99th edition published by Spotlight, 7 Leicester Place, London WC2H 7RJ
t: 020 7437 7631 f: 020 7437 5881  e-mail: questions@spotlight.com  www.spotlight.com

## What is Contacts?

g to work
ght since
ndividuals
e updated

ore about
e valuable
t starting

tion to

next
isit:

ops.

© COPYRIGHT - publishers everywhere are cautioned against using any of the contents of this
publication wholly or in part. This directory must not be copied or compiled for use as mailing lists
or telemarketing or database applications. Traceable material of an insignificant nature is
incorporated throughout the text to detect unauthorised use of data.
If you appear in Contacts please inform us of any change to contact details as soon as possible.
We update records throughout the year. Please note that the inclusion of a listing or a paid advert
is not an endorsement by Spotlight of any company or individual contained in the edition. All
content provided on the information pages, including third party contributions, is intended for
general guidance only and is by no means a definitive.

**Mixed Sources**
Product group from well-managed
forests and other controlled sources
www.fsc.org  Cert no. SA-COC-1565
© 1996 Forest Stewardship Council

Printed & bound in Great Britain by MPG Books Group

# SPOTLIGHT

**PARTNERS**

Nigel Seale, Ben Seale, Emma Smith, Philppa Burton

**EDITOR**

Kate Poynton

**DESIGN & LAYOUT**

Kathy Norrish

**ACCOUNTS**

Nas Fokeerchand - Head of Accounts
Amelia Barnham
Laura Ruocco

**CLIENT RELATIONS**

Pippa Harrison - Head of Client Relations
Joe Bates
Will Davies
Thom Hammond
Micki Ling
Nicholas Peel

**DATA PROCESSING**

Joanna MacLeod - Head of Data Processing
Caroline Taylor
Angie Drake
Amanda Lawrence
Emma Lear
Sharon Mulcahy
Helene Van De Langenberg

**EDITORIAL**

Cindy Lemmer
Christine Barry
Angela Cottrell
Nick Goldfinch
Martin Pavey

**HR**

Marilyn Peach

**IT**

Dylan Beattie - Head of IT
Dave Clements
Matthew Forest
Paul Goldsmith
Christina Kassimatis
Isabelle Kosciusko
Dan Woodhead

**MARKETING**

Laura Albery -  Head of Sales, Marketing &
Customer Relations
Sally Barnham
Thomas Bracewell
Elaine Compton
Lisa McGeoch
Frances Mordue
Joan Queva
Elinor Samuels
Kelly Taylor
Denise Teh

**PRODUCTION**

Hannah Witzenfeld
Louise Fairweather
Neill Kennedy
David McCarthy
Jaime Robb

# Contents
See pages 4-5

# Index To Advertisers
See page 409

[ CONTACTS 2010 ]

# A

**Accountants, Insurance & Law**
**Agents**
*Agents & Personal Managers*
*Children's & Teenagers'*
*Concert & Concert Promoters*
*Dance*
*Literary & Play*
*Presenters*
*Voice-Over*
*Walk-On & Supporting Artists*

PMA: For information regarding membership of the **Personal Managers' Association** please contact PO Box 63819, London N1P 1HL
t: 0845 6027191 w: www.thepma.com

CPMA: For information regarding membership of the **Co-operative Personal Management Association** please contact
The Secretary, CPMA
c/o 30 Ambleside, Southfields, London SW19 6JY
t: 07973 173988  w: www.cpma.coop

NASAA: For information regarding membership of the **National Association of Supporting Artistes Agents** please see
w: www.nasaa.org.uk

Members of the above organisations are clearly marked as such in the appropriate listings.

**Animals**
**Arts Centres**
**Arts Councils**

# [ CONTACTS 2010 ]

## AON Ltd /ALBERT G. RUBEN
(Insurance Brokers)
Pinewood Studios
Pinewood Road
Iver, Bucks SL0 0NH
Website: www.aon.co.uk
Fax: 01753 785861          Tel: 01753 785859

## ATKINS Chris & COMPANY
(Accountants & Business Consultants)
Astra House, Arklow Road
London SE14 6EB          Tel: 020-8691 4100
Website: www.chrisatkins.co.uk
e-mail: info@chrisatkins.co.uk

## BLACKMORE Lawrence
(Production Accountant)
Suite 5
26 Charing Cross Road
London WC2H 0DG          Tel: 020-7240 1817

## BLAKE LAPTHORNE
(Solicitors)
Watchmaker Court
33 St John's Lane
London EC1M 4DB
Website: www.bllaw.co.uk
e-mail: info@bllaw.co.uk
Fax: 020-7814 9421          Tel: 020-7405 2000

## BLINKHORNS
27 Mortimer Street
London W1T 3BL          Tel: 020-7636 3702
Website: www.blinkhorns.co.uk
e-mail: joel.trott@blinkhorns.co.uk

## BOWKER ORFORD
(Chartered Accountants)
15-19 Cavendish Place
London W1G 0DD
Website: www.bowkerorford.com
e-mail: mail@bowkerorford.com
Fax: 020-7580 3909          Tel: 020-7636 6391

## BREBNERS
(Chartered Accountants)
180 Wardour Street
London W1F 8LB
Website: www.brebners.com
e-mail: partners@brebners.com
Fax: 020-7287 5315          Tel: 020-7734 2244

## BRECKMAN & COMPANY
(Chartered Certified Accountants)
49 South Molton Street
London W1K 5LH          Tel: 020-7499 2292
Website: www.breckmanandcompany.co.uk

## CARR Mark & Co Ltd
(Chartered Accountants)
Garrick House
26-27 Southampton Street
Covent Garden
London WC2E 7RS
Website: www.markcarr.co.uk
e-mail: mark@markcarr.co.uk
Tel: 01273 778802          Tel: 020-7717 8474

**CARTER BACKER WINTER**
(Chartered Accountants, Business Advisers)
Enterprise House
21 Buckle Street
London E1 8NN
Website: www.cbw.co.uk
e-mail: info@cbw.co.uk
Fax: 020-7309 3801          Tel: 020-7309 3800

**COLLINS & COMPANY**
(Chartered Accountants)
2nd Floor
116 College Road
Harrow
Middlesex HA1 1BQ
e-mail: hq@collins116.com
Fax: 020-8863 0068          Tel: 020-8427 1888

**COUNT AND SEE Ltd**
(Tax, Accountancy & Book-keeping Services)
219 Macmillan Way
London SW17 6AW
Website: www.countandsee.com
e-mail: info@countandsee.com
Fax: 0845 0043454          Tel: 020-8767 7882

**EQUITY INSURANCE SERVICES**
131-133 New London Road
Chelmsford
Essex CM2 0QZ
Website: www.equity-ins-services.com
e-mail: enquiries@equity-ins-services.com
Fax: 01245 491641          Tel: 01245 357854

**FISHER BERGER & ASSOCIATES**
(Chartered Accountants)
Devonshire House
582 Honeypot Lane
Stanmore HA7 1JS
e-mail: nik@fisherberger.com
Fax: 020-8732 5500          Tel: 020-8732 5501

**FORD Jonathan & Co**
(Chartered Accountants)
The Coach House
31 View Road
Rainhill, Merseyside L35 0LF          Tel: 0151-426 4512
Website: www.jonathanford.co.uk
e-mail: info@jonathanford.co.uk

**GLOBAL MOBILITY LAW**
Contact: Julia de Cadenet (US Legal & Visa Consultancy.
Advice on all aspects of work visas and US green cards for
members of performing arts and associated industries).
Lawyers offices in California with liaison, contacts
in London & Paris
Website: www.globalmobilitylaw.com
e-mail: visas@legalbrain.eu
Tel: +33 62 62 18 58 (Paris)          Tel: 020-8940 1310

**HARDWICKE BUILDING**
Lincoln's Inn
London WC2A 3SB
Website: www.hardwicke.co.uk
e-mail: mark.engleman@hardwicke.co.uk
Fax: 020-7691 1234          Mobile: 07720 294667

# info**page**

### Why might I need this section?

This section contains listings for a number of companies and services which exist to help performers with the day-to-day administration of their working lives. Performers need to manage their business affairs personally, in ways that those in 'normal' jobs do not. For example, unlike most employees, a performer does not have an accounts department to work out their tax and national insurance, or an HR department to take care of contracts or health insurance on their behalf. On top of which, performers can often be away on tour or on set for many months and unable to attend to these matters themselves.

### Areas covered in this section include:

### Accountants and other financial services

Dedicated companies exist which can help you to manage key financial issues, including national insurance, taxation, benefits, savings and pensions. Specialist mortgage companies also exist for performers and other self-employed workers within the entertainment industry. If you are a member of Equity you can also ask them for free financial advice, and an Equity pension scheme exists into which the BBC, ITV, PACT, TV companies and West End Theatre producers will pay when you have a main part with one of them. Similar schemes also exist for dancers and other performers.

### Insurance

Performers may often need specialist insurance for specific jobs, as well as the standard life and health insurance policies held by most people. A number of specialist insurers are listed in the pages overleaf. Equity also offers a specialist backstage/accident and public liability insurance policy to all of its members.

### Legal

There may be times in a performer's career when he/she needs specialist legal advice or representation. This could be because of a performer's high profile, complicated contractual details, or international employment issues. Legal advisors and solicitors are listed in this section and general information is given overleaf. In addition, as part of their membership, Equity performers can also obtain free legal advice regarding professional engagements or personal injury claims.

### How should I use these listings?

As when looking to hire any company or individual, contact a number of different companies and carefully compare the services they offer. Ask others in the industry for recommendations. If you are an Equity member, don't forget to check first that the service isn't already available free of charge, as part of your annual membership.

**Henna Riaz is a media and entertainment lawyer with a great deal of experience in music, entertainment, digital, technology, and mobile. Henna also has extensive corporate experience and specialises in setting up corporate vehicles, reorganising company structures, and joint ventures. Henna's experience includes working as a lawyer both in the UK and the USA and her clients include high profile media companies and celebrities. She currently works for international law firm Hill Dickinson.**

Performers are more creative individuals than most. They are able to draw inspiration for their roles in ways that others might not, however this quality does not assist performers in dealing with the business side of their affairs, and many are more comfortable seeking advice from experts. Performers today are not just required to perform; they must also attend to a complex managerial and legal infrastructure. A performer's success depends heavily on good management and reliable, sound legal advice.

An appreciation of strength of bargaining power is, therefore, a major reason why a performer might wish to rely on a lawyer. No matter how friendly or well-intentioned a prospective employer might appear to be, the fundamental principle behind their negotiations is to secure a deal that ultimately reflects their own interests. There is nothing sinister about this practice, but is to be expected as both parties have differing objectives and priorities. A manager or agent might be more inclined to keep their client happy, but as they are paid by commission they are, in a similar way to the employer, looking out for the best commercial deal in the first instance. A lawyer on the other hand is only concerned with the best interests of the client performer, both financially and creatively.

A lawyer with knowledge of the media market will secure the very best deal available in the circumstances: something which managers and agents will usually admit is best left to the lawyers. Lawyers are neutral in the proceedings and can go beyond what managers and agents are able to achieve as they are not constrained by existing relationships with opposing parties (such as casting directors). This is, unfortunately, a reality of the industry.

The suggestion that a lawyer is only required when a contract is put before the performer is naïve and is a practice that I discourage. It is often very useful to have your lawyer involved from the outset. The point at which initial negotiations take place is often when most of the crucial issues are decided by the parties. It is often frustrating for a lawyer to be appointed at the contracts stage, only to discover that the negotiation process has come to an end. Once issues have been agreed it is incredibly difficult for the lawyer to try and change the terms as often at this stage the lawyer is simply expected to summarise everything in a legal document. The need to grasp the true strength of bargaining power, which is key in negotiating any contract prior to signature, is imperative for every performer. A good working relationship with a trusted lawyer will mean that the negotiation and contract process is smoother and more beneficial to the performer from the outset.

The media is a competitive business. The whole process of securing a deal, job or performance is naturally competitive. Having a lawyer by your side to guide you in securing the best deal is key. To suggest that a lawyer should always be by a performer's side will make many gasp at the thought of sky-high legal bills. Media lawyers are, however, pushing the boundaries of the client-lawyer relationship. Brief meetings for advice or a quick call to bounce ideas around will invariably not be charged. Of course, when the contract arrives then a lawyer has to charge for their work, but if a lawyer can be present in the background as a trustworthy source of advice, they can nip issues in the bud before they get to the point that further work, incurring fees, needs to be done. Should the matter develop, the lawyer will be fully appraised of the situation and be able to give quicker, more efficient advice.

It is, ultimately, not really the 'now' that causes problems. Today's decisions will impact on future events. A performer who uses a lawyer regularly will be able to have peace of mind knowing that their lawyer is always considering the ultimate impact of a step taken today. A performer or manager might not necessarily consider this angle. When a performer comes to rely on a contract or deal done, they need to know it is going to protect them against the claims of the other side. It is all very well not taking proper advice when relationships are going well, but it is the ability to regulate them when things turn bad that is particularly important. Lawyers are specialists at ensuring this is taken care of.

A media lawyer is not just someone that should be drafted in when documents start flying around. A media lawyer is able to be a friend and advisor to the performer on the everyday aspects of the industry which might make the difference between the chance that got away and the career-changing move.

Please visit www.hilldickinson.com for further information.

**HARVEYS LLP**
(Accountants)
The Old Winery, Lamberhurst Vineyard
Lamberhurst, Kent TN3 8ER
e-mail: tax@harveysllp.com
Fax: 01892 891892                    Tel: 01892 890388

**HILL DICKINSON LLP**
1 St Paul's Square
Old Hall Street, Liverpool L3 9SJ        Tel: 0161-817 7200
Website: www.hilldickinson.com
e-mail: mediateam@hilldickinson.com

**LARK INSURANCE BROKING GROUP**
(Insurance Brokers)
Wigham House, Wakering Road
Barking, Essex IG11 8PJ
Website: www.larkinsurance.co.uk
e-mail: mailbox@larkinsurance.co.uk
Fax: 020-8557 2430                    Tel: 020-8557 2300

**LONGREACH INTERNATIONAL Ltd**
(Specialist Insurance Brokers)
20-21 Tooks Court, London EC4A 1LB
Website: www.longreachint.com/theatre
e-mail: info@longreachint.com
Fax: 020-7421 7550                    Tel: 020-7421 7555

**MACINTYRE HUDSON LLP**
(Media & Entertainment Accountants)
New Bridge Street House
30-34 New Bridge Street
London EC4V 6BJ                    Tel: 020-7429 4100
Website: www.macintyrehudson.co.uk
e-mail: entertainment@mhllp.co.uk

**MEDIA INSURANCE BROKERS**
3rd Floor
St George's Buildings
Glasgow G1 2DH
Website: www.mediainsurance.com
e-mail: david.johnstone@mediainsurance.com
Fax: 0141-229 6489                    Tel: 0141-229 6480

**NYMAN LIBSON PAUL**
(Chartered Accountants)
Regina House
124 Finchley Road
London NW3 5JS
Website: www.nlpca.co.uk
e-mail: entertainment@nlpca.co.uk
Fax: 020-7433 2401                    Tel: 020-7433 2400

**PLANISPHERES**
(Business & Legal Affairs)
Sinclair House
2 Sinclair Gardens
London W14 0AT                    Tel/Fax: 020-7602 2038
Website: www.planispheres.com
e-mail: info@planispheres.com

**SUMMERS David & COMPANY**
(Chartered Accountants)
Argo House
Kilburn Park Road
London NW6 5LF
Website: www.dsummers.co.uk
e-mail: dsummersfca@hotmail.com
Fax: 020-7644 0678                    Tel: 0800 3288741

**TODS MURRAY LLP**
(Richard Findlay Entertainment Lawyer)
Edinburgh Quay
133 Fountainbridge
Edinburgh EH3 9AG
e-mail: richard.findlay@todsmurray.com
Fax: 0131-656 2023                    Tel: 0131-656 2000

**VANTIS**
(Accountants, Business & Tax Advisers)
Torrington House
47 Holywell Hill
St Albans, Hertfordshire AL1 1HD
Website: www.vantisplc.com/stalbanshh
e-mail: stalbans@vantisplc.com
Fax: 01727 861052                    Tel: 01727 838255

**Arnett Photography**
Pauline Arnett

**Casting Headshots  Student Rates**

m: 07951 991530
email: anetphotography@aim.com
www.arnett-photography.com

PMA: For information regarding membership of the **Personal Managers' Association** please contact
PO Box 63819, London N1P 1HL
t. 0845 6027191 w. www.thepma.com

CPMA: For information regarding membership of the **Co-operative Personal Management Association** please contact
The Secretary, CPMA
c/o 30 Ambleside, Southfields, London SW19 6JY
t: 07973 173988 w: www.cpma.coop

**Members of the above organisations are clearly marked as such in the following listings.**

**1984 PERSONAL MANAGEMENT Ltd**
(Personal Manager) (CPMA Member)
*Contact: David Meyer*
*By Post*
*24 Performers*
*Accepts Showreels*
Suite 508, Davina House, 137 Goswell Road
London EC1V 7ET
Website: www.1984pm.com
e-mail: info@1984pm.com
Fax: 020-7250 3031          Tel: 020-7251 8046

**21ST CENTURY ACTORS MANAGEMENT Ltd**
(CPMA Member)
*15 Performers*
*Contact: By e-mail*
*Commercials. Film. Singers. Stage. Television*
206 Panther House, 38 Mount Pleasant, London WC1X 0AN
Website: www.21stcenturyactors.co.uk
e-mail: mail@21stcenturyactors.co.uk    Tel: 020-7278 3438

**2MA Ltd**
*Sports. Stunts*
Spring Vale, Tutland Road
North Baddesley, Hants SO52 9FL
Website: www.2ma.co.uk
e-mail: info@2ma.co.uk
Fax: 023-8074 1355          Tel: 023-8074 1354

**A-LIST LOOKALIKES & ENTERTAINMENTS Ltd**
4th Floor Calls Landing
36-38 The Calls, Leeds LS2 7EW
Website: www.alistlookalikes.co.uk
e-mail: info@alistlookalikes.co.uk        Tel: 0113-243 6245

**A & B PERSONAL MANAGEMENT Ltd**
(Personal Manager) (PMA Member)
*Contact: By Post*
Suite 330, Linen Hall, 162-168 Regent Street
London W1B 5TD
e-mail: billellis@aandb.co.uk
Fax: 020-7038 3699              Tel: 020-7434 4262

**A & J MANAGEMENT**
242A The Ridgeway, Botany Bay, Enfield EN2 8AP
Website: www.ajmanagement.co.uk
e-mail: info@ajmanagement.co.uk
Fax: 020-8342 0842              Tel: 020-8342 0542

**ABA (ABACUS ADULTS)**
The Studio, 4 Bailey Road
Westcott, Dorking, Surrey RH4 3QS
Website: www.abacusaba.com
e-mail: aba@abacusagency.co.uk
Fax: 01306 877813              Tel: 01306 877144

**ABBOTT June ASSOCIATES**
Bowling Green Walk, 40 Pitfield Street, London N1 6EU
e-mail: jaa@thecourtyard.org.uk
Fax: 020-7251 6018              Tel: 020-7250 0520

**ACADEMY CASTINGS**
31 Chalmers Crescent, East Kilbride G75 0PE
Website: www.academycastings.co.uk
e-mail: robert@academycastings.co.uk
Mobile: 07961 536972              Tel: 01355 230896

**ACCESS ARTISTE MANAGEMENT Ltd**
*Contact: Sarah Bryan*
*By Post/e-mail*
*Accepts Showreels*
11-15 Betterton Street, Covent Garden, London WC2H 9BP
Website: www.access-uk.com
e-mail: mail@access-uk.com          Tel: 020-7866 5444

Bill Ward

# PETER SIMPKIN
P H O T O G R A P H Y

**t** 020 8364 2634
**m** 07973 224 084
**e** petersimpkin@aol.com
**w** www.petersimpkin.co.uk

Stephanie Leonidas

**ACE AGENCY**
7A Melish House, Harrington Way
London SE18 5NR
Website: www.aircraftcircus.com
e-mail: lucy@aircraftcircus.com          Tel: 020-8317 8401

**ACROBAT PRODUCTIONS**
*Advisors. Artists*
12 Oaklands Court
Hempstead Road, Watford WD17 4LF
Website: www.acrobatproductions.com
e-mail: roger@acrobatproductions.com     Tel: 01923 224938

**ACT OUT AGENCY**
22 Greek Street
Stockport
Cheshire SK3 8AB
e-mail: ab22actout@aol.com               Tel/Fax: 0161-429 7413

**ACTING ASSOCIATES**
(Personal Manager)
*Contact: Fiona Farley. By Post*
*Accepts Showreels/Voicereels*
*1 Agent represents 40 Performers*
*Commercials. Corporate. Film. Musicals. Radio. Stage*
*Television*
71 Hartham Road, London N7 9JJ
Website: www.actingassociates.co.uk
e-mail: fiona@actingassociates.co.uk  Tel/Fax: 020-7607 3562

**ACTOR MUSICIANS @ ACCESS**
(Personal Manager)
*Contact: Sarah Bryan. By Post/e-mail*
*Actor/Musician Productions. Commercials. Musicals. Stage*
11-15 Betterton Street, Covent Garden, London WC2H 9BP
Website: www.access-uk.com
e-mail: mail@access-uk.com                Tel: 020-7866 5444

Alistair McGowan                                    Rachel Weisz

# CAROLE LATIMER Photography

T: 020 7727 9371   www.carolelatimer.com   e-mail: carole.latimer@freenet.co.uk

# infopage

## Who are agents and personal managers?

There are hundreds of Agents and Personal Managers in the UK, representing thousands of actors and artists. It is their job to promote their clients to casting opportunities and negotiate contracts on their behalf. In return they take commission ranging from 10-15%. Larger agencies can have hundreds of clients on their books, smaller ones may only have a handful. Agents usually try to represent a good range of artists (age, sex, type) to fill the diverse role types required by casting directors. A personal manager is someone who manages an artist's career on a more one-on-one basis.

## What is a co-operative agency?

Co-operative agencies are staffed by actors themselves, who take turns to handle the administrative side of the agency and promote themselves to casting opportunities as a team. If you want more control over your career and can handle the pressures and responsibility that an agent takes away from you, then you might consider joining a co-operative agency. However it is very important that you think carefully about what you are signing up for. You will be responsible for the careers of others as well as yourself, so you must first of all be able to conduct yourself well when speaking to casting professionals. You will also have to commit some of your time to administrative jobs. You must be prepared to deal with finances and forms - all the boring paperwork you usually hand over to your agent! You must also be aware that the other actors in the agency will want to interview you and, if you are successful, to give you a trial period working with them. The Co-operative Personal Management Association (CPMA) provides advice on joining a co-operative agency on page 16.

## Why do I need an agent?

A good agent will have contacts and authority in the entertainment industry that you, as an individual actor, would find more difficult to acquire. Agents, if you want them to, can also deal with matters such as Equity and Spotlight membership renewal. They can offer you advice on which headshot would be best to send out to casting directors, what to include or exclude in your CV as you build on your skills and experience, what a particular casting director might expect when you are invited to an audition, and so on.

## How should I use these listings?

If you are an actor getting started in the industry, or looking to change your agent, the following pages will supply you with up-to-date contact details for many of the UK's leading agencies. Every company listed is done so by written request to us. Members of the Personal Managers' Association (PMA) and the Co-operative Personal Management Association (CMPA) have indicated their membership status under their name. Some agencies have also chosen to list other information such as relevant contact names, their preferred method of contact from new applicants, whether or not they will accept showreels and/or voicereels with your CV and headshot, the number of performers represented by the agency, the number of agents working for the company, and/or a description of the performance areas they cover. Use this information to narrow down your search for a suitable agent.

## How do I choose a new agent?

When writing to agencies, try to research the different companies instead of just sending a 'blanket' letter to every single one. This way you can target your approaches to the most suitable agencies and avoid wasting their time (and yours). As well as using the listing information provided here, look at agency websites and ask around for personal recommendations. Unfortunately Spotlight is not able to offer personalised advice on choosing an agent, nor is it in a position to handle any financial or contractual queries or complaints, but we have prepared some useful career advice on our website: www.spotlight.com/artists/advice. Click on our Frequently Asked Questions page for general guidance regarding agents, or you may wish to try consulting our list of Independent Advisory Services if you want one-to-one tailored advice. You can also contact The Agents Association www.agents-uk.com or The Personal Managers' Association (PMA) www.thepma.com. If you are a member of Equity then you can contact their legal and welfare department with general information about issues including commissions, fees and contracts. However, Equity is not able to recommend specific agencies or agents.

## How do I approach agencies?

Once you have made a list of suitable agencies, consult the listings again. Some agencies have indicated their preferred method of initial contact, whether by post, e-mail or telephone. Do not e-mail them, for example, if they have stated that they wish to receive your headshot, CV and covering letter by post. If they have not given a preference, you should send your CV by post as this is the traditional method of contacting agents. You should always include a stamped-addressed envelope (SAE) big enough to contain your 10 x 8 photo and with sufficient postage. This will increase your chances of getting a reply. Write your name and telephone number on the back of your headshot in case it gets separated from your CV.

Remember that agents receive hundreds of letters each week, so try to keep your communication concise, and be professional at all times. We also recommend that your covering letter has some kind of focus: perhaps you can tell them about your next showcase, or where they can see you currently appearing on stage. Ideally this should be addressed to an individual, not "To whom it may concern" or "Dear Sir or Madam". Some agents have indicated a specific contact to whom you can direct correspondence in their listing.

Some agents have indicated that they are happy to receive a showreel and/or voicereel with your CV, but it would be best to exclude these from your correspondence if they are not mentioned. Point out in your covering letter that one is available and the agent can contact you if they want to find out more.

## Should I pay an agent to join their books? Or sign a contract?

Equity (the actors' trade union) does not recommend that artists pay an agent to join their client list. Before signing a contract, you should be very clear about the terms and commitments involved. For advice on both of these issues, or if you experience any problems with a current agent, we recommend that you contact Equity www.equity.org.uk. They also publish the booklet *You and your Agent* which is free to all Equity members.

## How do I become an agent?

Budding agents will need to get experience of working in an agent's office; usually this is done by working as an assistant. It can be extremely hard work, and you will be expected to give up a lot of your evenings to attend productions. There are two organisations you may find it useful to contact: the Agents' Association www.agents-uk.com and the Personal Managers' Association www.thepma.com

# infopage

**Almost all actors' co-operative agencies belong to the CPMA (Co-operative Personal Management Association), which was created in 2002 to promote co-op agencies in the profession, encourage the highest professional standards, and represent the interests of co-op agencies to outside bodies, such as Equity and Government departments.**

Actors represented by co-operative agencies run the agency themselves, through a democratic structure, and work as unpaid agents for each other. Some co-ops employ a co-ordinator or administrator (who is not an actor). Co-op agencies are non-profit making and surplus funds are put back into the business. Co-op agencies began in the UK in 1970. Since then, many more have been established and thrive. Co-ops access the same casting information as conventional agents and suggest actors for jobs, negotiate contracts and fees, take commission on jobs, and advise and promote their clients to casting directors and others.

There is often a fee to join a co-op, which is refunded when you leave. Other, non-refundable, fees may be charged. There could also be a voluntary monthly levy to cover office costs, co-ordinator's fees, etc. Co-op members work in the office (typically two to four times a month), attend business meetings (usually monthly) to discuss aspects of running the agency, oversee the work of other co-op members (often with casting directors) and consider the work of applicants.

You quickly learn how the industry works by working as part of a co-op, which can be very useful for newcomers and those returning to the profession. You are in contact with many industry professionals, which could help you get work. You get support from other actors in the agency, some of whom will have a lot of experience. You know which jobs you have been suggested for and can monitor them. You have more influence over how you are represented and can be more pro-active in your career. You can say which type of work you will or won't do, without fear of being asked to leave the agency. Usually, more than one person decides who to suggest for a job. Many casting directors acknowledge that co-ops often know their clients much better and can sell them with honesty and confidence. Co-ops have smaller lists of clients, tend to avoid clashes and commission rates are lower.

However, you should be aware that there can be drawbacks to being part of a co-op. As with conventional agents, standards vary. A co-op is only as good and professional as its members. Can you be sure that other members are working as hard for you, as you are for them? Continuity can be a problem, with so many people involved. Although co-ops with a co-ordinator may have an advantage on this point, measures such as detailed note-taking and not changing negotiators on a contract still need to be taken. Casting directors also tend to send breakdowns for major TV and film roles to the top agencies in the industry, but other parts will be sent to good co-ops.

To join a co-op you need to be a good agent (not just a good actor), committed, reliable and keen to support fellow actors. You must be able to use a computer and learn the software the agency uses. You must be prepared to get on the phone, talk to casting directors, and sell your clients with knowledge and conviction. You must be able to make intelligent and credible suggestions for roles. Think about personal commitments, such as doing non-acting jobs to earn money, and expenses, such as travel to and from the office, and joining/training fees.

If you are thinking of applying, first ask if applications are being considered. Many co-ops, like conventional agents, do not accept e-mail applications. Check CVs and photos on the agency's website to identify potential gaps. Send your photograph and CV. Say why a co-op agency interests you and stress skills and any contacts which could be useful. Co-ops usually want to see an applicant's work, so send a showreel or details of the show you're in. Co-ops tend not to go to drama school shows or showcases, unless someone has expressed interest. To find out more about the agency, talk to members and ex-members. You might want to know when the agency was established, if any ex-members have returned, the extent of their contacts with casting directors and theatres, the range of casting information they receive and whether they belong to the CPMA, which has a code of conduct. Equity particularly welcomed the creation of the CPMA for this reason. If the co-op is interested in your application, you will be interviewed by all available members. If offered a place, you will usually have a three to six month trial period. After discussion to see how both sides feel, you may be offered full membership.

Please visit www.cpma.coop for further information.

DERREN NESBITT

NATALIE TURNER-JONES

KIKA MARKHAM

LUKE TREADAWAY

# CATHERINE SHAKESPEARE LANE

PHOTOGRAPHER

**020 7226 7694   www.csl-art.co.uk**

Joanna Page

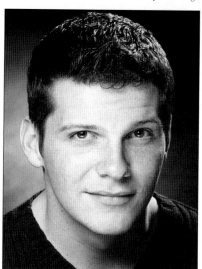

Nigel Harman

## ACTORS AGENCY
1 Glen Street, Tollcross
Edinburgh EH3 9JD
Website: www.stivenchristie.co.uk
e-mail: info@stivenchristie.co.uk
Fax: 0131-228 4645          Tel: 0131-228 4040

## ACTORS ALLIANCE
(CPMA Member)
*Contact: By Post*
*Commercials. Corporate. Film. Stage. Stills. Television*
Disney Place House
14 Marshalsea Road
London SE1 1HL          Tel/Fax: 020-7407 6028
e-mail: actors@actorsalliance.co.uk

## ACTORS' CREATIVE TEAM
(CPMA Member)
Panther House, 38 Mount Pleasant
London WC1X 0AN
Website: www.actorscreativeteam.co.uk
e-mail: office@actorscreativeteam.co.uk
Fax: 020-7833 5086          Tel: 020-7278 3388

## ACTORS DIRECT Ltd
Gainsborough House
109 Portland Street
Manchester M1 6DN
Website: www.actorsdirect.org.uk
e-mail: info@actorsdirect.org.uk
Mobile: 07985 760226          Tel/Fax: 0161-237 1904

## ACTORS FILE The
(Personal Manager) (CPMA Member)
*Contact: By Post/e-mail*
Spitfire Studios
63-71 Collier Street, London N1 9BE          Tel: 020-7278 0087
Website: www.theactorsfile.co.uk
e-mail: mail@theactorsfile.co.uk

## ACTORS' GROUP The (TAG)
(Personal Manager) (CPMA Member)
21-31 Oldham Street
Manchester M1 1JG          Tel/Fax: 0161-834 4466
Website: www.theactorsgroup.co.uk
e-mail: enquiries@theactorsgroup.co.uk

## ACTORS IN SCANDINAVIA
Tarkk'ampujankatu 14
00150 Helsinki, Finland
Website: www.actors.fi
e-mail: laura@actors.fi
Fax: 00 358 9 68 40 4422          Tel: 00 358 9 68 40 440

## ACTORS INTERNATIONAL Ltd
The White House
52-54 Kennington Oval, London SE11 5SW
e-mail: mail@actorsinternational.co.uk
Fax: 020-7820 0990          Tel: 020-3268 0023

## ACTORS IRELAND
Crescent Arts Centre
2-4 University Road
Belfast BT7 1NH          Tel: 028-9024 8861
Website: www.actorsireland.net
e-mail: actorsireland@aol.com

## ACTOR'S TEMPLE The
13 Warren Street, London W1T 5LG
Website: www.actorstemple.com
e-mail: info@actorstemple.com
Mobile: 07771 734670          Tel: 020-3004 4537

**ACTORS WORLD CASTING**
13 Briarbank Road, London W13 0HH
Website: www.actors-world-production.com
e-mail: katherine@actors-world-production.com
Mobile: 07960 332846            Tel: 020-8998 2579

**ACTORUM Ltd**
(Personal Manager)
9 Bourlet Close, London W1W 7BP
Website: www.actorum.com
e-mail: info@actorum.com
Fax: 020-7636 6975            Tel: 020-7636 6978

**AFA ASSOCIATES**
Unit 101
Business Design Centre
52 Upper Street, London N1 0QH    Tel: 020-7682 3677
e-mail: afa-associates@hotmail.com

**AFFINITY MANAGEMENT**
The Coach House
Down Park
Turners Hill Road, Crawley Down
West Sussex RH10 4HQ
e-mail: jstephens@affinitymanagement.co.uk
Fax: 01342 715800            Tel: 01342 715275

**AGENCY Ltd The**
Contact: Teri Hayden, Karl Hayden
47 Adelaide Road, Dublin 2, Ireland
Website: www.the-agency.ie
e-mail: admin1@tagency.ie
Fax: 00 353 1 6760052            Tel: 00 353 1 6618535

**AHA**
(See HOWARD Amanda ASSOCIATES Ltd)

**AIM (ASSOCIATED INTERNATIONAL MANAGEMENT)**
(PMA Member)
Fairfax House, Fulwood Place, London WC1V 6HU
Website: www.aimagents.com
e-mail: info@aimagents.com
Fax: 020-7242 0810            Tel: 020-7831 9709

**ALANDER AGENCY**
10 Ingram Close, Stanmore
Middlesex HA7 4EW            Tel: 020-8954 7685

**ALEXANDER PERSONAL MANAGEMENT Ltd**
Pinewood Studios, Pinewood Road
Iver Heath, Bucks SL0 0NH
Website: www.apmassociates.net
e-mail: apm@apmassociates.net
Fax: 01753 639205            Tel: 01753 639204

PETE LE MAY
PHOTOGRAPHY
LONDON
WWW.PETELEMAY.CO.UK
07703 649246
STUDENT RATES AVAILABLE

**ALL TALENT - THE SONIA SCOTT AGENCY**
*Contact: Sonia Scott Mackay*
*By Post/e-mail/Telephone*
*Accepts Showreels/Voicereels*
*2 Agents represent 40 Performers*
*Film. Modelling. Television. Voice Overs. Walk-on &*
*Supporting Artists*
Unit 325
95 Morrison Street
Glasgow G5 8BE
Website: www.alltalentuk.co.uk
e-mail: enquiries@alltalentuk.co.uk
Mobile: 07971 337074          Tel: 0141-418 1074

**ALLEN Debi ASSOCIATES**
(PMA Member)
22 Torrington Place
London WC1E 7HP          Tel: 020-7255 6123
Website: www.debiallenassociates.com
e-mail: info@debiallenassociates.com

**ALLSORTS AGENCY**
Suite 1 & 2 Marlborough Business Centre
96 George Lane, London E18 1AD
Website: www.allsortsagency.com
e-mail: bookings@allsortsagency.com
Fax: 020-8989 5600          Tel: 020-8989 0500

**ALLSORTS DRAMA FOR CHILDREN**
(In Association with Sasha Leslie Management)
34 Pember Road
London NW10 5LS          Tel/Fax: 020-8969 3249
e-mail: sasha@allsortsdrama.com

**ALLSTARS CASTING**
66 Hope Street
Liverpool L1 9BZ
Website: www.allstarsweb.co.uk
e-mail: allstarsweb@hotmail.co.uk
Mobile: 07739 359737          Tel: 0151-707 2100

**ALPHA PERSONAL MANAGEMENT**
(Co-operative) (CPMA Member)
Studio B4
3 Bradbury Street
London N16 8JN
Website: www.alphaactors.com
e-mail: alpha@alphaactors.com
Fax: 020-7241 2410          Tel: 020-7241 0077

**ALPHABET MANAGEMENT**
189 Southampton Way
London SE5 7EJ
Website: www.alphabetmanagement.co.uk
e-mail: contact@alphabetmanagement.co.uk
Fax: 020-7252 4341          Tel: 020-7252 4343

**ALRAUN Anita REPRESENTATION**
(PMA Member)
*Contact: By Post only (SAE)*
5th Floor
28 Charing Cross Road
London WC2H 0DB
e-mail: anita@cjagency.demon.co.uk
Fax: 020-7379 6865          Tel: 020-7379 6840

**ALTARAS Jonathan ASSOCIATES Ltd**
(PMA Member)
11 Garrick Street, Covent Garden
London WC2E 9AR
e-mail: info@jaa.ndirect.co.uk
Fax: 020-7836 6066          Tel: 020-7836 8722

**ALW ASSOCIATES**
1 Grafton Chambers
Grafton Place, London NW1 1LN
e-mail: alw_carolpaul@talktalk.net
Fax: 020-7813 1398          Tel: 020-7388 7018

**A M ENTERTAINMENTS**
*(Specialising only in Stand-up Comedians/Presenters)*
Suite 1, Townsend House
22-25 Dean Street
London W1D 3RY
e-mail: hilsjago@amentertainments.com
Mobile: 07970 524234          Tel: 020-7734 4588

**AMBER PERSONAL MANAGEMENT Ltd**
(PMA Member)
28 St Margaret's Chambers
5 Newton Street, Manchester M1 1HL
Website: www.amberltd.co.uk
e-mail: info@amberltd.co.uk
Fax: 0161-228 0235          Tel: 0161-228 0236
London          Tel: 020-7734 7887

**AMC MANAGEMENT**
*Contact: Anna McCorquodale*
31 Parkside
Welwyn, Herts AL6 9DQ
e-mail: anna@amcmanagement.co.uk
Fax: 01438 718669          Tel: 01438 714652

**AMCK MANAGEMENT Ltd**
125 Westbourne Studios
242 Acklam Road
Notting Hill
London W10 5JJ
Website: www.amck.tv
e-mail: info@amck.tv
Fax: 020-7524 7789          Tel: 020-7524 7788

**AMERICAN AGENCY The**
*Contact: By Post*
*3 Agents represent 70-80 Performers*
*Commercials. Corporate. Film. Musicals. Stage. Television*
*Voice Overs (American)*
14 Bonny Street
London NW1 9PG
Website: www.americanagency.tv
e-mail: americanagency@btconnect.com
Fax: 020-7482 4666          Tel: 020-7485 8883

**ANA (Actors Network Agency)**
(Personal Manager) (CPMA Member)
55 Lambeth Walk
London SE11 6DX
Website: www.ana-actors.co.uk
e-mail: info@ana-actors.co.uk
Fax: 020-7735 8177          Tel: 020-7735 0999

**ANDREWS Amanda AGENCY**
30 Caverswall Road
Blythe Bridge
Stoke-on-Trent
Staffordshire ST11 9BG
e-mail: amanda.andrews.agency@tesco.net
Mobile: 07711 379770 Tel/Fax: 01782 393889

**ANGEL Susan & FRANCIS Kevin Ltd**
(PMA Member)
*Contact: Kevin Francis. By Post*
*Accepts Showreels*
*3 Agents represent 5 Casting Directors & 80 Actors*
*Casting Directors. Film. Stage. Television*
1st Floor
12 D'Arblay Street
London W1F 8DU
e-mail: agents@angelandfrancis.co.uk
Fax: 020-7437 1712 Tel: 020-7439 3086

**ANTONY Christopher ASSOCIATES**
The Old Dairy
164 Thames Road
London W4 3QS
Website: www.christopherantony.co.uk
e-mail: info@christopherantony.co.uk
Fax: 020-8742 8066 Tel: 020-8994 9952

**A.P.M. ASSOCIATES (Linda French)**
(See ALEXANDER PERSONAL MANAGEMENT Ltd)

**ARAENA/COLLECTIVE**
10 Bramshaw Gardens
South Oxhey
Herts WD19 6XP Tel/Fax: 020-8428 0037
e-mail: info@collectivedance.co.uk

**ARC ENTERTAINMENTS**
*Contact: By e-mail*
*1 Agent represents 300 Active Performers*
10 Church Lane, Redmarshall
Stockton on Tees, Cleveland TS21 1EP Tel: 01740 631292
Website: www.arcents.co.uk
e-mail: arcents@hotmail.com

**ARCADIA ASSOCIATES**
18B Vicarage Gate
London W8 4AA Tel/Fax: 020-7937 0264
e-mail: info.arcadia@btopenworld.com

**ARENA ENTERTAINMENT (UK) Ltd**
Corporate Entertainment
Regent's Court
39 Harrogate Road
Leeds LS7 3PD
Website: www.arenaentertainments.co.uk
e-mail: info@arenaentertainments.co.uk
Fax: 0113-239 2016 Tel: 0113-239 2222

**ARENA PERSONAL MANAGEMENT Ltd**
(Co-operative)
Room 11, East Block, Panther House
38 Mount Pleasant
London WC1X 0AP Tel/Fax: 020-7278 1661
Website: www.arenapmltd.co.uk
e-mail: arenapmltd@aol.com

**A R G (ARTISTS RIGHTS GROUP Ltd)**
(PMA Member)
4 Great Portland Street
London W1W 8PA
e-mail: argall@argtalent.com
Fax: 020-7436 6700 Tel: 020-7436 6400

**ANTHONY BRITTON**
PHOTOGRAPHER
www.anthonybritton.co.uk
Email anthony-britton@btconnect.com
Tel: 01784-488343

**ARGYLE ASSOCIATES**
(Personal Manager)
*Contact: Richard Argyle. By Post (SAE)*
St John's Buildings
43 Clerkenwell Road
London EC1M 5RS
e-mail: argyle.associates@virgin.net
Fax: 0871 4336130     Tel: 020-7608 2095

**ARTIST MANAGEMENT UK Ltd**
PO Box 96
Liverpool L9 8WY
Website: www.artistmanagementuk.com
e-mail: chris@artistmanagementuk.com
Mobile: 07948 793552     Tel: 0151-523 6222

**ARTS MANAGEMENT**
First Floor
10 Goddard Place, Maidenbower
West Sussex RH10 7HR
Website: www.artsmanagement.co.uk
e-mail: artsmanagementltd@hotmail.com
Mobile: 07764 801167     Tel: 01293 885746

**ARUN Jonathan Ltd**
Studio 9
33 Stannary Street
London SE11 4AA
Website: www.jonathanarun.com
e-mail: jonathan@jonathanarun.com
Fax: 020-8249 0310     Tel: 020-7840 0123

**ASHCROFT Sharron MANAGEMENT Ltd**
c/o Dean Clough Mills
Halifax HX3 5AX     Tel: 01422 883090
Website: www.sharronashcroft.com
e-mail: info@sharronashcroft.com

**ASQUITH & HORNER**
(Personal Manager) (Consultant Elspeth Cochrane)
*Contact: By Post (SAE)/Telephone*
The Studio
14 College Road
Bromley, Kent BR1 3NS
Fax: 020-8313 0443     Tel: 020-8466 5580

**ASSOCIATED ARTS**
*Designers. Directors. Lighting & Sound Designers*
8 Shrewsbury Lane
London SE18 3JF
Website: www.associated-arts.co.uk
e-mail: karen@associated-arts.co.uk
Fax: 020-8856 8189     Tel: 020-8856 4958

**ASSOCIATED SPEAKERS**
*Lecturers & Celebrity Speakers*
24A Park Road
Hayes
Middlesex UB4 8JN     Tel: 020-8848 9048

**ASTRAL ACTORS MANAGEMENT**
7 Greenway Close, London NW9 5AZ     Tel: 020-8728 2782
Website: www.astralactors.com
e-mail: info@astralactors.com

**AVALON MANAGEMENT GROUP Ltd**
4A Exmoor Street
London W10 6BD
Website: www.avalonuk.com
e-mail: enquiries@avalonuk.com
Fax: 020-7598 7300     Tel: 020-7598 8000

**AVENUE ARTISTES Ltd**
PO Box 1573
Southampton SO16 3XS     Tel: 023-8076 0930
Website: www.avenueartistes.com
e-mail: info@avenueartistes.com

**AWA - ANDREA WILDER AGENCY**
23 Cambrian Drive
Colwyn Bay
Conwy LL28 4SL
Website: www.awagency.co.uk
e-mail: andreawilder@fastmail.fm
Fax: 07092 249314     Mobile: 07919 202401

**AXM**
(Actors' Exchange Management)
(Co-operative) (PMA Member)
308 Panther House
38 Mount Pleasant
London WC1X 0AN
Website: www.axmgt.com
e-mail: info@axmgt.com
Fax: 020-7837 7215     Tel: 020-7837 3304

**BALLROOM, LONDON THEATRE OF**
*Contact: Paul Harris®*
*Ballroom/Social Dancers for Film/TV/Theatre*
24 Montana Gardens
Sutton
Surrey SM1 4FP
Website: www.londontheatreofballroom.com
e-mail: office@londontheatreofballroom.com
Mobile: 07958 784462     Tel: 020-8722 8798

**B A M ASSOCIATES**
Benets
Dolberrow, Churchill
Bristol BS25 5NT     Tel: 01934 852942
Website: www.ebam.tv
e-mail: casting@ebam.tv

**BANANAFISH MANAGEMENT**
16 The Arts Village
20-26 Henry Street
Liverpool L1 5BS
Website: www.bananafish.co.uk
e-mail: info@bananafish.co.uk
Mobile: 07974 206622     Tel: 0151-324 2222

**BARKER Gavin ASSOCIATES Ltd**
(PMA Member)
*Contact: Gavin Barker, Michelle Burke*
2d Wimpole Street
London W1G 0EB
Website: www.gavinbarkerassociates.co.uk
e-mail: katie@gavinbarkerassociates.co.uk
Fax: 020-7499 3777     Tel: 020-7499 4777

Kika Mirylees

Greg Foreman

Jolyon Baker

Yolande Burke

# JOHN CLARK

London's leading theatrical photographer
actors-dancers-children

Kirsten Aarden

web contact sheet in B/W & colour
retouching
free image upload service to agents
on-line repro service
same day turnaround
online booking system

www.johnclarkphotography.com
info@johnclarkphotography.com

020 8854 4069
07702 627 237

**BARR Becca MANAGEMENT**
174 New Bond Street
London W1S 4RG                     Tel: 020-3137 2980
Website: www.beccabarrmanagement.co.uk
e-mail: info@beccabarrmanagement.co.uk

**BASHFORD Simon**
(See GLOBAL ARTISTS)

**B.A.S.I.C./JD AGENCY**
3 Rushden House
Tatlow Road
Glenfield
Leicester LE3 8ND                  Tel/Fax: 0116-287 9594
e-mail: jonny.dallas@ntlworld.com

**BELFIELD & WARD**
4th Floor
80-81 St Martin's Lane
London WC2N 4AA
e-mail: office@belfieldandward.com
Fax: 020-3292 9382                 Tel: 020-7395 7535

**BELFRAGE Julian ASSOCIATES**
(PMA Member)
Adam House
14 New Burlington Street
London W1S 3BQ
Fax: 020-7287 8832                 Tel: 020-7287 8544

**BELL Olivia Ltd**
(PMA Member)
*Contact: By Post*
*2 Agents represent 100 Performers*
*Commercials. Film. Musicals. Stage. Television*
189 Wardour Street
London W1F 8ZD
e-mail: info@olivia-bell.co.uk
Fax: 020-7439 3485                 Tel: 020-7439 3270

**BENJAMIN Audrey AGENCY**
278A Elgin Avenue
Maida Vale
London W9 1JR
e-mail: a.benjamin@btconnect.com
Fax: 020-7266 5480                 Tel: 020-7289 7180

**BERLIN ASSOCIATES**
(PMA Member)
7 Tyers Gate
London SE1 3HX
Website: www.berlinassociates.com
e-mail: agents@berlinassociates.com
Fax: 020-7632 5296                 Tel: 020-7836 1112

**BETTER CHEMISTRY**
1st & 2nd Floors
20 Stansfield Road
Stockwell, London SW9 9RZ          Tel/Fax: 020-7737 5300
Website: www.betterchemistry.co.uk
e-mail: info@betterchemistry.co.uk

**BETTS Jorg ASSOCIATES**
(PMA Member)
Gainsborough House
81 Oxford Street, London W1D 2EU
e-mail: agents@jorgbetts.com
Fax: 020-7903 5301                 Tel: 020-7903 5300

**BILLBOARD PERSONAL MANAGEMENT**
Unit 5
11 Mowll Street
London SW9 6BG
Website: www.billboardpm.com
e-mail: billboardpm@btconnect.com
Fax: 020-7793 0426                 Tel: 020-7735 9956

Koval Studio Photography - www.piotrkowalik.co.uk - 07946323631
Actors Dancers Singers Models

**BILLY MARSH DRAMA Ltd**
(Actors & Actresses)
(See MARSH Billy DRAMA Ltd)

**BIRD AGENCY**
(Personal Performance Manager)
Birkbeck Centre
Birkbeck Road
Sidcup
Kent DA14 4DE
Fax: 020-8308 1370      Tel: 020-8308 6994

**BLOND Rebecca ASSOCIATES**
(PMA Member)
69A Kings Road
London SW3 4NX
e-mail: info@rebeccablondassociates.com
Fax: 020-7351 4600      Tel: 020-7351 4100

**BLOOMFIELDS MANAGEMENT**
(PMA Member)
77 Oxford Street
London W1D 2ES
Website: www.bloomfieldsmanagement.com
e-mail: emma@bloomfieldsmanagement.com
Fax: 020-7659 2101      Tel: 020-7659 2001

**BLUE STAR ASSOCIATES**
Apartment 8 Shaldon Mansions
132 Charing Cross Road
London WC2H 0LA
e-mail: hopkinstacey@aol.com
Fax: 020-7836 2949      Tel: 020-7836 6220

**BMA MODELS/ACTORS**
346 High Street
Marlow House
Berkhamsted
Herts HP4 1HT
Website: www.bmamodels.com
e-mail: info@bmamodels.com
Fax: 01442 879879      Tel: 01442 878878

**BODENS AGENCY**
(Personal Manager)
Contact: Adam Boden, Katie McCutcheon, Sarah Christie
By Post/e-mail/Telephone
3 Agents represent 400 Performers. Children. Commercials.
Television. Walk-on & Supporting Artists
Bodens Studios & Agency
99 East Barnet Road
New Barnet, Herts EN4 8RF
Website: www.bodensagency.com
e-mail: info@bodensagency.com
Mobile: 07545 696888      Tel: 020-8447 0909

**BODYWORK AGENCY**
25-29 Glisson Road
Cambridge CB1 2HA
e-mail: agency@bodyworkds.co.uk
Fax: 01223 358923      Tel: 01223 309990

**BOSS CREATIVE ENTERTAINMENT**
Top Floor
81 Overhill Road
London SE22 0PQ
Website: www.bosscreativeentertainment.com
e-mail: enquiries@bosscreativeentertainment.com
Fax: 020-8516 1867      Tel: 020-8299 0478

**BOSS MODEL MANAGEMENT Ltd**
Fourways House
57 Hilton Street
Manchester M1 2EJ
Website: www.bossmodelmanagement.co.uk
e-mail: info@bossmodels.co.uk

**BOYCE Sandra MANAGEMENT**
(PMA Member)
1 Kingsway House
Albion Road, London N16 0TA
Website: www.sandraboyce.com
e-mail: info@sandraboyce.com
Fax: 020-7241 2313      Tel: 020-7923 0606

**B P A**
*Representing Artists of All Ages. Film. Musical Theatre
Specialists. New Media. Stage. Television*
83 Washington Avenue
Hemel Hempstead HP2 6AW
Website: www.boostpa.co.uk/agency
e-mail: agent@boostpa.co.uk      Tel: 0845 2260809

**BRADLEY Christina MANAGEMENT**
19 Jeffrey's Place
Camden, London NW1 9PP      Mobile: 07897 794728
Website: www.cbmlondon.com
e-mail: christina@cbmlondon.com

**BRAIDMAN Michelle ASSOCIATES Ltd**
(PMA Member)
2 Futura House
169 Grange Road
London SE1 3BN
Website: www.braidman.com
e-mail: info@braidman.com
Fax: 020-7231 4634      Tel: 020-7237 3523

**BRAITHWAITE'S THEATRICAL AGENCY**
8 Brookshill Avenue
Harrow Weald
Middlesex HA3 6RZ      Tel: 020-8954 5638

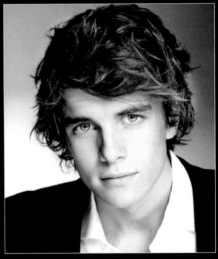

Artist Management
adults children

**Byron's Management**
Tel: 020 8444 4445
Fax: 020 8444 4040
byronsmanagement@aol.com
www.byronsmanagement.co.uk

**BREAK A LEG MANAGEMENT Ltd**
Units 2/3 The Precinct
Packington Square, London N1 7UP
Website: www.breakalegman.com
e-mail: agency@breakalegman.com
Fax: 020-7359 3660     Tel: 020-7359 3594

**BRIDGES: THE ACTORS' AGENCY**
St George's West
58 Shandwick Place
Edinburgh EH2 4RT     Tel: 0131-226 6433
Website: www.bridgesactorsagency.com
e-mail: admin@bridgesactorsagency.com

**BROADCASTING AGENCY**
Unit 36, Pall Mall Deposit
124 Barlby Road, London W10 6BL     Tel: 020-7490 4225
Website: www.broadcastingagency.co.uk
e-mail: info@broadcastingagency.co.uk

**BROOD MANAGEMENT**
*Contact: By e-mail*
*1 Agent represents 40 Performers*
High Street Buildings
134 Kirkdale, London SE26 4BB
Website: www.broodmanagement.com
e-mail: broodmanagement@aol.com
Fax: 020-8699 8787     Tel: 020-8699 1757

**BROOK Dolly AGENCY**
PO Box 5436
Dunmow CM6 1WW
e-mail: dollybrookcasting@btinternet.com
Fax: 01371 875996     Tel: 01371 875767

**BROOK Valerie AGENCY**
10 Sandringham Road
Cheadle Hulme
Cheshire SK8 5NH
e-mail: colinbrook@freenetname.co.uk
Fax: 0161-488 4206     Tel: 0161-486 1631

**BROOKS Claude ENTERTAINMENTS**
19 Sussex Place
Slough
Berks SL1 1NH
Fax: 01753 520424     Tel: 01753 520717

**BROWN & SIMCOCKS**
(PMA Member)
1 Bridgehouse Court
109 Blackfriars Road, London SE1 8HW
e-mail: mail@brownandsimcocks.co.uk
Fax: 020-7928 1909     Tel: 020-7928 1229

**BROWNE STREET Daniel**
18 Pinewood Place
Dartford DA2 7WQ     Tel: 01322 521239
Website: www.danielbrownestreet.co.uk
e-mail: daniel.browne@danielbrownestreet.co.uk

**BRUNO KELLY Ltd**
4th Floor
Albany House
324-326 Regent Street
London W1B 3HH
Website: www.brunokelly.com
e-mail: info@brunokelly.com
Fax: 020-7183 7332     Tel: 020-7183 7331

**BRUNSKILL MANAGEMENT Ltd**
(Personal Manager) (PMA Member)
*Contact: Aude Powell*
*By e-mail*
*Accepts Showreels/Voicereels*
*Commercials. Corporate. Film. Musicals. Radio. Stage*
*Television. Voice Overs*
Suite 8A
169 Queen's Gate
London SW7 5HE
e-mail: contact@brunskill.com
Fax: 020-7589 9460     Tel: 020-7581 3388

The Courtyard
Edenhall
Penrith, Cumbria CA11 8ST
e-mail: aude@brunskill.com
Fax: 01768 881850     Tel: 01768 881430

**BSA Ltd**
(See HARRISON Penny BSA Ltd)

**BSA MANAGEMENT**
First Floor
75 Brownlow Road
London N11 2BN
Website: www.bsa-management.co.uk
e-mail: info@bsa-management.co.uk
Mobile: 07532 158818     Tel: 020-3240 1064

**BUCHANAN Bronia ASSOCIATES Ltd**
(PMA Member)
First Floor
23 Tavistock Street
London WC2E 7NX
Website: www.buchanan-associates.co.uk
e-mail: info@buchanan-associates.co.uk
Fax: 020-7379 5560     Tel: 020-7395 1400

# Actors Headshot Photography

Aishwarya Rai

Dane Bowers

Francesca Kingdon

Dennis Quaid

Jonny Lee Miller

Jane Middlemiss

Martin Scorsese

Stella Rimington

Rachel Stevens

Michael Burke

Sophie Isaacs

Sam Kordbacheh

Steve Henry

Tedecia Wint

Terry Pratchett

Caroline Rovina

Vin Diesel

Jo Napthine

Eamonn Holmes

Karin Slaughter

**by celebrity photographer Jamie Hughes**

07850-122977  jhpixx@gmail.com

www.jamiehughesphotography.com/headshots

**BURNETT GRANGER CROWTHER Ltd**
(PMA Member)
*Contact: Barry Burnett, Lindsay Granger, Lizanne Crowther*
3 Clifford Street
London W1S 2LF
Website: www.bgcltd.org
e-mail: associates@bgcltd.org
Fax: 020-7287 3239                         Tel: 020-7437 8008

**BWH AGENCY Ltd The**
(PMA Member)
*Contact: By Post/e-mail*
*Accepts Showreels*
*4 Agents*
117 Shaftesbury Avenue, London WC2H 8AD
Website: www.thebwhagency.co.uk
e-mail: info@thebwhagency.co.uk
Fax: 020-7240 2287                         Tel: 020-7061 6399

**BYRON'S MANAGEMENT**
*Contact: By Post/e-mail*
*Accepts Showreels*
*Commercials. Film. Musicals. Stage. Television*
76 St James Lane
Muswell Hill
London N10 3DF
Website: www.byronsmanagement.co.uk
e-mail: byronsmanagement@aol.com
Fax: 020-8444 4040                         Tel: 020-8444 4445

**C.A. ARTISTES MANAGEMENT**
26-28 Hammersmith Grove
London W6 7BA                              Tel: 020-8834 1608
Website: www.caartistes.com
e-mail: casting@caartistes.com

**CALLUM Corinne ASSOCIATES**
(Personal Manager)
*Contact: Corinne Callum, Elena Melkis*
*By Post*
*Accepts Showreels/Voicereels*
*2 Agents represent 20 Clients*
*Commercials. Dancers. Musicals. Singers. Stage. Television*
46 Brightwell Crescent
Tooting Broadway
London SW17 9AE                     Mobile: 07504 987402
Website: www.corinnecallumassociates.co.uk
e-mail: corinnecallum@live.co.uk

**CAM**
(Personal Manager) (PMA Member)
*Contact: By Post*
First Floor
55-59 Shaftesbury Avenue
London W1D 6LD
Website: www.cam.co.uk
e-mail: reception@cam.co.uk
Fax: 020-7734 3205                         Tel: 020-7292 0600

**CAMBELL JEFFREY MANAGEMENT**
*Set, Costume, Lighting Designers*
6 Glenview
Dalmally
Argyll, Scotland PA33 1BE                  Tel: 01838 200707
e-mail: cambell@theatricaldesigners.co.uk

**CAMPBELL Alison MODEL & PROMOTION AGENCY**
381 Beersbridge Road
Belfast BT5 5DT
Website: www.alisoncampbellmodels.com
e-mail: info@alisoncampbellmodels.com
Fax: 028-9080 9808                         Tel: 028-9080 9809

**CANONGATE**
(Personal Manager)
*Contact: Alistair George*
*By e-mail*
*Accepts Showreels*
*1 Agent represents 5 Performers*
*Commercials. Modelling. Radio. Television*
9 Waters Close
Leith, Edinburgh EH6 6RB
Website: www.canongate.com
e-mail: al@canongate.com
Fax: 0131-555 2021                         Tel: 0131-555 4455

**CAPITAL VOICES**
*Contact: Anne Skates*
*Film. Session Singers. Stage. Studio. Television*
PO Box 364
Esher, Surrey KT10 9XZ
Website: www.capitalvoices.com
e-mail: capvox@aol.com
Fax: 01372 466229                          Tel: 01372 466228

**CARAVANSERAI ASSOCIATES Ltd**
Unit 30
Grand Union Centre
West Row, London W10 5AS                   Tel: 05601 534892
e-mail: info@cserai.co.uk

**CAREY Roger ASSOCIATES**
(Personal Manager) (PMA Member)
Suite 909
The Old House
Shepperton Film Studios
Studios Road, Shepperton
Middlesex TW17 0QD
e-mail: info@rogercarey.f2s.com
Fax: 01932 569602                          Tel: 01932 582890

**CARNEY Jessica ASSOCIATES**
(Personal Manager) (PMA Member)
4th Floor
23 Golden Square
London W1F 9JP
e-mail: info@jcarneyassociates.co.uk
Fax: 020-7434 4173                         Tel: 020-7434 4143

**CAROUSEL EVENTS**
*Entertainment for Corporate & Private Events*
Incentive House
23 Castle Street
High Wycombe
Bucks HP13 6RU
Website: www.carouselevents.co.uk
e-mail: enquiries@carouselevents.co.uk
Fax: 01494 511501                          Tel: 01494 511266

**CARR Norrie AGENCY**
Holborn Studios
49-50 Eagle Wharf Road
London N1 7ED
Website: www.norriecarr.com
e-mail: info@norriecarr.com
Fax: 020-7253 1772                         Tel: 020-7253 1771

**CASA MANAGEMENT**
Alison House
5 Highfield Road
Mellor, Stockport
Cheshire SK6 5AL
Website: www.casamanagement.co.uk
e-mail: casamgmt@aol.com
Fax: 0161-880 2056                         Tel: 0161-612 0082

philip quast
"georges" *la cage aux folles*

sheridan smith
"elle woods" *legally blonde*

oliver j hembrough
"sky" *mamma mia*

## 07961 122 030
## nickjamesphotography.co.uk

aneurin barnard
"melchior" *spring awakening*

chloe hart
"tracy turnblad" *hairspray*

PHOTOGRAPHY by
ANTHONY HEARN

07809 502763
hearn698@btinternet.com
www.aphearn-photography.com

**CASAROTTO MARSH Ltd**
Film Technicians
Waverley House
7-12 Noel Street, London W1F 8GQ
Website: www.casarotto.co.uk
e-mail: casarottomarsh@casarotto.co.uk
Fax: 020-7287 9128          Tel: 020-7287 4450

**CASTAWAY ACTORS AGENCY**
30-31 Wicklow Street, Dublin 2, Ireland
Website: www.irish-actors.com
e-mail: castaway@clubi.ie
Fax: 00 353 1 6719133        Tel: 00 353 1 6719264

**CASTCALL**
*Casting & Consultancy Service*
106 Wilsden Avenue, Luton LU1 5HR
Website: www.castcall.co.uk
e-mail: casting@castcall.co.uk
Fax: 01582 480736           Tel: 01582 456213

**CASTING DEPARTMENT The**
277 Chiswick Village
London W4 3DF              Tel: 020-8582 5523
Website: www.thecastingdept.co.uk
e-mail: thecastingdpt@aol.com

**CASTING SUITE AGENCY The**
8-10 Lower James Street, London W1F 9EL
Website: www.thecastingsuite.com
e-mail: agency@thecastingsuite.com
Fax: 020-7534 5799         Tel: 020-7534 5757

**CASTING UK**
Studio 125
77 Beak Street, London W1F 9DB     Tel: 020-7993 6042
Website: www.castinguk.com
e-mail: info@castinguk.com

**CAVAT AGENCY**
3, 97 Wardour Street
London W1F 0UF
Website: www.cavatagency.co.uk
e-mail: enquiries@cavatagency.co.uk  Tel: 020-8651 1099

**C B A INTERNATIONAL**
166 Waverley Avenue
Twickenham TW2 6DL          Mobile: 07789 991032
e-mail: cba_office@yahoo.co.uk

Contact: Cindy Brace
c/o C.M.S. Experts Associés
149 Boulevard Malesherbes
75017 Paris, France         Tel: 00 33 145 26 33 42
Website: www.cindy-brace.com
e-mail: c_b_a@club-internet.fr

**CBL MANAGEMENT**
*(Artistes & Creatives)*
20 Hollingbury Rise
Brighton, East Sussex BN1 7HJ
Website: www.cblmanagement.co.uk
e-mail: enquiries@cblmanagement.co.uk
Mobile: 07956 890307          Tel: 01273 321245

**C C A MANAGEMENT**
*(Personal Manager) (PMA Member)*
*Contact: By Post*
*Actors. Technicians*
Garden Level
32 Charlwood Street, London SW1V 2DY
e-mail: actors@ccamanagement.co.uk
Fax: 020-7630 7376            Tel: 020-7630 6303

**CCM**
*(CPMA Member)*
Panther House, 38 Mount Pleasant
London WC1X 0AP               Tel: 020-7278 0507
Website: www.ccmactors.com
e-mail: casting@ccmactors.com

**CDA**
*(PMA Member)*
*Contact: Belinda Wright*
125 Gloucester Road, London SW7 4TE
e-mail: cda@cdalondon.com
Fax: 020-7373 1110            Tel: 020-7373 3323

**CELEBRITY GROUP The**
13 Montagu Mews South
London W1H 7ER               Tel: 0871 2501234
Website: www.celebrity.co.uk
e-mail: info@celebrity.co.uk

**CENTER STAGE AGENCY**
*(Personal Manager) (PMA Member)*
*Contact: By e-mail*
*Accepts Showreels*
*55 Performers*
*Commercials. Film. Singers. Television*
7 Rutledge Terrace, South Circular Road
Dublin 8, Ireland            Tel/Fax: 00 353 1 4533599
Website: www.centerstageagency.com
e-mail: geraldinecenterstage@eircom.net

**CENTRAL LINE**
*(Personal Manager) (CPMA Member)*
*Contact: By Post*
11 East Circus Street
Nottingham NG1 5AF           Tel: 0115-941 2937
Website: www.the-central-line.co.uk
e-mail: centralline@btconnect.com

**CENTURY MODELS MANAGEMENT**
Unit D, Well House
23A Benwell Road, London N7 7BL
Website: www.century.com
e-mail: models@centurym.com
Mobile: 07984 055638         Tel: 020-3086 9031

**CHALICE PERSONAL MANAGEMENT Ltd**
*Contact: Haf Jones (Welsh Language)*
Temple Court, Cathedral Road
Cardiff CF11 9HA
Website: www.chalicepersonalmanagement.co.uk
e-mail: agent@chalicepersonalmanagement.co.uk
Mobile: 07794 051019         Tel: 029-2078 6537

Contact: Sarah Harding, Colin Scott
PO Box 59291
London NW3 9JW               Mobile: 07591 503980
e-mail: london@chalicepersonalmanagement.co.uk

**Representing Performers, Creative and Technical staff.**

**T: 0844 351 0223**
**E: info@dotted-line.co.uk**

**Agent Services**
Fixed fee contract negotiation. No weekly commission.  www.dotted-line.co.uk

**CHAMBERS MANAGEMENT**
*Comedians. Comic Actors*
23 Long Lane
Barbican, London EC1A 9HL
Website: www.chambersmgt.co.uk
e-mail: hannah@chambersmgt.com
Fax: 020-7796 3676                    Tel: 020-7796 3588

**CHAPMAN AGENCY**
BSA
Millennium Point
Curzon Street
Birmingham B4 7XG
e-mail: chapmanagency@bsa.bcu.ac.uk
Fax: 0121-331 7221                    Tel: 0121-331 7220

**CHARLESWORTH Peter & ASSOCIATES**
67 Holland Park Mews
London W11 3SS
e-mail: info@petercharlesworth.co.uk
Fax: 020-7792 1893                    Tel: 020-7792 4600

**CHATTO & LINNIT Ltd**
123A Kings Road
London SW3 4PL
e-mail: info@chattolinnit.com
Fax: 020-7352 3450                    Tel: 020-7352 7722

**CHP (CHARLOTTE HAMILTON PRODUCTIONS)**
(Personal Manager)
*Contact: By e-mail*
*Comedians. Commercials. Corporate. Film. Presenters*
*Radio. Television. Writers*
Meadowcroft Barn
Crowbrook Road
Askett, Princes Risborough
Buckinghamshire HP27 9LS
Website: www.chproductions.org.uk
e-mail: charlotte@chproductions.org.uk
Mobile: 07976 560580                  Tel: 01844 345630

**CHRYSTEL ARTS AGENCY**
6 Eunice Grove
Chesham, Bucks HP5 1RL
e-mail: chrystelarts@waitrose.com
Mobile: 07799 605489                  Tel/Fax: 01494 773336

**CINEL GABRAN MANAGEMENT**
(Personal Manager) (PMA Member)
*Contact: By Post*
*Accepts Showreels*
*60 Performers*
*Commercials. Corporate. Film. Musicals. Presenters. Radio.*
*Stage. Television. Voice Overs*
PO Box 5163, Cardiff CF5 9BJ
Website: www.cinelgabran.co.uk
e-mail: info@cinelgabran.co.uk
Fax: 0845 0666601                     Tel: 0845 0666605

PO Box 101
Newholm, Whitby
North Yorkshire YO21 3WT
e-mail: mail@cinelgabran.co.uk

**CIRCUIT PERSONAL MANAGEMENT Ltd**
*Contact: By Post/e-mail*
*Accepts Showreels*
*16 Performers*
*Commercials. Corporate. Film. Stage. Television*
Suite 71 S.E.C.
Bedford Street, Shelton
Stoke-on-Trent
Staffs ST1 4PZ
Website: www.circuitpm.co.uk
e-mail: mail@circuitpm.co.uk
Fax: 01782 206821                     Tel: 01782 285388

**CIRCUS MANIACS AGENCY**
*Corporate. Physical Artistes*
Office 8A
The Kingswood Foundation
Britannia Road
Kingswood, Bristol BS15 8DB
Website: www.circusmaniacs.com
e-mail: agency@circusmaniacs.com
Mobile: 07977 247287                  Tel/Fax: 0117-947 7042

**CITY ACTORS' MANAGEMENT**
(Personal Manager) (CPMA Member)
Oval House
52-54 Kennington Oval
London SE11 5SW                       Tel: 020-7793 9888
Website: www.cityactors.co.uk
e-mail: info@cityactors.co.uk

**C.K.K. ENTERTAINMENT**
PO Box 24550
London E17 9FG
e-mail: ckk.entertainment@virgin.net
Fax: 020-7515 6373                    Tel: 020-7531 6300

**CLARENDON ARTIST MANAGEMENT**
6 Old Lodge Place
St Margarets
Twickenham TW1 1RQ                    Tel: 020-8831 7221
Website: www.clarendonam.com
e-mail: info@clarendonam.com

**CLARKE AND JONES Ltd**
28 Fordwych Court
Shoot Up Hill
London NW2 3PH
e-mail: mail@clarkeandjones.plus.com
Fax: 0870 1313391                     Tel: 020-8438 0185

**CLASS - CARLINE LUNDON ASSOCIATES**
25 Falkner Square
Liverpool L8 7NZ                      Mobile: 07853 248957
e-mail: carline.lundon@ukonline.co.uk

**CLAYMAN Tony PROMOTIONS Ltd**
Vicarage House
58-60 Kensington Church Street
London W8 4DB
Website: www.tonyclayman.com
e-mail: tony@tonyclayman.com
Fax: 020-7368 3338                    Tel: 020-7368 3336

# Claire Grogan
## P h o t o g r a p h y

Anna-Maria Nabiyre

Ben Richards

Lindsey Coulson

Martin Freeman

Nicola Blackman

Duane Henry

Kerrie Andrews

Steve McFadden

Heather Peace

claire@clairegrogan.co.uk
www.clairegrogan.co.uk

**Film or Digital**

020 7272 1845
07932 635381

Kelly Schembri

Ericka Kamlert

Georgina Andrews

Sabastion Louis Blanc

Henreter Carey-Bryant

Musician Martin Fry ABC

# ACTORS/ACTRESSES PORTRAITS
## Photography for all your publicity and Spotlight needs
### We also photograph presenters, dancers, entertainers (musicians etc)

A Big Thank You to the following who we have photographed over the past 30 years:

| | | | |
|---|---|---|---|
| Richard Burton | Virginia McKenna | Diana Dors | Marie Helvin |
| Brigitte Bardot | Don Johnson | David Bellamy | Sam Fox |
| Sophia Loren | Grace Jones | Michael Bolton | Shirley Anne Field |
| Kojak | Roger Moore | Eric Morecambe | Will Young |
| Ronkey Philips | Bruce Willis | Vivien Creegor | Gareth Gates |
| Peter Sellers | Demi Moore | Martin Fry | Charles Dance |
| Dame Judi Dench | Patrick Swayze | Miyako Yoshida | Neil Diamond on |
| Derek Jacobi | Sir Richard Branson | Papillon Soo Lam | his recent 2008 tour |
| John Lennon | Sylvia Kristel | Richard O'Sullivan | and the rest, too |
| | | | many to mention... |

Phone or email for our special package.
A minimum of 80 colour and 80 B&W photos.
2 high resolution CDs to take away at the end of shoot.
Top hair and make-up artist supplied on request.

**Special offer to Spotlight and Contacts readers and subscribers: £170**
The highest quality photography by probably one of the best portrait photographers in the world at the most competitive prices

## Tel: 0208 438 0303 Mobile: 07712 669 953
e-mail: billy_snapper@hotmail.com
### www.london-photographer.com
www.theukphotographerexhibition.co.uk - www.billysnapper.com

Will C - Photographer to the Stars

**Picture Credits**  Sinitta actresss and singer, Martina Miss Slovakia, Sir Richard Branson Virgin, Andy Hamilton Whitbread, Jana Hyncociva, Miss Pinto with Rat, Kate Melton actress, Elizabeth actress

Will C specialises in actors, actresses and personalities in advertising, editorial, film and television. He has been principal photographer on over 30 major films and has directed and shot 40 commercials. Actors and actresses portraits can be taken in our fully equipped film and digital studio in NW2 - just 15 minutes from Marble Arch or Baker Street.

Tokyo  •  New York  •  Amsterdam  •  Paris  •  London

**CLAYPOLE MANAGEMENT**
PO Box 123
DL3 7WA
Website: www.claypolemanagement.co.uk
e-mail: info@claypolemanagement.co.uk
Fax: 0870 1334784                    Tel: 0845 6501777

**CLIC AGENCY**
Rhoslwyn
Rhoslsaf
Nr. Caernarfon
Gwynedd LL54 7NF                    Tel: 01286 831001
Website: www.clicagency.co.uk
e-mail: clic@btinternet.com

**CLOUD NINE AGENCY**
96 Tiber Gardens
Treaty Street
London N1 0XE
Website: www.cloudnineagency.co.uk
e-mail: email@cloudnineagency.co.uk
Mobile: 07506 579749              Tel/Fax: 020-7278 0029

**CMP MANAGEMENT**
8-30 Galena Road
Hammersmith
London W6 0LT
e-mail: info@ravenscourt.net
Fax: 020-8741 1786                    Tel: 020-8741 3400

**COCHRANE Elspeth PERSONAL MANAGEMENT**
(PMA Member)
*Existing clients only*
*No new applicants*
See ASQUITH & HORNER

**COLE KITCHENN PERSONAL MANAGEMENT Ltd**
(PMA Member)
212 Strand
London WC2R 1AP
Website: www.colekitchenn.com
e-mail: stuart@colekitchenn.com
Fax: 020-7353 9639                    Tel: 020-7427 5681

**COLLINS Shane ASSOCIATES**
(PMA Member)
11-15 Betterton Street
Covent Garden
London WC2H 9BP
Website: www.shanecollins.co.uk
e-mail: info@shanecollins.co.uk
Fax: 0870 460 1983                    Tel: 020-7470 8864

**COLLIS MANAGEMENT**
(PMA Member)
182 Trevelyan Road
London SW17 9LW
e-mail: marilyn@collismanagement.co.uk
Fax: 020-8682 0973                    Tel: 020-8767 0196

**COMEDY CLUB Ltd The**
2nd Floor, 28-31 Moulsham Street
Chelmsford, Essex CM2 0HX
Website: www.hahaheehee.com
e-mail: info@hahaheehee.com
Fax: 01245 255507                    Tel: 0870 0425656

**COMIC VOICE MANAGEMENT**
2nd Floor
28-31 Moulsham Street
Chelmsford, Essex CM2 0HX
Website: www.comicvoice.com
e-mail: info@comicvoice.com
Fax: 01245 255507                    Tel: 0870 0425656

**COMMERCIAL AGENCY The**
(See TCA)

**CONTI Italia AGENCY Ltd**
*Contact: By Post/Telephone*
23 Goswell Road
London EC1M 7AJ
e-mail: agency@italiaconti.co.uk
Fax: 020-7253 1430                    Tel: 020-7608 7500

**CONWAY Clive CELEBRITY PRODUCTIONS Ltd**
32 Grove Street, Oxford OX2 7JT
Website: www.celebrityproductions.info
e-mail: info@celebrityproductions.org
Fax: 01865 514409                    Tel: 01865 514830

**CONWAY VAN GELDER GRANT Ltd**
(Personal Manager) (PMA Member)
3rd Floor, 8-12 Broadwick Street
London W1F 8HW
Fax: 020-7287 1940                    Tel: 020-7287 0077

**COOKE Howard ASSOCIATES**
(PMA Member)
*Contact: Howard Cooke. By Post*
*2 Agents represent 50 Performers*
*Commercials. Film. Stage. Television*
19 Coulson Street
Chelsea, London SW3 3NA
Fax: 020-7591 0155                    Tel: 020-7591 0144

# Steve Lawton

PHOTOGRAPHY LONDON

07973 307487

www.stevelawton.com

Student rates

Dev Patel, Kerry Ellis, Adam-Joe Florentino

Kelly Adams, Robert Kazinsky, Natalie Cox

Steven Webb, Natalie Anderson, Douglas Booth

**icon** actors management

Tel: 0161 273 3344   Fax: 0161 273 4567
Tanzaro House, Ardwick Green North, Manchester. M12 6FZ
info@iconactors.net, www.iconactors.net

**COOPER Tommy AGENCY The**
*Comedy. Magicians*
21 Streatham Court
Ashley Cross
Poole, Dorset BH14 0EX          Mobile: 07860 290437
Website: www.tommycooperremembered.co.uk

**CORNER Clive ASSOCIATES**
*Contact: Duncan Stratton*
*By Post*
*Accepts Showreels*
*3 Agents represent 80 Performers*
*Commercials. Film. Musicals. Stage. Television*
'The Belenes'
60 Wakeham, Portland DT5 1HN          Tel: 01305 860267
e-mail: cornerassociates@aol.com

**CORNISH Caroline MANAGEMENT Ltd**
*Technicians only*
12 Shinfield Street
London W12 0HN
Website: www.carolinecornish.co.uk
e-mail: carolinecornish@btconnect.com
Fax: 020-8743 7887          Tel: 020-8743 7337

**COULSON Lou ASSOCIATES Ltd**
(PMA Member)
1st Floor
37 Berwick Street
London W1F 8RS
e-mail: info@loucoulson.co.uk
Fax: 020-7439 7569          Tel: 020-7734 9633

**COULTER MANAGEMENT AGENCY Ltd**
(PMA Member)
*Contact: Anne Coulter*
PO Box 2830
Glasgow G61 9BQ          Tel: 0141-357 6666
e-mail: coultermanagement@ntlworld.com

**COVENT GARDEN MANAGEMENT**
5 Denmark Street
London WC2H 8LP          Tel: 020-7240 8400
Website: www.coventgardenmanagement.com
e-mail: agents@coventgardenmanagement.com

**CPA MANAGEMENT**
The Studios
219B North Street
Romford
Essex RM1 4QA
Website: www.cpamanagement.co.uk
e-mail: julie@cpamanagement.co.uk
Fax: 01708 766077          Tel: 01708 766444

**CRAWFORDS**
PO Box 44394
London SW20 0YP
Website: www.crawfords.tv
e-mail: cr@wfords.com
Fax: 020-3258 5037          Tel: 020-8947 9999

**CREATIVE MEDIA MANAGEMENT**
(PMA Member)
*No Actors. Film, TV & Theatre Technical Personnel only*
Ealing Studios, Ealing Green
London W5 5EP
Website: www.creativemediamanagement.com
e-mail: enquiries@creativemediamanagement.com
Fax: 020-8566 5554          Tel: 020-8584 5363

**CREDITS ACTORS AGENCY Ltd**
29 Lorn Road
London SW9 0AB          Tel: 020-7737 0735
e-mail: credits@actors29.freeserve.co.uk

**CRESCENT MANAGEMENT**
(Personal Manager) (CPMA Member)
*Contact: By Post*
*Accepts Showreels*
10 Barley Mow Passage
Chiswick, London W4 4PH
Website: www.crescentmanagement.co.uk
e-mail: mail@crescentmanagement.co.uk
Fax: 020-8987 0207          Tel: 020-8987 0191

**CROWD PULLERS**
Street Performers
14 Somerset Gardens, London SE13 7SY
e-mail: jhole@crowdpullers.co.uk
Fax: 020-8469 2147          Tel: 020-8469 3900

**CRUICKSHANK CAZENOVE Ltd**
(PMA Member)
*Contact: Sky Macaskill*
*By Post*
*Accepts Showreels*
*2 Agents*
*Choreographers. Designers. Directors*
97 Old South Lambeth Road
London SW8 1XU
e-mail: mail@ccagents.co.uk
Fax: 020-7582 6405          Tel: 020-7735 2933

**CS MANAGEMENT**
(PMA Member)
The Croft, 7 Cannon Road
Southgate, London N14 7HE
Website: www.csmanagementuk.com
e-mail: carole@csmanagementuk.com
Fax: 020-8886 7555          Tel: 020-8886 4264

**CS PROMOTIONS**
*Contact: By e-mail/Telephone*
*300+ Performers*
*Commercials. Dancers. Modelling. Sports Models*
Jubilee Stand
Crystal Palace National Sports Centre
London SE19 2BB
Website: www.sportspromotions.co.uk
e-mail: agent@sportspromotions.co.uk
Fax: 020-8776 7772          Tel: 020-8659 4561

**C.S.A.**
(Christina Shepherd Advertising)
4th Floor
45 Maddox Street
London W1S 2PE
e-mail: csa@shepherdmanagement.co.uk
Fax: 020-7499 7534        Tel 020-7499 7534

**CURTIS BROWN GROUP Ltd**
(PMA Member)
Haymarket House
28-29 Haymarket
London SW1Y 4SP
e-mail: actorsagents@curtisbrown.co.uk
Fax: 020-7393 4401        Tel: 020-7393 4400

**DALY PEARSON ASSOCIATES**
(PMA Member)
*Contact: David Daly, Paul Pearson, Sophie Hirst*
586A King's Road, London SW6 2DX
Website: www.dalypearson.co.uk
e-mail: agent@dalypearson.co.uk
Fax: 020-7610 9512        Tel: 020-7384 1036

**DALY PEARSON ASSOCIATES (MANCHESTER)**
*Contact: Natalie Payne*
16 King Street
Knutsford WA16 6DL
Website: www.dalypearson.co.uk/manchester
e-mail: north@dalypearson.co.uk
Fax: 01565 755334        Tel: 01565 631999

paulcable
photography & design

www.paulcable.com
info@paulcable.com
07958 932 764

**DALZELL & BERESFORD Ltd**
26 Astwood Mews
London SW7 4DE
e-mail: mail@dblltd.co.uk
Fax: 020-7341 9412          Tel: 020-7341 9411

**DANCERS**
1 Charlotte Street
London W1T 1RD
Website: www.features.co.uk
e-mail: info@features.co.uk
Fax: 020-7637 0328          Tel: 020-7636 1473

**DARRELL Emma MANAGEMENT**
*Directors. Producers. Writers*
Hazelbank
3 Chalfont Lane
Chorleywood
Herts WD3 5PR
e-mail: emma.mc@virgin.net
Fax: 01923 284064          Tel: 01923 284061

**DAVID ARTISTES MANAGEMENT AGENCY Ltd The**
26-28 Hammersmith Grove
London W6 7BA          Tel: 020-8834 1615
Website: www.davidagency.net
e-mail: casting@davidagency.net

**DAVIS Chris MANAGEMENT Ltd**
(PMA Member)
Tenbury House
36 Teme Street
Tenbury Wells
Worcestershire WR15 8AA
Website: www.cdm-ltd.com
e-mail: info@cdm-ltd.com
Fax: 01584 819076          Tel: 01584 819005

**DAVIS Lena, JOHN BISHOP ASSOCIATES**
(Personal Manager)
*Contact: By Post*
*2 Agents*
Cotton's Farmhouse, Whiston Road
Cogenhoe, Northants NN7 1NL
e-mail: admin@cottonsfarmhouse.org          Tel: 01604 891487

**DEALERS AGENCY BELFAST**
Cathedral House
22-31 Waring Street
Belfast BT1 2DX
Website: www.dealersagency.co.uk
e-mail: patrickduncan609@msn.com
Tel: 00 44 28 90 43 66 39          Tel: 00 44 28 90 24 27 26

**DENMAN CASTING AGENCY**
*Contact: By Post/Telephone*
*2 Agents represent 100+ Performers*
Burgess House, Main Street
Farnsfield
Notts NG22 8EF          Tel/Fax: 01623 882272

**DENMARK STREET MANAGEMENT**
(Personal Manager) (CPMA Member)
*Contact: By Post (SAE)*
Suite 4
Clarendon Buildings
25 Horsell Road
Highbury N5 1XL
Website: www.denmarkstreet.net
e-mail: mail@denmarkstreet.net
Fax: 020-7607 8085          Tel: 020-7700 5200

**DEREK'S HANDS AGENCY**
Hand & Foot Modelling
26-28 Hammersmith Grove
London W6 7BA          Tel: 020-8834 1609
Website: www.derekshands.com
e-mail: casting@derekshands.com

**DEVINE ARTIST MANAGEMENT**
Mayfair House
16 Heddon Street
London W1B 4DA
e-mail: mail@devinemanagement.co.uk
Fax: 0844 8845083          Tel: 0844 8844578

**de WOLFE Felix**
(Personal Manager) (PMA Member)
*Contact: By Post*
*Accepts Showreels*
*3 Agents*
*Film. Musicals. Radio. Stage. Television*
Kingsway House
103 Kingsway
London WC2B 6QX
Website: www.felixdewolfe.com
e-mail: info@felixdewolfe.com
Fax: 020-7242 8119          Tel: 020-7242 5066

**DIAMOND MANAGEMENT**
(PMA Member)
31 Percy Street
London W1T 2DD
e-mail: agents@diman.co.uk
Fax: 020-7631 0500          Tel: 020-7631 0400

**DIESTENFELD Lily**
(Personal Manager Over 50+ ages)
*No unsolicited Mail/Calls from Actors*
28B Alexandra Grove
London N12 8HG          Tel: 020-8446 5379
e-mail: lilyd@talk21.com

**DIMPLES THEATRICAL ACADEMY**
*Contact: By Post/e-mail*
84 Kirkhall Lane
Leigh, Lancs WN7 5QQ          Tel: 01942 262012
Website: www.dimples-models.com
e-mail: info@dimples-models.com

**DIRECT PERSONAL MANAGEMENT**
(Personal Manager) (CPMA Member)
*Contact: Daphne Franks*
St John's House
16 St John's Vale
London SE8 4EN          Tel/Fax: 020-8694 1788
Website: www.directpm.co.uk
e-mail: daphne.franks@directpm.co.uk

Park House, 62 Lidgett Lane
Leeds LS8 1PL          Tel/Fax: 0113-266 4036

**DOE John MANAGEMENT**
26 Noko
3-6 Banister Road, London W10 4AR
Website: www.johndoemgt.com
e-mail: casting@johndoemgt.com
Mobile: 07957 114175          Tel: 020-8960 2848

**DON CAPO ENTERTAINMENT PRODUCTIONS**
Suite B, 5 South Bank Terrace
Surbiton, Surrey KT6 6DG
Website: www.doncapo.com
e-mail: doncapoandco@aol.com
Mobile: 07787 995604          Tel/Fax: 020-8390 8535

**DOTTED LINE**
13 Portman House, 136 High Road, London N22 6DF
Website: www.dotted-line.co.uk
e-mail: info@dotted-line.co.uk
Fax: 0844 3576764          Tel: 0844 3510223

**DOUBLE ACT CELEBRITY LOOK ALIKES**
PO Box 25574, London NW7 3GB
Website: www.double-act.co.uk
e-mail: info@double-act.co.uk
Fax: 020-8201 1795          Tel: 020-8381 0151

**DOUBLEFVOICES**
*Singers*
1 Hunters Lodge, Bodiam, East Sussex TN32 5UE
e-mail: rob@doublefvoices.com
Mobile: 07976 927764          Tel: 01580 830071

Robin Soans          Lauren Cohan          Leo Staar

# ric bacon
www.ricbacon.co.uk
**07970 970 799**
student rates

**CBA International**

Representing **Actors** and **Actresses** Bilingual in English, French & American

**Contact Cindy Brace**

T  00 (33) 1 4526 33 42
M  00 (33) 671 10 60 10
E  c_b_a@club-internet.fr

W  www.cindy-brace.com
M  07789 991032
E  cba_office@yahoo.co.uk

C/O C.M.S. Experts Associés, 149 Boulevard Malesherbes, 75017 Paris, France

**DOWNES PRESENTERS AGENCY**
96 Broadway
Bexleyheath, Kent DA6 7DE          Tel: 020-8304 0541
Website: www.presentersagency.com
e-mail: downes@presentersagency.com

**DP MANAGEMENT**
*Contact: Danny Pellerini*
*By Post*
*Accepts Showreels/Voicereels*
*1 Agent represents 60 Performers*
Argyle House
29-31 Euston Road, London NW1 2SD     Mobile: 07837 138892
e-mail: danny@dpmanagement.org

**DQ MANAGEMENT**
27 Ravenswood Park
Northwood, Middlesex HA6 3PR
Website: www.dqmanagement.com
e-mail: dq.management1@googlemail.com
Mobile: 07713 984633          Tel: 01273 721221

**DRAGON PERSONAL MANAGEMENT**
96 Diana Street
Roath, Cardiff CF24 4TU          Tel: 029-2019 3974
Website: www.dragon-pm.com
e-mail: casting@dragon-pm.com

**DRAKE Simon MANAGEMENT**
9 Golden Square
London W1F 9HZ
Website: www.simondrakemanagement.co.uk
e-mail: admin@simondrakemanagement.co.uk
Fax: 020-7183 9013          Tel: 020-7183 8995

**DRB ENTERTAINMENT AGENCY**
78 York Street
London W1H 1DP          Tel: 0118-941 5465
Website: www.drbentertainment.co.uk
e-mail: mail@drbentertainment.co.uk

**DREW Bryan Ltd**
(Personal Manager) Contact: By Post
Mezzanine
Quadrant House
80-82 Regent Street
London W1B 5AU
e-mail: bryan@bryandrewltd.com
Fax: 020-7437 0561          Tel: 020-7437 2293

**EARLE Kenneth PERSONAL MANAGEMENT**
214 Brixton Road
London SW9 6AP
Website: www.entertainment-kennethearle.co.uk
e-mail: kennethearle@agents-uk.com
Fax: 020-7274 9529          Tel: 020-7274 1219

**EARNSHAW Susi MANAGEMENT**
(Personal Manager)
The Bull Theatre, 68 High Street
Barnet, Herts EN5 5SJ
Website: www.susiearnshawmanagement.com
e-mail: casting@susiearnshaw.co.uk
Fax: 020-8364 9618          Tel: 020-8441 5010

**EDEN Shelly ASSOCIATES Ltd**
The Old Factory
Minus One House
Lyttelton Road
London E10 5NQ          Tel/Fax: 020-8558 3536
e-mail: shellyeden@aol.com

**EDLER Debbie MANAGEMENT Ltd (DEM)**
Little Friars Cottage
Lombard Street
Eynsham, Oxon OX29 4HT          Tel: 01865 884203
Website: www.demagency.co.uk
e-mail: info@demagency.co.uk

**EJA ASSOCIATES**
*Incorporating Simply Singers International*
PO Box 63617
London SW9 1AN
e-mail: ejaassociates@aol.com
Mobile: 07891 632946          Tel: 020-7564 2688

**EKA ACTOR MANAGEMENT**
(Personal Manager)
*Contact: Rebecca Keeley*
*By Post/e-mail*
*Accepts Showreels*
*6 Agents.*
*Commercials. Film. Television. Voice Overs*
The Warehouse Studios
Glaziers Lane
Culcheth
Warrington WA3 4AQ
Website: www.eka-agency.com
e-mail: castings@eka-agency.com
Fax: 01925 767563          Tel: 01925 761088

**ELITE TALENT Ltd**
9 Gloucester Avenue
Heywood OL10 2PU
Website: www.elite-talent.com
e-mail: jackie@elite-talent.com
Mobile: 07912 642946          Tel: 01706 623217

**ELLIOTT AGENCY Ltd The**
10 High Street
Shoreham-by-Sea BN43 5DA          Tel: 01273 454111
Website: www.elliottagency.co.uk
e-mail: elliottagency@btconnect.com

**ELLIS Bill Ltd**
(See A & B PERSONAL MANAGEMENT Ltd)

**ELLITE MANAGEMENT**
*Contact: By Post/e-mail*
*Accepts Showreels*
*3 Agents represent 40 Performers*
*Dancers*
'The Dancer'
8 Peterson Road
Wakefield WF1 4EB
Website: www.elliteproductions.co.uk
e-mail: enquiries@ellitemanagement.co.uk
Mobile: 07957 631510          Tel: 0845 6525361

**EMPTAGE HALLETT**
(PMA Member)
14 Rathbone Place, London W1T 1HT
e-mail: mail@emptagehallett.co.uk
Fax: 020-7580 2748　　　　Tel: 020-7436 0425

2nd Floor, 3-5 The Balcony
Castle Arcade, Cardiff CF10 1BU
e-mail: gemma.mcavoy@emptagehallett.co.uk
Fax: 029-2034 4206　　　　Tel: 029-2034 4205

**ENGLISH Doreen '95**
*Contact: By Post/Telephone*
4 Selsey Avenue, Aldwick, Bognor Regis
West Sussex PO21 2QZ　　　Tel/Fax: 01243 825968

**ENTERTAINMENT EXECUTIVES & TALENT**
24 Beehive Lane
Basildon SS14 2LG
Website: www.dan-blumenau.com
e-mail: info@dan-blumenau.com　　Tel: 020-7193 5978

**ENTERTAINMENT PEOPLE MANAGEMENT**
63 Blythe Road, Kensington, London W14 0HP
Website: www.ep-site.com
e-mail: russell.hawkins@ep-site.com
Fax: 020-7100 6090　　　　Tel: 020-7100 6070

**EORB CREATIVE**
The Thanet
Herbert Street
London NW5 4HD　　　　Tel: 020-7788 7737
Website: www.eorbcreative.co.uk
e-mail: info@eorbcreative.co.uk

**EPMC TALENT**
*Contact: Aldo Arcilla*
*By Post*
*Accepts Showreels/Voicereels*
Unit 67
Ability Plaza
Arbutus Street
London E8 4DT
Website: www.epmctalent.com
e-mail: info@epmctalent.com
Fax: 0871 5593947　　　　Tel: 0844 8243888

**EPSTEIN June ASSOCIATES**
*Contact: By Post/e-mail*
Flat 1
62 Compayne Gardens
London NW6 3RY
e-mail: june@june-epstein-associates.co.uk
Fax: 020-7328 0684　　　　Tel: 020-7328 0864

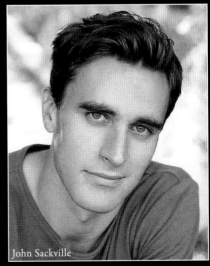

**ESSANAY**
(Personal Manager) (PMA Member)
*Contact: By Post*
PO Box 44394
London SW20 0YP
e-mail: info@essanay.co.uk
Fax: 020-3258 5037          Tel: 020-8549 4472

**ETHNICS ARTISTE AGENCY**
86 Elphinstone Road
Walthamstow
London E17 5EX
e-mail: info@ethnicsaa.co.uk
Fax: 020-8523 4523          Tel: 020-8523 4242

**EUROKIDS CASTING AGENCY**
*Contact: Rebecca Keeley*
*By Post/e-mail*
*Accepts Showreels*
*6 Agents*
*Children. Commercials. Film. Television. Walk-on &
Supporting Artists*
The Warehouse Studios, Glaziers Lane
Culcheth, Warrington WA3 4AQ
Website: www.eka-agency.com
e-mail: castings@eka-agency.com
Fax: 01925 767563          Tel: 01925 761088

**EVANS & REISS**
(PMA Member)
100 Fawe Park Road, London SW15 2EA
e-mail: janita@evansandreiss.co.uk
Fax: 020-8877 0307          Tel: 020-8877 3755

**EVANS Jacque MANAGEMENT Ltd**
Top Floor Suite
14 Holmesley Road, London SE23 1PJ
Website: www.jacqueevansltd.com
Fax: 020-8699 5192          Tel: 020-8699 1202

**EVANS Stephanie ASSOCIATES**
Rivington House
82 Great Eastern Street
London EC2A 3JF          Tel/Fax: 0870 6092629
Website: www.stephanie-evans.com
e-mail: steph@stephanie-evans.com

**EVOLUTION TALENT MANAGEMENT**
The Truman Brewery Building
Studio 21
91 Brick Lane, London E1 6QL
Website: www.evolutionmngt.com
e-mail: info@evolutionmngt.com
Fax: 020-7375 2752          Tel: 020-7770 6128

**EXPERTS MANAGEMENT SERVICES Ltd**
(T/A Jane Hughes Management)
PO Box 200
Stockport
Cheshire SK12 1GW
e-mail: gill@jhm.co.uk
Mobile: 07766 130604          Tel: 01625 858556

**EXPRESSIONS CASTING AGENCY**
3 Newgate Lane
Mansfield
Nottingham NG18 2LB
Website: www.expressionsperformingarts.co.uk
e-mail: expressions-uk@btconnect.com
Fax: 01623 647337          Tel: 01623 424334

**EYE MODELS The**
Tower Room
The Bath House
8 Chapel Place
Rivington Street
London EC2A 3DQ          Tel: 020-7729 9705
Website: www.theeyecasting.com
e-mail: bayo@theeyecasting.com

**FARINO Paola**
109 St Georges Road
London SE1 6HY          Tel: 020-7207 0858
Website: www.paolafarino.co.uk
e-mail: info@paolafarino.co.uk

**FARNES Norma MANAGEMENT**
9 Orme Court
London W2 4RL
Fax: 020-7792 2110          Tel: 020-7727 1544

**FAWKES Irene MANAGEMENT**
*Contact: Irene Fawkes*
*By Post*
*Accepts Showreels*
*1 Agent represents 40 Clients*
*Commercials. Film. Musicals. Stage. Television*
2nd Floor
91A Rivington Street
London EC2A 3AY
e-mail: irenefawkes@btconnect.com
Fax: 020-7613 0769          Tel: 020-7729 8559

**FBI AGENCY The**
PO Box 250
Leeds LS1 2AZ          Mobile: 07050 222747
Website: www.fbi-agency.co.uk
e-mail: casting@fbi-agency.co.uk

**Representing:-**
- Dancers, Choreographers and Singers in all aspects of TV, Film, Video, Theatre, Commercial and Cruise work.
- Specialising in Musical Theatre.
- Full Production Team available for Trade, Fashion & Corporate Events.
- Select actors' personal management service available.

**Visit our website: www.kmcagencies.co.uk**

PO Box 122
48 Great Ancoats Street
Manchester M4 5AB
**t:** 0161 237 3009
**f:** 0161 237 9812
**e:** casting@kmcagencies.co.uk

Garden Studios
11-15 Betterton Street
London WC2H 9BP
**t:** 0845 660 2459
**f:** 0870 442 1780
**e:** london@kmcagencies.co.uk

**FD MANAGEMENT**
*Contact: By e-mail*
*Accepts Showreels*
*1 Agent represents 15 Performers*
Little Benhams
Friday Street, Rusper RH12 4QA    Mobile: 07730 800679
e-mail: vivienwilde@mac.com

**FEA MANAGEMENT**
(Ferris Entertainment) London. Belfast. Cardiff
Number 8
132 Charing Cross Road
London WC2H 0LA    Tel: 08454 724725
Website: www.ferrisentertainment.com
e-mail: info@ferrisentertainment.com

**FEAST MANAGEMENT Ltd**
(PMA Member)
1st Floor
34 Upper Street, London N1 0PN
e-mail: office@feastmanagement.co.uk
Fax: 020-7354 8995    Tel: 020-7354 5216

**FEATURES**
1 Charlotte Street, London W1T 1RD
Website: www.features.co.uk
e-mail: info@features.co.uk
Fax: 020-7637 0328    Tel: 020-7637 1487

**FETCH**
c/o Mad Dog Casting Ltd
15 Leighton Place, London NW5 2QL
Website: www.fetchactors.com
e-mail: fetchtalent@maddogcasting.com
Fax: 020-7284 2689    Tel: 020-7482 0477

**FIELD Alan ASSOCIATES**
(Personal Manager)
*Contact: By e-mail*
*Celebrities. Musicals. Presenters. Singers*
3 The Spinney, Bakers Hill, Hadley Common, Herts EN5 5QJ
e-mail: alan@alanfield.com
Fax: 020-8447 0657    Tel: 020-8441 1137

**FILM CAST CORNWALL**
c/o 3 Church Walk, Truro TR1 1JH    Tel: 01326 311419
Website: www.filmcastcornwall.co.uk
e-mail: enquiries@filmcastcornwall.co.uk

**FILM RIGHTS Ltd**
(Personal Manager)
*Contact: By Post*
Mezzanine, Quadrant House
80-82 Regent Street, London W1B 5AU
Fax: 020-7734 0044    Tel: 020-7734 9911

**FINCH & PARTNERS**
Top Floor, 29-37 Heddon Street, London W1B 4BR
Website: www.finchandpartners.com
e-mail: kat@finchandpartners.com
Fax: 020-7287 6420    Tel: 020-7851 7140

**FIRST ACT PERSONAL MANAGEMENT**
(Personal Manager)
*Contact: John Burton*
*By Post*
*2 Agents represent 20-30 Performers*
*Commercials. Corporate. Film. Stage. Television*
2 Saint Michaels, New Arley
Coventry, Warwickshire CV7 8PY    Tel: 01676 540285
e-mail: firstactpm@aol.com

# Nick Gregan
## PHOTOGRAPHY

**The easiest and probably the best headshot you'll ever have by one of London's premier theatrical photographers**

**For contemporary, natural headshots for actors & performers, contact Nick on
Tel: 020 8533 3003    Mobile: 07774 421878    www.nickgregan.com
email: info@nickgregan.com
Special rates for theatre schools and group bookings**

**FIRST ARTIST MANAGEMENT**
3 Tenterden Street
Hanover Square
London W1S 1TD
Website: www.firstartist.co.uk
e-mail: info@firstartist.co.uk
Fax: 020-3205 2140     Tel: 020-7096 9999

**FIRST CALL MANAGEMENT**
29-30 Dame Street
Dublin 2
Ireland
e-mail: fcm@indigo.ie
Fax: 00 353 1 679 8353     Tel: 00 353 1 679 8401

**FITZGERALD Sheridan MANAGEMENT**
*Contact: By Post (SAE). No Phone Calls*
87 Western Road
Upton Park
London E13 9JE     Tel: 020-8471 9814

**FLAIR TALENT**
46 Barry Road
East Dulwich
London SE22 0HU     Tel: 020-8693 8649
Website: www.flairtalent.com
e-mail: aaron@flairtalent.com

**FLETCHER ASSOCIATES**
(Personal Manager)
*Contact: Francine Fletcher*
*By Telephone*
*Corporate. Experts. Radio. Stage. Television*
25 Parkway
London N20 0XN
Website: www.fletcherassociates.net
Fax: 020-8361 8866     Tel: 020-8361 8061

**FLETCHER JACOB**
(Artist Management)
Tower Room
Bath House
8 Chapel Place
Rivington Street, London EC2A 3DQ     Tel: 020-7617 7181
e-mail: info@fletcherjacob.co.uk

**FLP**
Hurlingham Studios
Unit 19A, Ranelagh Gardens
Fulham, London SW6 3PA
Website: www.formulaliveproductions.com
e-mail: info@formulaliveproductions.com
Fax: 020-7731 3422     Tel: 020-7371 0300

**FOSTER Sharon MANAGEMENT**
15A Hollybank Road
Birmingham B13 0RF     Tel: 0121-443 4865
Website: www.sharonfoster.co.uk
e-mail: mail@sharonfoster.co.uk

**FOX Clare ASSOCIATES**
Set, Lighting & Sound Designers
9 Plympton Road
London NW6 7EH     Tel/Fax: 020-7328 7494
Website: www.clarefox.co.uk
e-mail: cimfox@yahoo.co.uk

**FOX Julie ASSOCIATES**
(Personal Manager)
*Contact: Julie Fox*
*By e-mail only*
*Accepts Showreels/Voicereels*
*2 Agents represent 50 Performers*
9 Adam Street, London W1     Tel/Fax: 01628 777853
e-mail: agent@juliefoxassociates.co.uk

## Personal Management

### Agents:
Simon Bashford
Michael Garrett
Jessica Jones
Niki Winterson

### GLOBAL ARTISTS
23 Haymarket  London SW1Y 4DG
Tel: 020 7839 4888  Fax: 020 7839 4555
email: info@globalartists.co.uk
www.globalartists.co.uk
www.theatricalagent.co.uk

Members of the Personal Managers' Association

Michael Garrett Associates Ltd. Registered No. 4404385
Registered Office: 23 Haymarket, London SW1Y 4DG

Emma Akwafo · Antonio Salerno · Anna Nicolaus · Jemma Robinson · Stephen Duke

**FRENCH Linda**
(See ALEXANDER PERSONAL MANAGEMENT Ltd)

**FRESH AGENTS Ltd**
Suite 5
Saks House
19 Ship Street
Brighton BN1 1AD                    Tel: 0845 4080998
Website: www.freshagents.co.uk
e-mail: info@freshagents.co.uk

**FRESH PARTNERS**
1 Hardwick's Square
Wandsworth
London SW18 4AW                    Tel: 020-7198 8478
Website: www.fresh-partners.com
e-mail: hello@fresh-partners.com

**FRONTLINE ACTORS AGENCY DUBLIN**
30-31 Wicklow Street
Dublin 2
Ireland                    Tel: 00 353 1 6359882
Website: www.frontlineactors.com
e-mail: frontlineactors@eircom.net

**FUNKY BEETROOT CELEBRITY MANAGEMENT Ltd**
(Personal Manager)
*Actors. Television Celebrities*
PO Box 143
Faversham
Kent ME13 9LP
Website: www.funky-beetroot.com
e-mail: info@funky-beetroot.com
Fax: 01227 752300                    Tel: 01227 751549

**GAELFORCE 10 MANAGEMENT**
Film City
401 Govan Road
Glasgow G51 2QJ
Website: www.gaelforce10.com
e-mail: info@gaelforce10.com
Fax: 0871 7146275                    Tel: 0845 6031266

**GAGAN Hilary ASSOCIATES**
(Personal Manager) (PMA Member)
187 Drury Lane
London WC2B 5QD
e-mail: hilary@hgassoc.freeserve.co.uk
Fax: 020-7430 1869                    Tel: 020-7404 8794

**GALLOWAYS ONE**
15 Lexham Mews
London W8 6JW
Website: www.gallowaysone.com
e-mail: jill@gallowaysone.com
Fax: 020-7376 2416                    Tel: 020-7376 2288

**GANNON Kay**
Central Chambers
93 Hope Street
Glasgow G2 6LD                    Tel/Fax: 0141-221 8622
Website: www.revolutiontalentmanagement.com
e-mail: kay@revolutiontalentmanagement.com

**GARDNER HERRITY Ltd**
(PMA Member)
*Contact: Andy Herrity*
24 Conway Street, London W1T 6BG
Website: www.gardnerherrity.co.uk
e-mail: info@gardnerherrity.co.uk
Fax: 020-7388 0688                    Tel: 020-7388 0088

**GARRETT Michael**
(See GLOBAL ARTISTS)

**GARRICKS**
(PMA Member)
Angel House, 76 Mallinson Road, London SW11 1BN
e-mail: info@garricks.net
Fax: 020-7801 0088                    Tel: 020-7738 1600

**GAY Noel**
19 Denmark Street, London WC2H 8NA
Website: www.noelgay.com
e-mail: info@noelgay.com
Fax: 020-7287 1816                    Tel: 020-7836 3941

**GFI MANAGEMENT**
(Personal Manager)
Green Gables
47 North Lane
Teddington, Middlesex TW11 0HU
Website: www.goforitcentre.com
e-mail: agency@goforitcentre.com
Mobile: 07956 646412                    Tel: 020-8943 1120

**GILBERT & PAYNE**
Room 236, 2nd Floor
Linen Hall
162-168 Regent Street
London W1B 5TB
e-mail: ee@gilbertandpayne.com
Fax: 020-7494 3787                    Tel: 020-7734 7505

**GILLMAN Geraldine ASSOCIATES**
Malcolm House, Malcolm Primary School
Malcolm Road
Penge, London SE20 8RH
e-mail: geraldi.gillma@btconnect.com
Mobile: 07799 791586                    Tel: 0844 8005328

**GLASS Eric Ltd**
25 Ladbroke Crescent
Notting Hill
London W11 1PS
e-mail: eglassltd@aol.com
Fax: 020-7229 6220                    Tel: 020-7229 9500

**GLOBAL ARTISTS**
(PMA Member)
*Contact: By Post/e-mail*
*Accepts Showreels/Voicereels. 5 Agents*
23 Haymarket
London SW1Y 4DG
Website: www.globalartists.co.uk
e-mail: info@globalartists.co.uk
Fax: 020-7839 4555                    Tel: 020-7839 4888

Sarah Winn

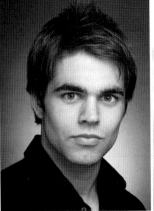

Jack Derges

Katherine Igoe

# robin savage photography

### www.robinsavage.co.uk

contact@robinsavage.co.uk

07901 927597

**GLOBAL7**
PO Box 56232, London N4 4XP
Website: www.global7casting.com
e-mail: global7castings@gmail.com
Mobile: 07956 956652 — Tel/Fax: 020-7281 7679

**GLYN MANAGEMENT**
The Old School House, Brettenham, Ipswich IP7 7QP
e-mail: glyn.management@tesco.net
Fax: 01449 736117 — Tel: 01449 737695

**GO ENTERTAINMENTS Ltd**
*Circus Artistes, Chinese State Circus, Cirque Surreal,*
*Bolshoi Circus "Spirit of The Horse"*
The Arts Exchange, Congleton, Cheshire CW12 1JG
Website: www.arts-exchange.com
e-mail: info@arts-exchange.com
Fax: 01260 270777 — Tel: 01260 276627

**GOLD AGENCY**
*Contact: By e-mail*
*Accepts Showreels*
*35 Performers*
Britannia House, Lower Road, Ebbsfleet, Kent DA11 9BL
Website: www.goldagency.co.uk
e-mail: ann@goldagency.co.uk — Tel/Fax: 01474 561200

**GORDON & FRENCH**
(PMA Member)
*Contact: By Post*
12-13 Poland Street, London W1F 8QB
e-mail: mail@gordonandfrench.net
Fax: 020-7734 4832 — Tel: 020-7734 4818

**GRAHAM David PERSONAL MANAGEMENT (DGPM)**
The Studio, 107A Middleton Road, London E8 4LN
e-mail: infodgpm@aol.com — Tel/Fax: 020-7241 6752

david price photography

jason bull

hana minett

pipa vanderfury

Studio based - London
Tel: 07950 542 494  info@davidpricephotography.co.uk / www.davidpricephotography.co.uk

**GRANTHAM-HAZELDINE Ltd**
(PMA Member)
Suite 315
The Linen Hall
162-168 Regent Street
London W1B 5TD
e-mail: agents@granthamhazeldine.com
Fax: 020-7038 3739                    Tel: 020-7038 3737

**GRAY Darren MANAGEMENT**
*Specialising in representing/promoting Australian Artists*
2 Marston Lane
Portsmouth
Hampshire PO3 5TW
Website: www.darrengraymanagement.co.uk
e-mail: darren.gray1@virgin.net
Fax: 023-9267 7227                    Tel: 023-9269 9973

**GRAYS MANAGEMENT & ASSOCIATES**
(Personal Manager)
Panther House
38 Mount Pleasant
London WC1X 0AP
Website: www.graysman.com
e-mail: grays.man@btconnect.com
Fax: 020-7278 1091                    Tel: 020-7278 1054

**GREEN & UNDERWOOD**
(Personal Manager)
*Contact: By Post*
PO Box 44394
London SW20 0YP
e-mail: info@greenandunderwood.com
Fax: 020-3258 5037                    Tel: 020-8546 2614

**GREGOR Katherine ASSOCIATES**
*Contact: By e-mail*
*1 Agent represents 40 Performers*
*Commercials. Film. Radio. Stage. Television*
The Colombo Centre
34-68 Colombo Street
London SE1 8DP                    Tel/Fax: 020-7261 9466
Website: www.katherinegregorassociates.co.uk
e-mail: agent@katherinegregorassociates.co.uk

**GRESHAM Carl GROUP**
PO Box 3
Bradford
West Yorkshire BD1 4QN
Website: www.carlgresham.com
e-mail: gresh@carlgresham.co.uk
Fax: 01274 827161                    Tel: 01274 735880

**GRIDMODELS UK Ltd**
*Contact: Rosie Beasley*
*By e-mail/Telephone*
*2 Agents represent 300 Performers*
*Modelling*
45 Garth Close
Morden, Surrey SM4 4NN
Website: www.gridmodels.com
e-mail: enquiries@gridmodels.com
Fax: 0844 8110347                    Tel: 020-7993 6512

**GRIFFIN Sandra MANAGEMENT Ltd**
6 Ryde Place
Richmond Road
East Twickenham
Middlesex TW1 2EH
Website: www.sandragriffin.com
e-mail: office@sandragriffin.com
Fax: 020-8744 1812                    Tel: 020-8891 5676

**GROVES Rob PERSONAL MANAGEMENT**
3 Melbourne House
London N3 1BX
Website: www.robgroves.co.uk
e-mail: rob@robgroves.co.uk
Fax: 07092 873538                    Tel: 020-8349 0111

**GUBBAY Louise ASSOCIATES**
26 Westmore Road
Tatsfield
Kent TN16 2AX                    Tel: 01959 573080
Website: www.louisegubbay.com
e-mail: louise@louisegubbay.com

**GURNETT J. PERSONAL MANAGEMENT Ltd**
12 Newburgh Street, London W1F 7RP
Website: www.jgpm.co.uk
e-mail: mail@jgpm.co.uk
Fax: 020-7287 9642                    Tel: 020-7440 1850

**HALL JAMES PERSONAL MANAGEMENT**
PO Box 604
Pinner, Middlesex HA5 9GH
Website: www.halljames.co.uk
e-mail: agents@halljames.co.uk
Fax: 020-8868 5825                    Tel: 020-8429 8111

**HALLY Yvette MANAGEMENT**
121 Grange Road
Rathfarnham
Dublin 14
Ireland
e-mail: yhmgt@eircom.net
Fax: 00 353 1 4933076                    Tel: 00 353 1 4933685

**HAMBLETON Patrick MANAGEMENT**
Top Floor
136 Englefield Road
London N1 3LQ
e-mail: patrick@phm.uk.com
Fax: 0870 2848554     Tel: 020-7226 0947

**HAMILTON HODELL Ltd**
(PMA Member)
5th Floor
66-68 Margaret Street
London W1W 8SR
Website: www.hamiltonhodell.co.uk
e-mail: info@hamiltonhodell.co.uk
Fax: 020-7636 1226     Tel: 020-7636 1221

**HAND MODELS 1**
Garden Studios
11-15 Betterton Street
Covent Garden
London WC2H 9BP     Tel: 020-7470 8739
Website: www.handmodels1.com
e-mail: info@handmodels1.com

**HandE CASTING ADVERTISING AGENCY**
Epping Film Studios, Brickfield Business Centre
Thornwood High Road, Epping, Essex CM16 6TH
Website: www.hande.org
e-mail: caa@hande.org
Fax: 01992 570601     Tel: 01992 570662

**HARGREAVES Alison MANAGEMENT**
*Designers*
27 Hamilton Road, London NW10 1NS     Tel: 020-8438 0112
Website: www.alisonhargreaves.co.uk
e-mail: agent@alisonhargreaves.co.uk

**HARRIS AGENCY Ltd The**
71 The Avenue, Watford, Herts WD17 4NU
e-mail: theharrisagency@btconnect.com
Fax: 01923 211666     Tel: 01923 211644

**HARRISON Penny BSA Ltd**
Trinity Lodge
25 Trinity Crescent, London SW17 7AG
e-mail: harrisonbsa@aol.com
Fax: 020-8672 8971     Tel: 020-8672 0136

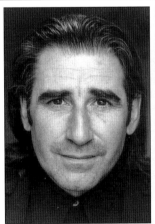

## Eliza Power Photography London

www.elizapower.co.uk    07590 370261    eliza.ckpower@gmail.com

**HARVEY VOICES**
4th Floor, 52-53 Margaret Street
London W1W 8SQ                    Tel: 020-7952 4361
Website: www.harveyvoices.co.uk

**HAT MANAGEMENT**
*Contact: Neil Howarth*
24 Thornley Rise, Audenshaw, Manchester M34 5JX
e-mail: hat.mgmt@hotmail.co.uk
Mobile: 07775 744438              Tel: 0161-370 8648

**HATTON McEWAN**
(Personal Manager)
*Contact: Stephen Hatton, Aileen McEwan, James Penford*
*By Post*
PO Box 37385, London N1 7XF
Website: www.hattonmcewan.com
e-mail: mail@hattonmcewan.com
Fax: 020-7251 9081               Tel: 020-7253 4770

**H C A**
(See COOKE Howard ASSOCIATES)

**HEADNOD TALENT AGENCY**
2nd Floor, 18 Kingsland Road
London E2 8DA                    Tel: 020-7502 9478
Website: www.headnodagency.com
e-mail: info@headnodagency.com

**HENRIETTA RABBIT CHILDREN'S ENTERTAINMENT AGENCY**
*Children's Entertainers. Balloonologists. Close-up*
*Magicians. Clowns. Face Painters. Jugglers. Punch & Judy*
*Stiltwalkers*
The Warren, 12 Eden Close
York YO24 2RD                    Tel: 0800 0965653
Website: www.henriettarabbit.co.uk
e-mail: info@henriettarabbit.co.uk

**HENRY'S AGENCY**
53 Westbury, Rochford, Essex SS4 1UL  Tel/Fax: 01702 541413
Website: www.henrysagency.co.uk
e-mail: info@henrysagency.co.uk

**HICKS Jeremy ASSOCIATES Ltd**
(Personal Manager)
*Contact: By Post/e-mail*
*Accepts Showreels*
*2 Agents represent 25 Performers*
*Chefs. Comedians. Presenters. Writers*
114-115 Tottenham Court Road, London W1T 5AH
Website: www.jeremyhicks.com
e-mail: info@jeremyhicks.com
Fax: 020-7383 2777               Tel: 020-7383 2000

**HILL Edward MANAGEMENT**
Website: www.edagent.com
e-mail: info@edagent.com
Tel: 01273 906781                Tel: 020-7558 8153

**HILTON Elinor ASSOCIATES**
2nd Floor
28 Charing Cross Road
London WC2H 0DB
Website: www.elinorhilton.com
e-mail: info@elinorhilton.com
Fax: 020-7836 3982               Tel: 020-7240 2555

**HINDIN Dee ASSOCIATES**
Existing Clients only
9B Brunswick Mews
Great Cumberland Place
London W1H 7FB
Fax: 020-7258 0651               Tel: 020-7723 3706

**HIRED HANDS**
12 Cressy Road
London NW3 2LY                   Tel: 020-7267 9212
Website: www.hiredhandsmodels.com
e-mail: hiredhandsagency@aol.com

**HOBBS Liz GROUP Ltd**
*Artiste Management*
65 London Road
Newark, Notts NG24 1RZ
Website: www.lizhobbsgroup.com
e-mail: casting@lizhobbsgroup.com
Fax: 0870 3337009                Tel: 0870 0702702

**HOBSONS ACTORS**
62 Chiswick High Road
Chiswick, London W4 1SY
Website: www.hobsons-international.com
e-mail: actors@hobsons-international.com
Fax: 020-8996 5350               Tel: 020-8995 3628

**HOLLOWOOD Jane ASSOCIATES Ltd**
Apartment 17
113 Newton Street
Manchester M1 1AE
e-mail: janehollowood@ukonline.co.uk
Fax: 0161-237 9142               Tel: 0161-237 9141

**HOLLY Dave ARTS MEDIA SERVICES**
The Annexe
23 Eastwood Gardens
Felling
Tyne & Wear NE10 0AH
Fax: 0191-438 2722               Tel: 0191-438 2711

# AM LONDON

## ACTORS HEADSHOTS

SIMON PEGG

CONNIE FISHER

SELINA SUFI

JOHN BARROWMAN

CATHERINE TATE

PETER SERAFINOWICZ

CARINA BIRRELL

CHRIS DALEY

## MODEL, DANCE & PERFORMER PORTFOLIOS

# WWW.AM-LONDON.COM

 STUDIO: 020 7193 1868    MOBILE: 07974 188 105

**Where culture and talent meet**
Multi-cultural representation for Film, TV, Stage and Commercials

Phone 020 7193 4230
info@epmctalent.com
www.epmctalent.com

**HOLMES Kim SHOWBUSINESS ENTERTAINMENT AGENCY Ltd**
8 Charles Close, Ilkeston
Derbyshire DE7 5AF
e-mail: kimholmesshowbiz@hotmail.co.uk
Fax: 0115-944 0390          Tel: 0115-930 5088

**HOPE Sally ASSOCIATES**
(PMA Member)
108 Leonard Street
London EC2A 4XS
Website: www.sallyhope.biz
e-mail: casting@sallyhope.biz
Fax: 020-7613 4848          Tel: 020-7613 5353

**HORSEY Dick MANAGEMENT Ltd**
(Personal Manager)
*Contact: By Post/e-mail/Telephone*
*Accepts Showreels/Voicereels*
*2 Agents represent 40 Performers*
*Corporate. Musicals. Stage. Television*
Suite 1, Cottingham House
Chorleywood Road
Rickmansworth,Herts WD3 4EP
Website: www.dhmlimited.co.uk
e-mail: roger@dhmlimited.co.uk
Mobile: 07850 112211          Tel: 01923 710614

**HOSKINS Steven MODEL AGENCY**
34 Queensland Avenue
Chapelfields
Coventry, West Midlands CV5 8FG      Mobile: 07760 414489
Website: www.shfashionfix.webs.com
e-mail: steven@stevenhoskins.com

**HOWARD Amanda ASSOCIATES Ltd**
(PMA Member)
*Contact: By Post*
21 Berwick Street
London W1F 0PZ
Website: www.amandahowardassociates.co.uk
e-mail: mail@amandahowardassociates.co.uk
Fax: 020-7287 7785          Tel: 020-7287 9277

**HOWARD Richard ASSOCIATES**
6 Upper Hollingdean Road
Brighton BN1 7GA          Tel/Fax: 01273 539530
Website: www.richardhowardassociates.co.uk
e-mail: info@richardhowardassociates.co.uk

**HOWE Janet**
(Personal Manager)
*4 Agents.*
*Children. Modelling. Television. Walk-on & Supporting Artists*
58 High Street
Newcastle-under-Lyme
Staffordshire ST5 1QE          Tel/Fax: 01782 661777
e-mail: info@janethowe.com

The Pie Factory
101 Broadway
Salford Quays
Manchester M50 2EQ
Tel: 0161-660 3633          Tel/Fax: 0161-263 0633

**HOWELL Philippa**
(See PHPM)

**HUDSON Nancy ASSOCIATES Ltd**
PO Box 1344
High Wycombe North
Bucks HP11 9ER          Tel: 020-7499 5548
Website: www.nancyhudsonassociates.com
e-mail: agents@nancyhudsonassociates.com

**HUNTER Bernard ASSOCIATES**
13 Spencer Gardens
London SW14 7AH
Fax: 020-8392 9334          Tel: 020-8878 6308

**HUNWICK HUGHES Ltd**
(Personal Manager) (PMA Member)
Suite 2F
45A George Street
Edinburgh EH2 2HT
Website: www.hunwickhughes.com
e-mail: maryam@hunwickhughes.com
Fax: 0131-225 4535          Tel: 0131-225 3585

**I-MAGE CASTINGS**
Regent House Business Centre
Suite 22, 24-25 Nutford Place
Marble Arch
London W1H 5YN
Website: www.i-mage.uk.com
e-mail: jane@i-mage.uk.com
Fax: 020-7725 7004          Tel: 020-7725 7003

**ICON ACTORS MANAGEMENT**
Tanzaro House
Ardwick Green North
Manchester M12 6FZ
Website: www.iconactors.net
e-mail: info@iconactors.net
Fax: 0161-273 4567          Tel: 0161-273 3344

**I.M.L.**
(Personal Manager) (CPMA Member)
The White House
52-54 Kennington Oval
London SE11 5SW          Tel/Fax: 020-7587 1080
Website: www.iml.org.uk
e-mail: info@iml.org.uk

**IMPACT INTERNATIONAL MANAGEMENT**
(Personal Manager)
*Contact: Cornelia Hefti*
*By e-mail*
*Accepts Showreels/Voicereels*
*1 Agent represents 10 Performers*
*Cruises. Musical Theatre. Speciality Acts & Events*
1st Floor Danceworks
16-18 Balderton Street
London W1K 6TN          Tel: 020-7495 6655
Website: www.impact-london.co.uk
e-mail: info@impact-london.co.uk

**IMPERIAL PERSONAL MANAGEMENT Ltd**
102 Kirkstall Road
Leeds
West Yorkshire LS3 1JA
Website: www.ipmcasting.com
e-mail: katie@ipmcasting.com
Mobile: 07890 387758          Tel: 0113-244 3222

**INDEPENDENT TALENT GROUP Ltd**
(Formerly ICM, London) (PMA Member)
Oxford House
76 Oxford Street
London W1D 1BS
Website: www.independenttalent.com
Fax: 020-7323 0101          Tel: 020-7636 6565

**INDEPENDENT THEATRE WORKSHOP The**
2 Mornington Road
Ranelagh
Dublin 6
Ireland          Tel/Fax: 00 353 1 4968808
Website: www.independent-theatre-workshop.com
e-mail: info@independent-theatre-workshop.com

**INSPIRATION MANAGEMENT**
(CPMA Member) (Co-operative)
Room 227
The Aberdeen Centre
22-24 Highbury Grove
London N5 2EA          Tel: 020-7704 0440
Website: www.inspirationmanagement.org.uk
e-mail: mail@inspirationmanagement.eclipse.co.uk

**INTER-CITY CASTING**
(Personal Manager)
*Contact: By Post*
*Accepts Showreels*
2 Agents represent 60 Performers
Portland Tower
Portland Street
Manchester M1 3LF          Tel/Fax: 0161-238 4950
e-mail: intercitycasting@btconnect.com

**INTERNATIONAL ARTISTES Ltd**
(PMA Member)
4th Floor, Holborn Hall
193-197 High Holborn
London WC1V 7BD
e-mail: reception@internationalartistes.com
Fax: 020-7404 9865          Tel: 020-7025 0600

**INTERNATIONAL COLLECTIVE ARTIST MANAGEMENT**
9-13 Grape Street
Covent Garden
London WC2H 8ED
Website: www.internationalcollective.com
e-mail: enquiries@internationalcollective.co.uk
Fax: 020-7557 6656          Tel: 020-7557 6650

**INTERNATIONAL MODEL MANAGEMENT Ltd**
(Incorporating Yvonne Paul Management)
Elysium Gate
Unit 15, 126-128 New Kings Road
London SW6 4LZ
e-mail: info@immmodels.com
Fax: 020-7736 2221          Tel: 020-7610 9111

**INTERNATIONAL MODELS & TALENT AGENCY**
1901 Avenue of The Stars
Suite #200
Century City, CA 90067
e-mail: int.talent@hotmail.com
Fax: (323) 644-5440          Tel: (310) 461-1550

**IPM CREW**
102 Kirkstall Road
Leeds, Yorkshire LS3 1JA          Tel: 0113-244 3222
Website: www.ipmcasting.com
e-mail: lee@ipmcasting.com

**IPM TALENT**
102 Kirkstall Road
Leeds, Yorkshire L53 1JA          Tel: 0113-244 3222
Website: www.ipmcasting.com
e-mail: stewart@ipmcasting.com

**IT&M MANAGEMENT**
Contact: Piers Chater Robinson
Garden Studios
11-15 Betterton Street
Covent Garden
London WC2H 9BP
Website: www.it-m.co.uk
e-mail: info@it-m.co.uk
Fax: 020-7379 0801          Tel: 020-7470 8786

**JAA**
(See ALTARAS Jonathan ASSOCIATES Ltd)

**JABBERWOCKY AGENCY**
*Contact: Christina Yates*
*By e-mail*
*4 Agents represent 135 Performers*
*Children. Teenagers*
Glassenbury Hill Farm
Glassenbury Road
Cranbrook
Kent TN17 2QF
Website: www.jabberwockyagency.com
e-mail: info@jabberwockyagency.com
Fax: 01580 714346          Tel: 01580 714306

**JAFFREY MANAGEMENT Ltd**
(Personal Manager) (PMA Member)
*Contact: Jennifer Jaffrey*
*By Post/e-mail*
*Accepts Showreels/Voicereels (SAE)*
*2 Agents represent 60 Performers*
*Commercials. Film. Stage. Television*
The Double Lodge
Pinewood Studios
Iver Heath, Bucks SL0 0NH
Website: www.jaffreyactors.co.uk
e-mail: castings@jaffreyactors.co.uk
Fax: 01753 785163          Tel: 01753 785162

**JAMESON Joy Ltd**
(Personal Manager)
21 Uxbridge Street
Kensington
London W8 7TQ
e-mail: joy@jote.freeuk.com
Fax: 020-7985 0842          Tel: 020-7221 0990

**JAMES Susan**
(See SJ MANAGEMENT)

**JAY Alex PERSONAL MANAGEMENT**
8 Higher Newmarket Road
Newmarket
Gloucestershire GL6 0RP          Tel/Fax: 01453 834783
e-mail: alexjay@alex-jay-pm.freeserve.co.uk

**JB ASSOCIATES**
(Personal Manager) (PMA Member)
*Contact: John Basham*
*By Post/email*
*Accepts Showreels/Voicereels*
*2 Agents represent 60 Performers*
*Commercials. Radio. Stage. Television*
4th Floor
Manchester House
84-86 Princess Street
Manchester M1 6NG
Website: www.j-b-a.net
e-mail: info@j-b-a.net
Fax: 0161-237 1809          Tel: 0161-237 1808

## Caroline Summers

Film or Digital
Session includes make-up
Short notice possible

020 7223 7669    07931 301234

www.gallery.me.com/carolinesummers

**JEFFREY & WHITE MANAGEMENT Ltd**
(Personal Manager) (PMA Member)
2 Ladygrove Court, Hitchwood Lane
Preston, Hitchin
Hertfordshire SG4 7SA          Tel: 01462 433752
Website: www.jeffreyandwhite.co.uk
e-mail: info@jeffreyandwhite.co.uk

**JERMIN Mark MANAGEMENT**
*Contact: By Post/e-mail*
*Accepts Showreels*
*2 Agents*
8 Heathfield, Swansea SA1 6EJ
Website: www.markjermin.co.uk
e-mail: info@markjermin.co.uk
Fax: 01792 458844          Tel: 01792 458855

**J.G.M.**
15 Lexham Mews, London W8 6JW
Website: www.jgmtalent.com
e-mail: mail@jgmtalent.com
Fax: 020-7376 2416          Tel: 020-7376 2414

**JLM PERSONAL MANAGEMENT**
(Personal Manager) (PMA Member)
*Contact: Sharon Henry*
*By Post*
*Accepts Showreels*
*2 Agents*
*Commercials. Film. Radio. Stage. Television*
4th Floor
Holborn Hall, 193-197 High Holborn, London WC1V 7BD
e-mail: info@jlmpm.co.uk
Fax: 020-7404 9865          Tel: 020 7025 0630

**J.M. MANAGEMENT**
*Personal representation to a small number of*
*Actors/Actresses in film work*
20 Pembroke Road
North Wembley
Middlesex HA9 7PD          Tel: 020-8908 0502

**JOHNSON WHITELEY Ltd**
12 Argyll Mansions
Hammersmith Road, London W14 8QG
e-mail: johnsonwhiteley@btconnnect.com
Fax: 020-7348 0164          Tel: 020-7348 0163

**JOHNSTON & MATHERS ASSOCIATES Ltd**
PO Box 3167
Barnet EN5 2WA
Website: www.johnstonandmathers.com
e-mail: johnstonmathers@aol.com
Fax: 020-8449 2386          Tel: 020-8449 4968

**JOYCE Michael MANAGEMENT**
4th Floor
14-18 Heddon Street
London W1B 4DA
Website: www.michaeljoycemanagement.com
e-mail: info@michaeljoycemanagement.com
Fax: 020-7745 6275          Tel: 020-7745 6274

**JPA MANAGEMENT**
30 Daws Hill Lane
High Wycombe
Bucks HP11 1PW
Website: www.jpamanagement.co.uk
e-mail: jackie.palmer@btinternet.com
Fax: 01494 510479          Tel: 01494 520978

**K TALENT ARTIST MANAGEMENT**
(Personal Manager)
*Contact: By Post/e-mail*
*Accepts Showreels/Voicereels*
*3 Agents represent 45 Performers*
*Children. Commercials. Dancers. Film. Musicals. Singers*
*Stage. Television*
1st Floor, 28 Gray's Inn Road
London WC1X 8HR
Website: www.ktalent.co.uk
e-mail: mail@ktalent.co.uk
Tel: 0844 5672470               Tel: 020-7209 8154

**KAL MANAGEMENT**
*Contact: By Post*
95 Gloucester Road
Hampton, Middlesex TW12 2UW
Website: www.kaplan-kaye.co.uk
e-mail: kaplan222@aol.com
Fax: 020-8979 6487               Tel: 020-8783 0039

**KANAL Roberta AGENCY**
82 Constance Road
Twickenham
Middlesex TW2 7JA
e-mail: roberta.kanal@dsl.pipex.com
Tel/Fax: 020-8894 7952           Tel: 020-8894 2277

**KARUSHI MANAGEMENT**
*Contact: By e-mail*
*5 Agents represent 30+ Performers*
Unit 10, 7 Wenlock Road
London N1 7SL
Website: www.karushi.com
e-mail: lisa@karushi.com
Fax: 0845 9005522                Tel: 0845 9005511

**KEDDIE SCOTT ASSOCIATES Ltd**
(Personal Manager) (PMA Member)
*Contact: By Post*
*Accepts Showreels/Voicereels*
*4 Agents represent 145 Performers*
*Commercials. Corporate. Dancers. Film. Musicals*
*Presenters. Radio. Singers. Stage. Television. Writers*
Studio 1
17 Shorts Gardens
Covent Garden, London WC2H 9AT
Website: www.ks-ass.co.uk
e-mail: fiona@ks-ass.co.uk
Fax: 020-7147 1326              Tel: 020-7836 6802

KSA - SCOTLAND
*Contact: Paul Michael*
*By Post/e-mail. Accepts Showreels/Voicereels*
*2 Agents represent 30 Performers*
*Film. Musicals. Stage. Television*
(0/1) 430 Tantallon Road
Glasgow G41 3HR
e-mail: scotland@ks-ass.co.uk
Fax: 020-7147 1326              Mobile: 07980 121728

KSA - WALES
Studio 1, 17 Shorts Gardens
Covent Garden, London WC2H 9AT
Website: www.ks-ass.co.uk
e-mail: wales@ks-ass.co.uk
Mobile: 07917 272298           Tel: 020-7836 6802

**KELLY MANAGEMENT Ltd**
11-15 Betterton Street
Covent Garden, London WC2H 9BP
Website: www.kelly-management.com
e-mail: assistant@kelly-management.com
Fax: 020-7379 0801             Tel: 020-7470 8757

**KENIS Steve & Co**
(PMA Member)
Royalty House
72-74 Dean Street, London W1D 3SG
e-mail: sk@sknco.com
Fax: 020-7287 6328            Tel: 020-7434 9055

**KEW PERSONAL MANAGEMENT**
PO Box Office 56584
London SW18 9GE               Tel: 020-8871 3697
Website: www.kewpersonalmanagement.com
e-mail: info@kewpersonalmanagement.com

**KEYLOCK MANAGEMENT**
*Contact: By Post*
*Accepts Showreels*
*1 Agent represents 64 Performers*
*Commercials. Film. Stage. Television*
85 Rupert Avenue
High Wycombe, Bucks HP12 3NF
Website: www.keylockmanagement.com
e-mail: agency@keylockmanagement.com
Fax: 01245 328625             Tel: 01245 321638

**KING Adrian ASSOCIATES**
(PMA Member)
*Contact: Adrian King*
*By Post/e-mail*
*Accepts Showreels*
33 Marlborough Mansions
Cannon Hill, London NW6 1JS
e-mail: akassocs@aol.com
Fax: 020-7435 4100            Tel: 020-7435 4600

**K M C AGENCIES**
(Personal Manager)
*Commercials. Corporate. Dancers. Musicals*
Garden Studios
11-15 Betterton Street, London WC2H 9BP
e-mail: london@kmcagencies.co.uk
Fax: 0870 4421780            Tel: 0870 4604868

PO Box 122
48 Great Ancoats Street
Manchester M4 5AB
e-mail: casting@kmcagencies.co.uk
Fax: 0161-237 9812           Tel: 0161-237 3009

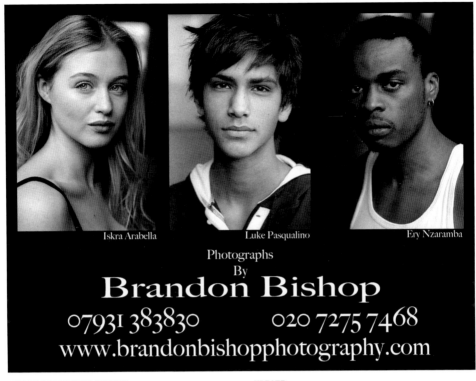

Iskra Arabella          Luke Pasqualino          Ery Nzaramba

Photographs
By
**Brandon Bishop**
07931 383830          020 7275 7468
www.brandonbishopphotography.com

**KNIGHT AYTON MANAGEMENT**
35 Great James Street
London WC1N 3HB
Website: www.knightayton.co.uk
e-mail: info@knightayton.co.uk
Fax: 020-7831 4455
Tel: 020-7831 4400

**KNIGHT Ray CASTING**
21A Lambolle Place
London NW3 4PG
Website: www.rayknight.co.uk
e-mail: casting@rayknight.co.uk
Fax: 020-7722 2322
Tel: 020-7722 1551

**KNOCK2BAG MANAGEMENT**
60 Pasquier Road
London E17 6HB
Mobile: 07870 212189
Website: www.knock2bag.co.uk
e-mail: knock2bagmanagement@knock2bag.co.uk

**KORT Richard MANAGEMENT Ltd**
Theatre House
2-4 Clasketgate, Lincoln LN2 1JS
Website: www.richardkortassociates.com
e-mail: richardkort@dial.pipex.com
Fax: 01522 511116
Tel: 01522 526888

**KREATE**
Unit 232
30 Great Guildford Street, London SE1 0HS
e-mail: web@kreate.co.uk
Fax: 020-7401 3003
Tel: 020-7401 9007

**KREMER ASSOCIATES**
(See MARSH Billy DRAMA Ltd)

**KSA - SCOTLAND**
(See KEDDIE SCOTT ASSOCIATES Ltd)

**KSA - WALES**
(See KEDDIE SCOTT ASSOCIATES Ltd)

**KW PROMOTIONS Ltd**
9 College Road
Alsager, Stoke-on-Trent ST7 2SS
Mobile: 07835 316639
Website: www.kwpromotions.co.uk
e-mail: dkeeno1@hotmail.com

**L.A. MANAGEMENT**
10 Fairoak Close
Kenley
Surrey CR8 5LJ
Mobile: 07963 573538
Website: www.lamanagement.biz
e-mail: info@lamanagement.biz

**LADA MANAGEMENT**
Sparkhouse Studios
Rope Walk, Lincoln LN6 7DQ
Website: www.lada.org.uk/agency
e-mail: management@lada.org.uk
Fax: 01522 837201                    Tel: 01522 837243

**LADIDA**
*Contact: By Post*
*Accepts Showreels*
*2 Agents represent 75 Performers*
*Commercials. Creatives. Film. Musicals. Radio. Stage*
*Television. Writers*
Cambridge Theatre
Earlham Street, London WC2H 9HU
Website: www.ladidagroup.com
e-mail: m@ladidagroup.com
Fax: 020-7379 6198                    Tel: 020-7379 6199

**LAINE MANAGEMENT Ltd**
Laine House
131 Victoria Road
Hope, Salford M6 8LF
Website: www.lainemanagement.co.uk
e-mail: sam@lainemanagement.co.uk
Fax: 0161-787 7572                    Tel: 0161-789 7775

**LAINE Betty MANAGEMENT**
The Studios, East Street
Epsom, Surrey KT17 1HH              Tel/Fax: 01372 721815
e-mail: enquiries@betty-laine-management.co.uk

**LANGFORD ASSOCIATES Ltd**
*(Personal Manager)*
*Contact: Barry Langford*
*By Post/e-mail*
*Commercials. Film. Stage. Television*
17 Westfields Avenue
Barnes, London SW13 0AT
Website: www.langfordassociates.com
e-mail: barry.langford@btconnect.com
Fax: 020-8878 7078                    Tel: 020-8878 7148

**LAWRENCE Tonicha AGENCY**
Serenissima
Church Hill
Thorner, Leeds LS14 3EG
Website: www.tonichalaurence.co.uk
e-mail: tonichalaurence@fastmail.co.uk
Mobile: 07766 415996            Tel/Fax: 0113-289 3433

**LE BARS Tessa MANAGEMENT**
*(PMA Member)*
*Existing Clients only*
54 Birchwood Road
Petts Wood, Kent BR5 1NZ
Website: www.galtonandsimpson.com
e-mail: tessa.lebars@ntlworld.com
Mobile: 07860 287255               Tel: 01689 837084

**LEE Nina MANAGEMENT**
*Contact: By email*
PO Box 11328, Paisley PA3 9EJ       Tel: 0141-848 7693
Website: www.ninaleemanagement.com
e-mail: nina@ninaleemanagement.com

**LEE Wendy MANAGEMENT**
2nd Floor
36 Langham Street
London W1W 7AP                      Tel: 020-7703 5187
e-mail: wendy-lee@btconnect.com

**LEE GARRETT Anna MANAGEMENT**
24-26 Arcadia Avenue
Finchley Central, London N3 2JU      Tel: 020-8349 7184
Website: www.annaleegarrett.net
e-mail: contact@annaleegarrett.net

**LEHRER Jane ASSOCIATES**
*(Personal Manager) (PMA Member)*
*Contact: By Post/e-mail. 2 Agents*
100A Chalk Farm Road
London NW1 8EH
Website: www.janelehrer.co.uk
e-mail: janelehrer@aol.com
Fax: 020-7482 4899                   Tel: 020-7482 4898

**LEIGH MANAGEMENT**
14 St David's Drive
Edgware, Middlesex HA8 6JH     Tel/Fax: 020-8951 4449
e-mail: leighmanagement@aol.com

**LEIGH Mike ASSOCIATES**
37 Marylebone Lane
London W1U 2NW
Website: www.mikeleighassoc.com
Fax: 020-7486 5886      Tel: 020-7935 5500

**LESLIE Sasha MANAGEMENT**
(In Association with Allsorts Drama for Children)
34 Pember Road
London NW10 5LS      Tel/Fax: 020-8969 3249
e-mail: sasha@allsortsdrama.com

**LIME ACTORS AGENCY & MANAGEMENT Ltd**
*Contact: Georgina Andrew*
*By Post. Accepts Showreels*
Nemesis House
1 Oxford Court
Bishopsgate, Manchester M2 3WQ
Website: www.limemanagement.tv
e-mail: georgina@limemanagement.co.uk
Fax: 0161-228 6727      Tel: 0161-236 0827

**LINKSIDE AGENCY**
*Contact: By Post*
*2 Agents represent 30 Performers*
*Dancers. Musicals. Singers. Stage. Television*
21 Poplar Road
Leatherhead, Surrey KT22 8SF
e-mail: linkside_agency@yahoo.co.uk
Fax: 01372 378398      Tel: 01372 802374

**LINTON MANAGEMENT**
3 The Rock, Bury BL9 0JP
e-mail: carol@linton.tv
Fax: 0161-761 1999      Tel: 0161-761 2020

27-31 Clerkenwell Close
London EC1R 0AT
e-mail: london@linton.tv
Fax: 020-7785 7276      Tel: 020-7785 7275

**LONG Eva AGENTS**
*Contact: By Post/e-mail*
*2 Agents represent 30 Performers*
*Commercials. Corporate. Film. Musicals. Radio. Singers*
*Stage. Television. Voice Overs*
107 Station Road
Earls Barton, Northants NN6 0NX
Website: www.evalongagents.co.uk
e-mail: evalongagents@yahoo.co.uk
Fax: 01604 811921      Mobile: 07736 700849

**LONGRUN ARTISTES AGENCY**
*Contact: Gina Long, Irene Wernli*
*By e-mail. 3 Agents represent 120 Clients*
Marylebone Dance Studio
12 Lisson Grove
London NW1 6TS
Website: www.longrunartistes.co.uk
e-mail: gina@longrunartistes.co.uk
Mobile: 07748 723228      Tel: 020-8316 6662

**LOOKALIKES**
*Contact: Susan Scott*
106 Tollington Park, London N4 3RB
Website: www.lookalikes.info
e-mail: susan@lookalikes.info
Fax: 020-7281 1263      Tel: 020-7281 8029

Scott Wright

Emma Beever

# michael pollard
photographer
# manchester

tel : 0161 456 7470
email : info@michaelpollard.co.uk
website : www.michaelpollard.co.uk

studio/location/student rates

**LOOKS**
*Contact: By Post/e-mail/Telephone*
*200 Performers*
*Commercials. Corporate. Modelling. Presenters. Walk-on &*
*Supporting Artists*
PO Box 42783, London N2 0UF
Website: www.lookslondon.com
e-mail: lookslondonltd@btconnect.com
Fax: 020-8442 9190                    Tel: 020-8341 4477

**LOVETT LOGAN ASSOCIATES**
(Formerly PLA) (PMA Member)
5 Union Street, Edinburgh EH1 3LT
Website: www.lovettlogan.com
e-mail: edinburgh@lovettlogan.com
Fax: 0131-478 7070                    Tel: 0131-478 7878

40 Margaret Street, London W1G 0JH
e-mail: london@lovettlogan.com
Fax: 020-7495 6411                    Tel: 020-7495 6400

**LSW PROMOTIONS**
PO Box 31855
London SE17 3XP                    Tel/Fax: 020-7793 9755
e-mail: londonswo@hotmail.com

**LUXFACTOR GROUP (UK) The**
(Personal Manager)
*Contact: Michael D. Finch*
*By e-mail*
*1 Agent represents 20+ Performers*
*Creatives. Presenters. Television*
*Walk-on & Supporting Artists*
Fleet Place, 12 Nelson Drive
Petersfield, Hampshire GU31 4SJ
Website: www.luxfactor.co.uk
e-mail: info@luxfactor.co.uk
Fax: 0845 3700588                    Tel: 0845 3700589

**LYNE Dennis AGENCY**
(PMA Member)
503 Holloway Road, London N19 4DD
e-mail: info@dennislyne.com
Fax: 020-7272 4790                    Tel: 020-7272 5020

**MACFARLANE CHARD ASSOCIATES Ltd**
(PMA Member)
33 Percy Street
London W1T 2DF
Website: www.macfarlane-chard.co.uk
e-mail: enquiries@macfarlane-chard.co.uk
Fax: 020-7636 7751                    Tel: 020-7636 7750

**MACFARLANE CHARD ASSOCIATES IRELAND**
7 Adelaide Street, Dun Laoghaire
Co Dublin, Ireland
e-mail: enquiries@macfarlane-chard.ie
Fax: 00 353 1 663 8649          Tel: 00 353 1 663 8646

**MACNAUGHTON LORD REPRESENTATION**
(PMA Member)
*Choreographers. Composers. Designers. Directors. Lighting*
*Designers. Lyricists. Musical Directors. Writers*
Unit 10
The Broomhouse Studios
50 Sulivan Road, London SW6 3DX
Website: www.mlrep.com
e-mail: info@mlrep.com
Fax: 020-7371 7563                    Tel: 020-7384 9517

**MADELEY Paul ASSOCIATES**
17 Valley Road, Arden Park
Bredbury, Stockport
Cheshire SK6 2EA                    Tel/Fax: 0161-430 5380
e-mail: paulmadeley@amserve.com

**MAIDA VALE SINGERS**
*Contact: Christopher Dee*
*Singers for Recordings, Theatre, Film, Radio & Television*
7B Lanhill Road, Maida Vale, London W9 2BP
Website: www.maidavalesingers.co.uk
e-mail: maidavalesingers@cdtenor.freeserve.co.uk
Mobile: 07889 153145                Tel/Fax: 020-7266 1358

**MAIN ARTISTS**
(Personal Manager)
*Boutique Agency*
*Contact: Stephen Anderson*
*By Post/e-mail*
*Accepts Showreels*
*2 Agents represent 50 Performers*
*Commercials. Film. Stage. Television*
1 Union Street, Brighton BN1 1HA
Website: www.mainartists.com
e-mail: stephen@mainartists.com
Fax: 0870 1280003                    Tel: 01273 724001

**MAITLAND MANAGEMENT**
(Personal Manager)
*Contact: Anne Skates*
21A Harley Place, London W1G 8LZ
Website: www.maitlandmanagement.com
e-mail: maitmus@aol.com
Fax: 01372 466229                    Tel: 020-7636 7492

**MAMBAB AGENCY**
Contact: Nichola D. Hartwell
PO Box 51261, Kennington
London SE11 4SW
Website: www.mrandmissblackandbeautiful.com
e-mail: contacts@mrandmissblackandbeautiful.com
Mobile: 07868 728132　　　Tel: 020-7793 4848

**MANAGEMENT 2000**
*Contact: Jackey Gerling*
*By Post*
*Accepts Showreels*
*1 Agent represents 40 Performers*
*Commercials. Film. Radio. Stage. Television*
11 Well Street, Treuddyn
Flintshire CH7 4NH　　　Tel/Fax: 01352 771231
Website: www.management-2000.co.uk
e-mail: jackey@management-2000.co.uk

**MANNING TALENT**
21 Lynton Road
London SE1 5QR　　　Mobile: 07887 878052

**MANS Johnny PRODUCTIONS Ltd**
PO Box 196
Hoddesdon, Herts EN10 7WG
Website: www.johnnymansproductions.co.uk
e-mail: johnnymansagent@aol.com
Fax: 01992 470516　　　Tel: 01992 470907

**MARCUS & McCRIMMON MANAGEMENT**
(Personal Manager)
*Contact: By Post*
*Accepts Showreels*
*3 Agents represent 60 Performers*
*Film. Musicals. Stage. Television*
1 Heathgate Place, 75 Agincourt Road
Hampstead, London NW3 2NU
Website: www.marcusandmccrimmon.com
e-mail: info@marcusandmccrimmon.com
Fax: 020-3012 3478　　　Tel: 020-3012 3477

**MARKHAM & FROGGATT Ltd**
(Personal Manager) (PMA Member)
*Contact: By Post*
4 Windmill Street, London W1T 2HZ
Website: www.markhamfroggatt.com
e-mail: admin@markhamfroggatt.co.uk
Fax: 020-7637 5233　　　Tel: 020-7636 4412

**MARKHAM & MARSDEN Ltd**
(Personal Manager) (PMA Member)
*Contact: John Markham, David Marsden*
*By Post/e-mail*
*Accepts Showreels/Voicereels*
*2 Agents jointly represent 85 Clients*
405 Strand
London WC2R 0NE
Website: www.markham-marsden.com
e-mail: info@markham-marsden.com
Fax: 020-7836 4222　　　Tel: 020-7836 4111

**MARSH BEST ASSOCIATES**
*Film Technicians*
Waverley House
7-12 Noel Street
London W1F 8GQ
Website: www.casarotto.co.uk
e-mail: casarottomarsh@casarotto.co.uk
Fax: 020-7287 9128　　　Tel: 020-7287 4450

**MARSH Billy ASSOCIATES Ltd**
(PMA Member)
76A Grove End Road
St John's Wood
London NW8 9ND
Website: www.billymarsh.co.uk
e-mail: talent@billymarsh.co.uk
Fax: 020-7449 6933　　　Tel: 020-7449 6930

**MARSH Billy DRAMA Ltd**
Actors & Actresses
20 Garrick Street
London WC2E 9BT
e-mail: info@billymarshdrama.co.uk
Fax: 020-3178 5488　　　Tel: 020-3178 4748

**MARSHALL Ronnie AGENCY**
*Contact: Ronnie Marshall*
*By Post/Telephone*
*Accepts Showreels*
*1 Agent represents 25 Performers*
*Commercials. Film. Musicals. Stage. Television*
66 Ollerton Road
London N11 2LA　　　Mobile: 07965 731456
e-mail: ronniemarshallagency@yahoo.co.uk

**MARSHALL Scott PARTNERS Ltd**
(PMA Member)
*Contact: Amanda Evans, Suzy Kenway, Manon Palmer*
2nd Floor
15 Little Portland Street
London W1W 8BW
Website: www.scottmarshall.co.uk
Fax: 020-7636 9728　　　Tel: 020-7637 4623

**MARTIN Carol PERSONAL MANAGEMENT**
19 Highgate West Hill
London N6 6NP
Fax: 020-8340 4868　　　Tel: 020-8348 0847

**MASTERS ENTERTAINMENTS**
47 Staunton Street
Portsmouth PO1 4EJ
Website: www.masterentertainments.com
e-mail: soniamaster@aol.com　　　Mobile: 07709 527753

**MAY John**
46 Golborne Road
London W10 5PR　　　Tel: 020-8962 1606
Website: www.johnmaymanagement.co.uk
e-mail: john@johnmaymanagement.co.uk

Hugh Bonneville

Katherine Parkinson

John Altman

Freya Copeland

Ian McNeice

# philip thorne
*film stills and portraits*

www.philipthorne.co.uk/filmandportraits
**01582 873165**
**07799 350329**

**MAYER Cassie Ltd**
(PMA Member)
5 Old Garden House
The Lanterns, Bridge Lane
London SW11 3AD
e-mail: info@cassiemayerltd.co.uk
Fax: 020-7350 0890          Tel: 020-7350 0880

**MBA (Formerly John Mahoney Management)**
Concorde House
18 Margaret Street
Brighton BN2 1TS
Website: www.mbagency.co.uk
e-mail: mba.concorde@virgin.net
Fax: 01273 818306          Tel: 01273 685970

**McDONAGH Melanie ACADEMY OF PERFORMING ARTS & CASTING AGENCY The**
(Northwest)
14 Apple Tree Way, Oswaldtwistle
Accrington, Lancashire BB5 0FB
Website: www.mcdonaghmanagement.co.uk
e-mail: mcdonaghmgt@aol.com
Mobile: 07909 831409          Tel: 01254 392560

**McKENNA Deborah Ltd**
64-66 Glentham Road
London SW13 9JJ
Website: www.deborahmckenna.com
e-mail: info@deborahmckenna.com
Fax: 020-8846 0967          Tel: 020-8846 0966

**McKINNEY MACARTNEY MANAGEMENT Ltd**
Technicians
Gable House
18-24 Turnham Green Terrace,
London W4 1QP                    Tel: 020-8995 4747
Website: www.mckinneymacartney.com
e-mail: mail@mckinneymacartney.com

**McLEAN Bill PERSONAL MANAGEMENT**
(Personal Manager)
*Contact: By Post*
23B Deodar Road
London SW15 2NP                  Tel: 020-8789 8191

**McLEAN-WILLIAMS MANAGEMENT**
14 Rathbone Place
London W1T 1HT
Website: www.mclean-williams.com
e-mail: info@mclean-williams.com
Fax: 020-7631 3739               Tel: 020-7631 5385

**McLEOD AGENCY Ltd The**
Priory House
1133 Hessle Road
Hull HU4 6SB
Website: www.mcleodagency.co.uk
e-mail: info@mcleodagency.co.uk
Fax: 01482 353635                Tel: 01482 565444

**McREDDIE Ken ASSOCIATES Ltd**
(Personal Manager) (PMA Member)
*Contact: By Post only*
11 Connaught Place
London W2 2ET
Website: www.kenmcreddie.com
e-mail: email@kenmcreddie.com
Fax: 020-7734 6530               Tel: 020-7439 1456

**MCS AGENCY**
47 Dean Street, London W1D 5BE   Tel: 020-7734 9995
Website: www.mcsagency.co.uk
e-mail: info@mcsagency.co.uk

**MEDIA LEGAL**
Existing Clients only
West End House
83 Clarendon Road
Sevenoaks
Kent TN13 1ET                    Tel: 01732 460592

**MF MANAGEMENT**
55 Newman Street
London W1T 3EB                   Tel: 020-3291 2929
e-mail: mfmall@mfmanagement.com

**MGA MANAGEMENT**
1 Warwick Row
London SW1E 5ER
Website: www.themgacompany.com
e-mail: management@themgacompany.com
Fax: 0131-466 9392               Tel: 020-7808 7094

**MIME THE GAP**
*Mime Artistes. Physical Comedy Specialists*
23 Manor Place, Staines
Middlesex TW18 1AE               Mobile: 07970 685982
Website: www.mimethegap.com
e-mail: richard@mimethegap.com

**MINT MANAGEMENT**
Upper Chance, Churn Estate
Blewbury, Didcot, Oxon OX11 9HA
e-mail: lisinewent123@btinternet.com
Mobile: 07792 107644             Tel: 01235 851165

**MITCHELL MAAS McLENNAN**
MD2000 Offices
29 Thomas Street
Woolwich
London SE18 6HU                  Tel/Fax: 020-8301 8745
Website: www.mmm2000.co.uk
e-mail: agency@mmm2000.co.uk

**MLR**
(See MACNAUGHTON LORD REPRESENTATION)

**MONDI ASSOCIATES Ltd**
(Personal Manager)
*Contact: Michelle Sykes*
*By Post/e-mail*
*Accepts Showreels/Voicereels*
*1 Agent represents 60 Clients*
*Children. Commercials. Corporate. Dancers. Film. Musicals
Presenters. Radio. Singers. Stage. Television. Voice Overs*
Unit 3 O, Cooper House
2 Michael Road
London SW6 2AD                   Mobile: 07817 133349
Website: www.mondiassociates.com
e-mail: info@mondiassociates.com

**MONTAGU ASSOCIATES**
Ground Floor
13 Hanley Road
London N4 3DU                    Tel: 020-7263 3883
e-mail: montagus@btconnect.com

**MOORE Jakki MANAGEMENT**
Halecote
St Lukes Road
Haverigg, Cumbria LA18 4HB
e-mail: jakki@jakkimoore.com
Mobile: 07967 612784             Tel: 01229 776389

**MORELLO CHERRY ACTORS AGENCY**
Website: www.mcaa.co.uk
e-mail: info@mcaa.co.uk
Fax: 0871 5284214                Tel: 020-7993 5538

**MORGAN & GOODMAN**
Mezzanine, Quadrant House
80-82 Regent Street, London W1B 5RP
e-mail: mg1@btinternet.com
Fax: 020-7494 3446               Tel: 020-7437 1383

JAMES KEATES PHOTOGRAPHY

HEADSHOTS
£145

Inc. hair & make-up
All high-res images
on CD

www.jk-photography.net   07816 825578

**MORGAN Lee MANAGEMENT**
Cameo House
11 Bear Street
Leicester Square
London WC2H 7AS
Website: www.leemorganmanagement.co.uk
e-mail: leemorganmgnt@aol.com
Fax: 020-7839 1900                 Tel: 020-7766 5234

**MORRIS Andrew MANAGEMENT**
124 Cole Green Lane
Welwyn Garden City
Herts AL7 3JD
e-mail: morrisagent@yahoo.co.uk
Mobile: 07918 636775          Tel/Fax: 020-7482 0451

**MORSE & du FER MANAGEMENT**
27 Kingfisher Court,
Bridge Road
Hampton Court KT8 9HL
Website: www.morsedufer.com
e-mail: info@morsedufer.com
Mobile: 07796 166814                Tel: 020-8941 8122

**MOUTHPIECE MANAGEMENT**
PO Box 145
Inkberrow
Worcestershire WR7 4ZG
Website: www.mouthpiecemanagement.co.uk
e-mail: karin@mouthpiecemanagement.co.uk
Mobile: 07900 240904                Tel: 01527 850149

Photography by Marc Broussely

www.10x8headshots.com
LONDON
info@10x8headshots.com
07738 920225

**MPC ENTERTAINMENT**
*Contact: By e-mail/Telephone*
MPC House 15-16 Maple Mews
Maida Vale
London NW6 5UZ
Website: www.mpce.com
e-mail: mpc@mpce.com
Fax: 020-7624 4220
Tel: 020-7624 1184

**MR.MANAGEMENT**
(Personal Manager)
*Contact: Ross Dawes, Mark Pollard*
*By Post/e-mail*
*Accepts Showreels*
*2 Agents represent 60 Performers*
*Commercials. Film. Musicals. Stage. Television*
29 Belton Road
Brighton
East Sussex BN2 3RE
e-mail: info@mrmanagement.net
Fax: 020-8579 6360
Tel: 01273 232381

**MRS JORDAN ASSOCIATES**
*Contact: By e-mail only*
Mayfair House
14-18 Heddon Street
London W1B 4DA
Tel/Fax: 020-3151 0710
Website: www.mrsjordan.co.uk
e-mail: info@mrsjordan.co.uk

**MUGSHOTS AGENCY**
153 Buckhurst Avenue
Carshalton
Surrey SM5 1PD
e-mail: becky@mugshots.co.uk
Fax: 020-8296 8056
Mobile: 07880 896911

**MURPHY Elaine ASSOCIATES**
Suite 1
50 High Street
London E11 2RJ
e-mail: elaine@elainemurphy.co.uk
Fax: 020-8989 1400
Tel: 020-8989 4122

**MURRAY Vic TALENT Ltd**
(PMA Member)
185A/B Latchmere Road
London SW11 2JZ
Tel: 020-7924 4453
Website: www.vicmurraytalent.com
e-mail: info@vicmurraytalent.com

**MUSIC INTERNATIONAL**
13 Ardilaun Road
London N5 2QR
Website: www.musicint.co.uk
e-mail: music@musicint.co.uk
Fax: 020-7226 9792
Tel: 020-7359 5183

**MV MANAGEMENT**
*Clients must be graduates of Mountview Academy of Theatre Arts*
*Co-operative of 25 performers*
Ralph Richardson Memorial Studios
Kingfisher Place
Clarendon Road
London N22 6XF
e-mail: theagency@mountview.org.uk
Fax: 020-8829 1050
Tel: 020-8889 8231

**MY SPIRIT PRODUCTIONS Ltd**
*Mystics. Psychics*
Maidstone TV Studios
Vinters Park
Maidstone ME14 5NZ
Website: www.myspiritradio.com
e-mail: info@myspirittv.com
Tel: 01634 323376

**MYERS MANAGEMENT**
63 Fairfields Crescent
London NW9 0PR
Tel/Fax: 020-8204 8941

**NARROW ROAD COMPANY The**
(PMA Member)
3rd Floor
76 Neal Street
London WC2H 9PL
e-mail: agents@narrowroad.co.uk
Fax: 020-7379 9777
Tel: 020-7379 9598

182 Brighton Road
Coulsdon
Surrey CR5 2NF
e-mail: richardireson@narrowroad.co.uk
Fax: 020-8763 2558
Tel: 020-8763 9895

2nd Floor
Grampian House
144 Deansgate
Manchester M3 3EE
Tel/Fax: 0161-833 1605
e-mail: manchester@narrowroad.co.uk

**NE REPRESENTATION**
3-5 Bakehouse Hill, Darlington, Co. Durham DL1 5QA
Website: www.nerepresentation.co.uk
e-mail: info@nerepresentation.co.uk
Fax: 01325 488390     Tel: 01325 488385

**NELSON BROWNE MANAGEMENT Ltd**
40 Bowling Green Lane, London EC1R 0NE
Website: www.nelsonbrowne.com
e-mail: enquiries@nelsonbrowne.com
Fax: 020-7837 7612     Tel: 020-7970 6010

**NEVS AGENCY**
Regal House, 198 King's Road, London SW3 5XP
Website: www.nevs.co.uk
e-mail: getamodel@nevs.co.uk
Fax: 020-7352 6068     Tel: 020-7352 4886

**NEW CASEY AGENCY**
The Annexe, 129 Northwood Way
Northwood HA6 1RF     Tel: 01923 823182

**NEW FACES Ltd**
(Personal Manager)
*Contact: Val Horton*
*By Post/e-mail*
*Accepts Showreels*
*3 Agents represent 50 Performers*
*Children. Commercials. Film. Stage. Television*
2nd Floor, The Linen Hall
162-168 Regent Street, London W1B 5TB
Website: www.newfacestalent.co.uk
e-mail: info@newfacestalent.co.uk
Fax: 020-7287 5481     Tel: 020-7439 6900

**NFD - THE FILM & TV AGENCY**
PO Box 76
Leeds LS25 9AG     Tel/Fax: 01977 681949
Website: www.film-tv-agency.com
e-mail: info@film-tv-agency.com

**NICHOLSON Jackie ASSOCIATES**
(Personal Manager)
*Contact: By Post*
Suite 44
2nd Floor, Morley House
320 Regent Street
London W1B 3BD
e-mail: jnalondon@aol.com
Fax: 020-7580 4489     Tel: 020-7580 4422

**N M MANAGEMENT**
16 St Alfege Passage
Greenwich
London SE10 9JS     Tel: 020-8853 4337
e-mail: nmmanagement@hotmail.com

**NMP MANAGEMENT**
(Personal Manager)
*Contact: By e-mail*
*2 Agents represent 10 Performers*
*Comedians. Corporate. Presenters. Television*
PO Box 981
Wallington
Surrey SM6 8JU
Website: www.nmpmanagement.co.uk
e-mail: management@nmp.co.uk
Fax: 020-8404 2621     Tel: 020-8669 3128

EXCLUSIVE REPRESENTATION OF PROFESSIONAL ACTORS

Contact Debbie Pine
Pure Actors Agency & Management Ltd
44 Salisbury Road, Manchester M41 0RB
T. 0161 747 2377  F. 0161 746 9886
E. enquiries@pure-management.co.uk

pure-management.co.uk

**NORTH OF WATFORD ACTORS AGENCY**
(Co-operative)
Bridge Mill, Hebden Bridge
West Yorks HX7 8EX
Website: www.northofwatford.com
e-mail: info@northofwatford.com
Fax: 01422 846503                    Tel: 01422 845361

**NORTH WEST ACTORS**
(Personal Manager)
*Contact: Nigel Adams*
*By Post. Accepts Showreels/Voicereels*
*Commercials. Film. Radio. Stage. Television*
36 Lord Street, Radcliffe
Manchester M26 3BA          Tel/Fax: 0161-724 6625
Website: www.northwestactors.co.uk
e-mail: info@northwestactors.co.uk

**NORTHERN LIGHTS MANAGEMENT Ltd**
Dean Clough Mills
Halifax
West Yorks HX3 5AX
e-mail: northern.lights@virgin.net
Fax: 01422 330101                    Tel: 01422 382203

**NORTHERN PROFESSIONALS**
*Action Safety. Boat & Diving Equipment Hire. Casting*
*Technicians*
21 Cresswell Avenue
North Shields
Tyne & Wear NE29 9BQ                 Tel: 0191-257 8635
Website: www.northernprocasting.co.uk
e-mail: bill@northernprocasting.co.uk

**NORTHERN STAR ACTORS AGENCY**
332 Royal Exchange
Manchester M2 7BR                    Tel: 0161-832 3535
e-mail: mark@northernstaractors.co.uk

**NORTHERN STAR MEDIA Ltd**
BCR House
3 Bredbury Business Park
Stockport
Cheshire SK6 2SN                     Tel: 0161-408 3476
Website: www.nsmagency.com
e-mail: info@nsmagency.com

**NORTHONE MANAGEMENT**
(CPMA Member)
HG08 Aberdeen Studios
Highbury Grove
London N5 2EA               Tel/Fax: 020-7359 9666
Website: www.northone.co.uk
e-mail: actors@northone.co.uk

**NS ARTISTES MANAGEMENT**
10 Claverdon House
Holly Bank Road
Billesley
Birmingham B13 0QY
Website: www.nsmanagement.co.uk
e-mail: nsmanagement@fsmail.net
Mobile: 07870 969577                Tel: 0121-684 5607

**NSM**
(Natasha Stevenson Management Ltd (Personal Manager)
(PMA Member)
*Contact: By Post/e-mail/Telephone*
*3 Agents*
*Commercials. Film. Stage. Television*
Studio 7C
Clapham North Arts Centre
Voltaire Road
London SW4 6DH
Website: www.natashastevenson.co.uk
e-mail: inbox@natashastevenson.co.uk
Fax: 020-7720 5565                  Tel: 020-7720 3355

**NUMBER ONE CASTING & MODEL MANAGEMENT Ltd**
The Barn
Pasture Farm
Coventry Road
Solihull B92 0HH                    Tel: 01675 443900
Website: www.numberonemodelagency.co.uk
e-mail: info@numberonemodelagency.co.uk

**NYLAND MANAGEMENT**
20 School Lane
Heaton Chapel
Stockport SK4 5DG                   Tel: 0161-442 2224
Website: www.nylandmanagement.com
e-mail: nylandmgmt@freenet.co.uk

## OBJECTIVE TALENT MANAGEMENT
3rd Floor
Riverside Building
County Hall
Westminster Bridge Road
London SE1 7PB                    Tel/Fax: 020-7202 2300
Website: www.objectivetalentmanagement.com
e-mail: info@objectivetalentmanagement.com

## OFF THE KERB PRODUCTIONS
3rd Floor
Hammer House
113-117 Wardour Street
London W1F OUN
Website: www.offthekerb.co.uk
e-mail: info@offthekerb.co.uk
Fax: 020-7437 0647               Tel: 020-7437 0607

## OI OI AGENCY
*2 Agents represent 400 Performers*
*Adults. Children. Commercials. Corporate. Dancers*
*Disabled. Film. Modelling. Musicals. Presenters. Radio*
*Singers. Stage. Television. Voice Overs*
The Coach House, Pinewood Film Studios
Pinewood, Iver Heath
Buckinghamshire SL0 0NH
Website: www.oioi.org.uk
e-mail: info@oioi.org.uk
Fax: 01753 655622               Tel: 01753 852326

## ONE MAKE UP/ONE PHOTOGRAPHIC Ltd
4th Floor
48 Poland Street, London W1F 7ND
Website: www.onemakeup.com
e-mail: info@onemakeup.com
Fax: 020-7287 2313              Tel: 020-7287 2311

## OPERA & CONCERT ARTISTS
Musicals. Opera
75 Aberdare Gardens, London NW6 3AN
e-mail: enquiries@opera-and-concert-artists.co.uk
Fax: 020-7372 3537             Tel: 020-7328 3097

## ORDINARY PEOPLE
Actors. Modelling
16 Camden Road, London NW1 9DP
Website: www.ordinarypeople.co.uk
e-mail: info@ordinarypeople.co.uk
Fax: 020-7267 5677             Tel: 020-7267 7007

## OREN
(CPMA Member)
Chapter Arts Centre
Market Road, Cardiff CF5 1QE    Tel: 029-2023 3321
Website: www.oren20.com
e-mail: admin@oren20.com

## ORIENTAL CASTING AGENCY Ltd
*Contact: Peggy Sirr*
*By e-mail/Telephone*
*Accepts Showreels/Voicereels*
*1 Agent represents 200+ Performers*
*Afro/Asian Artists*
60 Downton Avenue
Streatham Hill, London SW2 3TR
Website: www.orientalcasting.com
e-mail: peggy.sirr@btconnect.com
Fax: 020-8674 9303             Tel: 020-8671 8538

**ORPIN ASSOCIATES**
Studio 54, 77 Beak Street
London W1F 9DB     Tel: 01462 672305
Website: www.orpinassociates.com
e-mail: enquiries@orpinassociates.com

**ORR MANAGEMENT AGENCY**
1st Floor
147-149 Market Street
Farnworth
Greater Manchester BL4 8EX     Tel: 01204 579842
Website: www.orrmanagement.co.uk
e-mail: barbara@orrmanagement.co.uk

**OTTO PERSONAL MANAGEMENT Ltd**
(Personal Manager) (CPMA Member)
S.I.F.
5 Brown Street
Sheffield S1 2BS
Website: www.ottopm.co.uk
e-mail: admin@ottopm.co.uk
Fax: 0114-279 5225     Tel: 0114-275 2592

**OUR COMPANY**
Poplar Dock Marina
Broadwick Place
London E14 5SH     Mobile: 07977 302250
Website: www.our-company.co.uk
e-mail: info@our-company.co.uk

**PADBURY David ASSOCIATES**
44 Summerlee Avenue
Finchley
London N2 9QP     Tel/Fax: 020-8883 1277
Website: www.davidpadburyassociates.com
e-mail: info@davidpadburyassociates.com

**PAN ARTISTS AGENCY Ltd**
Cornerways
34 Woodhouse Lane
Sale, Cheshire M33 4JX
Website: www.panartists.co.uk
e-mail: panartists@btconnect.com
Mobile: 07890 715115     Tel: 0800 6349147

**PANTO PEOPLE**
3 Rushden House
Tatlow Road
Glenfield
Leicester LE3 8ND     Tel/Fax: 0116-287 9594
e-mail: jonny.dallas@ntlworld.com

**PARAMOUNT INTERNATIONAL MANAGEMENT**
*30 Performers. International Comedians*
Talbot House
204-226 Imperial Drive
Harrow, Middlesex HA2 7HH
Website: www.ukcomedy.com
e-mail: mail@ukcomedy.com
Fax: 020-8868 6475     Tel: 020-8429 3179

**PARKER Cherry MANAGEMENT (RSM)**
(See RSM: Cherry Parker Management)

**PARSONS & BROOK**
*Contact: By e-mail*
*Accepts Showreels*
*2 Agents represent 65 Performers*
*Commercials. Corporate. Film. Musicals. Radio. Stage
Television*
37 Berwick Street, London W1F 8RS
e-mail: info@parsonsandbrook.co.uk
Fax: 020-7287 8016     Tel: 020-7434 0398

**PARSONS Cary MANAGEMENT**
*Set, Costume & Lighting Designers, Directors &
Choreographers*
3/1, 4 Lawrence Street
Glasgow G11 5HQ     Tel: 0141-357 6702
e-mail: carylparsons@gmail.com

**P B J MANAGEMENT Ltd**
(Personal Manager) (PMA Member)
*Contact: Janette Linden*
*By e-mail*
*Accepts Showreels*
*8 Agents represent 54 Performers*
*Comedians. Commercials. Corporate. Presenters. Radio
Stage. Television. Voice Overs. Walk-on & Supporting
Artists. Writers*
5 Soho Square, London W1D 3QA
Website: www.pbjmgt.co.uk
e-mail: general@pbjmgt.co.uk
Fax: 020-7287 1191     Tel: 020-7287 1112

**PC THEATRICAL, MODEL & CASTING AGENCY**
*Large Database of Twins*
13A Carlisle Road
Colindale, London NW9 0HD
Website: www.twinagency.com
e-mail: twinagy@aol.com
Fax: 020-8933 3418     Tel: 020-8381 2229

*Kate Loustau*    *Patrick Malahide*    *Ella Brown*    *Gary Pillai*    *Nadia Cameron Blakey*

## Dan Harwood-Stamper
photographer

Tel: 01442 242410 / 07779 165777    www.danharwoodstamper.co.uk

**PELHAM ASSOCIATES**
(Personal Manager) (PMA Member)
*Contact: Peter Cleall*
The Media Centre
9-12 Middle Street
Brighton BN1 1AL
Website: www.pelhamassociates.co.uk
e-mail: petercleall@pelhamassociates.co.uk
Fax: 01273 202492                Tel: 01273 323010

**PEMBERTON ASSOCIATES Ltd**
(PMA Member)
*Contact: Barbara Pemberton*
*By Post/e-mail*
*Showreels on request*
*5 Agents represent 130 Performers*
*Film. Musicals. Radio. Singers. Stage. Television*
*Voice Overs*
193 Wardour Street
London W1F 8ZF
Website: www.pembertonassociates.com
e-mail: general@pembertonassociates.com
Fax: 020-7734 2522            Tel: 020-7734 4144

Express Networks
1 George Leigh Street
Manchester M4 5DL
Fax: 0161-235 8442            Tel: 0161-235 8440

**PEOPLEMATTER.TV**
40 Bowling Green Lane
Clerkenwell, London EC1R ONE
Website: www.peoplematter.tv
e-mail: tony@peoplematter.tv
Fax: 020-7415 7074            Tel: 020-7415 7070

**PEPPERPOT PROMOTIONS**
*Bands*
Suite 20B, 20-22 Orde Hall Street, London WC1N 3JW
e-mail: chris@pepperpot.co.uk
Fax: 020-7405 6799            Tel: 020-7405 9108

**PERFORMANCE ACTORS AGENCY**
(Co-operative) (CPMA Member)
137 Goswell Road, London EC1V 7ET
Website: www.performanceactors.co.uk
e-mail: info@performanceactors.co.uk
Fax: 020-7251 3974            Tel: 020-7251 5716

**PERFORMING ARTS**
(Personal Manager) (PMA Member)
*Contact: By Post/e-mail*
*2 Agents represent 30 Performers*
*Creative Team Members only*
6 Windmill Street, London W1T 2JB
Website: www.performing-arts.co.uk
e-mail: info@performing-arts.co.uk
Fax: 020-7631 4631            Tel: 020-7255 1362

## www.headshotsbysimon.com
tel: +44 (0)7949 660043 email: simoncardwell@googlemail.com

**PERSONAL APPEARANCES**
20 North Mount
1147-1161 High Road
Whetstone N20 0PH          Tel/Fax: 020-8343 7748
Website: www.personalappearances.biz
e-mail: patsy@personalappearances.biz

**P F D**
(PMA Member)
Drury House
34-43 Russell Street
London WC2B 5HA
Website: www.pfd.co.uk
e-mail: info@pfd.co.uk
Fax: 020-7836 9539          Tel: 020-7344 1010

**PHA ACTORS MANAGEMENT**
Tanzaro House
Ardwick Green North
Manchester M12 6FZ
Website: www.pha-agency.co.uk
e-mail: casting@pha-agency.co.uk
Fax: 0161-273 4567          Tel: 0161-273 4444

**PHD ARTISTS**
*Contact: Paul Harris®*
24 Montana Gardens
Sutton, Surrey SM1 4FP          Tel/Fax: 020-7241 6601
Website: www.phdartists.com
e-mail: office@phdartists.com

**PHILLIPS Frances**
(Personal Manager) (PMA Member)
*Contact: Frances Zealander-Phillips*
*By e-mail*
*2 Agents represent 40 Performers*
89 Robeson Way
Borehamwood
Hertfordshire WD6 5RY
Website: www.francesphillips.co.uk
e-mail: derekphillips@talk21.com
Mobile: 07957 334328          Tel: 020-8953 0303

**PHPM**
(Philippa Howell Personal Management)
(Personal Manager)
*Contact: By Post (SAE)/e-mail*
*2 Agents represent 80 Performers*
*Commercials. Film. Musicals. Stage. Television*
184 Bradway Road
Sheffield S17 4QX
e-mail: philippa@phpm.co.uk
Mobile: 07790 969024          Tel/Fax: 0114-235 3663

**PHYSICK Hilda**
(Personal Manager)
*Contact: By Post*
78 Temple Sheen Road
London SW14 7RR
Fax: 020-8876 5561          Tel: 020-8876 0073

**PICCADILLY MANAGEMENT**
(Personal Manager)
23 New Mount Street
Manchester M4 4DE
Website: www.piccadillymanagement.com
e-mail: info@piccadillymanagement.com
Fax: 0161-953 4001          Tel: 0161-953 4057

**PINEAPPLE AGENCY**
Montgomery House
159-161 Balls Pond Road
London N1 4BG
Website: www.pineappleagency.com
e-mail: pineapple.agency@btconnect.com
Fax: 020-7241 3006          Tel: 020-7241 6601

**PLA**
(See LOVETT LOGAN ASSOCIATES)

**PLAIN JANE**
PO Box 2730
Romford
Essex RM7 1AB          Mobile: 07813 667319
Website: www.plain-jane.co.uk
e-mail: info@plain-jane.co.uk

**PLATER Janet MANAGEMENT Ltd**
*Contact: Janet Plater*
*By Post*
*Accepts Showreels*
*Commercials. Film. Radio. Stage. Television*
D Floor
Milburn House
Dean Street
Newcastle upon Tyne NE1 1LF          Tel: 0191-221 2490
Website: www.janetplatermanagement.co.uk
e-mail: magpie@tynebridge.demon.co.uk

**PLUNKET GREENE ASSOCIATES**
(In conjunction with James Sharkey Associates Ltd)
Existing Clients only
PO Box 8365
London W14 0GL
Fax: 020-7603 2221          Tel: 020-7603 2227

**POLLYANNA MANAGEMENT Ltd**
1 Knighten Street
Wapping
London E1W 1PH
Website: www.pollyannatheatre.org
e-mail: aliceharwood@talktalk.net
Fax: 020-8530 6722          Tel: 020-7481 1911

**POOLE Gordon AGENCY Ltd**
The Limes
Brockley
Bristol BS48 3BB
Website: www.gordonpoole.com
e-mail: agents@gordonpoole.com
Fax: 01275 462252          Tel: 01275 463222

**PORTABLE COMEDY CLUB The**
14 Dover Street
Mayfair
London W1S 4LY
Website: www.theportablecomedyclub.co.uk
e-mail: enquiries@theportablecomedyclub.co.uk
Fax: 020-7281 6520          Mobile: 07808 808080

**POWER MODEL MANAGEMENT CASTING AGENCY**
PO Box 1198
Salhouse
Norwich NR13 6WD          Tel: 01603 777190
Website: www.powermodel.co.uk
e-mail: info@powermodel.co.uk

**POWER PROMOTIONS**
PO Box 61
Liverpool L13 0EF
Website: www.powerpromotions.com
e-mail: tom@powerpromotions.co.uk
Fax: 0870 7060202          Tel: 0151-230 0070

**PREGNANT PAUSE AGENCY**
*Pregnant Models, Dancers, Actresses*
11 Matham Road
East Molesey KT8 0SX
Website: www.pregnantpause.co.uk
e-mail: sandy@pregnantpause.co.uk     Tel: 020-8979 8874

**PRESTON Morwenna MANAGEMENT**
Website: www.morwennapreston.com
e-mail: info@morwennapreston.com     Tel/Fax: 020-8835 8147

**PRICE GARDNER MANAGEMENT**
PO Box 59908
London SW16 5QH
Website: www.pricegardner.co.uk
e-mail: info@pricegardner.co.uk
Fax: 020-7381 3288          Tel: 020-7610 2111

**PRINCIPAL ARTISTES**
(Personal Manager)
*Contact: By Post*
4 Paddington Street
Marylebone
London W1U 5QE
Fax: 020-7486 4668          Tel: 020-7224 3414

**PRODUCTIONS & PROMOTIONS Ltd**
Apsley Mills Cottage, London Road
Hemel Hempstead, Herts HP3 9QU     Mobile: 07885 811757
Website: www.prodmotions.com
e-mail: reception@prodmotions.com

**PROJECT MODELS**
29C Friars Place Lane
London W3 7AQ          Tel: 020-8354 5256
Website: www.projectmodels.co.uk
e-mail: dean@projectmodels.co.uk

**PROSPECTS ASSOCIATIONS**
*Sessions. Singers. Voice Overs for Commercials, Film & Television*
28 Magpie Close
Forest Gate, London E7 9DE
e-mail: wasegun@yahoo.co.uk          Tel: 020-8555 3628

**PROVOKE MODELS**
26A Ganton Street
London W1F 7QZ
Website: www.provokemodels.com
e-mail: russ@provokemodels.com
Fax: 0845 1236005          Tel: 0845 1236004

**PURE ACTORS AGENCY & MANAGEMENT Ltd**
44 Salisbury Road
Manchester M41 0RB
Website: www.pure-management.co.uk
e-mail: enquiries@pure-management.co.uk
Fax: 0161-746 9886          Tel: 0161-747 2377

# John Colclough Advisory

*Practical independent guidance for actors and actresses*

**t:** 020 8873 1763   **e:** john@johncolclough.org.uk   www.johncolclough.co.uk

**PVA MANAGEMENT Ltd**
County House, St Mary's Street
Worcester WR1 1HB
Website: www.pva.co.uk
e-mail: post@pva.co.uk
Fax: 01905 610709                   Tel: 01905 616100

**PWE**
129 Rectory Road
Farnborough
Hampshire GU14 7HS
e-mail: pwe@london.com             Tel: 01276 58967

**QUICK Nina ASSOCIATES**
(See TAYLOR Brian ASSOCIATES)

**RAFFLES Tim ENTERTAINMENTS**
(Personal Manager)
*2 Agents represent 9 Performers*
*Corporate. Cruise Work. Singers. Television*
Victoria House
29 Swaythling Road
West End
Southampton SO30 3AG        Tel/Fax: 023-8046 5843
Website: www.timrafflesentertainments.co.uk
e-mail: info@timrafflesentertainments.co.uk

**RAGE MODELS**
Tigris House
256 Edgware Road, London W2 1DS
Website: www.ragemodels.org
e-mail: ragemodels@ugly.org
Fax: 020-7402 0507                 Tel: 020-7262 0515

**RAMA GLOBAL Ltd**
*Contact: Rachael Pacey*
*By Post. Accepts Showreels*
*1 Agent represents 10 Performers. Children*
*Commercials. Film. Stage. Television*
Huntingdon House
278-290 Huntingdon Street
Nottingham NG1 3LY
Website: www.rama-global.co.uk
e-mail: admin@rama global.co.uk
Fax: 0115-948 3696                 Tel: 0845 0540255

**RANDALL RICHARDSON ACTORS MANAGEMENT**
2nd Floor, 145-157 St John Street
London EC1V 4PY
Website: www.randallrichardson.co.uk
e-mail: mail@randallrichardson.co.uk
Fax: 0870 7623212                  Tel: 020-7060 1645

**RAPID TALENT Ltd**
5 Vancouver Road
Eastbourne
East Sussex BN23 5BF
Website: www.rapidtalent.co.uk
e-mail: enquiries@rapidtalent.co.uk
Mobile: 07980 899156              Tel: 020-7734 5775

**RARE TALENT ACTORS MANAGEMENT**
Tanzaro House
Ardwick Green North
Manchester M12 6FZ
Website: www.raretalentactors.com
e-mail: info@raretalentactors.com
Fax: 0161-273 4567                 Tel: 0161-273 4004

**RAVENSCOURT MANAGEMENT**
8-30 Galena Road
Hammersmith
London W6 0LT
Website: www.ravenscourt.net
e-mail: info@ravenscourt.net
Fax: 020-8741 1786                 Tel: 020-8741 0707

**RAW AGENCY Ltd**
Studio 1
Bizzy House
73A Mayplace Road West
Bexleyheath, Kent DA7 4JL
Website: www.rawagencyltd.com
e-mail: clients@rawagencyltd.com
Fax: 020-8303 2730          Tel: 020-8303 2627 Ext 25

**RAY KNIGHT CASTING**
(See KNIGHT Ray CASTING)

**RAZZAMATAZZ MANAGEMENT**
(Personal Manager)
*Contact: Jill Shirley*
*By e-mail/Telephone*
*1 Agent represents 10 Clients*
*Children. Dancers. Presenters. Singers*
204 Holtye Road
East Grinstead
West Sussex RH19 3ES
e-mail: razzamatazzmanagement@btconnect.com
Mobile: 07836 268292               Tel: 01342 301617

**RbA MANAGEMENT Ltd**
(Personal Manager) (CPMA Member)
*24 Performers*
*Contact: By e-mail*
*Accepts Showreels/Voicereels*
37-45 Windsor Street
Liverpool L8 1XE                   Tel: 0151-708 7273
Website: www.rbamanagement.co.uk
e-mail: info@rbamanagement.co.uk

**RBM ACTORS**
3rd Floor
168 Victoria Street
London SW1E 5LB
Website: www.rbmactors.com
e-mail: info@rbmactors.com
Fax: 020-7630 6549                 Tel: 020-7630 7733

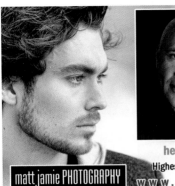   
**REACTORS AGENCY**
(CPMA Member)
*Contact: By Post/e-mail*
*Accepts Showreels*
*Co-operative of 23 Performers*
1 Eden Quay
Dublin 1, Ireland
Website: www.reactors.ie
e-mail: info@reactors.ie
Fax: 00 353 1 8783182          Tel: 00 353 1 8786833

**REAL PEOPLE, REAL TALENT**
Fourways House, 57 Hilton Street, Manchester M1 2EJ
Website: www.realpeople4u.com
e-mail: info@realpeople4u.com
Fax: 0161-236 1237          Tel: 0161-237 0101

**RE.ANIMATOR MANAGEMENT**
(PMA Member)
3rd Floor, The Priory
Syresham Gardens, West Sussex RH16 3LB
Website: www.reanimator.co.uk
e-mail: management@reanimator.co.uk
Fax: 01444 447030          Tel: 01444 447020

**RED&BLACK**
Website: www.red-black.co.uk
e-mail: info@red-black.co.uk          Mobile: 07722 887277

**RED CANYON MANAGEMENT**
Website: www.redcanyon.co.uk
e-mail: info@redcanyon.co.uk
Mobile: 07939 365578          Mobile: 07931 381696

**RED DOOR MANAGEMENT**
The Pie Factory
101 Broadway
Media City, Manchester M50 2EQ          Tel/Fax: 0161-425 6495
Website: www.the-reddoor.co.uk
e-mail: mail@the-reddoor.co.uk

**RED HOT ENTERTAINMENT**
*Contact: Nicky Raby*
*By e-mail*
*Accepts Showreels/Voicereels*
*4 Agents represent 23 Clients*
*Commercials. Disabled. Film. Musicals. Stage. Television*
*Writers*
6 Farriers Mews
London SE15 3XP
Website: www.redhotentertainment.biz
e-mail: info@redhotentertainment.biz
Fax: 020-7635 8988          Tel: 020-7635 0403

**RED ONION AGENCY**
*Session Fixer for Singers, Musicians and Gospel Choirs*
26-28 Hatherley Mews
London E17 4QP
Website: www.redonion.uk.com
e-mail: studio@redonion.uk.com
Fax: 020-8521 6646          Tel: 020-8520 3975

**REDDIN Joan**
(Personal Manager) Contact: By Post
Hazel Cottage, Frogg's Island, Wheeler End Common
Bucks HP14 3NL          Tel: 01494 882729

**REDROOFS ASSOCIATES**
Littlewick Green, Maidenhead, Berkshire SL6 3QY
Website: www.redroofs.co.uk
e-mail: agency@redroofs.co.uk
Fax: 01628 822461          Tel: 01628 822982

**REGAN RIMMER MANAGEMENT**
Contact: Leigh-Ann Regan
Ynyslas Uchaf Farm, Blackmill, Bridgend CF35 6DW
e-mail: regan-rimmer@btconnect.com
Fax: 01656 841815          Tel: 01656 841841

Contact: Debbie Rimmer
Room 412, Linen Hall
162/168 Regent Street, London W1B 5TE
e-mail: thegirls@regan-rimmer.co.uk
Fax: 020-7494 2444          Tel: 020-7494 2244

**REGENCY AGENCY**
25 Carr Road, Calverley
Leeds LS28 5NE          Tel: 0113-255 8980

**REPRESENTATION UPSON EDWARDS**
Voice Coaches only
23 Victoria Park Road
Stoke on Trent, Staffs ST6 6DX
Website: www.voicecoach.tv
e-mail: sarah.upson@voicecoach.tv
Fax: 01782 728004          Tel: 01782 827222

**REYNOLDS Sandra AGENCY**
Contact: By e-mail
8 Agents represent 150 Performers
Children. Commercials. Photographic Modelling. Presenters
Bacon House, 35 St Georges Street, Norwich NR3 1DA
Website: www.sandrareynolds.co.uk
e-mail: info@sandrareynolds.co.uk
Fax: 01603 219825          Tel: 01603 623842

Shakespeare House
168 Lavender Hill, London SW11 5TF
Fax: 020-7387 5848          Tel: 020-7387 5858

**RICHARDS Lisa AGENCY The**
108 Upper Leeson Street
Dublin 4
Ireland
e-mail: info@lisarichards.ie
Fax: 00 353 1 6671256          Tel: 00 353 1 6375000

The Space
57-61 Mortimer Street
London W1W 8HS          Tel: 020-3170 6205
Website: www.lisarichards.co.uk
e-mail: office@lisarichards.co.uk

**RICHARDS Stella MANAGEMENT**
Contact: Stella Richards, Julia Lintott
Existing Clients only
42 Hazlebury Road
London SW6 2ND
Website: www.stellarichards.com
e-mail: stellagent@aol.com
Fax: 020-7731 5082          Tel: 020-7736 7786

**RICHARD STONE PARTNERSHIP The**
(See STONE Richard PARTNERSHIP The)

**RICHMOND SHARPE AGENCY**
Merricourt
Windmill Lane
Appleton
Warrington
Cheshire WA4 5JP          Tel: 0161-858 0049
Website: www.richmondsharpe.com
e-mail: info@richmondsharpe.com

**RIDGEWAY MANAGEMENT**
Fairley House
Andrews Lane
Cheshunt
Herts EN7 6LB
e-mail: info@ridgewaystudios.co.uk
Fax: 01992 633844          Tel: 01992 633775

## RISQUE MODEL MANAGEMENT
32 Walter Walk
London HA8 9ES          Tel: 0870 2283890
Website: www.risquemodel.co.uk
e-mail: info@risquemodel.co.uk

## ROBERTS Nicola MANAGEMENT
149 Nelson Road
London N8 9RR          Tel/Fax: 020-8375 5555
Website: www.nicolarobertsmanagement.com
e-mail: info@nicolarobertsmanagement.com

## ROGUE MAIDENS AGENCY Ltd The
Netley Hall
Dorrington
Shrewsbury
Shropshire SY5 7JZ          Tel: 01743 719303
Website: www.roguemaidens.com
e-mail: info@roguemaidens.com

## ROGUES & VAGABONDS MANAGEMENT Ltd
(Personal Manager) (CPMA Member)
The Print House
18 Ashwin Street
London E8 3DL
e-mail: rogues@vagabondsmanagement.com
Fax: 020-7249 8564          Tel: 020-7254 8130

## ROLE MODELS
12 Cressy Road
London NW3 2LY          Tel: 020-7284 4337
Website: www.rolemodelsagency.com
e-mail: info@rolemodelsagency.com

## ROOM 3 AGENCY
64 Alma Road
Clifton
Bristol BS8 2DJ
Website: www.room3agency.com
e-mail: kate@room3agency.com
Fax: 0845 5679333          Tel: 0845 5678333

## ROSEBERY MANAGEMENT Ltd
(CPMA Member)
*Contact: Alan Bell*
*By Post*
*Accepts Showreels.*
*1 Agent represents 27 Performers*
*Commercials. Film. Musicals. Stage. Television. Voice Overs*
Hoxton Hall
130 Hoxton Street
London N1 6SH
Website: www.roseberymanagement.com
e-mail: admin@roseberymanagement.com
Fax: 020-7503 0517          Tel: 020-7684 0187

## ROSS Frances MANAGEMENT
(Personal Manager)
*Contact: Frances Ross*
*By Post/e-mail/Telephone*
*1 Agent represents 11 Performers*
*Commercials. Corporate. Film. Stage. Television*
Higher Leyonne
Golant
Fowey, Cornwall PL23 1LA
Website: www.francesrossmanagement.co.uk
e-mail: francesross@btconnect.com
Mobile: 07918 648330          Tel/Fax: 01726 832395

## STAGEWORKS® WORLDWIDE PRODUCTIONS

**agency**

SKATING
ICE DANCERS
FREE SKATERS
PAIR SKATERS
ADAGIO SKATERS
COMEDY SKATERS

DANCERS
ACTORS
SINGERS
MODELS

CIRCUS ARTISTS
SPECIALITY ACTS
MAGICIANS
ILLUSIONISTS
COSTUME CHARACTERS
STREET PERFORMERS

PROMOTIONAL PERSONNEL
HOSTS & HOSTESSES
GUEST SPEAKERS

SCRIPT WRITING

TECHNICAL STAGE MANAGEMENT

MUSIC PRODUCTION
PUBLISHING

MILLINERY AND COSTUMES

CHOREOGRAPHERS
DIRECTORS
PRODUCERS

**00 44 (0) 1253 342426**
**00 44 (0) 1253 336341**
**info@stageworkswwp.com**
**stageworkswwp.com**

## ROSS BROWN ASSOCIATES
(Personal Manager)
Rosedale House
Rosedale Road
Richmond
Surrey TW9 2SZ
e-mail: sandy@rossbrown.eu
Fax: 020-8398 4111                Tel: 020-8939 9000

## ROSSMORE MANAGEMENT
(PMA Member)
10 Wyndham Place
London W1H 2PU
Website: www.rossmoremanagement.com
e-mail: agents@rossmoremanagement.com
Fax: 020-7258 0124                Tel: 020-7258 1953

## ROUGH HANDS AGENCY The
29 James Street, Epping
Essex, London CM16 6RR
e-mail: roughhandsagency@yahoo.co.uk
Mobile: 07932 573228             Tel: 01992 578835

## ROWE ASSOCIATES
33 Percy Street
London W1T 2DF
Website: www.growe.co.uk
e-mail: agents@growe.co.uk
Mobile: 07887 898220             Tel/Fax: 01992 308519

## ROYCE MANAGEMENT
29 Trenholme Road
London SE20 8PP                  Tel/Fax: 020-8778 6861
Website: www.roycemanagement.co.uk
e-mail: office@roycemanagement.co.uk

## RPM2
Studio House, Delamare Road
Cheshunt, Herts EN8 9SH
Website: www.rhino2-rpm.com
e-mail: rhino-rpm2@hotmail.com
Tel: 0845 3625456                Tel/Fax: 0845 2415585

## RSM (Cherry Parker Management)
*Contact: Cherry Parker*
15 The Fairway SS9 4QN
Website: www.rsm.uk.net
e-mail: info@rsm.uk.net
Mobile: 07976 547066             Tel: 01702 522647

## RUBICON MANAGEMENT
27 Inderwick Road
Crouch End
London N8 9LB
e-mail: rubiconartists@blueyonder.co.uk
Mobile: 07957 358767             Tel/Fax: 020-8374 1836

## RUDEYE DANCE AGENCY
The Basement
73 St John Street
London EC1M 4NJ                  Tel: 020-7014 3023
Website: www.rudeye.com
e-mail: info@rudeye.com

## SANDERS Loesje Ltd
(PMA Member)
*Contact: Loesje Sanders, Jo Probitts*
*By Post*
*Choreographers. Designers. Directors. Lighting Designers*
Pound Square
1 North Hill
Woodbridge
Suffolk IP12 1HH
Website: www.loesjesanders.com
e-mail: loesje@loesjesanders.org.uk
Fax: 01394 388734                Tel: 01394 385260

## SANGWIN ASSOCIATES
(PMA Member)
8-30 Galena Road
Hammersmith
London W6 0LT
e-mail: info@sangwinassoc.com
Fax: 020-8741 1786               Tel: 020-8748 8698

## SARABAND ASSOCIATES
*Contact: Sara Randall, Bryn Newton*
265 Liverpool Road
London N1 1LX
e-mail: brynnewton@btconnect.com
Fax: 020-7609 2370               Tel: 020-7609 5313

## SASHAZE TALENT AGENCY
2 Gleannan Close
Omagh
Co. Tyrone BT79 7YA              Mobile: 07968 762942
Website: www.sashaze.com
e-mail: info@sashaze.com

**SCA MANAGEMENT**
Contact: By Post
77 Oxford Street
London W1D 2ES                        Tel: 020-7659 2027
Website: www.sca-management.co.uk
e-mail: agency@sca-management.co.uk

**SCHNABL Peter**
The Barn House
Cutwell, Tetbury
Gloucestershire GL8 8EB
e-mail: peter.schnabl@virgin.net
Fax: 01666 502998                     Tel: 01666 502133

**SCOTT MARSHALL PARTNERS Ltd**
(See MARSHALL Scott PARTNERS Ltd)

**SCOTT Tim**
PO Box 61776
London SW1V 3UX                       Tel/Fax: 020-7828 3824
e-mail: timscott@btinternet.com

**SCOTT-PAUL YOUNG ENTERTAINMENTS Ltd**
(Artists Representation & Promotions)
SPY Record Company
Northern Lights House
110 Blandford Road North
Langley, Nr Windsor
Berks SL3 7TA                         Tel/Fax: 01753 693250
Website: www.spy-artistsworld.com
e-mail: castingdirect@spy-ents.com

**SCRIMGEOUR Donald ARTISTS AGENT**
Choreographers. Principal Dancers. Producers
49 Springcroft Avenue
London N2 9JH
Website: www.donaldscrimgeour.com
e-mail: vwest@dircon.co.uk
Fax: 020-8883 9751                    Tel: 020-8444 6248

**SEARS MANAGEMENT Ltd**
2 Gumping Road
Orpington
Kent BR5 1RX
e-mail: lindasears@btconnect.com
Fax: 01689 862120                     Tel: 01689 861859

**SECOND SKIN AGENCY**
Foxgrove House
School Lane
Seer Green
Beaconsfield, Bucks HP9 2QJ           Tel/Fax: 01494 730166
Website: www.secondskinagency.com
e-mail: jenny@secondskinagency.com

**SEDGWICK Dawn MANAGEMENT**
3 Goodwins Court
Covent Garden
London WC2N 4LL
Fax: 020-7240 0415                    Tel: 020-7240 0404

**SELECT MANAGEMENT**
PO Box 748
London NW4 1TT
Website: www.selectmanagement.info
e-mail: mail@selectmanagement.info
Fax: 020-8203 8335                    Mobile: 07956 131494

**SHALIT GLOBAL MANAGEMENT**
4th Floor
34-35 Eastcastle Street
London W1W 8DW
Website: www.shalitglobal.com
e-mail: info@shalitglobal.com
Fax: 020-7462 9061                    Tel: 020-7462 9060

**SHAPER Susan MANAGEMENT**
5 Dovedale Gardens
465 Battersea Park Road
London SW11 4LR
e-mail: info@susanshapermanagement.com
Fax: 020-7350 1802                    Tel: 020-7585 1023

**SHEDDEN Malcolm MANAGEMENT**
1 Charlotte Street
London W1T 1RD
Website: www.features.co.uk
e-mail: info@features.co.uk
Fax: 020-7637 0328                    Tel: 020-7636 1876

**SHELDRAKE Peter AGENCY**
Contact: By e-mail
1 Agent represents 20 Clients
Commercials. Film. Musicals. Stage. Television
139 Lower Richmond Road
London SW14 7HX                       Tel: 020-8876 9572
e-mail: psagent@btinternet.com

**SHEPHERD MANAGEMENT Ltd**
(PMA Member)
4th Floor
45 Maddox Street
London W1S 2PE
e-mail: info@shepherdmanagement.co.uk
Fax: 020-7499 7535                    Tel: 020-7495 7813

**SHEPHERD MUSICAL ARTISTES**
(A Division of Shepherd Management Ltd)
4th Floor
25 Maddox Street
London W1S 2PE
e-mail: james@shepherdmusicalartistes.com
Fax: 020-7499 7535                    Tel: 020-7629 5268

**SHEPPERD-FOX**
5 Martyr Road
Guildford
Surrey GU1 4LF                        Mobile: 07957 624601
Website: www.shepperd-fox.co.uk
e-mail: info@shepperd-fox.co.uk

## SHOWSTOPPERS!
Events Management & Entertainment
42 Foxglove Close
Witham, Essex CM8 2XW
Website: www.showstoppers-group.com
e-mail: mail@showstoppers-group.com
Fax: 01376 510340                    Tel: 01376 518486

## SHOWTIME CASTINGS
112 Milligan Street
Docklands, London E14 8AS
Website: www.showtimecastings.com
e-mail: gemma@showtimecastings.com
Fax: 020-7987 3443                   Tel: 020-7068 6816

## SIBLEY Claire MANAGEMENT
15 Tweedale Wharf
Madeley
Shropshire TF7 4EW                   Tel: 01952 588951
Website: www.clairesibleymanagement.co.uk
e-mail: info@clairesibleymanagement.co.uk

## SILVEY Denise MANAGEMENT
St Martin's Theatre, West Street
London WC2N 9NH
e-mail: ds@denisesilvey.com
Mobile: 07711 245848                 Tel: 020-8743 7777

## SIMON & HOW ASSOCIATES
90-92 Ley Street, Ilford
Essex IG1 4BX                        Tel: 0845 0646666
Website: www.simon-how.com
e-mail: info@simon-how.com

## SIMPSON FOX ASSOCIATES Ltd
(PMA Member)
*Set, Costume and Lighting Designers. Directors*
*Choreographers*
52 Shaftesbury Avenue, London W1D 6LP
e-mail: info@simpson-fox.com
Fax: 020-7494 2887                   Tel: 020-7434 9167

## SINGER Sandra ASSOCIATES
(Personal Manager)
*Contact: By e-mail*
*2 Agents represent 40 Performers*
*Adults. Children. Choreographers. Commercials. Film*
*Musical Theatre. Television*
21 Cotswold Road
Westcliff-on-Sea, Essex SS0 8AA
Website: www.sandrasinger.com
e-mail: sandrasingeruk@aol.com
Fax: 01702 339393                    Tel: 01702 331616

## SINGERS INC
9-13 Grape Street, Covent Garden, London WC2H 8ED
Website: www.internationalcollective.com
e-mail: enquiries@internationalcollective.co.uk
Fax: 020-7557 6656                   Tel: 020-7557 6650

## SIRR Peggy
(See ORIENTAL CASTING AGENCY Ltd)

## SJ MANAGEMENT
8 Bettridge Road, London SW6 3QD
e-mail: sj@susanjames.demon.co.uk
Fax: 020-7371 0409                   Tel: 020-7371 0441

**Theatrical Agents • Actors • Dancers • Singers
Models • Presenters • Choreographers**

Room 236  Linen Hall  162-168 Regent Street  London W1B 5TB
**T** 020 7734 3356  **F** 020 7494 3787
www.successagency.co.uk  **e** ee@successagency.co.uk

**Success**

**SMART MANAGEMENT**
*Contact: Mario Renzullo*
PO Box 64377, London EC1P 1ND          Tel: 020-7837 8822
e-mail: smart.management@virgin.net

**SMEDLEY Tom MANAGEMENT**
28 White House
London SW11 3LJ                        Mobile: 07515 775220
Website: www.tomsmedleymanagement.com
e-mail: tom@tomsmedleymanagement.com

**SMILE TALENT**
The Office
55 Fitzwalter Place
Chelmsford Road
Great Dunmow, Essex CM6 1HB
Website: www.smiletalent.biz
e-mail: info@smiletalent.com
Fax: 01371 875270                      Tel: 01371 876757

**SONGTIME/CHANDLER'S MANAGEMENT**
10 Wallis Mews
Leatherhead
Surrey KT22 9DQ
Website: www.songtime.co.uk
e-mail: info@songtime.co.uk
Fax: 01372 362461                      Tel: 01372 372352

**SOPHIE'S PEOPLE**
*Choreographers. Dancers*
40 Mexfield Road, London SW15 2RQ
Website: www.sophiespeople.com
e-mail: sophies.people@btinternet.com
Fax: 0870 7876447                      Tel: 0870 7876446

**S.O.S.**
85 Bannerman House
Lawn Lane, London SW8 1UA
Website: www.sportsofseb.com
e-mail: info@sportsofseb.com
Mobile: 07740 359770                   Tel: 020-7735 5133

**SPACE PERSONAL MANAGEMENT**
PO Box 64412
London W5 9GU                          Tel: 020-8560 7709
Website: www.spacepersonalmanagement.co.uk
e-mail: katherine@spacepersonalmanagement.co.uk

**SPEAKERS CIRCUIT Ltd The**
After Dinner Speakers
The Priory
42 High Street
Frant, East Sussex TN3 9DU
e-mail: laura@allstarspeakers.co.uk
Fax: 01892 750089                      Tel: 01892 750131

**SPEAKERS CORNER**
*Facilitation & Cabaret for the Corporate Market
Presenters. Speakers*
207 High Road
London N2 8AN
Website: www.speakerscorner.co.uk
e-mail: info@speakerscorner.co.uk
Fax: 020-8883 7213                     Tel: 020-8365 3200

**SPIRE CASTING**
*(Personal Manager)*
*Contact: By Post/e-mail*
*1 Agent represents 6 Performers*
PO Box 372
Chesterfield S41 0XW
Website: www.spirecasting.com
e-mail: mail@spirecasting.com
Fax: 0870 4795321                      Mobile: 07900 517707

**SPLITTING IMAGES LOOKALIKES AGENCY**
25 Clissold Court
Greenway Close
London N4 2EZ
Website: www.splitting-images.com
e-mail: info@splitting-images.com
Fax: 020-8809 6103                     Tel: 020-8809 2327

# SIMON & HOW ASSOCIATES
## LONDON

T - 0845 064 6666
E - info@simon-how.com
W - www.simon-how.com
Representing - **Actors** & Extras for Advertising | Theatre | Television | Film | Photographic

**SPORTS OF SEB Ltd**
85 Bannerman House
Lawn Lane, London SW8 1UA
Website: www.sportsofseb.com
e-mail: info@sportsofseb.com
Mobile: 07740 359770     Tel: 020-7735 5133

**SPYKER Paul MANAGEMENT**
PO Box 48848, London WC1B 3WZ
e-mail: belinda@psmlondon.com
Fax: 020-7462 0047     Tel: 020-7462 0046

**SRA PERSONAL MANAGEMENT**
Lockhart Road
Cobham, Surrey KT11 2AX     Tel: 01932 863194
e-mail: agency@susanrobertsacademy.co.uk

**SSA MANAGEMENT**
37 Pageant Road
St Albans,
Hertfordshire AL1 1NB     Mobile: 07904 817229
Website: www.shootingstarsacademy.co.uk
e-mail: shootingstarsacademy@gmail.com

**STAFFORD Helen MANAGEMENT**
*Contact: Helen Stafford*
*1 Agent represents 30 Performers*
*Commercials. Film. Musicals. Television. Voice Overs*
14 Park Avenue
Bush Hill Park
Enfield EN1 2HP
e-mail: helen.stafford@blueyonder.co.uk
Fax: 020-8372 0611     Tel: 020-8360 6329

**JAMES LOOKER**
PHOTOGRAPHY
LONDON
www.jameslookerphotography.com
+44 (0) 7973 566537

**STAGE AND SCREEN PERSONAL MANAGEMENT**
20B Kidbrooke Grove
Blackheath SE3 0LF                    Mobile: 07958 648740
Website: www.stageandscreenpm.com
e-mail: info@stageandscreenpm.com

**STAGE CENTRE MANAGEMENT Ltd**
(Personal Manager) (CPMA Member)
Contact: Kelda Holmes
By e-mail
1 Lead Agent represents 23 Performers
Commercials. Film. Musicals. Stage. Television
41 North Road
London N7 9DP
Website: www.stagecentre.org.uk
e-mail: info@stagecentre.org.uk        Tel: 020-7607 0872

**STAGEWORKS ARTIST MANAGEMENT**
32 Brookfield Road
London E9 5AH                          Tel: 020-8525 0111

**STAGEWORKS WORLDWIDE PRODUCTIONS**
Contact: By e-mail
Cirque Artistes. Corporate. Dancers. Ice-Skaters. Musicals
525 Ocean Boulevard
Blackpool FY4 1EZ
Website: www.stageworkswwp.com
e-mail: simon.george@stageworkswwp.com
Fax: 01253 343702                     Tel: 01253 342426

**STAR MANAGEMENT Ltd**
16A Winton Drive, Glasgow G12 0QA    Tel: 0870 2422276
Website: www.starmanagement.co.uk
e-mail: star@starmanagement.co.uk

**STENTORIAN**
2 Aldersley Avenue
Skipton BD23 2LA                      Mobile: 07808 353611
Website: www.stentorian.freeuk.com
e-mail: stentorian@btinternet.com

**STEVENSON Natasha MANAGEMENT Ltd**
(See NSM)

**STIRLING MANAGEMENT**
Contact: Glen Mortimer
By e-mail
Accepts Showreels
3 Agents represent 40 Performers. Commercials. Film
Presenters. Stage. Television
Falcon Court
490 Halliwell Road, Bolton
Lancs BL1 8AN
Website: www.stirlingmanagement.co.uk
e-mail: admin@stirlingmanagement.co.uk
Fax: 0844 4128689                     Tel: 0845 0176500

**STIVEN CHRISTIE MANAGEMENT**
(Incorporating The Actors Agency of Edinburgh)
1 Glen Street
Tollcross
Edinburgh EH3 9JD
Website: www.stivenchristie.co.uk
e-mail: info@stivenchristie.co.uk
Fax: 0131-228 4645                    Tel: 0131-228 4040

**ST. JAMES'S MANAGEMENT**
(Personal Manager)
Contact: By Post (SAE)
19 Lodge Close
Stoke D'Abernon
Cobham
Surrey KT11 2SG
Fax: 01932 863152                     Tel: 01932 860666

**STONE Ian ASSOCIATES**
Suite 262
Maddison House
226 High Street
Croydon CR9 1DF                       Tel/Fax: 020-8667 1627

**STONE Richard PARTNERSHIP The**
(PMA Member)
2 Henrietta Street
London WC2E 8PS
Website: www.thersp.com
e-mail: all@thersp.com
Fax: 020-7497 0869                    Tel: 020-7497 0849

**STRAIGHT LINE MANAGEMENT**
(Division of Straight Line Productions)
58 Castle Avenue
Epsom
Surrey KT17 2PH
e-mail: hilary@straightlinemanagement.co.uk
Fax: 020-8393 8079                    Tel: 020-8393 4220

**STRANGE John MANAGEMENT**
Film City
401 Govan Road
Glasgow G51 2QJ
Website: www.strangemanagement.co.uk
e-mail: john@strangemanagement.co.uk
Fax: 0141-440 6769                    Tel: 0141-445 0444

**SUCCESS**
Room 236, 2nd Floor
Linen Hall
162-168 Regent Street
London W1B 5TB
Website: www.successagency.co.uk
e-mail: ee@successagency.co.uk
Fax: 020-7494 3787          Tel: 020-7734 3356

**SUMMERS Mark MANAGEMENT**
1 Beaumont Avenue
West Kensington
London W14 9LP          Tel: 020-7229 8413
Website: www.marksummers.com
e-mail: info@marksummers.com

**SUMMERTON Michael MANAGEMENT Ltd**
Choreographers. Dancers
Mimosa House
Mimosa Street
London SW6 4DS
Website: www.michaelsummerton.com
e-mail: msminfo@btconnect.com
Fax: 020-7731 0103          Tel: 020-7731 6969

**TAKE2 CASTING AGENCY & TALENT MANAGEMENT**
28 Beech Park Road
Foxrock
Dublin 18          Tel: 00 35 38 72 56 34 03
Website: www.take2.ie
e-mail: pamela@take2.ie

**TALENT4 MEDIA Ltd**
Studio LG16
Shepherds Building Central
Charecroft Way
London W14 0EH
Website: www.talent4media.com
e-mail: enquiries@talent4media.com
Fax: 020-7183 4331          Tel: 020-7183 4330

**TALENT ARTISTS Ltd**
(PMA Member)
Contact: Jane Wynn Owen
No Unsolicited Enquiries
59 Sydner Road
London N16 7UF
e-mail: talent.artists@btconnect.com
Fax: 020-7923 2009          Tel: 020-7923 1119

**TALENT SCOUT The**
19 Edge Road
Dewsbury WF12 0QA          Tel: 01924 464049
Website: www.thetalentscout.org
e-mail: connect@thetalentscout.org

**TAVISTOCK WOOD**
(PMA Member)
45 Conduit Street
London W1S 2YN
Website: www.tavistockwood.com
e-mail: info@tavistockwood.com
Fax: 020-7434 2017          Tel: 020-7494 4767

**TAYLOR Brian ASSOCIATES**
(PMA Member)
50 Pembroke Road
Kensington
London W8 6NX
e-mail: briantaylor@nqassoc.freeserve.co.uk
Fax: 020-7602 6301          Tel: 020-7602 6141

**TCA**
(The Commercial Agency)
12 Evelyn Mansions
Carlisle Place
London SW1P 1NH
Website: www.thecommercialagency.co.uk
e-mail: mail@thecommercialagency.co.uk
Fax: 020-7233 8110          Tel: 020-7233 8100

**TCG ARTIST MANAGEMENT Ltd**
*Contact: Kristin Tarry (Director), Johnny Muller*
*Emma Davidson, Jackie Davis*
*By Post/e-mail*
*Accepts Showreels*
*Commercials. Film. Musicals. Stage. Television*
14A Goodwin's Court
London WC2N 4LL
Website: www.tcgam.co.uk
e-mail: info@tcgam.co.uk
Fax: 020-7240 3606          Tel: 020-7240 3600

**TENNYSON AGENCY The**
10 Cleveland Avenue
Merton Park
London SW20 9EW          Tel: 020-8543 5939
e-mail: mail@tennysonagency.co.uk

**THOMAS & BENDA ASSOCIATES Ltd**
Top Floor
15-16 Ivor Place
London NW1 6HS          Tel/Fax: 020-7723 5509

**THOMPSON David ASSOCIATES**
7 St Peter's Close
London SW17 7UH
e-mail: montefioredt@aol.com
Mobile: 07889 191093          Tel: 020-8682 3083

**THOMSON Mia ASSOCIATES**
35 Central Avenue
Polegate
East Sussex BN26 6HA
Website: www.miathomsonassociates.co.uk
e-mail: info@miathomsonassociates.co.uk
Fax: 01323 489137          Tel: 01323 486143

**THORNTON AGENCY**
*(Specialist Agency for Small People)*
*Contact: By Post/e-mail/Telephone*
*50 Performers*
*Commercials. Corporate. Film. Stage. Television*
72 Purley Downs Road
South Croydon CR2 0RB          Tel/Fax: 020-8660 5588
Website: www.dwarfs4hire.com
e-mail: thorntons.leslie@tinyworld.co.uk

**THRELFALL Katie ASSOCIATES**
2A Gladstone Road
London SW19 1QT
e-mail: info@ktthrelfall.co.uk
Fax: 020-8543 7545          Tel: 020-8543 4344

**THRESH Melody MANAGEMENT ASSOCIATES Ltd (MTM)**
27 Ardwick Green North
Ardwick
Manchester M12 6FZ
e-mail: melodythreshmtm@aol.com
Fax: 0161-273 5455          Tel: 0161-273 5445

**TILDSLEY Janice ASSOCIATES**
*Contact: Kathryn Kirton*
*By Post*
*2 Agents represent 70 Performers*
47 Orford Road, London E17 9NJ
Website: www.janicetildsleyassociates.co.uk
e-mail: info@janicetildsleyassociates.co.uk
Fax: 020-8521 1174          Tel: 020-8521 1888

**TINKER Victoria MANAGEMENT**
*Technical, Non-Acting*
Birchenbridge House
Brighton Road
Mannings Heath, Horsham
West Sussex RH13 6HY          Tel/Fax: 01403 210653

**TOTAL VANITY Ltd**
15 Walton Way
Aylesbury
Buckinghamshire HP21 7JJ
Website: www.totalvanity.com
e-mail: richard.williams@totalvanity.com
Mobile: 07739 381788          Mobile: 07710 780152

**TRENDS AGENCY & MANAGEMENT Ltd**
*Contact: By e-mail*
*Commercials. Dancers. Musicals. Singers. Stage*
Sullom Lodge
Sullom Side Lane
Garstang PR3 1GH
Website: www.trendsgroup.co.uk
e-mail: info@trendsgroup.co.uk
Fax: 01253 407715          Tel: 0871 2003343

**TROIKA**
(PMA Member)
3rd Floor
74 Clerkenwell Road
London EC1M 5QA
e-mail: info@troikatalent.com
Fax: 020-7490 7642          Tel: 020 7336 7868

**TV MANAGEMENTS**
Brink House
Avon Castle
Ringwood
Hants BH24 2BL
e-mail: etv@tvmanagements.co.uk
Fax: 01425 480123          Tel: 01425 475544

**TWINS**
(See PC THEATRICAL, MODEL & CASTING AGENCY)

**TWITCH EVENT CHOREOGRAPHY**
Contact: By Post/e-mail/Telephone
Accepts Showreels
2 Agents represent 100 Performers
Circus Performers. Corporate. Dancers. Models. Stage
Television
5 Breakspears Mews
Brockley SE4 1PY
Website: www.twitch.uk.com
e-mail: info@twitch.uk.com
Mobile: 07932 656358          Mobile: 07747 770816

**TWO'S COMPANY**
Existing Clients only
Directors. Stage. Writers
244 Upland Road, London SE22 0DN
e-mail: graham@2scompanytheatre.co.uk
Fax: 020-8299 3714          Tel: 020-8299 4593

**UGLY MODELS**
Tigris House
256 Edgware Road, London W2 1DS
Website: www.ugly.org
e-mail: info@ugly.org
Fax: 020-7402 0507          Tel: 020-7402 5564

**UNITED AGENTS Ltd**
(Personal Manager) (PMA Member)
12-26 Lexington Street
London W1F 0LE          Tel: 020-3214 0800
Website: www.unitedagents.co.uk
e-mail: info@unitedagents.co.uk

**UPBEAT MANAGEMENT**
Theatre Touring & Events. No Actors
Larg House
Woodcote Grove
Coulsdon
Surrey CR5 2QQ
Website: www.upbeat.co.uk
e-mail: info@upbeat.co.uk
Fax: 020-8668 3922          Tel: 020-8668 3332

**UPSON EDWARDS**
(See REPRESENTATION UPSON EDWARDS)

**URBAN HEROES**
124 Boundary Road
London NW8 0RH
Website: www.theurbanheroes.com
e-mail: justin@theurbanheroes.com
Fax: 0870 4792458          Tel: 020-7043 1072

**URBAN TALENT**
Nemesis House
1 Oxford Court
Bishopsgate, Manchester M2 3WQ
Website: www.urbantalent.tv
e-mail: liz@nmsmanagement.co.uk
Fax: 0161-228 6727          Tel: 0161-228 6866

**UTOPIA MODEL MANAGEMENT**
348 Moorside Road
Swinton, Manchester M27 9PW
e-mail: kya@utopiamodels.co.uk
Fax: 0161-728 6600          Mobile: 07771 884844

**UVA MANAGEMENT Ltd**
Contact: By e-mail
Commercials. Film. Presenters. Stage. Television
Pinewood Film Studios
Pinewood Road, Iver Heath
Buckinghamshire SL0 0NH
Website: www.uvamanagement.com
e-mail: berko@uvamanagement.com
Mobile: 07716 777885          Tel: 0845 3700883

**VACCA Roxane MANAGEMENT**
73 Beak Street
London W1F 9SR
Fax: 020-7734 8086          Tel: 020-7734 8085

**VALLÉ ACADEMY THEATRICAL AGENCY The**
The Vallé Academy Studios, Wilton House
Delamare Road, Cheshunt, Herts EN8 9SG
Website: www.valleacademy.co.uk
e-mail: agency@valleacademy.co.uk
Fax: 01992 622868          Tel: 01992 622861

**VAMP JAZZ**
Bands. Entertainers. Musicians. Singers
Ealing House, 33 Hanger Lane
London W5 3HJ          Tel: 020-8997 3355
e-mail: vampjazz@aol.com

**VIDAL-HALL Clare**
(PMA Member)
Choreographers. Composers. Designers. Directors. Lighting Designers
57 Carthew Road, London W6 0DU
Website: www.clarevidalhall.com
e-mail: info@clarevidalhall.com
Fax: 020-8741 9459          Tel: 020-8741 7647

**VINE Michael ASSOCIATES**
Light Entertainment
1 Stormont Road, London N6 4NS          Tel: 020-8347 2580
e-mail: stephen@michaelvineassociates.com

**VisABLE PEOPLE**
Contact: Louise Dyson
Artists with Disabilities          Tel: 01905 776631
Website: www.visablepeople.com
e-mail: louise@visablepeople.com

**VSA Ltd**
(Formerly Vincent Shaw Associates) (PMA Member)
Contact: Andy Charles
186 Shaftesbury Avenue, London WC2H 8JB
Website: www.vsaltd.com
e-mail: info@vsaltd.com
Fax: 020-7240 2930          Tel: 020-7240 2927

**W ATHLETIC**
The Media Village
131-151 Great Titchfield Street
London W1W 5BB          Tel: 0845 2997798
Website: www.wathletic.com
e-mail: london@wathletic.com

**WADE Suzann**
(Personal Manager)
Contact: By Post only
Accepts Showreels
2 Agents represent 15 Clients
Film. Musicals. Stage. Television
9 Wimpole Mews, London W1G 8PG
Website: www.suzannwade.com
e-mail: info@suzannwade.com
Fax: 020-7486 5664          Tel: 020-7486 0746

**WALMSLEY Peter ASSOCIATES**
No Representation, Do Not Write
37A Crimsworth Road, London SW8 4RJ
e-mail: associates@peterwalmsley.net
Mobile: 07778 347312          Tel: 020-7787 6419

**WARING & McKENNA**
(PMA Member)
11-12 Dover Street
Mayfair, London W1S 4LJ
Website: www.waringandmckenna.com
e-mail: dj@waringandmckenna.com
Fax: 020-7629 6466     Tel: 020-7629 6444

**WELCH Janet PERSONAL MANAGEMENT**
*Contact: By Post*
Old Orchard, The Street, Ubley
Bristol BS40 6PJ     Tel/Fax: 01761 463238
e-mail: info@janetwelchpm.co.uk

**WEST CENTRAL MANAGEMENT**
(CPMA Member)
*Co-operative of 21 Performers*
*Contact: By Post/e-mail*
Room 4
East Block, Panther House
38 Mount Pleasant
London WC1X 0AN     Tel/Fax: 020-7833 8134
Website: www.westcentralmanagement.co.uk
e-mail: mail@westcentralmanagement.co.uk

**WEST END MANAGEMENT**
*Contact: Maureen Cairns, Allan Jones, Nina Lee*
2nd Floor, 34 Argyle Arcade Chambers
Buchanan Street, Glasgow G2 8BD     Tel: 0141-222 2333
Website: www.west-endmgt.com
e-mail: info@west-endmgt.com

**WHATEVER ARTISTS MANAGEMENT Ltd**
F24 Argo House
Kilburn Park Road
London NW6 5LF
Website: www.wamshow.biz
e-mail: info@wamshow.biz
Fax: 020-7372 5111     Tel: 020-7372 4777

**WHITEHALL ARTISTS**
10 Lower Common South
London SW15 1BP
e-mail: mwhitehall@msn.com
Fax: 020-8788 2340     Tel: 020-8785 3737

**WHITTINGHAM Ian Zachary AGENTS**
77 Brick Lane
Liverpool Street
London E1 6QL     Tel: 020-7246 0088
e-mail: zachwhittingham@ymail.com

**WILKINSON David ASSOCIATES**
(PMA Member) Existing Clients only
115 Hazlebury Road
London SW6 2LX
e-mail: info@dwassociates.net
Fax: 020-7371 5161     Tel: 020-7371 5188

**WILLIAMSON & HOLMES**
9 Hop Gardens
St Martin's Lane, London WC2N 4EH
e-mail: info@williamsonandholmes.co.uk
Fax: 020-7240 0408     Tel: 020-7240 0407

'the BIG agency for short & tall actors'

actors from 3ft to 5ft & over 7ft
for films, TV, theatre & advertising

tel: +44 (0)1733 240392 • email: office@willowmanagement.co.uk • on-line casting directory: willowmanagement.co.uk

**WILLOW PERSONAL MANAGEMENT**
Specialist Agency for Short Actors
151 Main Street
Yaxley
Peterborough
Cambs PE7 3LD                          Tel: 01733 240392
Website: www.willowmanagement.co.uk
e-mail: enquiries@willowmanagement.co.uk

**WILLS Newton MANAGEMENT**
(Personal Manager)
Contact: By Post/e-mail
Accepts Showreels/Voicereels
3 Agents represent 52 Performers
Commercials. Dancers. Singers. Stage
The Studio
29 Springvale Avenue
Brentford
Middlesex TW8 9QH
Website: www.newtonwills.com
e-mail: newtoncttg@aol.com
Fax: 00 33 468 218685                 Mobile: 07989 398381

**WINSLETT Dave ASSOCIATES**
4 Zig Zag Road
Kenley
Surrey CR8 5EL
Website: www.davewinslett.com
e-mail: info@davewinslett.com
Fax: 020-8668 9216                      Tel: 020-8668 0531

**WINTERSON Niki**
(See GLOBAL ARTISTS)

**WIS CELTIC MANAGEMENT**
Welsh, Irish, Scottish Performers
86 Elphinstone Road
Walthamstow
London E17 5EX
Fax: 020-8523 4523                     Tel: 020-8523 4234

**WISE BUDDAH TALENT**
Contact: Chris North
74 Great Titchfield Street
London W1W 7QP
Website: www.wisebuddah.com
e-mail: chris.north@wisebuddah.com
Fax: 020-7307 1601                     Tel: 020-7307 1600

**WMG MANAGEMENT EUROPE Ltd**
(Sports Management Company)
5th Floor
33 Soho Square
London W1D 3QU
Website: www.wmglk.com
Fax: 020-3230 1053                      Tel: 020-7009 6000

**WYMAN Edward AGENCY**
(English & Welsh Language)
Contact: Edward Wyman, Audrey Williams, Judith Gay
By Post
Accepts Showreels/Voicereels
3 Agents
Commercials. Corporate. Television. Voice Overs. Walk-on &
Supporting Artists
67 Llanon Road, Llanishen, Cardiff CF14 5AH
Website: www.wymancasting.co.uk
e-mail: edward.wyman@btconnect.com
Fax: 029-2075 2444                     Tel: 029-2075 2351

**XL MANAGEMENT**
Edmund House, Rugby Road
Leamington Spa
Warwickshire CV32 6EL
Website: www.xlmanagement.co.uk
e-mail: office@xlmanagement.co.uk
Fax: 01926 811420                       Tel: 01926 810449

**YAT MANAGEMENT**
(Young Actors Theatre Management)
70-72 Barnsbury Road, London N1 0ES
Website: www.yati.org.uk
e-mail: agent@yati.org.uk
Fax: 020-7833 9467                      Tel: 020-7278 2101

**YELLOW BALLOON PRODUCTIONS Ltd**
Contact: Mike Smith
Freshwater House
Outdowns
Effingham, Surrey KT24 5QR
e-mail: yellowbal@aol.com
Fax: 01483 281501                       Tel: 01483 281500

**ZWICKLER Marlene & ASSOCIATES**
1 Belgrave Crescent Lane
Edinburgh EH4 3AG                       Tel/Fax: 0131-343 3030
Website: www.mza-artists.com

**D&B MANAGEMENT**

In association with
D & B Theatre School
D & B School of Performing Arts Representing:
* Children * Young Adults

Tel: 020 8698 8880 Fax: 020 8697 8100
E-mail: bonnie@dandbmanagement.com Website: www.dandbperformingarts.co.uk
Agency Hours: Mon - Fri 8.30am - 9.00pm, Sat 8.30am - 6.00pm Central Studios, 470 Bromley Road, Kent BR1 4PN

**A & J MANAGEMENT**
242A The Ridgeway
Botany Bay, Enfield EN2 8AP
Website: www.ajmanagement.co.uk
e-mail: info@ajmanagement.co.uk
Fax: 020-8342 0842 Tel: 020-8342 0542

**ABACUS AGENCY**
The Studio, 4 Bailey Road
Westcott, Dorking, Surrey RH4 3QS
Website: www.abacusagency.co.uk
e-mail: admin@abacusagency.co.uk
Fax: 01306 877813 Tel: 01306 877144

**ABSTRACT MODELS / TALENT**
10-11 Navigation Street
Birmingham B2 4BS
Website: www.abstractmodelling.com
e-mail: info@abstractmodelling.com
Fax: 0121-633 9797 Tel: 0121-633 9765

**ACT OUT AGENCY**
(Children, Teenagers & New Graduates)
22 Greek Street, Stockport
Cheshire SK3 8AB Tel/Fax: 0161-429 7413
e-mail: ab22actout@aol.com

**ALL THE ARTS CHILDREN'S CASTING AGENCY**
5 Royal Oak Cottages, Main Road
Crockham Hill
Edenbridge, Kent TN8 6RD
Website: www.alltheartsagency.co.uk
e-mail: jillian@alltheartsagency.co.uk
Tel: 07908 618083 Tel: 01732 862067

**ALLSORTS AGENCY**
Suite 1 & 2 Marlborough Business Centre
96 George Lane, London E18 1AD
Website: www.allsortsagency.com
e-mail: bookings@allsortsagency.com
Fax: 020-8989 5600 Tel: 020-8989 0500

**ALLSORTS DRAMA FOR CHILDREN**
(In Association with Sasha Leslie Management)
34 Pember Road, London NW10 5LS
e-mail: sasha@allsortsdrama.com
Fax: 020-8969 3196 Tel: 020-8969 3249

**ALLSTARS CASTING**
Apt 4, 66 Hope Street
Liverpool L1 9BZ
Website: www.allstarsweb.co.uk
e-mail: allstarsweb@hotmail.co.uk
Mobile: 07739 359737 Tel/Fax: 0151-707 2100

**ALPHABET KIDZ ACTING & VOICE-OVER AGENCY**
189 Southampton Way
London SE5 7EJ
Website: www.alphabetkidz.co.uk
e-mail: contact@alphabetkidz.co.uk
Fax: 020-7252 4341 Tel: 020-7252 4343

**ANNA'S MANAGEMENT**
(Formerly of ALADDIN'S CAVE)
25 Tintagel Drive, Stanmore, Middlesex HA7 4SR
e-mail: annasmanage@aol.com
Fax: 020-8238 2899 Tel: 020-8958 7636

**AQUITAINE PERSONAL MANAGEMENT**
PO Box 1896
Stanford-Le-Hope, Essex SS17 0WR Tel: 01375 361888
Website: www.aquitainepersonalmanagement.co.uk
e-mail: apm@aquitaine.org.uk

**ARAENA/COLLECTIVE**
10 Bramshaw Gardens
South Oxhey, Herts WD19 6XP Tel/Fax: 020-8428 0037
e-mail: info@collectivedance.co.uk

**A.R.K. AGENCY**
(All Round Kids)
54 Oaklands, Curdworth
Sutton Coldfield
West Midlands B76 9HD Mobile: 07900 998090
Website: www.allroundkids.co.uk
e-mail: allroundkids@hotmail.co uk

**JACKIE PALMER AGENCY**

30 Daws Hill Lane
High Wycombe, Bucks
HP11 1PW
Office 01494 520978
Fax 01494 510479

E-mail jackie.palmer@btinternet.com
Website: www.jackiepalmer.co.uk

Well behaved, natural children,
teenagers and young adults.
All nationalities, many bi-lingual.
Pupils regularly appear in
West End Theatre, including
RSC, National Theatre and
in Fim and Television.

We are just off the M40
within easy reach of London, Oxford,
Birmingham and the South West.
Licensed tutors and chaperones

# infopage

## How can my child become an actor?

If a child is interested in becoming an actor, they should try to get as much practical experience as possible. For example, joining the drama club at school, taking theatre studies as an option, reading as many plays as they can, and going to the theatre on a regular basis. They could also attend local youth theatres or drama groups. Some theatres offer evening or Saturday classes.

## What are the chances of success?

As any agency or school will tell you, the entertainment industry is highly competitive and for every success story there are many children who will never be hired for paid acting work. Child artists and their parents should think very carefully before getting involved in the industry and be prepared for disappointments along the way.

## What is the difference between stage schools and agencies?

Stage schools provide specialised training in acting, singing and dancing for the under 18's. They offer a variety of full and part-time courses. Please see the 'Drama Training, Schools and Coaches' section for listings. Children's and Teenagers' agencies specialise in the representation of child artists, promoting them to casting opportunities and negotiating contracts on their behalf. In return they will take commission, usually ranging from 10-15%. Some larger stage schools also have agencies attached to them. A number of agents are listed in the following pages.

## Why does my child need an agent?

While many parents feel they want to retain control over their child's career, they will not have the contacts and authority a good agent will have in the industry. Casting directors are more likely to look to an agent they know and trust to provide the most suitable children for a job than an independent, unrepresented child. This does not mean to say that a child will never get work without an agent to put them forward for work, but it will certainly be more difficult.

## How should these listings be used?

The following pages list up-to-date contact details for agencies specialising in the representation of children and teenagers. Every company listed is done so by written request to us. Always research agencies carefully before approaching them to make sure they are suitable for your child. Many have websites you can visit, or ask around for personal recommendations. You should make a short-list of the ones you think are most appropriate rather than sending a standard letter to hundreds of agencies. Please see the main 'Agents and Personal Managers' advice section for further guidance on choosing and approaching agents.

## Can Spotlight offer me advice on choosing or changing my child's Agent?

Unfortunately Spotlight is not able to advise performers on specific agents, nor is it in a position to handle any financial or contractual queries or complaints. For agent-related queries we suggest you contact The Agents Association www.agents-uk.com or The Personal Managers' Association (PMA) www.thepma.com, or you could try one of the independent advisors on our website www.spotlight.com/artists/advice/independent

## Who can I contact for general advice?

Your local education authority should be able to help with most queries regarding your child's education, working hours, chaperones and general welfare if they are aged 16 or under. You could also try contacting an independent advisor (see website above) for advice, or for legal guidance please see the 'Accountants, Insurance & Law' section for listings.

## Should I pay an agent to represent my child? Or sign a contract?

Equity does not recommend that you pay an agent an upfront fee to place your child on their client list. Before signing a contract, you should be very clear about the terms and commitments involved. For advice on both of these issues, or if you experience any problems with a current agent, we recommend that you contact Equity www.equity.org.uk

## Why do child actors need licences?

Strict regulations apply to children working in the entertainment industry. These cover areas including the maximum number of performance hours per day / week, rest times, meal times and tutoring requirements. When any child under 16 performs in a professional capacity, the production company must obtain a Child Performance Licence from the child's local education authority.

## Who are chaperones?

Child artists must also be accompanied by a chaperone at all times when they are working. Registered chaperones are generally used instead of parents as they have a better understanding of the employment regulations involved, and they have professional experience of dealing with production companies. Registered chaperones have been police checked and approved by their local education authority to act in loco parentis. Always contact your local education authority if you have any questions or concerns.

## What is the Spotlight Children and Young Performers directory?

Children who are currently represented by an agent or attend a stage school can appear in the Spotlight Children and Young Performers directory. This is a casting directory, used by production teams to source child artists for TV, film, stage or commercial work. Each child pays an annual membership fee to have their photo featured in the printed directory along with others represented by the same agency or stage school, as well as having their own individual online CV on the Spotlight website, searchable by casting professionals. Please speak to your child's school or agency about joining Spotlight for ongoing promotion to hundreds of casting opportunities. For further information about the directory visit www.spotlight.com/join

# infopage

**Sylvia Young OBE has been a children's theatrical agent since 1974. Her young clients have been very successful in all areas of media - TV, film and musical theatre. Sylvia has a full-time theatre school in Central London for students aged between 10 and 16. She also runs holiday courses and part-time classes on Thursday evenings and Saturdays.**

I'm often asked what advice I'd give to a young person who wants to aim for a career as a professional actor, dancer or musician. Firstly, I believe that training is very important, whether it's part-time or full-time, as this is where you'll meet others with similar interests, explore ideas, build your confidence, and start to develop your potential. Classes give you a taste of performing in front of an audience, and if you enjoy it, you may decide you want to take it further.

If you do, the next step is to find an agent. Start by making a shortlist of agencies in Contacts which look most relevant to you. Prepare a CV, detailing any experience you already have, together with a list of relevant skills and hobbies and a clear, head and shoulders photograph and enclose an SAE. If an agency is interested in meeting you, they'll contact you to arrange a meeting, but do remember that agents are very busy so don't expect a reply immediately.

At the meeting, the agent will want to talk generally about you and your interests, before asking you to do some sight reading, possibly sing a verse or two of a song, and hear any accents, dialects or different languages you can speak. With younger children, they will want to see how confident the child is away from their parent. Once you've had meetings with a few agencies, you should decide which one suits you best as a performer, and who you felt most comfortable with.

A reputable agent should only work on commission from the earnings they get you, and shouldn't ask for a joining fee - although there are some additional expenses you should be prepared for at the start (see below). A children's agency will charge between 10% and 22.5% commission, depending on the type of work - this is a higher percentage than an agency for adults would charge, but this is because children's fees are minute compared to adult performers', whilst there is just as much (if not more!) work for the children's agent to do in order to find parts for their clients.

There are many more agencies today than there once were, and many more young performers looking for employment, so in order to stand out and get auditions there are a few expenses you'll need to be prepared to pay. Firstly, it's impossible for your new agent to represent you unless they have a good head and shoulders photo. This is the very first thing casting directors will see and it's important to make the right impression. Most agencies will have a photographer who they work with regularly - they will know exactly what's needed and they will often negotiate specially reduced rates. You should expect to pay about £45 for photos.

Next, you should strongly consider taking an entry in Spotlight. Every casting director has a copy of Spotlight Children & Young Performers directory, and the majority of casting directors ask agents to send suggestions via the Spotlight Link (Spotlight's online casting service), so if you don't have an entry you will be at a disadvantage. Spotlight members pay an annual fee - this is currently £86 for children joining in 2009.

Once your agent has your photos and details, they'll suggest you for any part that they think you're suitable for. It can take a while for a new face to be picked out, and the casting calls agents receive can be very specific, so be patient. If you haven't heard from your agent for a while, it doesn't mean that they're not thinking of you, just that they haven't managed to secure a casting for you yet. Agents have to do a lot of hard work before they can call you up for an audition!

The business moves very, very quickly, and it's not unusual for agents to call you about an audition the evening before, or even the same day! So it's essential to let them know if you're unavailable, even for a short time. Children's castings tend to be held between 4.30 and 6pm, and you may need to leave school early to get to them, so it's important that your school supports you.

The most important thing is to remember that you're doing this for fun, and for the experience, so don't take it too seriously. There will inevitably be disappointments along the way, so if you get downhearted easily, or if you are a parent and your child isn't enjoying it any more, then it's time to stop and try something else! But if you are willing to persevere, remember that no audition is ever a waste of time. Every time you meet a casting director or producer, you'll make an impression on them, and if you're not right for one part, you never know, you might be perfect for a different one next week!

**7 to 18 year olds**

Saturday classes in:
**Drama, Film, Singing,
Dance, Set & Costume Design**
Winner of four business awards!

**www.annafiorentini.com**
Tel/Fax: 020 7682 3677
Mobile: 07904 962779

## ANNA FIORENTINI
THEATRE & FILM SCHOOL'S AGENCY

Belinda Owusu
Elizabeth 'Squiggle' Fox- EastEnders

Charlie Jones
Ben Mitchell- EastEnders

Islington Business Design Centre, Unit 101, 52 Upper Street, London N1 0QH

---

**ARTS ACADEMY (T.A.A.) The**
15 Lexham Mews
London W8 6JW
e-mail: jill@galloways.ltd.uk
Fax: 020-7376 2416     Tel: 020-7376 0267

**ASHCROFT ACADEMY OF DRAMATIC ART & AGENCY**
Malcolm Primary School
Malcolm Road
Penge, London SE20 8RH
Website: www.ashcroftacademy.com
e-mail: geraldi.gillma@btconnect.com
Mobile: 07799 791586     Tel/Fax: 0844 8005328

**ASPARATIONS**
Arabesque School of Performing Arts
Quarry Lane, Chichester PO19 8NY    Mobile: 07825 239391
e-mail: asparations2006@aol.com

**AWA - ANDREA WILDER AGENCY**
23 Cambrian Drive
Colwyn Bay, Conwy LL28 4SL
Website: www.awagency.co.uk
e-mail: andreawilder@fastmail.fm
Fax: 07092 249314     Mobile: 07919 202401

**BABY BODENS**
Bodens Studios & Agency
99 East Barnet Road
New Barnet
Herts EN4 8RF
Website: www.bodensagency.com
e-mail: info@bodensagency.com
Fax: 020-8449 5212     Tel: 020-8447 1035

**BABYSHAK AGENCY**
Bizzy House
73A Mayplace Road West
Bexleyheath, Kent DA7 4JL
Website: www.babyshak.com
e-mail: clients@babyshak.com
Fax: 020-8303 2730     Tel: 020-8303 2627

**BANANAFISH MANAGEMENT**
16 The Arts Village
20-26 Henry Street, Liverpool L1 5BS
Website: www.bananafish.co.uk
e-mail: info@bananafish.co.uk
Mobile: 07974 206622     Tel: 0151-324 2222

**BIG ACT MANAGEMENT**
90 Chapel Way
Epsom, Surrey KT18 5SY
Website: www.bigacttheatre.co.uk
e-mail: lucy@bigacttheatre.co.uk
Mobile: 07816 524 066     Tel: 01737 211541

**BIZZYKIDZ**
Bizzy House, 73A Mayplace Road West
Bexleyheath, Kent DA7 4JL
Website: www.bizzykidz.com
e-mail: bookings@bizzykidz.com
Fax: 020-8303 2730     Tel: 020-8303 2627

**BODENS AGENCY**
99 East Barnet Road
New Barnet, Herts EN4 8RF     Tel: 020-8447 0909
Website: www.bodensagency.com
e-mail: info@bodensagency.com

Carousel Kidz
www.carouselkidz.co.uk
Child Modelling Agency
Tel/Fax: 020 8249 3597
info@carouselkidz.co.uk

**BONNIE AND BETTY Ltd**
County House
221-241 Beckenham Road
Beckenham, Kent BR3 4UF          Tel: 020-8676 6294
Website: www.bonnieandbetty.com
e-mail: agency@bonnieandbetty.com

**BOURNE Michelle ACADEMY & AGENCY The**
Studio 1, 22 Dorman Walk
Garden Way, London NW10 0PF          Mobile: 07956 853564
Website: www.michellebourneacademy.co.uk
e-mail: info@michellebourneacademy.co.uk

**BRUCE & BROWN**
203 Canalot Studios
222 Kensal Road, London W10 5BN
Website: www.bruceandbrown.com
e-mail: info@bruceandbrown.com
Fax: 020-8964 0457          Tel: 020-8968 5585

**BRUNO KELLY Ltd**
4th Floor, Albany House
324-326 Regent Street, London W1B 3HH
Website: www.brunokelly.com
e-mail: info@brunokelly.com
Fax: 020-7183 7332          Tel: 020-7183 7331

**BUBBLEGUM**
Pinewood Studios, Pinewood Road
Iver Heath, Bucks SL0 0NH
Website: www.bubblegummodels.com
e-mail: info@bubblegummodels.com
Fax: 01753 652521          Tel: 01753 632867

**BYRON'S MANAGEMENT**
(Children & Adults)
76 St James Lane
Muswell Hill
London N10 3DF
Website: www.byronsmanagement.co.uk
e-mail: byronsmanagement@aol.com
Fax: 020-8444 4040          Tel: 020-8444 4445

**CAROUSEL KIDZ**
1 Dukes Court
250 Croydon Road
Beckenham, Kent BR3 4DA          Tel/Fax: 020-8249 3597
Website: www.carouselkidz.co.uk
e-mail: info@carouselkidz.co.uk

**CARR Norrie AGENCY**
(Babies, Children & Adults)
Holborn Studios
49-50 Eagle Wharf Road
London N1 7ED
Website: www.norriecarr.com
e-mail: info@norriecarr.com
Fax: 020-7253 1772          Tel: 020-7253 1771

**CAVAT SCHOOL OF THEATRE ARTS & AGENCY**
16A Hook Hill
South Croydon
Surrey CR2 0LA          Tel: 020-8651 1099
Website: www.cavattheatrearts.co.uk
e-mail: enquiries@cavattheatrearts.co.uk

**CHADWICK Jacqueline ACADEMY The**
Oakdene Studios
Brewery Lane, Leigh WN7 2RJ
Website: www.jacquelinechadwickacademy.co.uk
e-mail: chadwickacademy@btconnect.com
Fax: 01942 609690          Tel: 01942 675747

**CHILDSPLAY MODELS LLP**
114 Avenue Road
Beckenham, Kent BR3 4SA
Website: www.childsplaymodels.co.uk
e-mail: info@childsplaymodels.co.uk
Fax: 020-8778 2672          Tel: 020-8659 9860

**CHILLI KIDS**
1 Badhan Court. Castle Street
Telford, TF1 5QX          Tel: 01952 320280
Website: www.chillimodels.com
e-mail: kids@chillimodels.com

**CHRYSTEL ARTS AGENCY**
6 Eunice Grove
Chesham, Bucks HP5 1RL
e-mail: chrystelarts@waitrose.com
Mobile: 07799 605489    Tel/Fax: 01494 773336

**CIRCUS MANIACS AGENCY**
(Circus, Theatre, Dance, Extreme Sports)
Office 8A
The Kingswood Foundation
Britannia Road
Kingswood, Bristol BS15 8DB
Website: www.circusmaniacsagency.com
e-mail: agency@circusmaniacs.com
Mobile: 07977 247287    Tel/Fax: 0117-947 7042

**COLIN'S PERFORMING ARTS AGENCY**
(Colin's Performing Arts Ltd)
The Studios
219B North Street
Romford
Essex RM1 4QA
Website: www.colinsperformingarts.co.uk
e-mail: agency@colinsperformingarts.co.uk
Fax: 01708 766077    Tel: 01708 766444

**CONTI Italia AGENCY Ltd**
23 Goswell Road
London EC1M 7AJ
e-mail: agency@italiaconti.co.uk
Fax: 020-7253 1430    Tel: 020-7608 7500

**CREATIVE KIDZ & Co**
(Incorporating NeighbourHood Productions)
9 Weavers Terrace
Fulham, London SW6 1QE    Mobile: 07958 377595
e-mail: info@creativekidzandco.co.uk

**CS MANAGEMENT**
(Children & Young Adults)
The Croft, 7 Cannon Road
Southgate, London N14 7HE
Website: www.csmanagementuk.com
e-mail: carole@csmanagementuk.com
Fax: 020-8886 7555    Tel: 020-8886 4264

**D & B MANAGEMENT & THEATRE SCHOOL**
470 Bromley Road, Bromley, Kent BR1 4PN
Website: www.dandbperformingarts.co.uk
e-mail: bonnie@dandbmanagement.com
Fax: 020-8697 8100    Tel: 020-8698 8880

**DD'S CHILDREN'S AGENCY**
6 Acle Close, Hainault, Essex IG6 2GQ
Website: www.ddtst.com
e-mail: ddsagency@yahoo.co.uk
Mobile: 07957 398501    Tel: 020-8502 6866

**DEBUT KIDS**
25 Crossways, Shenfield
Essex CM15 8QX    Mobile: 07946 618328
Website: www.debutkids.co.uk
e-mail: team@debutkids.co.uk

**DIMPLES MODEL & CASTING ACADEMY**
(Children, Teenagers & Adults)
84 Kirk Hall Lane
Leigh, Lancs WN7 5QQ    Tel: 01942 262012
e-mail: info@dimples-models.com

**DRAGON DRAMA**
(Drama for Children)
347 Hanworth Road TW12 3EJ    Tel/Fax: 020-8255 8356
Website: www.dragondrama.co.uk
e-mail: info@dragondrama.co.uk

**DRAMA STUDIO EDINBURGH The**
19 Belmont Road, Edinburgh EH14 5DZ    Tel: 0131-453 3284
Website: www.thedramastudio.com
e-mail: info@thedramastudio.com

**EARNSHAW Susi MANAGEMENT**
The Bull Theatre, 68 High Street, Barnet, Herts EN5 5SJ
Website: www.susiearnshawmanagement.com
e-mail: casting@susiearnshaw.co.uk
Fax: 020-8364 9618    Tel: 020-8441 5010

**ELITE ACADEMY OF PERFORMING ARTS**
City Studios, 4 Sandford Street
Lichfield, Staffs WS13 6QA    Mobile: 07976 971178
e-mail: elitedancing@hotmail.com

**ENGLISH Doreen '95**
Contact: Gerry Kinner
4 Selsey Avenue
Aldwick, Bognor Regis
West Sussex PO21 2QZ    Tel/Fax: 01243 825968

**EUROKIDS CASTING & MODEL AGENCY**
The Warehouse Studios, Glaziers Lane
Culcheth, Warrington, Cheshire WA3 4AQ
Website: www.eka-agency.com
e-mail: castings@eka-agency.com
Fax: 01925 767563    Tel: 01925 761088

**EXPRESSIONS CASTING AGENCY**
3 Newgate Lane, Mansfield
Nottingham NG18 2LB
Website: www.expressionsperformingarts.co.uk
e-mail: expressions-uk@btconnect.com
Fax: 01623 647337    Tel: 01623 424334

**FBI AGENCY Ltd The**
PO Box 250, Leeds LS1 2AZ    Tel/Fax: 07050 222747
Website: www.fbi-agency.co.uk
e-mail: casting@fbi-agency.co.uk

**FEA MANAGEMENT**
(Ferris Entertainment) (London, Belfast, Cardiff)
Number 8, 132 Charing Cross Road
London WC2H 0LA    Tel: 0845 4724725
Website: www.ferrisentertainment.com
e-mail: info@ferrisentertainment.com

**FILM CAST CORNWALL**
c/o 3 Church Walk, Truro TR1 1JH    Tel: 01326 311419
Website: www.filmcastcornwall.co.uk
e-mail: enquiries@filmcastcornwall.co.uk

**FIORENTINI Anna AGENCY**
Islington Business Design Centre
Unit 101, 52 Upper Street, London N1 0QH
Website: www.annafiorentini.co.uk
e-mail: info@annafiorentini.co.uk
Mobile: 07904 962779    Tel/Fax: 020-7682 3677

**FOOTLIGHTS AGENCY**
184 Katrina Grove, Featherstone
Pontefract WF7 5NT    Mobile: 07835 036347
Website: www.footlightsagency.co.uk
e-mail: agent@footlightsagency.co.uk

**FOOTSTEPS THEATRE SCHOOL CASTING AGENCY**
55 Pullan Avenue
Eccleshill, Bradford BD2 3RP
e-mail: helen@footsteps.fslife.co.uk
Tel/Fax: 01274 637429 Tel: 01274 636036

**FOX Betty AGENCY**
Slade Road, Erdington, Birmingham B23 7PX
e-mail: bettyfox.school@virgin.net
Mobile: 07703 436045 Tel/Fax: 0121-327 1020

**GENESIS THEATRE SCHOOL & AGENCY**
88 Hempland Close, Great Oakley
Corby, Northants NN18 8LT Tel: 01536 460928
e-mail: info@saracharles.com

**GLOBAL7**
PO Box 56232, London N4 4XP
Website: www.global7casting.com
e-mail: global7castings@gmail.com
Mobile: 07956 956652 Tel/Fax: 020-7281 7679

**GLYNNE Frances THEATRE STUDENTS & MANAGEMENT**
Flat 9, Elmwood, 6 The Avenue
Hatch End, Middlesex HA5 4EP Mobile: 07950 918355
e-mail: franandmo@googlemail.com

**GO FOR IT CHILDREN'S AGENCY**
(Children & Teenagers)
Green Gables, 47 North Lane
Teddington, Middlesex TW11 0HU
Website: www.goforitcentre.com
e-mail: agency@goforitcentre.com
Mobile: 07956 646412 Tel: 020-8943 1120

**GOBSTOPPERS MANAGEMENT**
37 St Nicholas Mount
Hemel Hempstead, Herts HP1 2BB
e-mail: chrisgobstoppers@btinternet.com
Mobile: 07961 372319 Tel: 01442 269543

**GP ASSOCIATES**
4 Gallus Close, Winchmore Hill, London N21 1JR
Website: www.greasepaintanonymous.co.uk
e-mail: info@gpassociates.co.uk
Fax: 020-8882 9189 Tel: 020-8886 2263

**GREVILLE Jeannine THEATRICAL AGENCY**
Melody House, Gillotts Corner
Henley-on-Thames, Oxon RG9 1QU
Website: www.jgdance.co.uk
e-mail: info@jgdance.co.uk
Fax: 01491 411533 Tel: 01491 572000

**HARLEQUIN STUDIOS AGENCY FOR CHILDREN**
122A Phyllis Avenue, Peacehaven
East Sussex BN10 7RQ Tel: 01273 581742

**HARRIS AGENCY Ltd The**
71 The Avenue, Watford
Herts WD17 4NU
e-mail: theharrisagency@btconnect.com
Fax: 01923 211666 Tel: 01923 211644

**HOBSONS KIDS**
62 Chiswick High Road, London W4 1SY
Website: www.hobsons-international.com
e-mail: kids@hobsons-international.com
Fax: 020-8996 5350 Tel: 020-8995 3628

**HOWE Janet CHILDREN'S CASTING & MODELLING AGENCY**
58A High Street
Newcastle, Staffordshire ST5 1QE Tel/Fax: 01782 661777
e-mail: info@janethowe.com

The Pie Factory, 101 Broadway
Salford Quays
Manchester M60 2EQ Tel/Fax: 0161-263 0633

Works Media Centre
36 White House Street
Hunslet, Leeds LS10 1AD Tel/Fax: 0113-242 5225

**INTER-CITY KIDS**
Portland Tower, Portland Street
Manchester M1 3LF Tel/Fax: 0161-238 4950
e-mail: intercitycasting@btconnect.com

**JABBERWOCKY AGENCY**
(Children & Teenagers)
Glassenbury Hill Farm
Glassenbury Road
Cranbrook, Kent TN17 2QF
Website: www.jabberwockyagency.com
e-mail: info@jabberwockyagency.com
Fax: 01580 714346                    Tel: 01580 714306

**JAM THEATRE COMPANY**
21 Beechtree Avenue, Marlow
Buckinghamshire SL7 3NH              Tel: 01628 487773
Website: www.jamtheatre.co.uk
e-mail: office@jamtheatre.co.uk

**JB ASSOCIATES**
(Children & Teenagers 13-18 Years)
4th Floor, Manchester House
84-86 Princess Street
Manchester M1 6NG
Website: www.j-b-a.net
e-mail: info@j-b-a.net
Fax: 0161-237 1809                   Tel: 0161-237 1808

**JERMIN Mark MANAGEMENT**
8 Heathfield, Swansea SA1 6EJ
Website: www.markjermin.co.uk
e-mail: info@markjermin.co.uk
Fax: 01792 458844                    Tel: 01792 458855

**JIGSAW ARTS MANAGEMENT**
(Representing Children & Young People from Jigsaw
Performing Arts Schools)
64-66 High Street
Barnet, Herts EN5 5SJ               Tel: 020-8447 4534
Website: www.jigsaw-arts.co.uk/agency
e-mail: admin@jigsaw-arts.co.uk

**JOHNSTON & MATHERS ASSOCIATES Ltd**
PO Box 3167
Barnet, Herts EN5 2WA
Website: www.johnstonandmathers.com
e-mail: johnstonmathers@aol.com
Fax: 020-8449 2386                   Tel: 020-8449 4968

**JUNIOR MODEL MANAGEMENT**
PO Box 61667, London SE9 9AT
Website: www.juniormm.com
e-mail: donia@juniormm.com
Fax: 0845 8388987                    Tel: 0845 8388985

**KELLY MANAGEMENT Ltd**
11-15 Betterton Street
Covent Garden, London WC2H 9BP
Website: www.kelly-management.com
e-mail: assistant@kelly-management.com
Fax: 020-7379 0801                   Tel: 020-7470 8757

**KIDS LONDON**
67 Dulwich Road, London SE24 0NJ
Website: www.kidslondonltd.com
e-mail: sue@kidslondonltd.com
Fax: 020-7924 9766                   Tel: 020-7924 9595

**KIDS PLUS**
Malcolm House, Malcolm Primary School
Malcolm Road, Penge, London SE20 8RH
Website: www.kidsplusagency.co.uk
e-mail: geraldi.gillma@btconnect.com
Mobile: 07799 791586                Tel: 0844 8005328

**KIDSHAK AGENCY**
Suite 3, 90 Frobisher Road
Erith, Kent DA8 2PQ                 Tel: 0845 4600623
Website: www.kidshak.com
e-mail: agency@kidshak.com

**KIDZ Ltd**
Beckinsdale, Ingol Lane
Hambleton SY6 9BJ
Website: www.kidzltd.com
e-mail: info@kidzltd.com
Tel/Fax: 0870 2416260               Tel: 0870 2414418

**KRACKERS KIDS THEATRICAL AGENCY**
6-7 Electric Parade, Seven Kings Road
Ilford, Essex IG3 8BY               Tel/Fax: 01708 502046
Website: www.krackerskids.co.uk
e-mail: krackerskids@hotmail.com

**KYT AGENCY**
Mulberry Croft
Mulberry Hill, Chilham CT4 8AJ
Website: www.kentyouththeatre.co.uk
e-mail: richard@kyt.org.uk
Mobile: 07967 580213                Tel/Fax: 01227 730177

**LAMONT CASTING AGENCY**
2 Harewood Avenue
Ainsdale, Merseyside PR8 2PH        Mobile: 07736 387543
Website: www.lamontcasting.co.uk
e-mail: diane@lamontcasting.co.uk

**LESLIE Sasha MANAGEMENT**
(In Association with Allsorts Drama for Children)
34 Pember Road
London NW10 5LS Tel/Fax: 020-8969 3249
e-mail: sasha@allsortsdrama.com

**LIFE AND SOUL THEATRE AGENCY**
Boxmoor Hall, St Johns Road, Hemel Hempstead
Herts HP1 1JR Tel/Fax: 01442 233050
Website: www.lifeandsoultheatreacademy.co.uk
e-mail: lifeandsoulta@hotmail.com

**LIL DEVILS AGENCY**
1st Floor, 76 School Road
Tilehurst, Reading, Berks RG31 5AW
Website: www.lildevils.co.uk
e-mail: kids@lildevils.co.uk
Fax: 0118-941 7273 Tel: 0118-943 3057

**LINTON MANAGEMENT**
3 The Rock, Bury BL9 0JP
e-mail: carol@linton.tv
Fax: 0161-761 1999 Tel: 0161-761 2020

**LIPSTICK, POWDER & PAINT TALENT & MODEL AGENCY**
480 Redford Close
Feltham TW13 4TP Tel: 020-8751 6750
Website: www.lipstickmodelagency.co.uk
e-mail: lipstickmodelagency@hotmail.com

**LITTLE ADULTS ACADEMY & MODELLING AGENCY Ltd**
Studio 1, Essex House
375-377 High Street
Stratford, London E15 4QZ
Website: www.littleadultsagency.co.uk
e-mail: info@littleadults.demon.co.uk
Fax: 020-8519 9797 Tel: 020-8519 9755

**LIVE & LOUD AGENCY**
Contact: Maureen Cairns, Hugh Hastie, Allan Jones
2nd Floor, 34 Argyle Arcade Chambers
Buchanan Street, Glasgow G2 8BD Tel: 0141-222 2333
e-mail: info@liveandloudagency.com

**McDONAGH Melanie ACADEMY OF PERFORMING ARTS & CASTING AGENCY The**
14 Apple Tree Way, Oswaldtwistle
Accrington, Lancashire BB5 0FB
Website: www.mcdonaghmanagement.co.uk
e-mail: mcdonaghmgt@aol.com
Mobile: 07909 831409 Tel: 01254 392560

**MONDI ASSOCIATES Ltd**
Contact: Michelle Sykes
Unit 3 0, Cooper House
2 Michael Road, London SW6 2AD Mobile: 07817 133349
Website: www.mondiassociates.com
e-mail: info@mondiassociates.com

**MONKEY MANAGEMENT**
47 Furze Platt Road
Maidenhead, Berks SL6 7NF Tel: 01628 777853
e-mail: agent@juliefoxassociates.co.uk

**MRS WORTHINGTON'S**
(6-16 Years)
16 Ouseley Road
London SW12 8EF Tel/Fax: 020-8767 6944

**NFD - THE FILM AND TV AGENCY**
PO Box 76, Leeds LS25 9AG Tel/Fax: 01977 681949
Website: www.film-tv-agency.com
e-mail: info@film-tv-agency.com

**O'FARRELL STAGE & THEATRE SCHOOL**
(Babies, Children, Teenagers & Young Adults)
36 Shirley Street, Canning Town, London E16 1HU
e-mail: linda@ofarrells.wanadoo.co.uk
Mobile: 07956 941497 Tel: 020-7511 9444

**ORR MANAGEMENT AGENCY**
(Children, Teenagers & Adults)
1st Floor, 147-149 Market Street
Farnworth, Greater Manchester BL4 8EX
Website: www.orrmanagement.co.uk
e-mail: barbara@orrmanagement.co.uk
Mobile: 07773 227784 Tel: 01204 579842

**PALMER Jackie AGENCY**
30 Daws Hill Lane
High Wycombe, Bucks HP11 1PW
Website: www.jackiepalmer.co.uk
e-mail: jackie.palmer@btinternet.com
Fax: 01494 510479                    Tel: 01494 520978

**PAUL'S THEATRE AGENCY**
Ardleigh House, 42 Ardleigh Green Road
Hornchurch, Essex RM11 2LG          Tel: 01708 446167
Website: www.paulstheatreschool.com
e-mail: info@paulstheatreschool.com

**PC THEATRICAL, MODEL & CASTING AGENCY**
13A Carlisle Road
Colindale, London NW9 0HD
Website: www.twinagency.com
e-mail: twinagy@aol.com
Fax: 020-8933 3418                   Tel: 020-8381 2229

**PERFORMERS AGENCY Ltd**
Southend Road,
Corringham, Essex SS17 8JT
Website: www.performersagency.biz
e-mail: mandy@performersagency.biz
Fax: 01375 672353                    Tel: 01375 665716

**PHA YOUTH**
Tanzaro House
Ardwick Green North
Manchester M12 6FZ
Website: www.pha-agency.co.uk
e-mail: youth@pha-agency.co.uk
Fax: 0161-273 4567                   Tel: 0161-273 4444

**PLATFORM TALENT MANAGEMENT Ltd**
16 Shelbourne Rise
Camberley, Surrey GU15 2EJ          Tel: 01276 23256
Website: www.kidsagency.tv
e-mail: castings@kidsagency.tv

**POLLYANNA MANAGEMENT Ltd**
1 Knighten Street, Wapping, London E1W 1PH
Website: www.pollyannatheatre.com
e-mail: aliceharwood@talktalk.net
Fax: 020-8530 6722                   Tel: 020-7481 1911

**POWER MODEL MANAGEMENT CASTING AGENCY**
PO Box 1198, Salhouse
Norwich NR13 6WD                     Tel: 01603 777190
Website: www.powermodel.co.uk
e-mail: info@powermodel.co.uk

**PWASSOCIATES**
7 Catherine Cottages, Calvert Road
Middle Claydon, Bucks MK18 2HA       Tel: 01296 733258
Website: www.premierperformers.co.uk
e-mail: emma@premierperformers.co.uk

**RAMA YOUNG ACTORS**
Huntingdon House
278-290 Huntingdon Street
Nottingham NG1 3LY
Website: www.ramayoungactors.co.uk
e-mail: martin@rama-global.co.uk
Fax: 0115-948 3696                   Tel: 0845 0540255

**RASCALS MODEL AGENCY**
13 Jubilee Parade, Snakes Lane East
Woodford Green, Essex IG8 7QG
Website: www.rascals.co.uk
e-mail: kids@rascals.co.uk
Fax: 020-8559 1035                   Tel: 020-8504 1111

**RAVENSCOURT MANAGEMENT**
8-30 Galena Road, Hammersmith, London W6 0LT
e-mail: info@ravenscourt.net
Fax: 020-8741 1786                   Tel: 020-8741 0707

**RDDC MANAGEMENT**
RDDC, 52 Bridleway, Waterfoot
Rossendale, Lancashire BB4 9DS
Website: www.rddc.co.uk
e-mail: rddc@btinternet.com
Mobile: 07792 309992                 Tel: 01706 211161

**REBEL SCHOOL OF THEATRE ARTS AND CASTING AGENCY Ltd**
(Based in Leeds)
PO Box 169, Huddersfield HD8 1BE     Mobile: 07808 803637
e-mail: suerebeltheatre@aol.com

**REDROOFS THEATRE SCHOOL AGENCY**
Littlewick Green, Maidenhead, Berks SL6 3QY
Website: www.redroofs.co.uk
e-mail: sam@redroofs.co.uk
Fax: 01628 822461                    Tel: 01628 822982

**REFLECTIONS AGENCY**
34 Knowle Avenue
Bexleyheath, Kent DA7 5LX
Website: www.reflectionsperfarts.tripod.com
e-mail: c.johnson717@ntlworld.com
Mobile: 07958 617976                 Tel/Fax: 01322 410003

# Tuesdays Child Agency

## Established 1976

### Babies, Children and Adults (0-80+)
### North and South UK

### Tel: 01625 501765

info@tuesdayschildagency.co.uk
www.tuesdayschildagency.co.uk

**RHODES AGENCY**
5 Dymoke Road
Hornchurch, Essex RM11 1AA
e-mail: rhodesarts@hotmail.com
Fax: 01708 730431          Tel: 01708 747013

**RIDGEWAY MANAGEMENT**
Fairley House
Andrews Lane
Cheshunt, Herts EN7 6LB
Website: www.ridgewaystudios.co.uk
e-mail: info@ridgewaystudios.co.uk
Fax: 01992 633844          Tel: 01992 633775

**RISING STARS AGENCY**
2 Parsonage Farmhouse, High Street
Eynsford, Kent DA4 0AB          Mobile: 07709 429354
Website: www.risingstarsmusicaltheatre.piczo.com
e-mail: risingstars_agency@yahoo.co.uk

**RISING STARS AGENCY**
16 Llwyn Yr Eos Grove
Penyard, Merthyr Tydfil
Mid Glamorgan
Wales CF47 0GD          Mobile: 07947 345434
Website: www.risingstarsagency.co.uk
e-mail: info@risingstarsagency.co.uk

**ROSS David ACTING ACADEMY**
8 Farrier Close
Sale, Cheshire M33 2ZL          Mobile: 07957 862317
Website: www.davidrossacting.com
e-mail: info@davidrossacting.com

**SCALA KIDS CASTING**
42 Rufford Avenue, Yeadon, Leeds LS19 7QR
Website: www.scalakids.com
e-mail: office@scalakids.com
Fax: 0113-250 8806          Tel: 0113-250 6823

**SCALLYWAGS AGENCY Ltd**
90-92 Ley Street, Ilford, Essex IG1 4BX
Website: www.scallywags.co.uk
e-mail: info@scallywags.co.uk
Fax: 020-8553 4849          Tel: 020-8553 9999

**SCREAM MANAGEMENT**
The Pie Factory, 101 Broadway
Media City, Manchester M50 2EQ          Tel: 0161-660 3652
Website: www.screammanagement.com
e-mail: info@screammanagement.com

**SELECT MANAGEMENT**
PO Box 748, London NW4 1TT
Website: www.selectmanagement.info
e-mail: mail@selectmanagement.info
Fax: 020-8203 2007          Mobile: 07956 131494

**SEQUINS THEATRICAL AGENCY**
8 Bideford Gardens, Bush Hill Park
Enfield, Middlesex EN1 2RP          Tel: 020-8360 6601

**SINGER Sandra ASSOCIATES**
21 Cotswold Road, Westcliff-on-Sea, Essex SS0 8AA
Website: www.sandrasinger.com
e-mail: sandrasingeruk@aol.com
Fax: 01702 339393          Tel: 01702 331616

**SMARTYPANTS AGENCY**
San-Marie Studios, Southend Road, Billericay CM11 2PZ
Website: www.smartypantsagency.co.uk
e-mail: office@smartypantsagency.co.uk
Fax: 01277 633998                    Tel: 01277 633772

**SMITH Elisabeth Ltd**
20 Chenies, Rickmansworth
Herts WD3 6ET                        Tel: 0845 8721331
Website: www.elisabethsmith.com
e-mail: models@elisabethsmith.com

**SPEAKE Barbara AGENCY**
East Acton Lane, London W3 7EG
e-mail: speakekids2@aol.com
Fax: 020-8740 6542                   Tel: 020-8743 6096

**SRA AGENCY**
Lockhart Road, Cobham
Surrey KT11 2AX                      Tel: 01932 863194
e-mail: agency@susanrobertsacademy.co.uk

**STAGE 84 YORKSHIRE SCHOOL OF PERFORMING ARTS**
Old Bell Chapel, Town Lane
Idle, Bradford, West Yorks BD10 8PR
e-mail: valeriejackson@stage84.com
Mobile: 07785 244984                 Tel: 01274 569197

**STAGE CENTRAL CASTING AGENCY**
14 Gilsforth Lane, Whixley YO26 8BF
Website: www.stagecentral.co.uk
e-mail: darren@stagecentral.co.uk
Mobile: 07940 014448                 Tel: 01423 331478

**STAGE KIDS AGENCY**
(Children, Teenagers & Adults)
1 Greenfield, Welwyn Garden City
Herts AL8 7HW                        Tel: 01707 328359
Website: www.stagekids.co.uk
e-mail: stagekds@aol.com

**STAGECOACH AGENCY UK & IRELAND**
PO Box 127, Ross-on-Wye HR9 6WZ
Website: www.stagecoachagency.co.uk
e-mail: tarquin@stagecoachagency.co.uk
Fax: 0845 4082464                    Tel: 0845 4082468

**STARDOM CASTING AGENCY & THEATRE SCHOOL**
16 Pinebury Drive, Queensbury, Bradford BD13 2TA
e-mail: liz.stardom@btinternet.com
Mobile: 07740 091019                 Tel/Fax: 01274 818051

**STARSTRUCK MANAGEMENT**
85 Hewson Road, Lincoln
Lincolnshire LN1 1RZ                 Tel: 01522 887894
e-mail: starstruckacademy@hotmail.com

**STOMP! MANAGEMENT**
Suite 5, Lyndhurst House
120 Bunns Lane, London NW7 2AR    Tel/Fax: 020-8959 5353
Website: www.stompmanagement.com
e-mail: stompmanagement@aol.com

**TAKE2 CASTING AGENCY & TALENT MANAGEMENT**
28 Beech Park Road
Foxrock, Dublin 18                   Tel: 00 35 38 72 56 34 03
Website: www.take2.ie
e-mail: pamela@take2.ie

**TALENTED KIDS PERFORMING ARTS SCHOOL & AGENCY**
23 Burrow Manor, Calverstown
Kilcullen, Co. Kildare, Ireland
Website: www.talentedkidsireland.com
e-mail: talentedkids@hotmail.com
Mobile: 00 353 87 2480348       Tel/Fax: 00 353 45 485464

**TANWOOD**
72 Nyland Road, Nythe
Swindon, Wilts SN3 3RJ                Mobile: 07774 517469
Website: www.tanwood.co.uk
e-mail: tanwood.agency2@ntlworld.com

**TELEVISION WORKSHOP The**
(Nottingham Group)
30 Main Street, Calverton
Notts NG14 6FQ                       Tel: 0115-845 0764
e-mail: ian@thetelevisionworkshop.co.uk

**THAMES VALLEY THEATRICAL AGENCY**
Dorchester House, Wimblestraw Road
Berinsfield, Oxfordshire OX10 7LZ
e-mail: donna@childactors.tv
Mobile: 07956 256189  Tel: 01865 340333

**TK MANAGEMENT**
Spires Meade, 4 Bridleways, Wendover, Bucks HP22 6DN
e-mail: tkpamanagement@aol.com
Fax: 01296 625763                    Mobile: 07985 510038

**TOMORROW'S TALENT THEATRE ARTS**
5 Beaumont Walk, Chelmsford
Essex CM1 2HF                        Tel: 01202 526667
Website: www.tomorrowstalent.co.uk
e-mail: enquiries@tomorrowstalent.co.uk

**TOP TALENT AGENCY Ltd**
(Representing Child Actors & Models from Babies to
Teenagers)
c/o Top Hat Stage & Screen School
PO Box 860, St Albans
Herts AL1 9BR                        Tel/Fax: 01727 812666
Website: www.toptalentagency.co.uk
e-mail: admin@toptalentagency.co.uk

**TRULY SCRUMPTIOUS Ltd**
66 Bidwell Gardens, London N11 2AU
Website: www.trulyscrumptious.co.uk
e-mail: bookings@trulyscrumptious.co.uk
Fax: 020-8888 4584          Tel: 020-8888 4204

**TUESDAYS CHILD**
(Children, Teenagers & Adults)
Oakfield House, Springwood Way
Macclesfield SK10 2XA          Tel/Fax: 01625 501765
Website: www.tuesdayschildagency.co.uk
e-mail: info@tuesdayschildagency.co.uk

**TURNSTONE CASTING**
Hilton Hall, Hilton Lane
Essington WV11 2BQ          Mobile: 07866 211647
Website: www.turnstonecasting.com
e-mail: mark_turner85@hotmail.co.uk

**TWINS**
(See PC THEATRICAL, MODEL & CASTING AGENCY)

**URBAN ANGELS**
7 Burnage Court, Lawrie Park Avenue, Sydenham SE26 6HS
e-mail: info@urbanangelsagency.com
Fax: 0870 8710046          Tel: 0870 8710045

**URBAN ANGELS NORTH**
Contact: Sarah Heeler
Churchill House, 12 Mosley Street
Newcastle NE1 1DE
Website: www.urbanangelsagency.com
e-mail: sarah@urbanangelsagency.com
Fax: 0191-230 6456          Tel: 0191-230 6455

**VALLÉ ACADEMY THEATRICAL AGENCY**
The Vallé Academy Studios
Wilton House, Delamare Road
Cheshunt, Herts EN8 9SG
Website: www.valleacademy.co.uk
e-mail: agency@valleacademy.co.uk
Fax: 01992 622868          Tel: 01992 622861

**W-A-P-A AGENCY**
6-8 Akroyd Place, Halifax, West Yorkshire HX1 1YH
Website: www.w-a-p-a.co.uk
e-mail: enquiries@w-a-p-a.co.uk
Fax: 01422 360958          Tel: 01422 351958

**WHITEHALL PERFORMING ARTS CENTRE**
Rayleigh Road, Leigh-on-Sea
Essex SS9 5UU          Tel/Fax: 01702 529290
Website: www.whitehallcollege.co.uk

**WILLIAMSON & HOLMES**
9 Hop Gardens, St Martin's Lane, London WC2N 4EH
e-mail: info@williamsonandholmes.co.uk
Fax: 020-7240 0408          Tel: 020-7240 0407

**WINGS AGENCY**
49 Midhurst Road, Fernhurst, Haslemere GU27 3EN
Website: www.angelstheatreschool.co.uk
e-mail: admin@wingsagency.co.uk
Fax: 01428 658990          Tel: 01428 658900

**WYSE AGENCY**
Hill House, 1 Hill Farm Road, Whittlesford
Cambs CB22 4NB          Tel: 01223 832288
e-mail: frances.wyse@btinternet.com

**YAT MANAGEMENT**
(Young Actors Theatre)
70-72 Barnsbury Road, London N1 0ES
Website: www.yati.org.uk
e-mail: agent@yati.org.uk
Fax: 020-7833 9467          Tel: 020-7278 2101

**YOUNG ACTORS COMPANY Ltd The**
3 Marshall Road, Cambridge CB1 7TY
Website: www.theyoungactorscompany.com
e-mail: info@theyoungactorscompany.com
Fax: 01223 416511          Tel: 01223 416474

**YOUNG ACTORS FILE The**
31 Nursery Road
Angmering, West Sussex BN16 4GQ
e-mail: young.actorsfile@btinternet.com
Mobile: 07789 888575          Tel: 01903 782354

**YOUNG Sylvia AGENCY**
Sylvia Young Theatre School, Rossmore Road
Marylebone, London NW1 6NJ
e-mail: info@sylviayoungagency.com
Fax: 020-7723 1040          Tel: 020-7723 0037

**YOUNGBLOOD THEATRE COMPANY**
c/o The BWH Agency Ltd
117 Shaftesbury Avenue, London WC2H 8AD
Website: www.thebwhagency.co.uk
e-mail: rep@thebwhagency.co.uk
Fax: 020-7240 2287          Tel: 020-7061 6399

**YOUNGSTARS**
Contact: Coralyn Canfor-Dumas
4 Haydon Dell, Bushey, Herts WD23 1DD
e-mail: coralyncd@gmail.com
Fax: 020-8950 5701          Mobile: 07966 176756

**ACORN ENTERTAINMENTS Ltd**
PO Box 64, Cirencester, Glos GL7 5YD
Website: www.acornents.co.uk
e-mail: info@acornents.co.uk
Fax: 01285 642291                    Tel: 01285 644622

**ARTISTE MANAGEMENT PRODUCTIONS Ltd**
(Concert Promotion)
13-14 Margaret Street
London W1W 8RN
Website: www.harveygoldsmith.com
e-mail: mail@harveygoldsmith.com
Fax: 020-7224 0111                   Tel: 020-7224 1992

**ASKONAS HOLT Ltd**
(Classical Music)
Lincoln House
300 High Holborn, London WC1V 7JH
Website: www.askonasholt.co.uk
e-mail: info@askonasholt.co.uk
Fax: 020-7400 1799                   Tel: 020-7400 1700

**AVALON PROMOTIONS Ltd**
4A Exmoor Street, London W10 6BD
Fax: 020-7598 7334                   Tel: 020-7598 7333

**BARRUCCI LEISURE ENTERPRISES Ltd**
(Promoters)
45-47 Cheval Place
London SW7 1EW
e-mail: barrucci@barrucci.com
Fax: 020-7581 2509                   Tel: 020-7225 2255

**BLOCK Derek ARTISTES AGENCY**
70-76 Bell Street
Marylebone, London NW1 6SP
e-mail: derekblock@derekblock.co.uk
Fax: 020-7724 2102                   Tel: 020-7724 2101

**FLYING MUSIC**
FM House, 110 Clarendon Road
London W11 2HR
Website: www.flyingmusic.com
e-mail: reception@flyingmusic.com
Fax: 020-7221 5016                   Tel: 020-7221 7799

**GUBBAY Raymond Ltd**
Dickens House, 15 Tooks Court
London EC4A 1QH
Website: www.raymondgubbay.co.uk
e-mail: info@raymondgubbay.co.uk
Fax: 020-7025 3751                   Tel: 020-7025 3750

**HOBBS Liz GROUP Ltd**
65 London Road
Newark
Nottinghamshire NG24 1RZ
Website: www.lizhobbsgroup.com
e-mail: events@lizhobbsgroup.com
Fax: 0870 3337009                    Tel: 0870 0702702

**HOCHHAUSER Victor**
4 Oak Hill Way
London NW3 7LR
e-mail: admin@victorhochhauser.co.uk
Fax: 020-7431 2531                   Tel: 020-7794 0987

**IMG ARTS & ENTERTAINMENT**
Pier House, Strand on the Green
Chiswick, London W4 3NN
Fax: 020-8233 5001                   Tel: 020-8233 5000

**McINTYRE Phil ENTERTAINMENT**
2nd Floor, 35 Soho Square
London W1D 3QX
e-mail: info@mcintyre-ents.com
Fax: 020-7439 2280                   Tel: 020-7439 2270

**MEADOW Jeremy Ltd**
73 Great Titchfield Street
London W1W 6RD
Website: www.jeremymeadow.com
e-mail: info@jeremymeadow.com
Fax: 0870 7627882                    Tel: 020-7436 2244

**RBM**
(Comedy)
3rd Floor
168 Victoria Street
London SW1E 5LB
Website: www.rbmcomedy.com
e-mail: info@rbmcomedy.com
Fax: 020-7630 6549                   Tel: 020-7630 7733

**T.A.P.**
(Tribute Attack Promotions)
99 Wellington Lane
Norwich NR2 1HJ
e-mail: jack.halpert@yahoo.co.uk     Mobile: 07979 895641

**WOW PRODUCTIONS Ltd**
81 Oxford Street, London W1D 2EU
Website: www.wow-productions.biz
e-mail: info@wow-productions.biz
Fax: 020-7903 5333                   Tel: 020-7903 5183

## ACCELERATE Ltd
374 Ley Street
Ilford IG1 4AE
Website: www.accelerate-productions.co.uk
e-mail: info@accelerate-productions.co.uk
Mobile: 07956 104086              Mobile: 07782 199181

## BLACKFISH PRODUCTIONS
4 Knox Road
London E7 9HW
Website: www.blackfishproductions.co.uk
e-mail: team@blackfishproductions.co.uk
Fax: 0845 8679307              Tel: 0845 4650735

## BODYWORK AGENCY
17-19 Brookside
Cambridge CB2 1JE
e-mail: agency@bodyworkds.co.uk
Fax: 01223 568231              Tel: 01223 309990

## CREATIVE KIDZ & Co
(Incorporating NeighbourHood Productions)
9 Weavers Terrace
Fulham, London SW6 1QE        Mobile: 07958 377595
e-mail: info@creativekidzandco.co.uk

## DANCERS
1 Charlotte Street, London W1T 1RD
Website: www.features.co.uk
e-mail: info@features.co.uk
Fax: 020-7636 1657            Tel: 020-7636 1473

## DANCERS INC. INTERNATIONAL COLLECTIVE
9-13 Grape Street
Covent Garden
London WC2H 8ED
Website: www.internationalcollective.co.uk
e-mail: enquiries@internationalcollective.co.uk
Fax: 020-7557 6656           Tel: 020-7557 6650

## ELLITE MANAGEMENT
'The Dancer'
8 Peterson Road
Wakefield WF1 4EB
Website: www.elliteproductions.co.uk
e-mail: enquiries@ellitemanagement.co.uk
Mobile: 07957 631510          Tel: 0845 6525361

## FEATURES
1 Charlotte Street
London W1T 1RD
Website: www.features.co.uk
e-mail: info@features.co.uk
Fax: 020-7636 1657           Tel: 020-7637 1487

## HEADNOD TALENT AGENCY
2nd Floor Office (Unit 4)
18 Kingsland Road
Shoreditch, London E2 8DA    Tel/Fax: 020-7502 9478
Website: www.headnodagency.com
e-mail: info@headnodagency.com

## JK DANCE PRODUCTIONS
South Manchester Film & Television Studios
Battersea Road
Stockport SK4 3EA            Tel: 0161-432 5222
Website: www.jkdance.co.uk
e-mail: info@jkdance.co.uk

## K TALENT
1st Floor, 28 Grays Inn Road
London WC1X 8HR
Website: www.ktalent.co.uk
e-mail: mail@ktalent.co.uk
Tel: 0844 5672470            Tel: 020-7209 8154

## KEW PERSONAL MANAGEMENT
PO Box Office 56584
London SW18 9GE              Tel: 020-8871 3697
Website: www.kewpersonalmanagement.com
e-mail: info@kewpersonalmanagement.com

## KMC AGENCIES
Garden Studios
11-15 Betterton Street
London WC2H 9BP
e-mail: london@kmcagencies.co.uk
Fax: 0870 4421780            Tel: 0845 6602459

PO Box 122
48 Great Ancoats Street
Manchester M4 5AB
e-mail: casting@kmcagencies.co.uk
Fax: 0161-237 9812           Tel: 0161-237 3009

## LONGRUN ARTISTES
Contact: Gina Long, Irene Wernli
Marylebone Dance Studios
12 Lisson Grove
London NW1 6TS
Website: www.longrunartistes.co.uk
e-mail: gina@longrunartistes.co.uk
Fax: 0871 5227926            Tel: 020-8316 6662

## MBK DANCE & ENTERTAINEMENT
(Existing Clients only)
10 St Julians Close
London SW16 2RY
Website: www.mbkonline.co.uk
e-mail: mbkdance@msn.com
Fax: 020-8488 9121           Tel: 020-8664 6676

## MITCHELL MAAS McLENNAN
MD2000 Offices
29 Thomas Street
Woolwich, London SE18 6HU    Tel/Fax: 020-8301 8745
Website: www.mmm2000.co.uk
e-mail: agency@mmm2000.co.uk

# infopage

## Why do I need a dance agent?

As with any other agent, a dance agent will submit their clients for jobs, negotiate contracts, handle paperwork and offer advice. In return for these services they will charge commission ranging from 10-15%. The agents listed on the following pages specialise in representing and promoting dancers. They will possess the relevant contacts in the industry that you need to get auditions and jobs.

## How should I use these listings?

If you are a dancer getting started in the industry, looking to change your existing agent, or wishing to take on an additional agent that represents you for dance alongside your main acting agent, the following pages will supply you with up-to-date contact details for dance agencies. Every company listed is done so by written request to us. Please see the main 'Agents and Personal Managers' advice section for further guidance on choosing and approaching agents.

## Should I pay an agent to join their books? Or sign a contract?

Equity (the actors' trade union) does not recommend that artists pay an agent to join their client list. Before signing a contract, you should be very clear about the terms and commitments involved. For advice on both of these issues, or if you experience any problems with a current agent, we recommend that you contact Equity www.equity.org.uk. They also publish the booklet *You and your Agent* which is free to all Equity members.

## What is Spotlight Dancers?

Spotlight Dancers is a specialist casting directory published annually by Spotlight. Members receive a page in the directory containing a headshot and body shot, agency contact details and selected credits as well as an online CV on the Spotlight website. These are used by dance employers throughout the UK to locate dancers and send out casting or audition information. Dancers who attend CDET (Council for Dance Education and Training) accredited schools receive a discount when applying in their graduating year. Dancers wishing to promote themselves for job opportunities in commercial theatre, musicals, opera, film, television, live music and video, corporate events and many other areas of the industry should consider joining: see www.spotlight.com/dancers for more information.

## Should I join Spotlight's Actors/Actresses directory or the Dancers directory?

Depending on your skills, training and experience, you may be eligible for both directories if you are interested in promoting yourself both as an actor and as a dancer. If you join both, you would receive an entry into each directory and two separate online CVs. You would also qualify for a 25% discount off the Dancers membership fee. If you only want to join one or the other, then you will need to consider which area of the industry you want to focus on in your career. Musical theatre experience can qualify you for either directory, depending on whether your role involved mainly dancing or acting. This is something you will need to think about, and something you should discuss with your agent if you sign with one.

## Where can I find more information?

Please refer to the guest article on the next page and the info pages preceding the 'Dance Companies' listings for further information about the dance industry.

**Stuart Bishop is an international choreographer, agent, and director of the renowned Rudeye Dance Agency. Stuart has worked with top brands and artists from Pepsi to Playstation, BT to the BBC, choreographing everything from music videos to award shows and on a daily basis casting dancers for jobs for all aspects of the dance industry including TV, fashion and film.**

As a choreographer and agent, I am in contact with dancers every day either via professional work (casting or choreographic) or via my teaching of workshops and masterclasses. I am frequently asked for advice on how to build a successful dancing career so here are my thoughts...

A dancer's life should be no different to being in any other business or profession - if you work hard and smart you will have a long and successful career. The correct training is essential. Technique is key - as a dancer it's important not to pigeon hole yourself as only a ballet boy or maybe a jazz girl. It is more than possible to achieve a high standard in a number of styles and the more you can do, the more jobs an agent can put you up for.

Upon completion of training it is important for dancers to remember that they are the new kids on the block, so do not get downbeat if you do not get jobs immediately - only a small number will be lucky enough to work straight away. For the other 90% it's important to remain positive and start to get to know everything about your business. Find out who the choreographers and agents are and find out which studios are best to take classes with, or even which are best just to hang around for inspiration. Find out and learn the latest dance styles, what to wear, how to look. You have to live the life of a professional dancer. For me it is so important for dancers to live in London in order for faces and places to become second nature to you - it makes attending auditions less scary as the more comfortable you are, the more confident you will be.

As dancers find their feet they often have to get an additional job to pay the bills - again, you have to be clever about this by keeping within the industry. Teaching dance for £20 to £30 pounds an hour is smarter than working in a bar for maybe £7 an hour! By teaching you are developing your dance skills and, most importantly, keeping yourself open to taking the next step up if the opportunity arises to become a choreographer.

During the first couple of years of being a professional, a dancer has to maintain focus, discipline and determination to succeed. You must resist the temptation of listening too much to the gossip mill - what other people are up to or what work they have been offered - and solely concentrate on yourself.

Applying to agencies is a priority - dancers are fortunate in that they can sign with as many as they can get without a stigma being attached, unlike actors, which provides them with more chance of finding work. Some agents will take you on just from your photo and CV - these agencies are good to get you started in the industry, however the top agencies will only accept new dancers after seeing them at an audition being taught by one of their choreographers.

Rudeye will normally have one agency audition each year as well as inviting dancers that impress in our choreographers' classes to castings and auditions for jobs. As an agency we look to take on dancers who we think will benefit and impress our clients and most importantly get jobs! Personally I look for dancers who are multi-skilled with ballet and jazz technique, funk styles and a good commercial look. Discipline and professionalism are also very important as dancers need to be able to be responsible and respectful when amongst clients and fellow dancers. As an agent I work hard to get the best jobs with the best pay and conditions, so dancers need to keep up standards and skills at all times to represent their worth to the agent and client.

**Some quick tips which could help a dancer impress me and my team here at Rudeye:**

1  Only e-mail top quality, up-to-date glossy pictures with a CV when applying for the agency.

2  Master our choreographers' styles before you get to the audition at Rudeye classes.

3  At an agency audition dress funky, colourful and confident and make sure you arrive on time and are mentally prepared to dance your best!

**TOP SECRET TIP: for the last three years the routine that has been taught in our annual agency audition is the routine taught at my Friday professional class the week before the audition date!**

Please visit www.rudeye.com for further information.

**PINEAPPLE AGENCY**
Montgomery House
159-161 Balls Pond Road
Islington
London N1 4BG
Website: www.pineappleagency.com
e-mail: pineapple.agency@btconnect.com
Fax: 020-7241 3006       Tel: 020-7241 6601

**RAZZAMATAZZ MANAGEMENT**
204 Holtye Road
East Grinstead RH19 3ES
e-mail: razzamatazzmanagement@btconnect.com
Mobile: 07836 268292       Tel/Fax: 01342 301617

**RE.ANIMATOR**
3rd Floor, The Priory
Syresham Gardens
West Sussex RH16 3LB
Website: www.reanimator.co.uk
e-mail: management@reanimator.co.uk
Fax: 01444 447030       Tel: 01444 447020

**RED & BLACK**
Website: www.red-black.co.uk
e-mail: info@red-black.co.uk       Mobile: 07722 887277

**RUDEYE DANCE AGENCY**
The Basement
73 St John Street
London EC1M 4NJ       Tel: 020-7014 3023
Website: www.rudeye.com
e-mail: info@rudeye.com

**SCRIMGEOUR Donald ARTISTS AGENT**
49 Springcroft Avenue
London N2 9JH
e-mail: vwest@dircon.co.uk
Fax: 020-8883 9751       Tel: 020-8444 6248

**SHOW TEAM PRODUCTIONS The**
(Dancers & Choreographers)
9 Church Street
Brighton BN1 1US       Tel: 0845 4671010
Website: www.theshowteam.co.uk
e-mail: info@theshowteam.co.uk

**SINGER Sandra ASSOCIATES**
(Dancers & Choreographers)
21 Cotswold Road, Westcliff-on-Sea, Essex SS0 8AA
Website: www.sandrasinger.com
e-mail: sandrasingeruk@aol.com
Fax: 01702 339393       Tel: 01702 331616

**S.O.S.**
85 Bannerman House
Lawn Lane, London SW8 1UA
Website: www.sportsofseb.com
e-mail: info@sportsofseb.com
Mobile: 07740 359770       Tel: 020-7735 5133

**SUCCESS**
Room 236, 2nd Floor, Linen Hall
162-168 Regent Street, London W1B 5TB
Website: www.successagency.co.uk
e-mail: ee@successagency.co.uk
Fax: 020-7494 3787       Tel: 020-7734 3356

**TWITCH EVENT CHOREOGRAPHY**
5 Breakspears Mews, Brockley SE4 1PY
Website: www.twitch.uk.com
e-mail: info@twitch.uk.com
Mobile: 07932 656358       Mobile: 07747 770816

**T W MANAGEMENT AGENCY**
66-74 The Promenade
Blackpool, Lancashire FY1 1HB       Tel: 01253 749332
Website: www.twmanagementagency.co.uk
e-mail: marie.cavney@twmanagementagency.co.uk

**UNITED PRODUCTIONS**
(Choreographers, Dancers, Stylists)
6 Shaftesbury Mews
Clapham, London SW4 9BP       Tel/Fax: 020-7498 6563
Website: www.unitedproductions.biz
e-mail: info@unitedproductions.biz

**W ATHLETIC**
The Media Village
131-151 Great Titchfield Street
London W1W 5BB       Tel: 0845 2997798
Website: www.wathletic.com
e-mail: talent@wathletic.com

**SPOTLIGHT DANCERS**

**SPOTLIGHT'S** latest directory, created especially for dancers
Promote yourself to dance jobs across the UK and worldwide

To join call 020 7437 7631 or visit www.spotlight.com/dancers

**SAMUEL FRENCH LTD**

*Publishers of Plays • Agents for the Collection of Royalties*
*Specialist Booksellers*
52 Fitzroy Street London W1T 5JR
Tel 020 7255 4300 (Bookshop) 020 7387 9373 (Enquiries)
Fax 020 7387 2161 www.samuelfrench-london.co.uk
e-mail: theatre@samuelfrench-london.co.uk

**A & B PERSONAL MANAGEMENT Ltd**
(PMA Member)
Suite 330, Linen Hall
162-168 Regent Street
London W1B 5TD
e-mail: billellis@aandb.co.uk
Fax: 020-7038 3699    Tel: 020-7434 4262

**ABNER STEIN**
10 Roland Gardens
London SW7 3PH
e-mail: abner@abnerstein.co.uk
Fax: 020-7370 6316    Tel: 020-7373 0456

**AGENCY (LONDON) Ltd The**
(PMA Member)
24 Pottery Lane
Holland Park, London W11 4LZ
Website: www.theagency.co.uk
e-mail: info@theagency.co.uk
Fax: 020-7727 9037    Tel: 020-7727 1346

**A R G (ARTISTS RIGHTS GROUP Ltd)**
(PMA Member)
4 Great Portland Street
London W1W 8PA
e-mail: argall@argtalent.com
Fax: 020-7436 6700    Tel: 020-7436 6400

**ASPER Pauline MANAGEMENT**
(PMA Member)
Jacobs Cottage
Reservoir Lane
Sedlescombe
East Sussex TN33 0PJ    Tel/Fax: 01424 870412
e-mail: pauline.asper@virgin.net

**BERLIN ASSOCIATES**
(PMA Member)
7 Tyers Gate, London SE1 3HX
Website: www.berlinassociates.com
e-mail: agents@berlinassociates.com
Fax: 020-7632 5296    Tel: 020-7836 1112

**BLAKE FRIEDMANN**
(Novels, Non-Fiction & TV/Film Scripts)
122 Arlington Road
London NW1 7HP
Website: www.blakefriedmann.co.uk
e-mail: julian@blakefriedmann.co.uk
Fax: 020-7284 0442    Tel: 020-7284 0408

**BRITTEN Nigel MANAGEMENT**
(PMA Member)
Riverbank House
1 Putney Bridge Approach
London SW6 3JD
e-mail: office@nbmanagement.com
Fax: 020-7384 3862    Tel: 020-7384 3842

**BRODIE Alan REPRESENTATION Ltd**
(PMA Member)
6th Floor
Fairgate House
78 New Oxford Street
London WC1A 1HB
Website: www.alanbrodie.com
e-mail: abr@alanbrodie.com
Fax: 020-7079 7999    Tel: 020-7079 7990

**CANN Alexandra REPRESENTATION**
(PMA Member)
52 Beauchamp Place
London SW3 1NY    Tel: 020-7584 9047
e-mail: alex@alexandracann.co.uk

**CASAROTTO RAMSAY & ASSOCIATES Ltd**
(PMA Member)
Waverley House
7-12 Noel Street, London W1F 8GQ
Website: www.casarotto.co.uk
e-mail: agents@casarotto.co.uk
Fax: 020-7287 9128    Tel: 020-7287 4450

**CLOWES Jonathan Ltd**
(PMA Member)
10 Iron Bridge House
Bridge Approach
London NW1 8BD
e-mail: admin@jonathanclowes.co.uk
Fax: 020-7722 7677    Tel: 020-7722 7674

**COCHRANE Elspeth PERSONAL MANAGEMENT**
(PMA Member)
Existing clients only
No new applicants
See ASQUITH & HORNER page 22

**CULVERHOUSE & JAMES Ltd**
Halsall Business Park
Orchard House
17 Summerwood Lane
Halsall L39 8TH
Website: www.culverhousejames.co.uk
e-mail: enquiries@culverhousejames.co.uk

Shepperton Studios
Shepperton
Middlesex TW17 0QD
Fax: 01932 592233    Tel: 01932 592546

**CURTIS BROWN GROUP Ltd**
(PMA Member)
5th Floor
Haymarket House
28-29 Haymarket, London SW1Y 4SP
e-mail: cb@curtisbrown.co.uk
Fax: 020-7393 4401    Tel: 020-7393 4400

---

# Culverhouse and James limited Literary Agents

Halsall Business Park, Orchard House
17 Summerwood Lane, Halsall L39 8TH **e:** enquiries@culverhousejames.co.uk
Shepperton Studios, Shepperton, Middx TW17 0QD
**t:** 01932 592546 **f:** 01932 592233 www.culverhousejames.co.uk

---

**DAISH Judy ASSOCIATES Ltd**
(PMA Member)
2 St Charles Place, London W10 6EG
Website: www.judydaish.com
e-mail: judy@judydaish.com
Fax: 020-8964 8966    Tel: 020-8964 8811

**DENCH ARNOLD AGENCY The**
(PMA Member)
10 Newburgh Street
London W1F 7RN
Website: www.dencharnold.com
e-mail: contact@dencharnold.com
Fax: 020-7439 1355    Tel: 020-7437 4551

**de WOLFE Felix**
(PMA Member)
Kingsway House
103 Kingsway, London WC2B 6QX
Website: www.felixdewolfe.com
e-mail: info@felixdewolfe.com
Fax: 020-7242 8119    Tel: 020-7242 5066

**DREW Bryan Ltd**
Mezzanine, Quadrant House
80-82 Regent Street, London W1B 5AU
e-mail: bryan@bryandrewltd.com
Fax: 020-7437 0561    Tel: 020-7437 2293

**FARNES Norma MANAGEMENT**
9 Orme Court, London W2 4RL
Fax: 020-7792 2110    Tel: 020-7727 1544

**FILLINGHAM Janet ASSOCIATES**
(PMA Member)
52 Lowther Road, London SW13 9NU
Website: www.janetfillingham.com
e-mail: info@jfillassoc.co.uk
Fax: 020-8748 7374    Tel: 020-8748 5594

**FILM RIGHTS Ltd**
Mezzanine, Quadrant House
80-82 Regent Street
London W1B 5AU
Website: www.filmrights.ltd.uk
e-mail: information@filmrights.ltd.uk
Fax: 020-7734 0044    Tel: 020-7734 9911

**FITCH Laurence Ltd**
Mezzanine, Quadrant House
80-82 Regent Street, London W1B 5AU
Fax: 020-7734 0044    Tel: 020-7734 9911

**FOSTER Jill Ltd**
(PMA Member)
9 Barb Mews, London W6 7PA
Website: www.jflagency.com
e-mail: agents@jflagency.com
Fax: 020-7602 9336    Tel: 020-7602 1263

**FRENCH Samuel Ltd**
(PMA Member)
52 Fitzroy Street
Fitzrovia, London W1T 5JR
Website: www.samuelfrench-london.co.uk
e-mail: theatre@samuelfrench-london.co.uk
Fax: 020-7387 2161    Tel: 020-7387 9373

**FUTERMAN, ROSE & ASSOCIATES**
(PMA Member) (TV/Film, Showbiz & Music Biographies)
91 St Leonards Road
London SW14 7BL
Website: www.futermanrose.co.uk
e-mail: guy@futermanrose.co.uk
Fax: 020-8286 4860    Tel: 020-8255 7755

**GILLIS Pamela MANAGEMENT**
46 Sheldon Avenue
London N6 4JR
Fax: 020-8341 5564    Tel: 020-8340 7868

**GLASS Eric Ltd**
25 Ladbroke Crescent
Notting Hill, London W11 1PS
e-mail: eglassltd@aol.com
Fax: 020-7229 6220    Tel: 020-7229 9500

**HALL Rod AGENCY Ltd The**
(PMA Member)
6th Floor
Fairgate House
78 New Oxford Street
London WC1A 1HB
Website: www.rodhallagency.com
e-mail: office@rodhallagency.com
Fax: 0845 6384094    Tel: 020-7079 7987

**HANCOCK Roger Ltd**
(PMA Member)
7 Broadbent Close
Highgate Village, London N6 5JW
Fax: 020-8348 4087    Tel: 020-8341 7243

**HIGHAM David ASSOCIATES Ltd**
(PMA Member)
5-8 Lower John Street
Golden Square
London W1F 9HA
Website: www.davidhigham.co.uk
e-mail: dha@davidhigham.co.uk
Fax: 020-7437 1072    Tel: 020-7434 5900

**HOSKINS Valerie ASSOCIATES Ltd**
(PMA Member)
20 Charlotte Street
London W1T 2NA
e-mail: vha@vhassociates.co.uk
Fax: 020-7637 4493    Tel: 020-7637 4490

**HOWARD Amanda ASSOCIATES Ltd**
(PMA Member)
21 Berwick Street, London W1F 0PZ
Website: www.amandahowardassociates.co.uk
e-mail: mail@amandahowardassociates.co.uk
Fax: 020-7287 7785                    Tel: 020-7287 9277

**HURLEY LOWE MANAGEMENT**
(PMA Member)
27 Rosenau Crescent
London SW11 4RY                    Mobile: 07812 165998
e-mail: kate@hurleylowemanagement.com

**INDEPENDENT TALENT GROUP Ltd**
(PMA Member) (Formerly ICM, London)
Oxford House, 76 Oxford Street, London W1D 1BS
Website: www.independenttalent.com
Fax: 020-7323 0101                    Tel: 020-7636 6565

**KASS Michelle ASSOCIATES**
(PMA Member)
85 Charing Cross Road
London WC2H 0AA
e-mail: office@michellekass.co.uk
Fax: 020-7734 3394                    Tel: 020-7439 1624

**KENIS Steve & Co**
(PMA Member)
Royalty House
72-74 Dean Street, London W1D 3SG
e-mail: sk@sknco.com
Fax: 020-7287 6328                    Tel: 020-7434 9055

**MACFARLANE CHARD ASSOCIATES Ltd**
(PMA Member)
33 Percy Street
London W1T 2DF
Website: www.macfarlane-chard.co.uk
e-mail: louise@macfarlane-chard.co.uk
Fax: 020-7636 7751                    Tel: 020-7636 7750

**MACNAUGHTON LORD REPRESENTATION**
(PMA Member)
Unit 10, The Broomhouse Studios
50 Sulivan Road, London SW6 3DX
Website: www.mlrep.com
e-mail: info@mlrep.com
Fax: 020-7371 7563                    Tel: 020-7384 9517

**MANN Andrew Ltd**
(PMA Member)
1 Old Compton Street, London W1D 5JA
Website: www.andrewmann.co.uk
e-mail: info@andrewmann.co.uk
Fax: 020-7287 9264                    Tel: 020-7734 4751

**MANS Johnny PRODUCTIONS Ltd**
PO Box 196
Hoddesdon, Herts EN10 7WQ
Website: www.johnnymansproductions.co.uk
e-mail: johnnymansagent@aol.com
Fax: 01992 470516                    Tel: 01992 470907

**MARJACQ SCRIPTS Ltd**
34 Devonshire Place
London W1G 6JW
Website: www.marjacq.com
e-mail: enquiries@marjacq.com
Fax: 020-7935 9115                    Tel: 020-7935 9499

**MARVIN Blanche**
(PMA Member)
21A St Johns Wood High Street
London NW8 7NG                    Tel/Fax: 020-7722 2313
e-mail: blanchemarvin17@hotmail.com

**M.B.A. LITERARY AGENTS Ltd**
(PMA Member)
62 Grafton Way
London W1T 5DW
Website: www.mbalit.co.uk
e-mail: agent@mbalit.co.uk
Fax: 020-7387 2042                    Tel: 020-7387 2076

**McLEAN Bill PERSONAL MANAGEMENT**
23B Deodar Road
London SW15 2NP                    Tel: 020-8789 8191

**MLR**
(See MACNAUGHTON LORD REPRESENTATION)

**MORRIS William ENDEAVOR ENTERTAINMENT**
(PMA Member)
Centre Point
103 New Oxford Street
London WC1A 1DD
Fax: 020-7534 6900                    Tel: 020-7534 6800

**NARROW ROAD COMPANY The**
(PMA Member)
182 Brighton Road
Coulsdon, Surrey CR5 2NF
e-mail: richardireson@narrowroad.co.uk
Fax: 020-8763 2558                    Tel: 020-8763 9895

**PFD**
(PMA Member)
Drury House
34-43 Russell Street
London WC2B 5HA
Website: www.pfd.co.uk
e-mail: info@pfd.co.uk
Fax: 020-7836 9539                    Tel: 020-7344 1000

**POLLINGER Ltd**
9 Staple Inn
Holborn, London WC1V 7QH
Website: www.pollingerltd.com
e-mail: info@pollingerltd.com
Fax: 020-7242 5737                    Tel: 020-7404 0342

**ROSICA COLIN Ltd**
1 Clareville Grove Mews
London SW7 5AH
Fax: 020-7244 6441                    Tel: 020-7370 1080

**SAYLE SCREEN Ltd**
(PMA Member) (Screenwriters & Directors for Film & TV)
11 Jubilee Place
London SW3 3TD
Fax: 020-7823 3363                    Tel: 020-7823 3883

**SEIFERT Linda MANAGEMENT Ltd**
(PMA Member)
22 Poland Street
London W1F 8QQ
Website: www.lindaseifert.com
e-mail: contact@lindaseifert.com
Fax: 020-7292 7391                    Tel: 020-7292 7390

**SHARLAND ORGANISATION Ltd**
(PMA Member)
The Manor House
Manor Street
Raunds, Northants NN9 6JW
e-mail: tso@btconnect.com
Tel: 01933 626600

**SHEIL LAND ASSOCIATES Ltd**
(PMA Member) (Literary, Theatre & Film)
52 Doughty Street, London WC1N 2LS
e-mail: info@sheilland.co.uk
Fax: 020-7831 2127
Tel: 020-7405 9351

**STAGESCRIPTS Ltd**
Lantern House, 84 Littlehaven Lane
Horsham, West Sussex RH12 4JB
Website: www.stagescripts.com
e-mail: sales@stagescripts.com
Fax: 0700 5810582
Tel: 0700 5810581

**STEEL Elaine**
(PMA Member) (Writers' Agent)
110 Gloucester Avenue, London NW1 8HX
e-mail: ecmsteel@aol.com
Fax: 01273 772400
Tel: 01273 739022

**STEINBERG Micheline ASSOCIATES**
(PMA Member)
104 Great Portland Street
London W1W 6PE
Website: www.steinplays.com
e-mail: info@steinplays.com
Tel: 020-7631 1310

**STEVENS Rochelle & Co**
(PMA Member)
2 Terretts Place
Upper Street, London N1 1QZ
e-mail: info@rochellestevens.com
Fax: 020-7354 5729
Tel: 020-7359 3900

**TENNYSON AGENCY The**
10 Cleveland Avenue
Merton Park, London SW20 9EW
e-mail: submissions@tenagy.co.uk
Tel: 020-8543 5939

**THURLEY J M MANAGEMENT**
Archery House, 33 Archery Square
Walmer, Deal CT14 7JA
e-mail: jmthurley@aol.com
Tel: 01304 371721

**TYRRELL Julia MANAGEMENT**
(PMA Member)
57 Greenham Road
London N10 1LN
Website: www.jtmanagement.co.uk
e-mail: julia@jtmanagement.co.uk
Fax: 020-8374 5580
Tel: 020-8374 0575

**WARE Cecily LITERARY AGENTS**
(PMA Member)
19C John Spencer Square
London N1 2LZ
Website: www.cecilyware.com
e-mail: info@cecilyware.com
Fax: 020-7226 9828
Tel: 020-7359 3787

**WEINBERGER Josef Ltd**
(PMA Member)
12-14 Mortimer Street
London W1T 3JJ
Website: www.josef-weinberger.com
e-mail: general.info@jwmail.co.uk
Fax: 020-7436 9616
Tel: 020-7580 2827

**WESSON Penny**
(PMA Member)
26 King Henry's Road, London NW3 3RP
e-mail: penny@pennywesson.demon.co.uk
Fax: 020-7483 2890
Tel: 020-7722 6607

**ALLEN Debi ASSOCIATES**
22 Torrington Place, London WC1E 7HP
Website: www.debiallenassociates.com
e-mail: info@debiallenassociates.com
Fax: 020-7317 2245                    Tel: 020-7255 6123

**APM ASSOCIATES**
Contact: Linda French
Pinewood Studios
Pinewood Road
Iver Heath, Bucks SL0 0NH
Website: www.apmassociates.net
e-mail: apm@apmassociates.net
Fax: 01753 639205                    Tel: 01753 639204

**ARLINGTON ENTERPRISES Ltd**
1-3 Charlotte Street, London W1T 1RD
Website: www.arlingtonenterprises.co.uk
e-mail: info@arlington-enterprises.co.uk
Fax: 020-7580 4994                   Tel: 020-7580 0702

**BARR Becca MANAGEMENT**
174 New Bond Street
London W1S 4RG                       Tel: 020-3137 2980
Website: www.beccabarrmanagement.co.uk
e-mail: becca@beccabarrmanagement.co.uk

**BLACKBURN SACHS ASSOCIATES**
Argyll House
All Saints Passage, London SW18 1EP
Website: www.blackburnsachsassociates.com
e-mail: presenters@blackburnsachsassociates.com
Fax: 020-8875 8301                   Tel: 020-7292 7555

**CAMERON Sara MANAGEMENT**
(See TAKE THREE MANAGEMENT)

**CHASE PERSONAL MANAGEMENT**
2nd Floor, 3 Kew Road, Richmond, Surrey TW9 2NQ
Website: www.chasepersonalmanagement.co.uk
e-mail: sue@chasemanagement.co.uk
Mobile: 07775 683955                 Tel: 020-8940 7198

**CINEL GABRAN MANAGEMENT**
PO Box 101, Newholm, Whitby
North Yorkshire YO21 3WT
Website: www.cinelgabran.co.uk
e-mail: mail@cinelgabran.co.uk
Fax: 0845 0666601                    Tel: 0845 0666605

PO Box 5163, Cardiff CF5 9BJ
e-mail: info@cinelgabran.co.uk

**CRAWFORDS**
PO Box 44394, London SW20 0YP
Website: www.crawfords.tv
e-mail: cr@wfords.com
Fax: 020-3258 5037                   Tel: 020-8947 9999

**CURTIS BROWN GROUP Ltd**
Haymarket House, 28-29 Haymarket, London SW1Y 4SP
Website: www.curtisbrown.co.uk
e-mail: presenters@curtisbrown.co.uk
Fax: 020-7393 4401                   Tel: 020-7393 4460

**DAVID ANTHONY PROMOTIONS**
PO Box 286, Warrington, Cheshire WA2 8GA
Website: www.davewarwick.co.uk
e-mail: dave@davewarwick.co.uk
Fax: 01925 416589                    Tel: 01925 632496

**DOWNES PRESENTERS AGENCY**
96 Broadway, Bexleyheath
Kent DA6 7DE                         Tel: 020-8304 0541
Website: www.presentersagency.com
e-mail: downes@presentersagency.com

**EVANS Jacque MANAGEMENT Ltd**
Top Floor Suite, 14 Holmesley Road, London SE23 1PJ
e-mail: jacque@jacqueevans.com
Fax: 020-8699 5192                   Tel: 020-8699 1202

**EXCELLENT**
118-120 Great Titchfield Street, London W1W 6SS
Website: www.excellenttalent.com
e-mail: marie-claire@excellenttalent.com
Fax: 020-7637 4091                   Tel: 0845 2100111

**EXPERTS MANAGEMENT SERVICES Ltd**
(T/A Jane Hughes Management)
PO Box 200, Stockport, Cheshire SK12 1GW
e-mail: gill@jhm.co.uk
Mobile: 07766 130604                 Tel: 01625 858556

**FBI AGENCY Ltd The**
PO Box 250, Leeds LS1 2AZ            Tel/Fax: 07050 222747
Website: www.fbi-agency.co.uk
e-mail: casting@fbi-agency.co.uk

**FIRST ARTIST MANAGEMENT**
3 Tenterden Street, Hanover Square, London W1S 1TD
Website: www.firstartist.co.uk
e-mail: info@firstartist.co.uk
Fax: 020-3205 2140                   Tel: 020-7096 9999

**FLETCHER ASSOCIATES**
(Broadcast & Media)
25 Parkway, London N20 0XN
Website: www.fletcherassociates.net
Fax: 020-8361 8866                   Tel: 020-8361 8061

**FORD-CRUSH June PERSONAL MANAGEMENT & REPRESENTATION**
PO Box 57948, London W4 2UJ
Website: www.junefordcrush.com
e-mail: june@junefordcrush.com
Mobile: 07711 764160                 Tel/Fax: 020-8742 7724

**GAY Noel**
19 Denmark Street, London WC2H 8NA
Website: www.noelgay.com
e-mail: info@noelgay.com
Fax: 020-7287 1816                   Tel: 020-7836 3941

**GLOBAL7**
PO Box 56232, London N4 4XP
Website: www.global7casting.com
e-mail: global7castings@gmail.com
Mobile: 07956 956652                 Tel/Fax: 020-7281 7679

# infopage

## How do I become a presenter?

There is no easy answer to this question. Some presenters start out as actors and move into presenting work, others may be 'experts' such as chefs, designers or sports people who are taken on in a presenting capacity. Others may have a background in stand-up comedy. All newsreaders are professional journalists with specialist training and experience. Often presenters work their way up through the production side of broadcasting, starting by working as a runner or researcher and then moving to appear in front of the camera. To get this kind of production work you could contact Film and TV Production companies, many of whom are listed in this book. A number of Performing Arts Schools, Colleges and Academies also offer useful part-time training courses for presenters. See the 'Drama Training, Schools and Coaches' section of this book for college / school listings.

## Why do I need a presenting agent?

As with any other agent, a presenting agent will promote their clients to job opportunities, negotiate contracts on their behalf, handle paperwork and offer advice. In return for these services they take commission ranging from 10-15%. The following pages contain contact details for the UK's leading presenter agencies. They will possess the relevant contacts in the industry that you need to get auditions and jobs.

## How should I use these listings?

Before you approach any agency looking for representation, do some research into their current client list and the areas in which they specialise. Many have websites you can visit. Once you have made a short-list of the ones you think are most appropriate, you should send them your CV with a covering letter and a good quality, recent photograph which is a genuine likeness of you. Showreels can also be a good way of showcasing your talents, but only send these if you have checked with the agency first. Enclosing a stamped-addressed envelope with sufficient postage (SAE) will also give you a better chance of a reply. Please see the main 'Agents and Personal Managers' advice section for further guidance on choosing and approaching agents.

## Should I pay a presenter's agent to join their books? Or sign a contract?

As with other types of agencies, Equity does not generally recommend that artists pay an agent to join their client list. Before signing any contract, you should be clear about the terms and commitments involved. Always speak to Equity www.equity.org.uk if you have any concerns or queries.

## What is Spotlight Presenters?

Spotlight Presenters is a specialist casting directory published annually. It contains photographs and contact details for over seven hundred professional TV and radio presenters and is a great way of promoting yourself for work. It is used by production companies, casting directors, TV and radio stations, advertising agencies and publicists to browse and locate talent for future productions. Membership is available to any presenter with proven professional broadcast experience. This year Spotlight's Presenters directory will also feature a new 'Emerging Talent' section for those who have a limited amount of broadcast experience or training and are just starting out with their presenting careers. Please see www.spotlight.com to join or for more information.

## Should I join the Spotlight Actors/Actresses directory or the Presenters directory?

Depending on your skills, training and experience, you may be eligible for both directories if you are interested in promoting yourself as an actor and as a presenter. You would receive an entry into each directory and two separate online CVs. You would also qualify for a 25% discount off the Presenters membership fee. You will however have to prove that you already have professional experience and/or relevant training.

**Knight Ayton Management represent journalists and presenters covering news and current affairs, and a wide range of factual programming in television and radio.**

One of the first things to remember in the current climate is that the old rule of good manners, patience and doing your homework still applies, but with greater intensity.

Those two words "television presenter" have become aspirational for many young people but the harsh reality is that there will never be enough programmes to fulfil all these ambitions. The public's thirst for news and entertainment never seems to diminish so there is no let-up in production; however with more and more budgets being cut, producers ultimately rely on people who they know will deliver.

Young people stand more chance than ever of forging a career in broadcasting but you do need to decide what specialist areas interest you and you must have a goal in mind. Think about how to use skills learnt elsewhere, gain experience, train, watch, listen and continue to learn. Study the best course of action to get you to the position of a fully rounded and grounded broadcaster who adds value, honesty and integrity to all the programmes you present.

Skills in production will always help on the way to becoming a presenter - the ability to write and edit a story will be more valuable than just looking into the camera and delivering someone else's lines. Writing and producing skills (however minimal) will always hold you in good stead for on-screen work.

The expansion of experts, be it historians, scientists or designers, offers more opportunities to work in television, providing a base to spring from in an area of interest. Programmes on cooking and property don't go out of fashion - the way they are produced and presented does. Here at Knight Ayton Management we work with many specialists in current affairs, history and science, and as well as representing those at the top of the tree, we always welcome new authors in academia set to be the next generation of TV historians and scientists.

New research published in magazines or books is always a good point of entry into broadcasting. As broadcast agents, we work with literary agents to ensure our clients are put forward for new programming as contributors or presenters - no role is too small to act as a showcase. Fees are non-existent or minimal but the exposure is invaluable.

If news and current affairs is your passion, then study your idol's career. Again the old rules apply: a news presenter needs to have experience in the field - and that doesn't have to be in a war zone. Local news reporters gain wonderful experience: working to deadlines and flushing out a story; remaining unflappable; doing the research; getting on with the job in hand; working as part of a team; learning your craft and aiming for the top job in the main anchor's chair in the studio.

Check the biogs of the greats - Jon Snow, Peter Sissons - and you will see a pattern which continues today. One of our clients spent three weeks on the front line in Afghanistan in Summer 2009 and knows he will be a better studio presenter as a result.

There are no short cuts. Your agent will help find those elusive opportunities and get you through that door to meet the people who may ultimately hold your fate in their hands. However you must prepare in advance and never turn up to a job without thoroughly researching what kind of programmes are made by the production company or broadcaster. Rejection is tough for everyone but it's important to hold on to the fact that each rejection is not the end of the game. If you don't fit the bill this time round, then you just might at the next audition or meeting.

Your agent can't perform miracles and all producers know what they are looking for, so it's not just a matter of changing your hairstyle or getting a set of newly whitened teeth to impress. Don't ever act a part - television is the great leveller and that small screen can show up anyone who is false in a heartbeat. Producers want genuine people - passionate about their beliefs, able to put up a good argument and to hold their own, so be brave, honest and true to yourself.

All agents are bombarded by showreels and CVs and we have to make a quick judgement when these arrive on our desks. We check the CV first, look at the track record and then view the showreel. We judge on presentation style, a natural ability in front of the camera and some kind of experience in newspapers, magazines, local radio, or anything else that shows effort to learn the craft.

Breaking new talent is the most difficult thing for an agent - opening up opportunities, although exciting, is challenging and very hard work. But the delight when a new client gets their first job with a chance to develop and thrive is still fantastic and all agents will find that a thrill.

At Knight Ayton Management we have always found it deeply fulfilling to work together with our clients to grow their careers and to help them reach where they want to be. It's a bumpy road, but an exciting one.

Please visit www.knightayton.co.uk for further information.

**GLORIOUS MANAGEMENT**
Lower Ground Floor
79 Noel Road, London N1 8HE
e-mail: lisa@glorioustalent.co.uk
Tel: 020-7704 6555

**GRANT James MEDIA**
94 Strand on The Green, London W4 3NN
Website: www.jamesgrant.co.uk
e-mail: enquiries@jamesgrant.co.uk
Fax: 020-8742 4951
Tel: 020-8742 4950

**GURNETT J. PERSONAL MANAGEMENT Ltd**
12 Newburgh Street, London W1F 7RP
Website: www.jgpm.co.uk
e-mail: info@jgpm.co.uk
Fax: 020-7287 9642
Tel: 020-7440 1850

**HICKS Jeremy ASSOCIATES Ltd**
114-115 Tottenham Court Road, London W1T 5AH
Website: www.jeremyhicks.com
e-mail: info@jeremyhicks.com
Fax: 020-7383 2777
Tel: 020-7383 2000

**INTERNATIONAL ARTISTES Ltd**
4th Floor, Holborn Hall
193-197 High Holborn
London WC1V 7BD
Website: www.internationalartistes.com
e-mail: reception@internationalartistes.com
Fax: 020-7404 9865
Tel: 020-7025 0600

**JLA (Jeremy Lee Associates Ltd)**
(Supplies celebrities and after dinner speakers)
80 Great Portland Street
London W1W 7NW
e-mail: talk@jla.co.uk
Fax: 020-7907 2801
Tel: 020-7907 2800

**JOYCE Michael MANAGEMENT**
4th Floor
14-18 Heddon Street, London W1B 4DA
Website: www.michaeljoycemanagement.com
e-mail: info@michaeljoycemanagement.com
Fax: 020-7745 6275
Tel: 020-7745 6274

**KBJ MANAGEMENT Ltd**
(TV Presenters)
5 Soho Square, London W1D 3QA
Website: www.kbjmgt.co.uk
e-mail: general@kbjmgt.co.uk
Fax: 020-7287 1191
Tel: 020-7434 6767

**KNIGHT AYTON MANAGEMENT**
35 Great James Street, London WC1N 3HB
Website: www.knightayton.co.uk
e-mail: info@knightayton.co.uk
Fax: 020-7831 4455
Tel: 020-7831 4400

**KNIGHT Hilary MANAGEMENT Ltd**
Grange Farm, Church Lane
Old, Northamptonshire NN6 9QZ
Website: www.hkmanagement.co.uk
e-mail: hilary@hkmanagement.co.uk
Tel: 01604 781818

**LEIGH Mike ASSOCIATES**
37 Marylebone Lane, London W1U 2NW
Website: www.mikeleighassoc.com
Fax: 020-7486 5886
Tel: 020-7935 5500

**LYTE Seamus MANAGEMENT Ltd**
Apt 5, Oswald Building, Chelsea Bridge Wharf
374 Queenstown Road
London SW8 4NU
e-mail: seamus@seamuslyte.com
Mobile: 07930 391401

**MACFARLANE CHARD ASSOCIATES Ltd**
33 Percy Street, London W1T 2DF
Website: www.macfarlane-chard.co.uk
e-mail: enquiries@macfarlane-chard.co.uk
Fax: 020-7636 7751
Tel: 020-7636 7750

**MARKS PRODUCTIONS Ltd**
2 Gloucester Gate Mews
London NW1 4AD
Tel: 020-7486 2001

**MARSH Billy ASSOCIATES Ltd**
76A Grove End Road, St John's Wood, London NW8 9ND
Website: www.billymarsh.co.uk
e-mail: talent@billymarsh.co.uk
Fax: 020-7449 6933
Tel: 020-7449 6930

**MEDIA PEOPLE**
(The Celebrity Group)
13 Montagu Mews South
London W1H 7ER
Website: www.celebrity.co.uk
e-mail: info@celebrity.co.uk
Tel: 0871 2501234

**MILES John ORGANISATION**
Cadbury Camp Lane
Clapton-in-Gordano, Bristol BS20 7SB
Website: www.johnmilesorganisation.org.uk
e-mail: john@johnmiles.org.uk
Fax: 01275 810186
Tel: 01275 854675

**MONDI ASSOCIATES Ltd**
Contact: Michelle Sykes
Unit 3 0, Cooper House
2 Michael Road, London SW6 2AD
Website: www.mondiassociates.com
e-mail: michelle@mondiassociates.com
Mobile: 07817 133349

**MPC ENTERTAINMENT**
MPC House, 15-16 Maple Mews, London NW6 5UZ
Website: www.mpce.com
e-mail: info@mpce.com
Fax: 020-7624 4220
Tel: 020-7624 1184

**MTC (UK) Ltd**
20 York Street, London W1U 6PU
Website: www.mtc-uk.com
e-mail: kirsty@mtc-uk.com
Fax: 020-7935 8066
Tel: 020-7935 8000

**MURRAY Vic TALENT Ltd**
185A/B Latchmere Road
London SW11 2JZ
Website: www.vicmurraytalent.com
e-mail: info@vicmurraytalent.com
Tel: 020-7924 4453

**NEWPORT GROUP**
59 Richmond Avenue
Chadderton, Oldham OL9 8LG
e-mail: simonmallitt@live.co.uk
Mobile: 07896 680657

**NOEL John MANAGEMENT**
Block B, Imperial Works
Perren Street, London NW5 3ED
Website: www.johnnoel.com
e-mail: john@johnnoel.com
Fax: 020-7428 8401
Tel: 020-7428 8400

**OFF THE KERB PRODUCTIONS**
(Comedy Presenters & Comedians)
3rd Floor, Hammer House
113-117 Wardour Street, London W1F 0UN
Website: www.offthekerb.co.uk
e-mail: westend@offthekerb.co.uk
Fax: 020-7437 0647
Tel: 020-7437 0607

**PANMEDIA UK Ltd**
18 Montrose Crescent
London N12 0ED Tel: 020-8446 9662
Website: www.panmediauk.co.uk
e-mail: enquiries@panmediauk.co.uk

**PVA MANAGEMENT Ltd**
County House
St Mary's Street, Worcester WR1 1HB
Website: www.pva.co.uk
e-mail: post@pva.co.uk
Fax: 01905 610709 Tel: 01905 616100

**RARE TALENT ACTORS MANAGEMENT**
Tanzaro House
Ardwick Green North, Manchester M12 6FZ
Website: www.raretalentactors.com
e-mail: info@raretalentactors.com
Fax: 0161-273 4567 Tel: 0161-273 4004

**RAZLAND**
6/3, 200 Lincoln Avenue
Glasgow G13 3PP Tel: 0141-950 2434
Website: www.razland.com
e-mail: kandi_razan@hotmail.com

**RAZZAMATAZZ MANAGEMENT**
204 Holtye Road
East Grinstead, West Sussex RH19 3ES
e-mail: razzamatazzmanagement@btconnect.com
Mobile: 07836 268292 Tel/Fax: 01342 301617

**RED 24 MANAGEMENT**
Crown House, 72 Hammersmith Road
London W14 8TH Tel: 020-7559 3611
Website: www.red24management.com
e-mail: info@red24management.com

**RED CANYON MANAGEMENT**
Website: www.redcanyon.co.uk
e-mail: info@redcanyon.co.uk
Mobile: 07939 365578 Mobile: 07931 381696

**RPM2**
Studio House, Delamare Road
Cheshunt, Hertfordshire EN8 9SH
Website: www.rhino2-rpm.com
e-mail: rhino-rpm2@hotmail.com
Tel: 0845 3625456 Tel/Fax: 0845 2415585

**SINGER Sandra ASSOCIATES**
21 Cotswold Road
Westcliff-on-Sea, Essex SS0 8AA
Website: www.sandrasinger.com
e-mail: sandrasingeruk@aol.com
Fax: 01702 339393 Tel: 01702 331616

**SOMETHIN' ELSE**
20-26 Brunswick Place, London N1 6DZ
Website: www.somethinelse.com
e-mail: info@somethinelse.com
Fax: 020-7250 0937 Tel: 020-7250 5500

**SPEAK-EASY Ltd**
PO Box 648, Draughton
Northampton, NN6 9XT Tel: 01604 686100
Website: www.speak-easy.co.uk
e-mail: enquiries@speak-easy.co.uk

**STAR MANAGEMENT Ltd**
16A Winton Drive, Glasgow G12 0QA Tel: 0870 2422276
Website: www.starmanagement.co.uk
e-mail: star@starmanagement.co.uk

**TAKE THREE MANAGEMENT**
110 Gloucester Avenue
Primrose Hill, London NW1 8HX
Website: www.take3management.co.uk
e-mail: info@take3management.com
Fax: 020-7209 3770 Tel: 020-7209 3777

**TALENT4 MEDIA Ltd**
Studio LG16
Shepherds Building Central
Charecroft Way, London W14 0EH
Website: www.talent4media.com
e-mail: enquiries@talent4media.com
Fax: 020-7183 4331 Tel: 020-7183 4330

**TROIKA**
3rd Floor
74 Clerkenwell Road, London EC1M 5QA
Website: www.troikatalent.com
e-mail: info@troikatalent.com
Fax: 020-7490 7642 Tel: 020-7336 7868

**WANDER Jo MANAGEMENT**
110 Gloucester Avenue
Primrose Hill, London NW1 8HX Tel: 020-7209 3777
Website: www.jowandermanagement.com
e-mail: jo@jowandermanagement.com

**WILLCOCKS John MEDIA AGENCY Ltd**
34 Carisbrook Close
Enfield, Middlesex EN1 3NB Tel/Fax: 020-8364 4556
e-mail: john.willcocks@blueyonder.co.uk

**WISE BUDDAH TALENT**
74 Great Titchfield Street, London W1W 7QP
Website: www.wisebuddah.com
e-mail: talent@wisebuddah.com
Fax: 020-7307 1601 Tel: 020-7307 1600

**WWW.PEOPLEMATTER.TV**
Contact: Tony Fitzpatrick
40 Bowling Green Lane
Clerkenwell, London EC1R ONE
Website: www.peoplematter.tv
e-mail: tony@peoplematter.tv
Fax: 020-7415 7074 Tel: 07000 300707

**ZWICKLER Marlene & ASSOCIATES**
1 Belgrave Crescent Lane
Edinburgh EH4 3AG Tel/Fax: 0131-343 3030
Website: www.mza-artists.com

**We offer a complete voice-over artists agency service as well as providing a full voice production studio.**

**Specialising in high quality voice-over showreels at realistic prices.**

**ACCENT BANK**
420 Falcon Wharf
34 Lombard Road
London SW11 3RF
Website: www.accentbank.co.uk
e-mail: info@accentbank.co.uk
Tel: 020-7223 5160

**AD VOICE**
Oxford House
76 Oxford Street
London W1D 1BS
Website: www.advoice.co.uk
e-mail: info@advoice.co.uk
Fax: 020-7323 0101
Tel: 020-7323 2345

**AGENCY OAKROYD**
Oakroyd, 89 Wheatley Lane
Ben Rhydding
Ilkley LS29 8PP
Website: www.agencyoakroyd.com
e-mail: paula@agencyoakroyd.com
Mobile: 07840 784337
Tel: 01943 600820

**ALPHABET KIDZ ACTING & VOICE-OVER AGENCY**
189 Southampton Way
London SE5 7EJ
Website: www.alphabetkidz.co.uk
e-mail: contact@alphabetkidz.co.uk
Fax: 020-7252 4341
Tel: 020-7252 4343

**AMERICAN AGENCY VOICES The**
14 Bonny Street
London NW1 9PG
Website: www.americanagency.tv
e-mail: americanagency@btconnect.com
Fax: 020-7482 4666
Tel: 020-7485 8883

**ANOTHER TONGUE VOICES Ltd**
The Basement
10-11 D'Arblay Street
London W1F 8DS
Website: www.anothertongue.com
e-mail: john@anothertongue.com
Fax: 020-7494 7080
Tel: 020-7494 0300

**ASQUITH & HORNER**
Contact: By Post (SAE)
The Studio, 14 College Road
Bromley, Kent BR1 3NS
Fax: 020-8313 0443
Tel: 020-8466 5580

**BRAIDMAN Michelle ASSOCIATES**
2 Futura House
169 Grange Road, London SE1 3BN
e-mail: info@braidman.com
Fax: 020-7231 4634
Tel: 020-7237 3523

**CALYPSO VOICES**
25-26 Poland Street
London W1F 8QN
Website: www.calypsovoices.com
e-mail: calypso@calypsovoices.com
Fax: 020-7437 0410
Tel: 020-7734 6415

**CASTAWAY**
Suite 3, 15 Broad Court
London WC2B 5QN
Website: www.castaway.org.uk
e-mail: info@castaway.org.uk
Fax: 020-7240 2772
Tel: 020-7240 2345

**CINEL GABRAN MANAGEMENT**
PO Box 5163
Cardiff CF5 9BJ
Website: www.cinelgabran.co.uk
e-mail: info@cinelgabran.co.uk
Fax: 0845 0666601
Tel: 0845 0666605

PO Box 101
Newholm, Whitby
North Yorkshire YO21 3WT
e-mail: mail@cinelgabran.co.uk

**COLE KITCHENN PERSONAL MANAGEMEMENT Ltd**
212 Strand, London WC2R 1AP
Website: www.colekitchenn.com
e-mail: stuart@colekitchenn.com
Fax: 020-7353 9639
Tel: 020-7427 5681

**CONWAY VAN GELDER GRANT Ltd**
3rd Floor
8-12 Broadwick Street
London W1F 8HW
Website: www.conwayvangeldergrant.com
e-mail: kate@conwayvg.co.uk
Fax: 020-7287 1940
Tel: 020-7287 1070

**CREATIVE KIDZ & Co**
(Incorporating NeighbourHood Productions)
9 Weavers Terrace
Fulham, London SW6 1QE
Mobile: 07958 377595
e-mail: info@creativekidzandco.co.uk

# info**page**

### How do I become a voice-over artist?

The voice-over business has opened up a lot more to newcomers in recent years; you don't have to be a celebrity already to be booked for a job. However, it is a competitive industry, and it is important to bear in mind that only a select few are able to earn a living from voice-over work. It is more likely that voice-over work could become a supplement to your regular income.

In order to get work you must have a great voice and be able to put it to good use. Being able to act does not necessarily mean that you will also be able to do voice-overs. Whether your particular voice will get you the job or not will ultimately depend on the client's personal choice, so your technical ability to do voice-over work initially comes second in this industry. Once the client has chosen you, however, then you must be able to consistently demonstrate that you can take direction well, you don't need numerous takes to get the job finished, you have a positive attitude and you don't complain if recording goes a little over schedule.

Before you get to this stage, however, you will need a professional-sounding voicereel and, in the majority of cases, an agent.

### How do I produce a voicereel?

Please see the 'Promotional Services' section for advice on creating your voicereel.

### Why do I need a voice-over agent?

As with any other agent, a voice-over agent will promote their clients to job opportunities, negotiate contracts on their behalf, handle paperwork and offer advice. In return for these services they take commission ranging from 10-15%. The agents listed on the following pages specialise in representing and promoting voice-over artists, mostly in the commercial and corporate sectors, but also areas such as radio and animation. They will possess the relevant contacts in the industry that you need to get auditions and jobs. In this industry in particular, time is money, and clients are often more likely to trust that an agent can provide someone who can get the job done in the least amount of takes but still sounds good in every project, rather than taking on an unknown newcomer.

### How do I find work in radio?

Please see the 'Radio' section of Contacts for further information on this specific area of voice work.

### How should I use these listings?

Whether you are completely new to the industry, looking to change your existing agent, or wishing to take on an additional agent to represent you for voice-overs alongside your main acting or presenting agent, the following pages will supply you with up-to-date contact details for voice-over agencies. Every company listed is done so by written request to us. Please see the main 'Agents and Personal Managers' advice section for further guidance on choosing and approaching agents.

### Should I pay an agent to join their books? Or sign a contract?

Equity (the actors' trade union) does not recommend that artists pay an agent to join their client list. Before signing a contract, you should be very clear about the terms and commitments involved. For advice on both of these issues, or if you experience any problems with a current agent, we recommend that you contact Equity www.equity.org.uk. They also publish the booklet *You and your Agent* which is free to all Equity members.

# infopage

Alex Lynch-White joined Earache Voices five years ago and became Managing Agent three years ago. Beforehand she had been working at Ad Voice, part of ICM. Earache was created to offer an alternative to the bland "rich, warm, smooth" voices that were favoured by advertisers in the past, and instead they specialise in artistes who have naturally interesting and distinctive voices which are bursting with character, but most importantly who are also excellent actors.

## Auntie Alex's "Dos" and "Don'ts" of the Voice-over Industry:

### DO get a good showreel

You would be amazed by the number of potential artistes we have calling up, enquiring about representation, without a voice-over showreel. Unless you are a high-profile actor, it's pretty unlikely an agent will take you on without one, quite simply because your voice showreel is your tool for the trade.

With this in mind, you'll need to find a suitable studio and engineer, preferably with directing experience, who can also supply you with relevant scripts.

### DON'T be lazy and copy scripts that are irrelevant to you!

There is very little point attempting to rehash well-known scripts for your voice showreel, such as those of a certain mobile phone network renowned for using a familiar Yorkshire actor! The idea behind doing a showreel is that the commercials are supposed to sound as real as possible, making the listener believe that these are commercials which have actually gone to air with your voice.

### DON'T forget that just because your Great Aunt Ethel says you do an amazing impression of Oliver Reed, it doesn't mean you actually can!

Unless you are renowned for, or have an absolute genuine talent for accents or impersonations, stay well clear. With so many available voice-over artistes to pick from now, if a producer needs a proper 'Geordie Lass', then they can get someone who is actually from Newcastle.

### DO get yourself an agent

Before you do, you need to be aware that most voice-over agents receive huge numbers of queries from actors every day, either via post or e-mail. And this isn't even the main part of the job! Generally, agents tend to allot a couple of hours on a specific day to deal with these, so calling up every few days to chase doesn't tend to help! Doing research before approaching an agency is quite a clever way to at least get them to notice you. Check out their current client list - see what gaps they might have and whether you could possibly fill them. Also check out who could be direct competition to you. Be aware though that even if there is a gap, if an agency have just taken on a few new artistes they will want to concentrate on those new people first. Try to be understanding - you'd want the same treatment!

### DO get on with your agent

I only ever take on artistes if I genuinely like them. I think you need to have a good rapport with your agent, because you need to trust them to act on your behalf and also offer their advice. Having an agent who is up on current TV, films and theatre is massively important too - how else are they going to promote you when your guest turn comes on? When you've done a voice-over job, ask your agent to try and get copies so you can keep your showreel fresh and up-to-date. Most good agents will already do this before you ask.

### DON'T be late for a job

They are paying you after all! If you are running late, let your agent know as soon as possible so they can let the producers and the studio know. Don't forget that not only does your agent represent you, but you are representing the agency.

### DO report back to your agent

Especially if the session went really well (or really badly), and of course if it runs over the allotted time. But let's not be penny-pinching here - that extra five minutes over could have been caused by the time you took taking off your coat, sipping your green tea and chatting about the next series of Big Brother!

So in summary, DO make sure your voicereel is as good as it possibly can be. Research which agents and agencies would be right for you. Be professional, punctual and polite with everyone. And DON'T go ordering your Maserati just because you've got your first voice-over job!

Please visit www.earachevoices.com for further information. You may also wish to refer to the 'Promotional Services' section of Contacts for more information about producing a voicereel.

**CUT GLASS VOICES**
Studio 187
181-187 Queens Crescent
Camden, London NW5 4DS          Tel: 020-7267 2339
Website: www.cutglassproductions.com
e-mail: info@cutglassproductions.com

**DIAMOND MANAGEMENT**
31 Percy Street
London W1T 2DD
e-mail: hj@diman.co.uk
Fax: 020-7631 0500              Tel: 020-7631 0400

**DREW Bryan Ltd**
Mezzanine
Quadrant House
80-82 Regent Street
London W1B 5AU
e-mail: bryan@bryandrewltd.com
Fax: 020-7437 0561             Tel: 020-7437 2293

**EARACHE VOICES**
177 Wardour Street
London W1F 8WX
Website: www.earachevoices.com
e-mail: alex@earachevoices.com
Fax: 020-7287 2288             Tel: 020-7287 2291

**EVANS O'BRIEN**
2 Lampmead Road
London SE12 8QL               Tel: 020-8318 9058
Website: www.evansobrien.co.uk
e-mail: info@evansobrien.co.uk

**EXCELLENT**
118-120 Great Titchfield Street
London W1W 6SS
Website: www.excellenttalent.com
e-mail: info@excellenttalent.com
Fax: 020-7637 4091            Tel: 0845 2100111

**FERRIS ENTERTAINMENT VOICES**
(London, Belfast, Cardiff)
Number 8
132 Charing Cross Road
London WC2H 0LA              Tel: 0845 4724725
Website: www.ferrisentertainment.com
e-mail: info@ferrisentertainment.com

**FIRST VOICE AGENCY**
Foxgrove House
School Lane
Seer Green HP9 2QJ
Website: www.firstvoiceagency.com
e-mail: jenny@firstvoiceagency.com
Fax: 01494 730166            Tel: 01494 678277

**FOREIGN LEGION**
1 Kendal Road, London NW10 1JH    Tel: 020-8450 4451
Website: www.foreignlegion.co.uk
e-mail: voices@foreignlegion.co.uk

**FOREIGN VERSIONS Ltd**
(Translation)
Website: www.foreignversions.com
e-mail: info@foreignversions.co.uk    Tel: 0333 123 2001

**GAY Noel VOICES**
19 Denmark Street
London WC2H 8NA
Website: www.noelgay.com
e-mail: info@noelgay.com
Fax: 020-7287 1816           Tel: 020-7836 3941

**GLOBAL7**
PO Box 56232
London N4 4XP
Website: www.global7casting.com
e-mail: global7castings@gmail.com
Mobile: 07956 956652         Tel/Fax: 020-7281 7679

**GORDON & FRENCH**
Contact: By Post
12-13 Poland Street
London W1F 8QB
Website: www.gordonandfrench.co.uk
e-mail: voices@gordonandfrench.net
Fax: 020-7734 4832           Tel: 020-7734 4818

**HAMILTON HODELL Ltd**
Contact: Louise Donald
5th Floor
66-68 Margaret Street
London W1W 8SR
Website: www.hamiltonhodell.co.uk
e-mail: louise@hamiltonhodell.co.uk
Fax: 020-7636 1226           Tel: 020-7636 1221

**HARVEY VOICES**
(No unsolicited correspondence)
52-53 Margaret Street
London W1W 8SQ                    Tel: 020-7952 4361
Website: www.harveyvoices.co.uk
e-mail: info@harveyvoices.co.uk

**HOBSONS SINGERS**
62 Chiswick High Road
London W4 1SY
Website: www.hobsons-international.com
e-mail: singers@hobsons-international.com
Fax: 020-8996 5350               Tel: 020-8995 3628

**HOBSONS VOICES**
62 Chiswick High Road
London W4 1SY
Website: www.hobsons-international.com
e-mail: voices@hobsons-international.com
Fax: 020-8996 5350               Tel: 020-8995 3628

**HOPE Sally ASSOCIATES**
108 Leonard Street
London EC2A 4XS
Website: www.sallyhope.biz
e-mail: casting@sallyhope.biz
Fax: 020-7613 4848               Tel: 020-7613 5353

**HOWARD Amanda ASSOCIATES**
(See JONESES The)

**J H A VOICE**
114-115 Tottenham Court Road
London W1T 5AH
Website: www.jeremyhicks.com
e-mail: info@jeremyhicks.com
Fax: 020-7383 2777               Tel: 020-7383 2000

**JONESES The**
21 Berwick Street
London W1F 0PZ
Website: www.meetthejoneses.co.uk
e-mail: mail@meetthejoneses.co.uk
Fax: 020-7287 7785               Tel: 020-7287 9666

**JUST VOICES AGENCY The**
140 Buckingham Palace Road
London SW1W 9SA
Website: www.justvoicesagency.com
e-mail: info@justvoicesagency.com
Fax: 020-7881 2569               Tel: 020-7881 2567

**KIDZTALK Ltd**
(Young Voices, Children, Teenagers, Twenties)
Website: www.kidztalk.com
e-mail: studio@kidztalk.com
Fax: 01737 352456                Tel: 01737 350808

**LIP SERVICE CASTING Ltd**
60-66 Wardour Street, London W1F 0TA
Website: www.lipservice.co.uk
e-mail: bookings@lipservice.co.uk
Fax: 020-7734 3373               Tel: 020-7734 3393

**MARCUS & McCRIMMON VOICES**
1 Heathgate Place, 75 Agincourt Road, London NW3 2NU
Website: www.marcusandmccrimmon.com
e-mail: voices@marcusandmccrimmon.com
Fax: 020-3012 3478               Tel: 020-3012 3477

**MARKHAM & FROGGATT Ltd**
4 Windmill Street
London W1T 2HZ
Website: www.markhamfroggatt.com
e-mail: millie@markhamfroggatt.co.uk
Fax: 020-7637 5233                    Tel: 020-7636 4412

**McREDDIE Ken ASSOCIATES Ltd**
Contact: Jan Thornton
11 Connaught Place, London W2 2ET
e-mail: jan@kenmcreddie.com
Fax: 020-7734 6530                    Tel: 020-7439 1456

**PEMBERTON VOICES**
193 Wardour Street
London W1F 8ZF
Website: www.pembertonassociates.com
e-mail: general@pembertonassociates.com
Fax: 020-7734 2522                    Tel: 020-7734 4144

Express Networks
1 George Leigh Street
Manchester M4 5DL
Fax: 0161-235 8442                    Tel: 0161-235 8440

**QVOICE**
4th Floor, Holborn Hall
193-197 High Holborn, London WC1V 7BD
Website: www.qvoice.co.uk
e-mail: info@qvoice.co.uk
Fax: 020-7025 0659                    Tel: 020-7025 0660

**RABBIT VOCAL MANAGEMENT**
2nd Floor
18 Broadwick Street
London W1F 8HS
Website: www.rabbit.uk.net
e-mail: info@rabbit.uk.net
Fax: 020-7287 6566                    Tel: 020-7287 6466

**RED 24 VOICES**
Crown House
72 Hammersmith Road
London W14 8TH                    Tel: 020-7559 3611
Website: www.red24voices.com
e-mail: paul@red24voices.com

**RED CANYON MANAGEMENT**
Website: www.redcanyon.co.uk
e-mail: info@redcanyon.co.uk
Mobile: 07931 381696              Mobile: 07939 365578

**RHUBARB VOICES**
1st Floor
1A Devonshire Road
London W4 2EU
Website: www.rhubarbvoices.co.uk
e-mail: enquiries@rhubarbvoices.co.uk
Fax: 020-8742 8693                    Tel: 020-8742 8683

**RPM2**
Studio House
Delamare Road
Cheshunt, Hertfordshire EN8 9SH
Website: www.rhino2-rpm.com
e-mail: rhino-rpm2@hotmail.com
Tel: 0845 3625456                    Tel/Fax: 0845 2415585

**SHINING MANAGEMENT Ltd**
12 D'Arblay Street
London W1F 8DU
Website: www.shiningvoices.com
e-mail: info@shiningvoices.com
Fax: 020-7734 2528                    Tel: 020-7734 1981

**SPEAK-EASY Ltd**
PO Box 648, Draughton
Northampton NN6 9XT
Website: www.speak-easy.co.uk
e-mail: enquiries@speak-easy.co.uk
Tel: 01604 686100                    Tel: 0870 0135126

**SVMK Ltd**
Studio 1A
151 Tower Bridge Road
London SE1 3LW
Website: www.svmk.co.uk
e-mail: info@svmk.co.uk
Fax: 020-7407 9661                    Tel: 020-7407 9660

**TALKING HEADS**
Argyll House, All Saints Passage
London SW18 1EP
Website: www.talkingheadsvoices.com
e-mail: voices@talkingheadsvoices.com
Fax: 020-7292 7576                    Tel: 020-7292 7575

**TERRY Sue VOICES Ltd**
3rd Floor, 18 Broadwick Street
London W1F 8HS
Website: www.sueterryvoices.co.uk
e-mail: sue@sueterryvoices.co.uk
Fax: 020-7434 2042                    Tel: 020-7434 2040

**TONGUE & GROOVE**
4th Floor, Manchester House
84-86 Princess Street
Manchester M1 6NG
Website: www.tongueandgroove.co.uk
e-mail: info@tongueandgroove.co.uk
Fax: 0161-237 1809                    Tel: 0161-228 2469

**VOCAL POINT**
25 Denmark Street
London WC2H 8NJ
Website: www.vocalpoint.net
e-mail: enquiries@vocalpoint.net
Fax: 020-7419 0699                    Tel: 020-7419 0700

**VOICE BANK Ltd**
1st Floor, 100 Talbot Road
Old Trafford
Manchester M16 0PG
Website: www.voicebankltd.co.uk
e-mail: elinors@voicebankltd.co.uk
Fax: 0161-888 2242                Tel: 0161-874 5741

**VOICE MASTER STUDIO**
(Specialising in Foreign Language Voice-Overs)
88 Erskine Hill
London NW11 6HR                Tel: 020-8455 2211
Website: www.voicemaster.co.uk
e-mail: stevehudson@voicemaster.co.uk

**VOICE SHOP**
First Floor, Thomas Place
1A Devonshire Road
London W4 2EU
Website: www.voice-shop.co.uk
e-mail: info@voice-shop.co.uk
Fax: 020-8742 7011                Tel: 020-8742 7077

**VOICE SQUAD**
1 Kendal Road
London NW10 1JH                Tel: 020-8450 4451
Website: www.voicesquad.com
e-mail: voices@voicesquad.com

**VOICEBANK, THE IRISH VOICE-OVER AGENCY**
The Barracks
76 Irishtown Road
Dublin 4, Ireland
Website: www.voicebank.ie
e-mail: voicebank@voicebank.ie
Fax: 00 353 1 6607850                Tel: 00 353 1 6687234

**VOICECALL**
67A Gondar Gardens
London NW6 1EP                Tel: 020-7209 1064
Website: www.voicecall-online.co.uk
e-mail: voices@voicecall-online.co.uk

**VOICEOVER GALLERY The**
London E3                Tel: 020-7987 0951
Website: www.thevoiceovergallery.co.uk
e-mail: london@thevoiceovergallery.co.uk

Manchester M16                Tel: 0161-881 8844
e-mail: manchester@thevoiceovergallery.co.uk

**VOICEOVERS.CO.UK**
PO Box 326, Plymouth
Devon PL4 9YQ                Tel: 01752 207313
Website: www.voiceovers.co.uk
e-mail: info@voiceovers.co.uk

**VSI - VOICE & SCRIPT INTERNATIONAL**
(Foreign Language Specialists)
132 Cleveland Street, London W1T 6AB
Website: www.vsi.tv
e-mail: info@vsi.tv
Fax: 020-7692 7711                Tel: 020-7692 7700

**WAM VOICES**
(The Voice Agency of Waring & McKenna)
11-12 Dover Street
Mayfair, London W1S 4LJ
Website: www.wamvoices.com
e-mail: info@wamvoices.com
Fax: 020-7629 6466                Tel: 020-7495 6665

**WOOTTON Suzy VOICES**
72 Towcester Road, Far Cotton
Northampton NN4 8LQ
Website: www.suzywoottonvoices.com
e-mail: suzy@suzywoottonvoices.com
Fax: 0870 7659668                Tel: 0870 7659660

**YAKETY YAK**
7A Bloomsbury Square
London WC1A 2LP
Website: www.yaketyyak.co.uk
e-mail: info@yaketyyak.co.uk
Fax: 020-7404 6109                Tel: 020-7430 2600

**AVENUE ARTISTES LTD** *The South's most efficient casting service*
ACTORS, SUPPORTING ARTISTES, EXTRAS & WALK ONS AVAILABLE
FOR TELEVISION, FILMS, COMMERCIALS, ADVERTISING etc
PO Box 1573, Southampton SO16 3XS   TEL: 02380 760930
EMAIL: info@avenueartistes.com   WEBSITE: www.avenueartistes.com

**10 TWENTYTWO CASTING**
(NASAA Member)
PO Box 1022, Liverpool L69 5WZ
Website: www.10twentytwo.com
e-mail: contact@10twentytwo.com
Fax: 0151-207 4230                    Tel: 0871 7891022

**2020 CASTING Ltd**
(NASAA Member)
2020 Hopgood Street, London W12 7JU
Website: www.2020casting.com
e-mail: info@2020casting.com
Fax: 020-8735 2727                    Tel: 020-8746 2020

**AD AGENCY**
1st Floor Danceworks, 16-18 Balderton Street
London W1K 6TN                       Tel: 020-7493 5235
Website: www.adagency-london.com
e-mail: info@adagency-london.com

**AGENCY OAKROYD**
Oakroyd, 89 Wheatley Lane
Ben Rhydding, Ilkley, Yorkshire LS29 8PP
Website: www.agencyoakroyd.com
e-mail: paula@agencyoakroyd.com
Mobile: 07840 784337                 Tel: 01943 600820

**ALLSORTS AGENCY**
(Modelling)
Suite 1 & 2 Marlborough Business Centre
96 George Lane, London E18 1AD
Website: www.allsortsagency.com
e-mail: bookings@allsortsagency.com
Fax: 020-8989 5600                   Tel: 020-8989 0500

**ARTIST MANAGEMENT UK Ltd**
PO Box 96, Liverpool L9 8WY          Tel: 0151-523 6222
Website: www.artistmanagementuk.com
e-mail: chris@artistmanagementuk.com

**AVENUE ARTISTES Ltd**
PO Box 1573, Southampton SO16 3XS    Tel: 023-8076 0930
Website: www.avenueartistes.com
e-mail: info@avenueartistes.com

**WA - ANDREA WILDER AGENCY**
23 Cambrian Drive, Colwyn Bay, Conwy LL28 4SL
Website: www.awagency.co.uk
e-mail: andreawilder@fastmail.fm
Fax: 07092 249314                Mobile: 07919 202401

**BENNETTON - CMP**
Raines Business Centre
Raines House, Denby Dale Road
Wakefield, West Yorkshire WF1 1HR
Website: www.bennetton-cmp.co.uk
e-mail: enquiries@bennetton-cmp.co.uk
Mobile: 07540 693657                 Tel: 01924 291008

**BODENS ADVANCED**
Bodens Studios & Agency
99 East Barnet Road, New Barnet, Herts EN4 8RF
Website: www.bodensagency.com
e-mail: info@bodensagency.com
Mobile: 07545 696888                 Tel: 020-8447 1226

**BROADCASTING AGENCY**
Unit 36 Pall Mall Deposit
124 Barlby Road, London W10 6BL      Tel: 020-7490 4225
Website: www.broadcastingagency.co.uk
e-mail: info@broadcastingagency.co.uk

**BROOK Dolly CASTING AGENCY**
PO Box 5436, Dunmow CM6 1WW
e-mail: dollybrookcasting@btinternet.com
Fax: 01371 875996                    Tel: 01371 875767

**CAIRNS AGENCY The**
Contact: Maureen Cairns, Allan Jones
2nd Floor, 34 Argyle Arcade Chambers
Buchanan Street, Glasgow G2 8BD      Tel: 0141-222 2333
e-mail: info@thecairnsagency.com

**CAMCAST**
(NASAA Member)
Laragain, Upper Banavie
Fort William, Inverness-shire PH33 7PB
Website: www.camcast.co.uk
e-mail: anne@camcast.co.uk
Fax: 01397 772456                    Tel: 01397 772523

**CASTING COLLECTIVE Ltd The**
(NASAA Member)
Olympic House
317-321 Latimer Road, London W10 6RA
Website: www.castingcollective.co.uk
e-mail: enquiries@castingcollective.co.uk
Fax: 020-8962 0333                   Tel: 020-8962 0099

**CASTING NETWORK Ltd The**
4 Vidler Close, Chessington, Surrey KT9 2GL
Website: www.thecastingnetwork.co.uk
e-mail: info@thecastingnetwork.co.uk
Fax: 020-8391 5119                   Tel: 020-8391 2979

**CASTING STUDIO The**
PO Box 167, Middleton
Manchester M24 5WY                 Tel/Fax: 07806 538243
Website: www.thecastingstudio.co.uk
e-mail: info@thecastingstudio.co.uk

**CELEX CASTING Ltd**
(NASAA Member) (Children available)
PO Box 7317, Derby DE1 0GS
e-mail: anne@celex.co.uk
Fax: 01332 232115                    Tel: 01332 232445

**CENTRAL CASTING Ltd**
(See also KNIGHT Ray CASTING)
21A Lambolle Place
Belsize Park, London NW3 4PG
Website: www.rayknight.co.uk
e-mail: casting@rayknight.co.uk
Fax: 020-7722 2322                   Tel: 020-7722 1551

**CREATIVE KIDZ & Co**
(Incorporating NeighbourHood Productions)
9 Weavers Terrace, Fulham
London SW6 1QE                   Mobile: 07958 377595
e-mail: info@creativekidzandco.co.uk

## arguably the north of england's most established casting agency...

...and our Casting Booker is Cath Ashworth, a former 2nd A.D. who knows what the industry expectations are and how important it is to provide the right people. Select from a pool of 350 artists ranging from age sixteen to eighty three, with both Equity and non-Equity experience and one thing in common - a dedicated, enthusiastic and professional attitude

As part of Boss Agencies, Nidges also has unique access to Boss's catwalk and high end fashion models nationally and internationally, and Real People's range of commercial and photographic models for any assignment...this is the classic "one stop shop"

**BOSS agencies**
Fourways House, 57 Hilton St
Manchester M1 2EJ
Tel: 0161 237 0101  Fax: 0161 236 1237
www.nidgescasting.co.uk
www.bossmodelmanagement.co.uk
www.realpeople4u.com

---

**CS PROMOTIONS Ltd**
Jubilee Stand
Crystal Palace National Sports Centre, London SE19 2BB
Website: www.sportspromotions.co.uk
e-mail: agent@sportspromotions.co.uk
Fax: 020-8776 7772    Tel: 020-8659 4561

**DAVID AGENCY The**
(NASAA Member)
26-28 Hammersmith Grove
London W6 7BA    Tel: 020-8834 1615
Website: www.davidagency.net
e-mail: casting@davidagency.net

**DOE John ASSOCIATES**
26 Noko, 3-6 Banister Road, London W10 4AR
Website: www.johndoemgt.com
e-mail: casting@johndoemgt.com
Mobile: 07957 114175    Tel: 020-8960 2848

**ELLIOTT AGENCY Ltd The**
(NASAA Member)
10 High Street
Shoreham-by-Sea BN43 5DA    Tel: 01273 454111
Website: www.elliottagency.co.uk
e-mail: elliottagency@btconnect.com

**ETHNIKA CASTING**
14 Bowmont Gardens
Glasgow G12 9LR
Website: www.ethnikacasting.co.uk
e-mail: ethnikacasting@yahoo.co.uk
Mobile: 07778 296002    Tel/Fax: 0845 6031266

**EUROKIDS & EUROXTRAS CASTING AGENCY**
The Warehouse Studios
Glaziers Lane
Culcheth, Warrington
Cheshire WA3 4AQ
Website: www.eka-agency.com
e-mail: castings@eka-agency.com
Fax: 01925 767563    Tel: 01925 761088

**EXTRASPECIAL Ltd**
4th Floor, 20 Bedford Street
Covent Garden, London WC2E 9HP
e-mail: info@extraspecialartists.com
Fax: 020-7240 4879    Tel: 020-7240 9240

**FACE MUSIC**
(Musician's Agency)
13 Elvedon Road, London N13 4SJ    Tel: 020-8889 3969
e-mail: facemusic@btinternet.com

# infopage

## Who are Walk-on and Supporting Artists?

Sometimes known as 'Extras', walk-on and supporting artists appear in the background of TV and film scenes in order to add a sense of realism, character or atmosphere. They do not have individual speaking roles, unless required to make background / ambient noise. Working as a walk-on or supporting artist does not require any specific 'look', training or experience as such; however it does involve more effort than people think. Artists are often required to start very early in the morning (6am is not uncommon), and days can be long with lots of waiting around, sometimes in tough conditions on location. It is certainly not glamorous, nor is it a way to become a TV or film star! Artists must be reliable and available at very short notice, which can make it difficult to juggle with other work or family commitments. Requirements vary from production to production and, as with mainstream acting work, there are no guarantees that you will get regular work, let alone be able to earn a living as a walk-on.

## How should I use these listings?

If you are serious about working as a walk-on artist, you will need to register with an agency in order to be put forward for jobs. In return for finding you work, you can expect an agency to take between 10-15% in commission. The following pages contain contact details of many walk-on and supporting artist agencies. Some will specialise in certain areas, so make sure you research the different companies carefully to see if they are appropriate for you. Many have websites you can visit. It is also worth asking questions about how long an agency has existed, and about their recent production credits. When approaching an agency for representation, you should send them your CV with a covering letter and a recent photograph which is a genuine, natural likeness of you. Enclosing a stamped-addressed envelope with sufficient postage (SAE) will give you a better chance of a reply.

## Should I pay a Walk-on Agent to join their books? Or sign a contract?

As with other types of agencies, Equity does not generally recommend that artists pay an agent to join their client list. Before signing any contract, you should be clear about the terms and commitments involved. Always speak to Equity www.equity.org.uk or BECTU www.bectu.org.uk if you have any concerns or queries.

## Where can I find more information?

You may find it useful to contact the Film Artists Association, part of BECTU www.bectu.org.uk, or the National Association of Supporting Artistes Agents www.nasaa.org.uk. NASAA members listed in the following pages have indicated their status under their agency name.

**Ray Knight Casting was founded in 1988 and is an Agency specialising in the supply of walk-on and supporting artists for Film, Television and Commercials. They have a main workforce of approximately 1800 artists on their books. Ray Knight offers the following advice to budding supporting artists:**

Supporting artist work is not for everybody. You need to have endless patience, a very compliant and tolerant attitude, and the ability to get on with other people in close and often awkward circumstances. The vast majority of employment is handled by agencies specialising in this field of work. I have been such an agent since 1988 and like to think I have done a good job for both artist and client, building a reputation for fairness and reliability.

When seeking an agent to represent you, please bear the following useful pointers in mind. There are unfortunately some real cowboys in the field. Do not part with any money in advance of receiving any viable work, whatever the explanation you are given. Be it for registration, photographs, advertising or promotional material or for any other reason, do not pay anything 'up-front'. Honest agencies will make a nominal charge for promotional material they produce on behalf of their artists, but this will always be taken from fees earned from work supplied. It will be a one-off annual charge and by law, only based on an estimate of cost basis.

A good agent will want to see you before he or she will offer to put you forward for employment, be keen to make an appointment. This will give you an opportunity to check that the agent has proper premises and is operating in a viable fashion. Get to know as much as you can about your agent, both before and after you join. Check to see if they are members of the trade association NASAA www.nasaa.org.uk

Supporting artist work does not lead to stardom. If you want to be an actor, go to drama school. It is essentially a part-time occupation for those who have a good level of availability, often at short notice, and find it both rewarding and interesting. Much depends on types and age groups. Over the years it has been my perception that 60% of work goes to men and 40% to women, with the greatest demand being for men aged between 25 and 45, and women between 20 and 40. This does not mean that there is no work for those outside those rough parameters, but just that it is likely to be more erratic than for those in the categories for which there is a concentration of demand. It also helps to be of average size and measurements.

Please remember that leading artists are carrying the burden of scripted lines, close up action and focusing on their work. They may not welcome chatting to the supporting artists, even though at other times they would be very approachable. Do not bother them unless they invite you to socialise with them, give them space and respect their need for concentration.

The best supporting artists are the ones who turn up on time, wearing the right clothes where appropriate, only need telling once, are quick to re-position, and are amenable to all they work with be it fellow artist or crew. Do not adopt a high profile - people who try to get noticed are only seen as irritating. There is enough ego on a film set already, it is not a good idea for supporting artists to add to it.

Having said all of this, supporting artists can have an interesting, rewarding and enjoyable time with the right attitude and approach. I have been fortunate to represent some lovely people whom I have very much enjoyed having on my books. I hope they have thought as well of me as I of them.

Please visit www.rayknight.co.uk for further information.

**FACEBOOK EXTRAS**
Cambridge Chambers, 200-202 High Street
Bromley, Kent BR1 1PW
Website: www.facebookextras.co.uk
e-mail: info@facebookextras.co.uk
Fax: 0870 2853250                    Tel: 0844 2572327

**FBI AGENCY The**
(NASAA Member)
PO Box 250, Leeds LS1 2AZ           Mobile: 07050 222747
Website: www.fbi-agency.co.uk
e-mail: casting@fbi-agency.co.uk

**FILM CAST CORNWALL**
c/o 3 Church Walk, Truro TR1 1JH      Tel: 01326 311419
Website: www.filmcastcornwall.co.uk
e-mail: enquiries@filmcastcornwall.co.uk

**FRESH AGENTS Ltd**
Suite 5, Saks House, 19 Ship Street, Brighton BN1 1AD
Website: www.freshagents.co.uk
e-mail: info@freshagents.co.uk
Tel: 0845 4080998                    Tel: 01273 711777

**FTS CASTING AGENCY**
55 Pullan Avenue, Eccleshill, Bradford BD2 3RP
e-mail: helen@footsteps.fslife.co.uk
Fax: 01274 637429                    Tel: 01274 636036

**GUYS & DOLLS CASTING**
(NASAA Member)
Trafalgar House, Grenville Place, Mill Hill, London NW7 3SA
Website: www.guysanddollscasting.com
e-mail: info@guysanddollscasting.com
Mobile: 07890 774454                 Tel: 020-8906 4144

**HOWE Janet CASTING AGENCY**
The Pie Factory, 101 Broadway
Salford Quays, Manchester M50 2EQ
e-mail: info@janethowe.com
Mobile: 07801 942178                 Tel/Fax: 0161-263 0633

The Works Media Centre
36 White House Street, Hunslet, Leeds LS10 1AD
Mobile: 07801 942178                 Tel/Fax: 0113-242 5225

58 High Street, Newcastle-under-Lyme
Staffordshire ST5 1QE
e-mail: info@janethowe.com
Mobile: 07801 942178                 Tel: 01782 661777

**INDUSTRY CASTING**
332 Royal Exchange, Manchester M2 7BR
Website: www.industrycasting.co.uk
e-mail: mark@industrypeople.co.uk
Fax: 0161-839 1661                   Tel: 0161-839 1551

## Bennetton-cmp

Bennetton casting, modelling and promotions (cmp) has been involved in the media for 2 decades providing hands on experience, to both clients and associates, which is second to none.

Our assignments are many fold with television work, film & cinema, advertising, modelling and promotions. Our work also extends into magazine & editorial assignments, exhibition and events.

Bennetton is renowned for building an excellent rapport with each individual on our books. We pride ourselves on first class dedication to our client's specification, to ensure we make the right choice for all assignments delivering high quality services.

Contact us at:
Bennetton-cmp, Raines Business Centre, Raines House, Denby Dale Road, WAKEFIELD, West Yorkshire, WF1 1HR.
T: 01924 882414   T: 07540 693657   Fax: 01924 291008
E: enquiries@bennetton-cmp.co.uk  www.bennetton-cmp.co.uk

**IPM EXTRAS**
102 Kirkstall Road, Leeds
West Yorkshire LS3 1JA               Tel: 0113-244 4222
Website: www.ipmcasting.com
e-mail: dean@ipmcasting.com

**JACLYN AGENCY**
(NASAA Member)
52 Bessemer Road
Norwich, Norfolk NR4 6DQ            Tel: 01603 622027
Website: www.jaclynagency.co.uk
e-mail: info@jaclynagency.co.uk

**JB AGENCY ONLINE Ltd**
(NASAA Member)
26 Onslow Gardens, London SW7 3AG
Website: www.jb-agency.com
e-mail: info@jb-agency.com
Mobile: 07962 434111                 Tel: 0845 6384984

**JPM EXTRAS**
(A Division of Janet Plater Management Ltd)
D Floor, Milburn House, Dean Street
Newcastle upon Tyne NE1 1LF         Tel: 0191-221 2491
Website: www.janetplatermanagement.co.uk
e-mail: extras@tynebridge.demon.co.uk

**KNIGHT Ray CASTING**
(NASAA Member)
21A Lambolle Place, Belsize Park, London NW3 4PG
Website: www.rayknight.co.uk
e-mail: casting@rayknight.co.uk
Fax: 020-7722 2322                   Tel: 020-7722 4111

**KREATE PROMOTIONS**
Unit 232, 30 Great Guildford Street, London SE1 0HS
Website: www.kreate.co.uk
e-mail: enquiries@kreatepromotions.co.uk
Fax: 020-7401 3003                   Tel: 020-7401 9007

**LEMON CASTING Ltd**
The Pie Factory, 101 Broadway
Salford Quays, Manchester M50 2EQ
e-mail: lemon.tv@btconnect.com
Mobile: 07723 317489                 Tel: 0161-876 0088

**LINTON MANAGEMENT**
3 The Rock, Bury BL9 0JP
e-mail: mail@linton.tv
Fax: 0161-761 1999                   Tel: 0161-761 2020

**MAD DOG CASTING Ltd**
(NASAA Member)
Third Floor, 15 Leighton Place, London NW5 2QL
e-mail: info@maddogcasting.com
Fax: 020-7284 2689                   Tel: 020-7482 4703

**M.E.P. MANAGEMENT**
1 Malvern Avenue, Highams Park
London E4 9NP                        Tel/Fax: 020-8523 3540
Website: www.mepmanagementagency.co.uk
e-mail: mep@btclick.com

**NE REPRESENTATION**
(Models, Photographers, Hair & Make-up artists, Stylists and Film Extras)
3-5 Bakehouse Hill, Darlington, Co. Durham DL1 5QA
Website: www.nerepresentation.co.uk
e-mail: info@nerepresentation.co.uk
Fax: 01325 488390                    Tel: 01325 488385

**NEMESIS AGENCY Ltd**
Nemesis House, 1 Oxford Court
Bishopsgate, Manchester M2 3WQ
Website: www.nemesisagency.co.uk
e-mail: ros@nmsmanagement.co.uk
Fax: 0161-228 6727                   Tel: 0161-228 6404

---

Supplying experienced background artists, walk-ons and photographic characters to the television, film and advertising industries.

Representing a large selection of professional artistes based in the North West.

**'No brief is out of our reach'**

Tel 0161 839 1551        Fax 0161 839 1661

**industrycasting**

332 Royal Exchange
Manchester M2 7BR

www.industrycasting.co.uk
mark@industrypeople.co.uk

---

**NIDGES CASTING AGENCY**
Fourways House, 57 Hilton Street
Manchester M1 2EJ
e-mail: cath@nidgescasting.co.uk
Fax: 0161-236 1237                    Tel: 0161-237 0101

**NORTHERN PROFESSIONALS CASTING COMPANY**
21 Cresswell Avenue, North Shields
Tyne & Wear NE29 9BQ
Website: www.northernprocasting.co.uk
e-mail: bill@northernprocasting.co.uk
Fax: 0191-296 3243                    Tel: 0191-257 8635

**ORIENTAL CASTING AGENCY Ltd (Peggy Sirr)**
(NASAA Member) (Afro/Asian Artists)
60 Downton Avenue, Streatham Hill, London SW2 3TR
Website: www.orientalcasting.com
e-mail: peggy.sirr@btconnect.com
Fax: 020-8674 9303                    Tel: 020-8671 8538

**PAN ARTISTS AGENCY Ltd**
Cornerways, 34 Woodhouse Lane, Sale, Cheshire M33 4JX
Website: www.panartists.co.uk
e-mail: panartists@btconnect.com
Mobile: 07890 715115                  Tel: 0800 6349147

**PC THEATRICAL MODEL & CASTING AGENCY**
13A Carlisle Road, Colindale, London NW9 0HD
Website: www.twinagency.com
e-mail: twinagy@aol.com
Fax: 020-8933 3418                    Tel: 020-8381 2229

**PERFORMERS LEAGUE AGENCY Ltd The**
21 Clothworkers Road, Plumstead, London SE18 2PD
Website: www.tpla.co.uk
e-mail: info@tpla.co.uk
Mobile: 07886 319807                  Tel: 020-8854 4576

**PHA CASTING**
Tanzaro House, Ardwick Green North
Manchester M12 6FZ
Website: www.pha-agency.co.uk
e-mail: info@pha-agency.co.uk
Fax: 0161-273 4567                    Tel: 0161-273 4444

**PHOENIX CASTING AGENCY**
(NASAA Member)
PO Box 387, Bristol BS99 3JZ
Website: www.phoenixagency.biz
e-mail: info@phoenixagency.biz
Fax: 0117-973 4160                    Tel: 0117-973 1100

**POLEASE**
1 Noake Road, Hucclecote
Gloucester GL3 3PE
Website: www.polease.co.uk
e-mail: info@polease.co.uk
Mobile: 07811 504079                  Tel: 05600 650524

**POLICE ACTION**
39 Gregson Close
Borehamwood WD6 5RW
e-mail: police-action@hotmail.co.uk
Mobile: 07920 421347              Mobile: 07005 993434

**POWER MODEL MANAGEMENT CASTING AGENCY**
PO Box 1198, Salhouse
Norwich NR13 6WD                      Tel: 01603 777190
Website: www.powermodel.co.uk
e-mail: info@powermodel.co.uk

**PRAETORIAN ASSOCIATES**
(Specialist Action Extras)
Room 501, 2 Old Brompton Road
London SW7 3DG                   Tel/Fax: 020-7096 1827
Website: www.praetorianasc.com
e-mail: info@praetorianasc.com

**RAPID TALENT Ltd**
5 Vancouver Road, Eastbourne
East Sussex BN23 5BF
Website: www.rapidtalent.co.uk
e-mail: enquiries@rapidtalent.co.uk
Mobile: 07980 899156                  Tel: 020-7734 5775

**RAY'S NORTHERN CASTING AGENCY**
7 Wince Close, Alkrington
Middleton, Manchester M24 1UJ    Tel/Fax: 0161-643 6745
e-mail: rayscasting@yahoo.co.uk

**REGENCY AGENCY**
25 Carr Road, Calverley
Pudsey, West Yorks LS28 5NE          Tel: 0113-255 8980

**RENTACROWD CASTING AGENCY**
14 Craigelvan Drive, Condorrat
Cumbernauld, Scotland G67 4RL     Mobile: 07877 984636
Website: www.rentacrowd.co.uk
e-mail: alana@rentacrowd.co.uk

**REVOLUTION TALENT MANAGEMENT**
Central Chambers
93 Hope Street, Glasgow, G2 6LD
Website: www.revolutionmanagement.com
e-mail: enquiries@revolutionmanagement.com
Fax: 0141-221 8622          Tel: 0141-221 2258

**REYNOLDS Sandra AGENCY**
Bacon House
35 St Georges Street
Norwich NR3 1DA
Website: www.sandrareynolds.co.uk
e-mail: info@sandrareynolds.co.uk
Fax: 01603 219825          Tel: 01603 623842

Shakespeare House
168 Lavender Hill, London SW11 5TF
Fax: 020-7387 5848          Tel: 020-7387 5858

**RHODES AGENCY**
5 Dymoke Road
Hornchurch, Essex RM11 1AA
e-mail: rhodesarts@hotmail.com
Fax: 01708 730431          Tel: 01708 747013

**SA19 - THE UNIFORMED ARTISTE AGENCY**
(NASAA Member)
2020 Hopgood Street
Shepherds Bush, London W12 7JU
Website: www.sa19.co.uk
e-mail: info@sa19.co.uk
Fax: 020-8735 2727          Tel: 020-8746 2523

**SAPPHIRES MODEL MANAGEMENT**
The Makers Dozen
Studio 11, 8 Wulfruna Street
Wolverhampton WV1 1LW
Website: www.sapphiresmodel.com
e-mail: contact@sapphiresmodel.com
Fax: 0870 9127563          Tel: 0844 8845404

**SCREAM MANAGEMENT**
The Pie Factory, 101 Broadway
Media City, Manchester M50 2EQ
Website: www.screammanagement.com
e-mail: info@screammanagement.com
Fax: 01253 309069          Tel: 0161-660 3653

**SCREENLITE AGENCY**
(NASAA Member)
Pinewood Studios, Pinewood Road
Iver Heath, Bucks SL0 0NH          Tel: 01753 785372
Website: www.screenliteagency.co.uk
e-mail: enquiries@screenliteagency.co.uk

**SHARMAN Alan AGENCY**
P2 Wexler Lofts, 100 Carver Street
Birmingham B1 3AQ          Tel: 0121-212 0090
Website: www.alansharmanagency.com
e-mail: info@alansharmanagency.com

**SOLOMON ARTISTES**
30 Clarence Street
Southend-on-Sea, Essex SS1 1BD
Website: www.solomon-artistes.co.uk
e-mail: info@solomon-artistes.co.uk
Tel: 01702 437118          Tel: 020-7748 4409

**SUMMERS Mark MANAGEMENT**
(Formerly Extras Unlimited)
1 Beaumont Avenue, West Kensington
London W14 9LP          Tel: 020-7229 8413
Website: www.marksummers.com
e-mail: info@marksummers.com

**TUESDAYS CHILD Ltd**
(Children & Adults)
Oakfield House, Springwood Way
Macclesfield SK10 2XA          Tel/Fax: 01625 501765
Website: www.tuesdayschildagency.co.uk
e-mail: info@tuesdayschildagency.co.uk

**TURNSTONE CASTING AGENCY**
Suite 8, Hilton Hall, Hilton Lane
Essington WV11 2BQ
info@turnstonecasting.com
Mobile: 07590 038241          Mobile: 07891 642627

**UNI-VERSAL EXTRAS**
Pinewood Studios
Pinewood Road, Iver Heath
Buckinghamshire SL0 0NH          Tel: 0845 0090344
Website: www.universalextrascasting.co.uk
e-mail: wayne.berko@universalextras.co.uk

**A-Z ANIMALS Ltd**
The Bell House, Bell Lane, Fetcham, Surrey KT22 9ND
Website: www.a-zanimals.com
e-mail: info@a-zanimals.com
Fax: 01372 377666 Tel: 01372 377111

**A1 ANIMALS**
(Farm, Domestic & Exotic Animals)
9 The Drive, Enstone
Oxon OX7 4NQ Tel/Fax: 01608 677348
Website: www.a1animals.co.uk
e-mail: a1animals@btinternet.com

**ACTION STUNT DOGS & ANIMALS**
3 The Chestnuts, Clifton, Deddington
Oxon OX15 0PE Tel/Fax: 01869 338546
e-mail: gill@stuntdogs.net

**ALTERNATIVE ANIMALS**
Contact: Trevor Smith (Animatronics/Taxidermy)
19 Greaves Road, High Wycombe, Bucks HP13 7JU
Website: www.animalswork.co.uk
e-mail: animalswork1@yahoo.co.uk
Fax: 01494 441385 Mobile: 07956 564715

**ANIMAL ACTING**
(Animals, Stunts, Props, Horse-Drawn Vehicles)
7 Dovedale Court, Windermere Road
Middleton, Manchester M24 5QT
Website: www.animalacting.com
e-mail: information@animalacting.com
Mobile: 07831 800567 Tel: 0161-655 3700

**ANIMAL ACTORS**
(Animals, Birds, Reptiles)
95 Ditchling Road, Brighton
Sussex BN1 4ST Tel: 020-8654 0450

**ANIMAL AMBASSADORS**
Old Forest, Hampstead Norreys Road
Hermitage, Berks RG18 9SA
Website: www.animalambassadors.co.uk
e-mail: kayweston@tiscali.co.uk
Mobile: 07831 558594 Tel/Fax: 01635 200900

**ANIMAL CASTING**
119 Magdalen Road, London SW18 3ES
e-mail: silcresta@aol.com
Mobile: 07956 246450 Tel: 020-8874 9530

**ANIMAL WELFARE FILMING FEDERATION**
(Free Consultancy Service)
28 Greaves Road, High Wycombe, Bucks HP13 7JU
Website: www.animalworld.org.uk
e-mail: animalswork1@yahoo.co.uk
Fax: 01494 441385 Mobile: 07770 666088

**ANIMALS GALORE Ltd**
208 Smallfield Road, Horley, Surrey RH6 9LS
Website: www.animals-galore.co.uk
Fax: 01342 841546 Tel: 01342 842400

**ANIMALS O KAY**
16 Queen St, Chipperfield, Kings Langley
Herts WD4 9BT Tel: 01923 291277
Website: www.animalsokay.com
e-mail: kayraven@btinternet.com

**ANIMALS WORK WITH ANIMAL WORLD**
Contact: Trevor Smith
28 Greaves Road, High Wycombe, Bucks HP13 7JU
Website: www.blinkx.com/channel/wildthingtv
e-mail: animalswork1@yahoo.co.uk
Fax: 01494 441385 Mobile: 07956 564715

**CANINE FILM ACADEMY The**
57C Cheapside Road, Ascot, Berks SL5 7QR
Website: www.caninefilmacademy.com
e-mail: katie@caninefilmacademy.com
Mobile: 07767 341424 Tel: 01344 291465

**CELEBRITY REPTILES**
11 Tramway Close
London SE20 7DF Tel/Fax: 020-8659 0877
Website: www.celebrityreptiles.co.uk
e-mail: info@celebrityreptiles.co.uk

**CHEESEMAN Virginia**
21 Willow Close, Flackwell Heath
High Wycombe, Bucks HP10 9LH
Website: www.virginiacheeseman.co.uk
e-mail: virginia@virginiacheeseman.co.uk
Mobile: 07971 838724 Tel: 01628 522632

**COTSWOLD FARM PARK**
(Rare Breed Farm Animals)
Guiting Power, Cheltenham, Gloucestershire GL54 5UG
e-mail: info@cotswoldfarmpark.co.uk
Fax: 01451 850423 Tel: 01451 850307

**CREATURE FEATURE**
(Animal Agent)
Gubhill Farm, Ae, Dumfries, Scotland DG1 1RL
Website: www.creaturefeature.co.uk
e-mail: david@creaturefeature.co.uk
Mobile: 07770 774866 Tel/Fax: 01387 860648

**DOG EXTRAS**
11 Colster Way, Colsterworth, Grantham, Lincs NG33 5JT
Website: www.dog-extras.co.uk
e-mail: info@dog-extras.co.uk
Mobile: 07956 369890 Tel/Fax: 01476 862028

**DOLBADARN FILM HORSES**
Dolbadarn Hotel, High Street
Llanberis, Gwynedd, North Wales LL55 4SU
Website: www.filmhorses.co.uk
e-mail: info@filmhorses.co.uk
Mobile: 07710 461341 Tel/Fax: 01286 870277

**ANIMALS**

**DUDLEY Yvonne LRPS**
(Glamour Dogs & Stories)
55 Cambridge Park, Wanstead
London E11 2PR                    Tel: 020-8989 1528

**FILM HORSES**
(Horses, Saddlery, Equestrian Centre)
Free Range Farm, Oakleigh Green Road
Windsor, Berks SL4 4GW
Website: www.filmhorses.com
e-mail: filmhorses@yahoo.co.uk
Mobile: 07831 629662          Tel/Fax: 01628 675105

**GET STUFFED**
(Taxidermy)
105 Essex Road, London N1 2SL
Website: www.thegetstuffed.co.uk
e-mail: taxidermy@thegetstuffed.co.uk
Fax: 020-7359 8253                Tel: 020-7226 1364

**GRAY Robin COMMENTARIES**
(Equestrian Equipment, Horse Race Commentaries, Voice Overs)
Comptons, Isington, Alton, Hants GU34 4PL
e-mail: gray@isington.fsnet.co.uk
Mobile: 07831 828424              Tel: 01420 23347

**HILTON HORSES**
Contact: Samantha Jones
478 London Road, Ashford
Middlesex TW15 3AD         Mobile: 07958 292222
Website: www.hilton-horses.com
e-mail: samantha@hilton-horses.com

**KNIGHTS OF MIDDLE ENGLAND The**
(Horses & Riders for Film, Opera & TV)
Warwick International School of Riding, Guys Cliffe
Coventry Road, Warwick CV34 5YD    Tel: 01926 400401
Website: www.knightsofmiddleengland.co.uk
e-mail: info@knightsofmiddleengland.co.uk

**KNIGHTS OF ARKLEY The**
Glyn Sylen Farm, Five Roads
Llanelli SA15 5BJ             Tel/Fax: 01269 861001
Website: www.knightsofarkley.com
e-mail: penny@knightsofarkley.fsnet.co.uk

**MILLENNIUM BUGS**
(Live Insects)
28 Greaves Road, High Wycombe, Bucks HP13 7JU
Website: www.animalworld.org.uk
e-mail: animalswork1@yahoo.co.uk
Fax: 01494 441385                 Tel: 01494 442750

**MORTON Geoff**
(Shire Horse & Equipment)
Hasholme Carr Farm
Holme on Spalding Moor
York YO43 4BD                     Tel: 01430 860393

**NOLTON STABLES**
Nolton, Nr Newgale, Haverfordwest
Pembrokeshire SA62 3NW
Website: www.noltonstables.com
e-mail: noltonstables@aol.com
Fax: 01437 710967                 Tel: 01437 710360

**OTTERS**
Contact: Daphne & Martin Neville (Tame Otters)
Baker's Mill, Frampton Mansell
Stroud, Glos GL6 8JH              Tel: 01285 760234
e-mail: martin_neville_bakers_mill@yahoo.co.uk

**PROP FARM Ltd**
Contact: Pat Ward
Grange Farm
Elmton, Nr Creswell
North Derbyshire S80 4LX
e-mail: les@propfarm.co.uk
Fax: 01909 721465                 Tel: 01909 723100

**ROCKWOOD ANIMALS ON FILM**
Lewis Terrace
Llanbradach, Caerphilly CF83 3JZ
Website: www.rockwoodanimals.com
e-mail: martin@rockwoodanimals.com
Mobile: 07973 930983             Tel: 029-2088 5420

**SCHOOL OF NATIONAL EQUITATION Ltd**
Contact: Sam Humphrey
Bunny Hill Top
Costock, Loughborough
Leicestershire LE12 6XE
Website: www.bunnyhill.co.uk
e-mail: sam@bunnyhill.co.uk
Mobile: 07977 930083             Tel: 01509 852366

**TATE Olive**
(Trained Dogs & Cats)
49 Upton Road
Bexleyheath, Kent DA6 8LW
Mobile: 07504 113298        Tel/Fax: 020-8303 0683

**WHITE DOVES COMPANY Ltd The**
(Provision of up to 150 Doves for Release)
Suite 210 Sterling House
Langston Road
Loughton, Essex IG10 3TS
Website: www.thewhitedovecompany.co.uk
e-mail: thewhitedovecompany@yahoo.co.uk
Fax: 020-8502 2461               Tel: 020-8508 1414

**WOLF SPECIALISTS The**
The UK Wolf Conservation Trust
UK Wolf Centre, Butlers Farm
Beenham, Berks RG7 5NT           Tel: 0118-971 3330
Website: www.ukwolf.org
e-mail: ukwct@ukwolf.org

**WOODS Sue**
(Animal Promotions, Specialising in Dogs, Domestic Cats Rodents, Poultry & Farm Stock)
White Rocks Farm, Underriver
Sevenoaks, Kent TN15 0SL
Website: www.animalpromotions.co.uk
e-mail: sue.woods@animalpromotions.co.uk
Fax: 01732 763767                Tel: 01732 761888

**YORKSHIRE TERRIER**
17 Gardnor Road
London NW3 1HA              Mobile: 07963 818845
e-mail: woodlandcreature10@hotmail.com

**ALDERSHOT**
West End Centre, Queens Road
Aldershot, Hants GU11 3JD
Website: www.westendcentre.co.uk
e-mail: westendcentre@hants.gov.uk
BO: 01252 330040                    Admin: 01252 408040

**BARNET**
Churchill Studio, Unit 8, Alston Works
Alston Road, Barnet EN5 4EL
Website: www.churchillstudio.co.uk
e-mail: info@churchillstudio.co.uk
Mobile: 07794 366725                    Tel: 020-3231 1057

**BILLERICAY**
Billericay Arts Association
The Fold, 72 Laindon Road, Billericay
Essex CM12 9LD                    Tel: 01277 659286
e-mail: baathefold@yahoo.co.uk

**BINGLEY**
Bingley Arts Centre, Main Street, Bingley
West Yorkshire BD16 2LZ                    Tel: 01274 431576
e-mail: community-halls@bradford.gov.uk

**BIRMINGHAM**
The Custard Factory
Gibb Street, Digbeth, Birmingham B9 4AA
Website: www.custardfactory.co.uk
e-mail: info@custardfactory.co.uk
Fax: 0121-604 8888                    Tel: 0121-693 7777

**BOSTON**
Blackfriars Arts Centre
Spain Lane, Boston, Lincolnshire PE21 6HP
Website: www.blackfriars.uk.com
e-mail: director@blackfriars.uk.com
Contact: Mike Raymond
Fax: 01205 358855                    Tel: 01205 363108

**BRACKNELL**
South Hill Park Arts Centre
Ringmead, Bracknell
Berkshire RG12 7PA
Website: www.southhillpark.org.uk
Chief Executive: Ron McAllister
Fax: 01344 411427
BO: 01344 484123                    Admin: 01344 484858

**BRADFORD**
Theatre in The Mill, University of Bradford
Shearbridge Road, Bradford, West Yorkshire BD7 1DP
e-mail: theatre@bradford.ac.uk
BO: 01274 233200                    Tel: 01274 233185

**BRAINTREE**
The Town Hall Centre, Market Square
Braintree, Essex CM7 3YG
Tourism Manager: Marie Orpe                    Tel: 01376 557776

**BRENTFORD**
Watermans Arts Centre
40 High Street, Brentford TW8 0DS
e-mail: info@watermans.org.uk
Fax: 020-8232 1030
BO: 020-8232 1010                    Admin: 020-8232 1020

**BRIDGWATER**
Bridgwater Arts Centre
11-13 Castle Street, Bridgwater
Somerset TA6 3DD                    Tel: 01278 422700
Website: www.bridgwaterartscentre.co.uk
e-mail: info@bridgwaterartscentre.co.uk

**BRISTOL**
Arnolfini, 16 Narrow Quay, Bristol BS1 4QA
e-mail: boxoffice@arnolfini.org.uk
Fax: 0117-917 2303                    Tel: 0117-917 2300

**BUILTH WELLS**
Wyeside Arts Centre
Castle Street, Builth Wells, Powys LD2 3BN
Fax: 01982 553995                    Tel: 01982 553668

**BURY**
The Met, Market Street, Bury, Lancs BL9 0BW
e-mail: post@themet.biz
Director: David Agnew
Fax: 0870 0520297
BO: 0161-761 2216                    Admin: 0161-761 7107

**CANNOCK**
Prince of Wales Centre
Church Sreet, Cannock
Staffs WS11 1DE
e-mail: princeofwales@cannockchasedc.gov.uk
General Manager: Richard Kay
Fax: 01543 574439
BO: 01543 578672                    Tel: 01543 466453

**CARDIFF**
Chapter Arts Centre
Market Road, Canton
Cardiff CF5 1QE
BO: 029-2030 4400                    Admin: 029-2031 1050

**CHIPPING NORTON**
The Theatre, 2 Spring Street
Chipping Norton, Oxon OX7 5NL
Website: www.chippingnortontheatre.com
e-mail: admin@chippingnortontheatre.com
Director: John Terry
Head of Operations: Ambereene Hitchcox
Fax: 01608 642324
BO: 01608 642350                    Admin: 01608 642349

**CHRISTCHURCH**
The Regent Centre
51 High Street, Christchurch
Dorset BH23 1AS
Website: www.regentcentre.co.uk
e-mail: info@regentcentre.co.uk
General Manager: Keith Lancing                    BO: 01202 499199

**CIRENCESTER**
New Brewery Arts
Brewery Court
Cirencester, Glos GL7 1JH
Website: www.newbreweryarts.org.uk
e-mail: admin@newbreweryarts.org.uk
Fax: 01285 644060                    Admin 01285 657181

**COLCHESTER**
Colchester Arts Centre
Church Street, Colchester, Essex CO1 1NF
Website: www.colchesterartscentre.com
e-mail: info@colchesterartscentre.com
Director: Anthony Roberts                    Tel: 01206 500900

**COVENTRY**
Warwick Arts Centre
University of Warwick, Coventry CV4 7AL
Website: www.warwickartscentre.co.uk
e-mail: arts.centre@warwick.ac.uk
Director: Alan Rivett
BO: 024-7652 4524                    Admin: 024-7652 3734

**CUMBERNAULD**
Cumbernauld Theatre
Kildrum
Cumbernauld G67 2BN
Website: www.cumbernauldtheatre.co.uk
e-mail: info@cumbernauldtheatre.co.uk
Fax: 01236 738408
BO: 01236 732887                    Admin: 01236 737235

**DARLINGTON**
Darlington Arts Centre
Vane Terrace, Darlington
County Durham DL3 7AX
Website: www.darlingtonarts.co.uk
BO: 01325 486555                    Admin: 01325 348843

**EDINBURGH**
Scottish Storytelling Centre
43-45 High Street
Edinburgh EH1 1SR
Website: www.scottishstorytellingcentre.co.uk
e-mail: reception@scottishstorytellingcentre.com
Director: Dr Donald Smith            Tel: 0131-556 9579

**EDINBURGH**
Theatre Workshop
34 Hamilton Place
Edinburgh EH3 5AX
Website: www.theatre-workshop.com
Director: Robert Rae
Fax: 0131-220 0112                   Tel: 0131-225 7942

**EPSOM**
Playhouse, Ashley Avenue
Epsom, Surrey KT18 5AL
Website: www.epsomplayhouse.co.uk
e-mail: tmitchell@epsom-ewell.gov.uk
General Manager/Artistic Director: Trevor Mitchell
Fax: 01372 726228
BO: 01372 742555                    Admin: 01372 742226

**EXETER**
Exeter Phoenix
Bradninch Place, Gandy Street
Exeter, Devon EX4 3LS
Website: www.exeterphoenix.org.uk
e-mail: admin@exeterphoenix.org.uk
Director: Patrick Cunningham
Fax: 01392 667599
BO: 01392 667080                    Admin: 01392 667060

**FAREHAM**
Ashcroft Arts Centre
Osborn Road
Fareham, Hants PO16 7DX
Website: www.ashcroft.org.uk
e-mail: info@ashcroft.org.uk
Director/Programmer: Annabel Cook
Fax: 01329 825661
BO: 01329 223100                     Tel: 01329 235161

**FROME**
Merlin Theatre, Bath Road
Frome, Somerset BA11 2HG
Website: www.merlintheatre.co.uk
BO: 01373 465949                    Admin: 01373 461360

**GAINSBOROUGH**
Trinity Arts Centre
Trinity Street, Gainsborough
Lincolnshire DN21 2AL
Fax: 01427 811198               BO/Admin: 01427 676655

**GREAT TORRINGTON**
The Plough Arts Centre
9-11 Fore Street, Great Torrington
Devon EX38 8HQ
Website: www.plough-arts.org
BO: 01805 624624                    Admin: 01805 622552

**HARLECH**
Theatr Harlech, Harlech, Gwynedd LL46 2PU
e-mail: clare@theatrharlech.com
Theatre Director: Clare Williams      BO: 01766 780667

**HAVANT**
Havant Arts Centre
East Street, Havant, Hants PO9 1BS
Website: www.havantartscentre.co.uk
e-mail: info@havantartsactive.co.uk
Director: Amanda O'Reilly           BO: 023-9247 2700

**HELMSLEY**
Helmsley Arts Centre
Meeting House Court
Helmsley, York YO62 5DW
Website: www.helmsleyarts.co.uk
e-mail: clairehelmsleyarts@yahoo.co.uk
Marketing & Theatre Manager: Claire Lishman
BO: 01439 771700                     Tel: 01439 772112

**HEMEL HEMPSTEAD**
Old Town Hall Theatre
High Street, Hemel Hempstead, Herts HP1 3AE
Website: www.oldtownhall.co.uk
e-mail: othadmin@dacorum.gov.uk
Art & Entertainment Manager: Sara Railson
BO: 01442 228091                    Admin: 01442 228095

**HEXHAM**
Queens Hall Arts
Beaumont Street, Hexham
Northumberland NE46 3LS
Website: www.queenshall.co.uk
e-mail: boxoffice@queenshall.co.uk
Artistic Director: Geof Keys
Fax: 01434 652478
BO: 01434 652477                    Admin: 01434 652476

**HORSHAM**
The Capitol, North Street, Horsham
West Sussex RH12 1RG
Website: www.thecapitolhorsham.com
Fax: 01403 756092                    Tel: 01403 756080

**HUDDERSFIELD**
Kirklees (various venues)
Kirklees Culture & Leisure Services
The Stadium Business & Leisure Complex
Stadium Way, Huddersfield HD1 6PG
BO: 01484 223200                    Admin: 01484 234000

**INVERNESS**
Eden Court, Bishop's Road
Inverness IV3 5SA
e-mail: admin@eden-court.co.uk
Director: Colin Marr
BO: 01463 234234                    Admin: 01463 239841

**JERSEY**
Jersey Arts Centre
Phillips Street, St Helier, Jersey JE2 4SW
Website: www.artscentre.je
Fax: 01534 700401
BO: 01534 700444                    Admin: 01534 700400

**KENDAL**
Brewery Arts Centre
Highgate, Kendal, Cumbria LA9 4HE
Website: www.breweryarts.co.uk
e-mail: admin@breweryarts.co.uk
Chief Executive: Sam Mason
BO: 01539 725133        Admin: 01539 722833

**KING'S LYNN**
King's Lynn Arts Centre
29 King Street, King's Lynn, Norfolk PE30 1HA
Website: www.kingslynnarts.co.uk
Fax: 01553 762141
BO: 01553 764864        Tel: 01553 765565

**LEICESTER**
Phoenix Arts Centre
21 Upper Brown Street, Leicester LE1 5TE
e-mail: admin@phoenix.org.uk
BO: 0116-255 4854        Admin: 0116-224 7700

**LICHFIELD**
Lichfield District Arts Association
Donegal House
Bore Street, Lichfield WS13 6LU
Website: www.lichfieldarts.org.uk
e-mail: info@lichfieldarts.org.uk
Director: Brian Pretty
Fax: 01543 308211        Tel: 01543 262223

**LISKEARD**
Sterts Theatre & Arts Centre
Upton Cross, Liskeard, Cornwall PL14 5AZ
Website: www.sterts.co.uk
Tel/Fax: 01579 362382        Tel/Fax: 01579 362962

**LONDON**
The Albany, Douglas Way, London SE8 4AG
Website: www.thealbany.org.uk
e-mail: reception@thealbany.org.uk
Fax: 020-8469 2253        Tel: 020-8692 4446

**LONDON**
Artsdepot
5 Nether Street, Tally Ho Corner
North Finchley, London N12 0GA     BO: 020-8369 5454
Website: www.artsdepot.co.uk
e-mail: info@artsdepot.co.uk

**LONDON**
BAC
Lavender Hill, Battersea, London SW11 5TN
Website: www.bac.org.uk
e-mail: mailbox@bac.org.uk
Fax: 020-7978 5207
BO: 020-7223 2223        Admin: 020-7223 6557

**LONDON**
Chats Palace
42-44 Brooksby's Walk, Hackney, London E9 6DF
Website: www.chatspalace.com
e-mail: info@chatspalace.com
Centre Director: Sarah Wickens    BO/Admin: 020-8533 0227

**LONDON**
Cockpit Theatre
Gateforth Street, London NW8 8EH
Website: www.cockpittheatre.org.uk
e-mail: dave.wybrow@cwc.ac.uk
Fax: 020-7258 2921
BO: 020-7258 2925        Admin: 020-7258 2920

**LONDON**
The Drill Hall
16 Chenies Street
London WC1E 7EX
Website: www.drillhall.co.uk
e-mail: box.office@drillhall.co.uk
Fax: 020-7307 5062
BO: 020-7307 5060        Admin: 020-7307 5061

**LONDON**
The Hangar Arts Trust
7A Melish House
Harrington Way
London SE18 5NR        Tel: 020-8317 8401
Website: www.hangaruk.com
e-mail: alex@aircraftcircus.com
Space Manager/Trust Chairman: Alex Frith

**LONDON**
Hoxton Hall Arts Centre
130 Hoxton Street
London N1 6SH
Website: www.hoxtonhall.co.uk
e-mail: info@hoxtonhall.co.uk
Operations Manager: Jane Caley
Fax: 020-7729 3815        Admin: 020-7684 0060

**LONDON**
Institute of Contemporary Arts
(No in-house productions or castings)
The Mall, London SW1Y 5AH
Website: www.ica.org.uk
Live & Media Arts Director: Emma Quinn
Fax: 020-7306 0122
BO: 020-7930 3647        Admin: 020-7930 0493

**LONDON**
Islington Arts Factory
2 Parkhurst Road
London N7 0SF
e-mail: iaf@islingtonartsfactory.fsnet.co.uk
Fax: 020-7700 7229        Tel: 020-7607 0561

**LONDON**
Jacksons Lane
269A Archway Road
London N6 5AA
Website: www.jacksonslane.org.uk
e-mail: reception@jacksonslane.org.uk
Fax: 020-8348 2424
BO: 020-8341 4421        Admin: 020-8340 5226

**LONDON**
Menier Chocolate Factory
53 Southwark Street
London SE1 1RU
Website: www.menierchocolatefactory.com
e-mail: office@menierchocolatefactory.com
Artistic Director: David Babani
Fax: 020-7378 1713
BO: 020-7907 7060        Admin: 020-7378 1712

**LONDON**
The Nettlefold
West Norwood Library Centre
1 Norwood High Street
London SE27 9JX
Centre Development Officers: Joanne Johnson,
Mark Sheehan        Admin/BO: 020-7926 8070

**LONDON**
October Gallery
24 Old Gloucester Street
London WC1N 3AL
Website: www.octobergallery.co.uk
e-mail: rentals@octobergallery.co.uk
Contact: Danielle Nunez
Fax: 020-7405 1851               Tel: 020-7831 1618

**LONDON**
Oval House Theatre
52-54 Kennington Oval, London SE11 5SW
Website: www.ovalhouse.com
e-mail: info@ovalhouse.com
Programmer: Ben Evans
Director: Deborah Bestwick         Tel: 020-7582 0080

**LONDON**
Polish Social & Cultural Association
238-246 King Street, London W6 0RF    Tel: 020-8741 1940

**LONDON**
Riverside Studios
Crisp Road
Hammersmith, London W6 9RL
Website: www.riversidestudios.co.uk
e-mail: admin@riversidestudios.co.uk
Fax: 020-8237 1001
BO: 020-8237 1111                 Tel: 020-8237 1000

**LONDON**
The Stables Gallery & Arts Centre
Gladstone Park, Dollis Hill Lane
London NW2 6HT
Website: www.brentarts.org.uk
e-mail: stablesgallery@msn.com      Tel: 020-8452 8655

**MAIDENHEAD**
Norden Farm Centre For The Arts
Altwood Road, Maidenhead SL6 4PF
Website: www.nordenfarm.org
e-mail: admin@nordenfarm.org
Director: Jane Corry
Fax: 01628 682525
BO: 01628 788997               Admin: 01628 682555

**MAIDSTONE**
Hazlitt Arts Centre, Earl Street
Maidstone, Kent ME14 1PL
Theatre & Events Manager: Mandy Hare
Fax: 01622 602194
BO: 01622 758611               Admin: 01622 753922

**MANCHESTER**
Greenroom
54-56 Whitworth Street West
Manchester M1 5WW
Website: www.greenroomarts.org
e-mail: info@greenroomarts.org
Artistic Director: Garfield Allen
Fax: 0161-615 0516
BO: 0161-615 0500              Admin: 0161-615 0515

**MANCHESTER**
The Lowry
Pier 8, Salford Quays M50 3AZ
Website: www.thelowry.com
e-mail: info@thelowry.com
Theatre Production Bookings: Steve Cowton
Fax: 0161-876 2021
BO: 0870 1112000              Admin: 0870 1112020

**MILFORD HAVEN**
Torch Theatre, St Peter's Road
Milford Haven
Pembrokeshire SA73 2BU
Website: www.torchtheatre.co.uk
e-mail: info@torchtheatre.co.uk
Artistic Director: Peter Doran
Fax: 01646 698919
BO: 01646 695267               Admin: 01646 694192

**NEWPORT (Isle of Wight)**
Quay Arts
Sea Street, Newport Harbour
Isle of Wight PO30 5BD
Website: www.quayarts.org
e-mail: info@quayarts.org
Fax: 01983 526606                 Tel: 01983 822490

**NORTH SHIELDS**
North Tyneside Arts
Saville Exchange
Howard Street
North Shields NE30 1SE              Tel: 0191-643 7090
e-mail: saville-arts@northtyneside.gov.uk

**NORWICH**
Norwich Arts Centre
St Benedicts Street
Norwich, Norfolk NR2 4PG
Website: www.norwichartscentre.co.uk
e-mail: stuart@norwichartscentre.co.uk
BO: 01603 660352               Admin: 01603 660387

**NUNEATON**
Abbey Theatre & Arts Centre
Pool Bank Street
Nuneaton, Warks CV11 5DB
Website: www.abbeytheatre.co.uk
e-mail: admin@abbeytheatre.co.uk
Chairman: Tony Deeming
Tel: 024-7632 7359              BO: 024-7635 4090

**PLYMOUTH**
Plymouth Arts Centre
38 Looe Street
Plymouth, Devon PL4 0EB
Website: www.plymouthartscentre.org
e-mail: info@plymouthartscentre.org
Director: Ian Hutchinson
Fax: 01752 206118                 Tel: 01752 206114

**POOLE**
Lighthouse Poole Centre for The Arts
Kingland Road, Poole
Dorset BH15 1UG              BO/Admin: 0844 4068666
Website: www.lighthousepoole.co.uk

**RADLETT**
The Radlett Centre, 1 Aldenham Avenue
Radlett, Herts WD7 8HL
Website: www.radlettcentre.co.uk
e-mail: admin@radlettcentre.com
Fax: 01923 857592                 Tel: 01923 857546

**ROTHERHAM**
Rotherham Civic Theatre
Catherine Street
Rotherham, South Yorkshire S65 1EB
Website: www.rotherham.gov.uk/theatres
Theatre Manager: Mark Scott
BO: 01709 823621               Admin: 01709 823641

**SALISBURY**
Salisbury Arts Centre, Bedwin Street
Salisbury, Wiltshire SP1 3UT
e-mail: info@salisburyarts.co.uk
Fax: 01722 343030                    BO: 01722 321744

**SHREWSBURY**
Shrewsbury & District Arts Association
The Gateway, Chester Street
Shrewsbury, Shropshire SY1 1NB        Tel: 01743 355159
e-mail: gateway.centre@shropshire-cc.gov.uk

**SOUTHPORT**
Southport Arts Centre
Lord Street, Southport
Merseyside PR8 1DB
Website: www.seftonarts.co.uk
e-mail: artsops@seftonarts.co.uk
BO: 01704 540011                 Admin: 0151-934 2131

**STAMFORD**
Stamford Arts Centre
27 St Mary's Street
Stamford, Lincolnshire PE9 2DL
Website: www.stamfordartscentre.co.uk
General Manager: David Popple
Fax: 01780 766690
BO: 01780 763203                 Admin: 01780 480846

**STIRLING**
MacRobert Arts Centre
University of Stirling
Stirling FK9 4LA
Website: www.macrobert.org
e-mail: info@macrobert.org
BO: 01786 466666                 Admin: 01786 467155

**SWANSEA**
Taliesin Arts Centre
Swansea University
Singleton Park, Swansea SA2 8PZ       Tel: 01792 295238
Website: www.taliesinartscentre.co.uk
e-mail: s.e.crouch@swansea.ac.uk
Head of Cultural Services: Sybil Crouch

**SWINDON**
Wyvern Theatre, Theatre Square
Swindon, Wiltshire SN1 1QN
BO: 01793 524481                 Admin: 01793 535534

**TAUNTON**
Brewhouse Theatre & Arts Centre
Coal Orchard
Taunton, Somerset TA1 1JL
Website: www.thebrewhouse.net
e-mail: info@thebrewhouse.net
Director: Robert Miles
BO: 01823 283244                 Admin: 01823 274608

**TOTNES**
The Arts at Dartington
The Barn, Dartington Hall
Totnes, Devon TQ9 6DE
Website: www.dartington.org/arts
e-mail: arts@dartington.org
BO: 01803 847070                 Admin: 01803 847074

**TUNBRIDGE WELLS**
Trinity Theatre, Church Road
Tunbridge Wells, Kent TN1 1JP
e-mail: info@trinitytheatre.net
BO: 01892 678678                 Admin: 01892 678670

**ULEY**
Prema
South Street, Uley
Nr Dursley, Glos GL11 5SS
Website: www.prema.demon.co.uk
e-mail: info@prema.demon.co.uk
Director: Gordon Scott               Tel: 01453 860703

**VALE OF GLAMORGAN**
St Donats Arts Centre
St Donats Castle
The Vale of Glamorgan CF61 1WF
e-mail: janetsmith@stdonats.com
General Manager: Janet Smith
Fax: 01446 799101
BO: 01446 799100                 Tel: 01446 799095

**WAKEFIELD**
Wakefield Arts Centre
Wakefield College
Thornes Park Centre, Thornes Park
Horbury Road, Wakefield WF2 8QZ
Website: www.theatreroyalwakefield.co.uk
BO: 01924 211311             Admin: 01924 215531

**WASHINGTON**
The Arts Centre Washington
Biddick Lane, Fatfield
Washington, Tyne & Wear NE38 8AB
e-mail: matthew.blylh@sunderland.gov.uk
Fax: 0191-219 3458               Tel: 0191-219 3455

**WELLINGBOROUGH**
The Castle, Castle Way
Wellingborough, Northants NN8 1XA
Website: www.thecastle.org.uk
e-mail: info@thecastle.org.uk
Executive Director: Gail Arnott
Artistic Director: Nik Ashton
Fax: 01933 229888                Tel: 01933 229022

**WIMBORNE**
Layard Theatre
Canford School
Canford Magna
Wimborne, Dorset BH21 3AD
e-mail: layardtheatre@canford.com
Director of Drama: Stephen Hattersley
Administrator: Christine Haynes
BO/Fax: 01202 847525             Admin: 01202 847529

**WINCHESTER**
The Tower @ Kings
Romsey Road, Winchester
Hampshire SO22 5PW
Website: www.towerarts.co.uk
Tower Co-ordinator: Ben Ward          Tel: 01962 867986

**WINDSOR**
The Firestation
The Old Court
St Leonards Road
Windsor, Berks SL4 3BL               Tel: 01753 866865
Website: www.firestationartscentre.com
e-mail: info@firestationartscentre.com

**WREXHAM**
Oriel Wrecsam/Wrexham Arts Centre
Rhosddu Road, Wrexham LL11 1AU
e-mail: arts.centre@wrexham.gov.uk
Fax: 01978 292611                Tel: 01978 292093

**ARTS COUNCIL ENGLAND, EAST**
(Norfolk, Suffolk, Bedfordshire, Cambridgeshire, Essex, Hertfordshire and the unitary authorities of Luton, Peterborough, Southend-on-Sea and Thurrock)

Eden House, 48-49 Bateman Street, Cambridge CB2 1LR
Website: www.artscouncil.org.uk
Fax: 0870 2421271                    Tel: 0845 3006200

**ARTS COUNCIL ENGLAND, EAST MIDLANDS**
(Derbyshire, Leicestershire, Lincolnshire excluding North and North East Lincolnshire, Northamptonshire, Nottinghamshire and the unitary authorities of Derby, Leicester, Nottingham and Rutland)

St Nicholas Court, 25-27 Castle Gate, Nottingham NG1 7AR
Website: www.artscouncil.org.uk
Fax: 0115-950 2467                   Tel: 0845 3006200

**ARTS COUNCIL ENGLAND, LONDON**
(Greater London)

14 Great Peter Street, London SW1P 3NQ
Website: www.artscouncil.org.uk
Fax: 020-7608 4100                   Tel: 0845 3006200

**ARTS COUNCIL ENGLAND, NORTH EAST**
(Durham, Northumberland, metropolitan authorities of Gateshead, Newcastle upon Tyne, North Tyneside, South Tyneside, Sunderland and the unitary authorities of Darlington, Hartlepool, Middlesborough, Red Car and Cleveland, Stockton-on-Tees)

Central Square, Forth Street, Newcastle upon Tyne NE1 3PJ
Website: www.artscouncil.org.uk
Fax: 0191-230 1020                   Tel: 0845 3006200

**ARTS COUNCIL ENGLAND, NORTH WEST**
(Lancashire, Cheshire, Cumbria and the metropolitan authorities of Bolton, Bury, Knowsley, Liverpool, Manchester, Oldham, Rochdale, St Helens, Salford, Sefton, Stockport, Tameside, Trafford, Wigan, Wirral and the unitary authorities of Blackburn with Darwen, Blackpool, Halton & Warrington)

Manchester House, 22 Bridge Street, Manchester M3 3AB
Website: www.artscouncil.org.uk
Fax: 0161-834 6969                   Tel: 0845 3006200

**ARTS COUNCIL ENGLAND, SOUTH EAST**
(Buckinghamshire, East Sussex, Hampshire, Isle of Wight, Kent, Oxfordshire, Surrey, West Sussex and the unitary authorities of Bracknell Forest. Brighton & Hove, Medway Towns, Milton Keynes, Portsmouth)

Sovereign House, Church Street, Brighton BN1 1RA
Website: www.artscouncil.org.uk
Fax: 0870 2421257                    Tel: 0845 3006200

**ARTS COUNCIL ENGLAND, SOUTH WEST**
(Cornwall, Devon, Dorset, Gloucestershire, Somerset and Wiltshire and the unitary authorities of Bristol, Bath, Bournemouth, Plymouth, Poole, Torbay and Swindon)

Senate Court, Southernhay Gardens, Exeter, Devon EX1 1UG
Website: www.artscouncil.org.uk
e-mail: enquiries@artscouncil.org.uk    Tel: 0845 3006200

**ARTS COUNCIL ENGLAND, WEST MIDLANDS**
(Herefordshire, Worcestershire, Staffordshire, Warwickshire and Shropshire, Stoke-on-Trent, Telford and Wrekin and districts of Birmingham, Coventry, Dudley, Sandwell, Solihull, Walsall & Wolverhampton)

82 Granville Street, Birmingham B1 2LH
Website: www.artscouncil.org.uk
Fax: 0121-643 7239                   Tel: 0845 3006200

**ARTS COUNCIL ENGLAND, YORKSHIRE**
(North Yorkshire, metropolitan authorities of Barnsley, Bradford, Calderdale, Doncaster, Kirklees, Leeds, Rotherham, Sheffield, Wakefield and the unitary authorities of East Riding of Yorkshire, Kingston upon Hull, North Lincolnshire, North East Lincolnshire)

21 Bond Street, Dewsbury, West Yorkshire WF13 1AX
Website: www.artscouncil.org.uk
Fax: 01924 466522                    Tel: 0845 3006200

**ARTS COUNCIL OF WALES, NORTH WALES OFFICE**
(Isle of Anglesey, Gwynedd, Conwy, Denbighshire, Flintshire, Wrexham)

36 Prince's Drive, Colwyn Bay, Conwy LL29 8LA
Website: www.artswales.org.uk
e-mail: north@artswales.org.uk
Fax: 01492 533677                    Tel: 01492 533440

**ARTS COUNCIL OF WALES, SOUTH WALES & CENTRAL OFFICE**
(Vale of Glamorgan, Cardiff, Newport, Monmouthshire, Torfaen, Blaenau Gwent, Caerphilly, Merthyr Tydfil, Rhonda Cynon Taff, Bridgend)

Bute Place, Cardiff CF10 5AL
Website: www.artswales.org.uk
e-mail: info@artswales.org.uk
Fax: 029-2041 1400                   Tel: 0845 8734900

**ARTS COUNCIL OF WALES, MID & WEST WALES OFFICE**
(Ceredigion, Carmarthenshire, Pembrokeshire, Powys, Swansea, Neath & Port Talbot)

6 Gardd Llydaw, Jacksons Lane, Carmarthen SA31 1QD
Website: www.artswales.org
Fax: 01267 233084                    Tel: 01267 234248

**Casting Directors**

For information regarding membership of
the Casting Directors' Guild (CDG) please see
www.thecdg.co.uk

**Consultants**
**Costumes, Wigs & Make-up**
**Critics**

**A C A CASTING**
*Contact: Catherine Arton*
32A Edenvale Street
London SW6 2SF          Tel/Fax: 020-7384 2635
e-mail: catherine@acacasting.com

**ADAMSON Jo**
Northern Spirit Creative (Casting)
PO Box 140, Leeds LS13 9BS
Website: www.northernspiritcreative.co.uk
e-mail: jo@northernspiritcreative.co.uk
Mobile: 07787 311270          Tel: 0113-219 2896

**AILION Pippa**
(CDG Member)
3 Towton Road, London SE27 9EE    Tel/Fax: 020-8670 4816
e-mail: enquiries@pippaailioncasting.co.uk

**ALL DIRECTIONS OF LONDON**
*Contact: By Post only*
7 Rupert Court, Off Wardour Street
London W1D 6EB          Tel: 020-7437 5879

**ANDERSON Jane**
(CDG Member)
e-mail: casting@janeandersononline.com

**ANDREW Dorothy CASTING**
(CDG Member)
Campus Manor, Childwall Abbey Road
Childwall, Liverpool L16 0JP
Fax: 0151-737 4006          Tel: 0151-737 4042

**AP CASTING**
*Contact: Annelie Powell*
Website: www.powellcasting.com

**ASHTON HINKINSON CASTING**
1 Charlotte Street, London W1T 1RD
Website: www.ashtonhinkinson.com
e-mail: casting@ahcasting.com
Fax: 020-7637 0328          Tel: 020-7580 6101

**BAIG Shaheen CASTING**
e-mail: shaheen.baig@btconnect.com    Tel: 020-7613 3173

**BARNES Derek**
(CDG Member)
BBC DRAMA SERIES CASTING
BBC Elstree, Room N221
Neptune House, Clarendon Road
Borehamwood, Herts WD6 1JF
Fax: 020-8228 8311          Tel: 020-8228 7096

**BATH Andrea**
*Contact: By Post/e-mail/Telephone*
*Accepts Showreels*
*Television. Theatre*
85 Brightwell Road
Watford WD18 0HR          Tel: 01923 333067
e-mail: andreabath@btinternet.com

**BEACH CASTING Ltd**
*Contact: Brendan McNamara*
1st Floor, 21 Whiston Road, London E2 8EX
Website: www.beach-casting.com
Mobile: 07903 630964          Tel: 020-7749 6910

**BEASTALL AND NORTH Ltd**
*Contact: Lesley Beastall, Sophie North*
41E Elgin Crescent, London W11 2JD
e-mail: lesley@beastallnorth.co.uk
Mobile: 07956 516606 (Sophie)    Mobile: 07956 516603 (Lesley)

**[ CONTACTS 2010 ]**

# infopage

## Who are casting directors?

Casting directors are employed by directors / production companies to source the best available actors for roles across TV, film, radio, theatre and commercials. They do the groundwork and present a shortlist of artists to the director, who often makes the final selection. Many casting directors work on a freelance basis, others are employed permanently by larger organisations such as the BBC or the National Theatre. Discovering new and emerging talent also plays an important part in their job.

## Why should I approach them?

If you are an actor looking for work, you can promote yourself directly to casting directors by sending them your photo and CV. They keep actors' details on file and may consider you for future productions. Bear in mind that you will not be guaranteed a response as casting directors are physically unable to reply to every one of the vast numbers of letters they receive from actors, but it is worth your while to explore this opportunity to find work.

## How should I approach them?

Many of the following casting directors have indicated the method in which they prefer actors to contact them for the first time. This tends to be by post but some accept or prefer e-mails. Some are happy to receive telephone calls, but be aware that casting directors are very busy and you should not continually call them with questions or updates once you have sent your CV. If they have not specified whether they prefer postal or e-mail contact, you should send them your CV, a headshot and a covering letter by post only, as this is the traditional method of contacting casting professionals. You should always include a stamped-addressed envelope (SAE) big enough to contain your 10 x 8 photo and with sufficient postage. This will increase your chances of getting a reply. Write your name and telephone number on the back of your headshot in case it gets separated from your CV.

## Should I send a casting director my showreel and/or voicereel?

Some casting directors have also indicated that they are happy for actors to send showreels and/or voicereels along with their CVs and headshots, but if this is not indicated, we would recommend that you leave these out of your correspondence but indicate in your covering letter that they are available. If a casting director is interested in you, they can contact you later for these items, but they usually prefer not to sift through hundreds of unsolicited showreels until they have first established an interest in an actor.

## How do I target my search?

It is not advisable to send a generic CV to every casting director listed in the following pages. Research the following names and companies and then target your letters accordingly. Find out what areas of the industry each one usually casts for (some specify this in their listing) and what productions they have previously cast. Keep an eye on TV, film and theatre credits so you become familiar with the casting directors used for different productions. Some of these casting directors have their own websites. If a casting director has 'CDG' after their name, it means they are a member of the Casting Directors' Guild, the professional organisation of casting directors working in the UK (see www.thecdg.co.uk for more information and their article on page 152).

## How do I write an effective CV and covering letter?

Once you have made a short-list of suitable casting directors you should send them your CV, your headshot, and an individually tailored covering letter. The covering letter should demonstrate that you have researched the casting director, and ideally you will have a particular reason for contacting them at this time: perhaps you can tell them about your next showcase, or where they can see you currently appearing on stage. Your CV should be no longer than one page, up-to-date and spell-checked. Please see the 'Promotional Services' section of Contacts for further advice on writing CVs and covering letters.

## How do I prepare for a casting/audition?

Make sure you are fully prepared with accurate information about the audition time, venue, format and the people you will be meeting. Unless it's a last minute casting, you should always read the script in advance and try to have some opinions on it. If you are asked in advance to prepare a piece, always stick to the brief with something suitable and relevant. On the day, allow plenty of time to get there so you are not flustered when you arrive. Try to be positive and enjoy yourself. Remember, the casting director doesn't want to spend several days auditioning - they want you to get the job! Never criticise previous productions you have worked on. And at the end of the casting, remember to take your script away unless you are asked to leave it, otherwise it can look as if you're not interested. Please see 'Rehearsal Rooms and Casting Suites' for more detailed advice on preparing for and attending auditions.

## Should I attend a casting in a house or flat?

Professional auditions are rarely held anywhere other than an official casting studio or venue. Be very wary if you are asked to go elsewhere. Trust your instincts. If something doesn't seem right to you, it probably isn't. Always take someone with you if you are in any doubt.

## How do I become a casting director?

The best way to gain experience in this field is to work as a casting assistant. Vacancies are sometimes advertised in The Stage www.thestage.co.uk or PCR www.pcrnewsletter.com. Alternatively you could try sending your CV to casting directors asking for an internship. Just as we advise actors, remember to research any casting director you are considering approaching to make sure they actually work in the area you are interested in. The internship is likely to be unpaid, but the experience and contacts you gain will be invaluable.

# infopage

**When you read CDG after a Casting Director's name, you know he/she is a member of The Casting Directors' Guild and will therefore have a minimum of five years' experience. The current CDG Committee has prepared the following advice for actors.**

Casting directors are there to help actors and not to hinder them. We want you to do your best as that reflects back on us, and you should realise that we are only as good as the actors we submit for each role.

Much of our work consists of creating a shortlist of potential actors and reducing it to a suitably sized group to present for audition. We also spend a great deal of time watching you work. Members of the CDG endeavour to cover as many performances as possible on film, television and in the theatre. There is no substitute to seeing you act.

When asked to attend an interview or audition, an actor should feel confident in asking his/her agent any relevant questions about the role and the project. If this is not forthcoming, arrive early and seek information from the casting director or, better still, contact him/her the day before. If it is only possible to speak to the casting director on the day, preferably do so before entering the audition room, rather than in front of the director or producer. The casting director will be happy to help.

Sometimes you will only receive pages for a role, but a casting director will always endeavour to give you as much information about a character as is available. When possible, read the entire play/screenplay rather than just the scenes your 'character' appears in, and ideally be able to talk about the script as a whole during the interview. Take your time when reading; preparation is worth a lot but don't be fazed if you get lost over their script. If you feel that a scene is going terribly it's ok to start again.

For most non-theatre jobs these days you will find that your meeting will be recorded on video tape. These tapes are then shown to the various producers involved, and this is when the process can slow down. It takes time to build a company and for final casting choices to be made.

Casting is a matter of interpretation. As well as character information derived from the script, the vision of the producer, director, casting director and indeed the actor all come into play. There are many reasons why one actor will be chosen over another, and even the best audition might not necessarily secure a part. Every aspect of the actor comes into play. Is he/she too young or too mature? Do they work as a family? Could they be mother and son? Does the chemistry work? There is also the frustrating problem of scripts, and parts, being re-written. A character may have an entirely different physical description in a later draft. Sadly we do not have control over this.

When it comes to contacting casting directors, most are happy to receive letters, updated photos and CVs. The best correspondence for casting directors to receive is performance information. Letters should be brief and to the point, with the production name, director, venue and/or TV channel clearly stated. If you are enquiring about work be as specific as possible, e.g. "I would like to be seen for the part of ... in ... because ..." or something similar. Dear Sir or Madam letters just don't work.

CVs should be well laid out. List most recent work first and use your spell checker. 6x4 photos are fine to send but include an SAE if you want them returned. Casting directors rarely like unsolicited DVDs and showreels: you must be aware that we do get inundated. Also bear in mind that not receiving a response to your letter does not mean it hasn't been read and filed: it is virtually impossible to reply to the volume of mail received from actors.

In our greener world it's great that Spotlight and other web media now have the facility for us to view CVs, photos and showreels online. Use the technology: it's very easy to keep your CV up-to-date online and you can change your photo at any time of year without having to do a huge mail out to let people know.

Actors are a fundamental tool of this industry: CDG members are aware of this and aim to put actors at their ease. Audition nerves are a given but you should feel secure that the reason you are in the room is because someone wants you to get that role and not because they want to see you fail.

Please visit www.thecdg.co.uk for further information.

## STUART**ALLEN**
### P H O T O G R A P H E R

# 07776 258829
www.stuartallenphotos.com

Production, Publicity, Portraits

## STUDENT DISCOUNTS

Sean Gleeson

Natalie Barrett

**BEATTIE Victoria**
*Contact: By e-mail*
*Accepts Showreels*
*Commercials. Feature Films. Television Drama*
Flat 1, Kenmore Mansions, Gondar Gardens
London NW6 1ET          Mobile: 07976 395996
e-mail: victoria@victoriabeattie.com

**BEAUCHAMP Lauren CASTING**
34A Brightside
Billericay CM12 0LJ
e-mail: laurenbeauchamp@tiscali.co.uk
Fax: 01277 656147          Mobile: 07961 982198

**BECKLEY Rowland**
BBC DRAMA SERIES CASTING, BBC Elstree
Room N222
Neptune House
Clarendon Road
Borehamwood, Herts WD6 1JF
Fax: 020-8228 7130

**BERTRAND Leila CASTING**
53 Hormead Road
London W9 3NQ          Tel/Fax: 020-8964 0683
e-mail: leilabcasting@aol.com

**BEVAN Lucy**
2nd Floor, 138 Portobello Road
London W11 2DZ          Tel: 020-7727 5572

**BEWICK Maureen CASTING**
104A Dartmouth Road, London NW2 4HB

**BEXFIELD DEITCH ASSOCIATES**
80-81 St Martin's Lane
London WC2N 4AA          Tel: 020-7395 7525
e-mail: casting@bexfielddeitch.co.uk

**BILL The**
TalkbackThames Studios
1 Deer Park Road
London SW19 3TL          Tel: 020-8540 0600

**BIRD Sarah**
(CDG Member)
PO Box 32658, London W14 0XA
Fax: 020-7602 8601          Tel: 020-7371 3248

**BIRKETT Hannah CASTING**
26 Noko, 3/6 Banister Road
London W10 4AR
e-mail: hannah@hbcasting.com
Mobile: 07957 114175          Tel: 020-8960 2848

**BRACKE Siobhan**
(CDG Member)
*Contact: By Post*
Basement Flat, 22A The Barons
St Margaret's TW1 2AP          Tel: 020-8891 5686

**BUCKINGHAM Jo**
*Comedy. Entertainment*
BBC Television Centre
Wood Lane, London W12 7RJ          Tel: 020-8225 7585
e-mail: jo.buckingham@bbc.co.uk

**CANDID CASTING**
1st Floor, 32 Great Sutton Street, London EC1V 0NB
Website: www.candidcasting.co.uk
e-mail: mail@candidcasting.co.uk
Fax: 020-7490 8966          Tel: 020-7490 8882

IMELDA STAUNTON

## PHOTOGRAPHY BY
## BEAJ JOHNSON

# 07973 382859
www.beajpix.com
info@beajpix.com

**CANNON DUDLEY & ASSOCIATES**
*Contact: Carol Dudley (CDG Member)*
*By Post*
*Film. Stage. Television*
43A Belsize Square, London NW3 4HN
e-mail: cdacasting@blueyonder.co.uk
Fax: 020-7813 2048     Tel: 020-7433 3393

**CANNON John**
(CDG Member)
BBC DRAMA SERIES CASTING, BBC Elstree
Room N223, Neptune House
Clarendon Road
Borehamwood, Herts WD6 1JF
Fax: 020-8228 8311     Tel: 020-8228 7322

**CARLING Di CASTING**
(CDG Member)
1st Floor, 49 Frith Street, London W1D 4SG
Fax: 020-7287 6844     Tel: 020-7287 6446

**CARROLL Anji**
(CDG Member)
*Contact: By e-mail (Small Attachments only)*
*Film. Television. Theatre*
4 Nesfield Drive, Winterley
Cheshire CW11 4NT     Tel: 01270 250240
e-mail: anji@anjicarroll.tv

**CASTING COMPANY (UK) The**
*Contact: Michelle Guish*
3rd Floor
112-114 Wardour Street, London W1F 0TS
Fax: 020-7434 2346     Tel: 020-7734 4954

**CASTING CONNECTION The**
*Contact: Michael Syers*
Dalrossie House, 16 Victoria Grove
Stockport, Cheshire SK4 5BU
Fax: 0161-442 7280     Tel: 0161-432 4122

**CASTING COUCH The**
*Contact: Moira Townsend*
213 Trowbridge Road
Bradford on Avon
Wiltshire BA15 1EU
e-mail: moiratownsend@yahoo.co.uk     Mobile: 07932 785807

**CASTING UK**
Studio 125, 77 Beak Street
London W1F 9DB     Tel: 020-7993 5165
Website: www.castinguk.com
e-mail: casting@castinguk.com

**CATLIFF Suzy**
(CDG Member)
PO Box 39492, London N10 3YX     Tel: 020-8442 0749
e-mail: soose@soose.co.uk

**CHAND Urvashi**
(CDG Member)
Cinecraft, 69 Teignmouth Road
London NW2 4EA     Tel: 020-8208 3861
e-mail: urvashi@cinecraft.biz

**CHARD Alison**
(CDG Member)
23 Groveside Court, 4 Lombard Road
Battersea, London SW11 3RQ     Tel: 020-7223 9125
e-mail: chardcasting@btinternet.com

**CHARKHAM CASTING**
*Contact: Beth Charkham*
Suite 361, 14 Tottenham Court Road
London W1T 1JY     Mobile: 07956 456630
e-mail: charkhamcasting@btconnect.com

**CLARK Andrea**
*Contact: By Post*
*Accepts Showreels*
*Children & Adults. Commercials. Film. Stage. Television*
PO Box 28895, London SW13 0WG     Tel: 020-8876 6869
Website: www.aclarkcasting.com
e-mail: andrea@aclarkcasting.com

**CLAYPOLE Sam**
*(Live Stream Casting)*
PO Box 123, Darlington
Durham DL3 7WA     Tel: 0845 6501777
Website: www.claypolemanagement.co.uk
e-mail: info@claypolemanagement.co.uk

**CLAYTON Rosalie**
(CDG Member)
e-mail: rosalie@rosalieclayton.com    Tel/Fax: 020-7242 8109

**COGAN Ben**
BBC DRAMA SERIES CASTING
BBC Elstree, Room N221, Neptune House, Clarendon Road
Borehamwood, Herts WD6 1JF
Fax: 020-8228 8311     Tel: 020-8228 7516

**COLLINS Jayne CASTING**
(CDG Member)
4th Floor, 20 Bedford Street, London WC2E 9HP
Website: www.jaynecollinscasting.com
e-mail: info@jaynecollinscasting.com
Fax: 020-7240 5323     Tel: 020-7836 9792

**COMMERCIALS CASTING UK Ltd**
*Contact: Michelle Smith (CDG Member)*
*By Post*
*Accepts Showreels/Voicereels*
*Commercials. Photographic. Street Casting. Voice Overs*
*Streaming/Uploading Service Available*
220 Church Lane, Stockport SK7 1PQ
Fax: 0161-439 0622                    Tel: 0161-439 6825

**CORDORAY Lin**
66 Cardross Street, London W6 0DR

**COTTON Irene**
(CDG Member)
25 Druce Road
Dulwich Village, London SE21 7DW
e-mail: irenecotton@btinternet.com
Tel/Fax: 020-8299 2787               Tel: 020-8299 1595

**CRAMPSIE Julia**
*(Casting Executive)*
BBC DRAMA SERIES CASTING
BBC Elstree, Room N224
Neptune House, Clarendon Road
Borehamwood, Herts WD6 1JF
Fax: 020-8228 8311                   Tel: 020-8228 7170

**CRANE Carole CASTING**
e-mail: crane.shot@virgin.net        Mobile: 07976 869442

**CRAWFORD Kahleen CASTING**
Film City Glasgow
Govan Town Hall
401 Govan Road, Glasgow G51 2QJ
Website: www.kahleencrawford.com
e-mail: casting@kahleencrawford.com
Mobile: 07950 414164                 Tel: 0141-425 1725

**CRAWFORD Margaret**
92 Castlenau, London SW13 9EU    Tel/Fax: 020-8748 8929
e-mail: margaretcrawford.casting@virgin.net

**CROCODILE CASTING COMPANY The**
*Contact: Claire Toeman, Tracie Saban*
*By e-mail only*
Website: www.crocodilecasting.com
e-mail: croccast@aol.com             Tel: 020-8203 7009

**CROSS Louise**
(CDG Member)
128A North View Road
London N8 7LP                        Tel: 020-8341 2200

**CROWE Sarah CASTING**
75 Amberley Road, London W9 2JL
e-mail: sarah@sarahcrowecasting.co.uk
Fax: 020-7286 5030                   Tel: 020-7286 5080

**CROWLEY POOLE CASTING**
*Contact: Suzanne Crowley (CDG Member)*
*Gilly Poole (CDG Member)*
11 Goodwins Court, London WC2N 4LL
Fax: 020-7379 5971                   Tel: 020-7379 5965

**CROWLEY Suzanne**
(CDG Member)
(See CROWLEY POOLE CASTING)

**DAVIES Jane CASTING**
*Contact: Jane Davies (CDG Member)*
*John Connor (CDG Member)*
PO Box 680, Sutton, Surrey SM1 3ZG
e-mail: info@janedaviescasting.co.uk
Fax: 020-8644 9746                   Tel: 020-8715 1036

**DAVIS Leo (Miss)**
(JUST CASTING)
20th Century Theatre
291 Westbourne Grove, London W11 2QA
Fax: 020-7792 2143                   Tel: 020-7229 3471

**DAVY Gary**
(CDG Member) *Film. Television*
e-mail: casting@garydavy.com

**DAWES Gabrielle**
*(CDG Member)*
PO Box 52493
London NW3 9DZ                       Tel: 020-7435 3645
e-mail: gdawescasting@tiscali.co.uk

**DAWES Stephanie**
(CDG Member)
13 Nevern Square
London SW5 9NW
e-mail: stephaniedawes5@gmail.com
Mobile: 07802 566642

**DAY Kate**
(CDG Member)
Pound Cottage
27 The Green South
Warborough, Oxon OX10 7DR
Tel/Fax: 01865 858709

**DE FREITAS Paul**
(CDG Member)
e-mail: info@pauldefreitas.com

**DENMAN Jack CASTING**
*Contact: By Post/Telephone*
*Commercials. Film. Role Play. Television*
Burgess House
Main Street
Farnsfield, Notts NG22 8EF
Tel/Fax: 01623 882272

**DICKENS Laura**
(CDG Member)
197 Malpas Road
London SE4 1BH
Mobile: 07958 665468
e-mail: dickenscasting@aol.com

**DOWD Kate**
74 Wells Street, London W1T 3QG
Fax: 020-7580 6688
Tel: 020-7580 8866

**DRURY Malcolm**
(CDG Member)
34 Tabor Road, London W6 0BW
Tel: 020-8748 9232

**DUDLEY Carol**
(CDG Member)
(See CANNON DUDLEY & ASSOCIATES)

**DUFF Julia**
(CDG Member)
73 Wells Street, London W1T 3QG
Fax: 020-7436 8859
Tel: 020-7436 8860

**DUFF Maureen**
(CDG Member)
PO Box 47340, London NW3 4TY
e-mail: belgrove@dircon.co.uk
Fax: 020-7681 7172
Tel: 020-7586 0532

**DUFFY Jenny**
(CDG Member)
e-mail: casting@jennyduffy.co.uk
Tel: 020-7582 1348

**EARNSHAW Rob**
35 Bishops Hill, Hexham
Northumberland NE46 4NH
Website: www.robertearnshawcasting.co.uk
e-mail: robertearnshaw@btinternet.com
Mobile: 07707 083674

117 Park Lane, London W1K 7AH
Mobile: 07707 083674

**EAST Irene CASTING**
(CDG Member)
*Contact: By Post. Film. Theatre*
40 Brookwood Avenue, Barnes
London SW13 0LR
Tel: 020-8876 5686
e-mail: irneast@aol.com

**EH7 CASTING**
9 Claremont Bank
Edinburgh EH7 4DR
Website: www.eh7casting.com
e-mail: contact@eh7casting.com
Tel: 0131-556 9339

**EJ CASTING**
PO Box 63617, London SW9 1AN
e-mail: info@ejcasting.com
Mobile: 07891 632946
Tel: 020-7564 2688

**EMMERSON Chloe**
46 Bassein Park Road
London W12 9RZ
Tel: 020-8740 0982
e-mail: c@chloeemmerson.com

**EPMC TALENT & CASTINGS**
*Contact: Aldo Arcilla*
*By Post. Accepts Showreels/Voicereels*
*Commercials. Film. Television*
Unit 67, Ability Plaza
Arbutus Street, London E8 4DT
Website: www.epmctalent.com
e-mail: info@epmctalent.com
Fax: 0871 5593947
Tel: 0844 8243888

**EVANS Camilla CASTING**
2 Dalberg Road
London SW2 1AN
Mobile: 07768 977050
e-mail: camilla@camillaevans.com

**EVANS Richard**
(CDG Member)
10 Shirley Road
London W4 1DD
Website: www.evanscasting.co.uk
e-mail: contact@evanscasting.co.uk
Tel: 020-8994 6304

**EYE CASTING The**
Tower Room, The Bath House
8 Chapel Place, Rivington Street
London EC2A 3DQ
Website: www.theeyecasting.com
e-mail: jody@theeyecasting.com
Fax: 05602 059199
Tel: 020-7729 9705

**FEARNLEY Ali CASTING**
3rd Floor
58-60 Rivington Street
London EC2A 3AU
Tel/Fax: 020-7613 7320
e-mail: cast@alifearnley.com

**FIGGIS Susie**
19 Spencer Rise, London NW5 1AR
Tel: 020-7482 2200

**FILDES Bunny CASTING**
(CDG Member)
56 Wigmore Street, London W1
Tel: 020-7935 1254

ANNA ISOLA CROLLA
PHOTOGRAPHER
annaisolacrolla.co.uk  07980 551 468

Alex Kelly

Reginald D Hunter

Carey Mulligan

# Charlie Carter PHOTOGRAPHER

## 020 8222 8742    www.charliecarter.com

---

**FINCHER Sally**
(CDG Member)
e-mail: sally.fincher@btinternet.com

**FOX CASTING**
47 Furze Platt Road
Maidenhead, Berks SL6 7NF        Tel: 01628 777853
e-mail: julie@juliefox.net

**FOX Celestia**
23 Leppoc Road, London SW4 9LS        Tel: 020-7720 6143
e-mail: celestia.fox@virgin.net

**FRAZER Janie**
(CDG Member)
e-mail: janiefrazercasting@gmail.com        Tel: 020-7652 4077

**FRECK Rachel**
(CDG Member)
e-mail: casting@rachelfreck.com        Tel/Fax: 020-8673 2455

**FREND Amanda**
87 Swindon Road, Horsham
West Sussex RH12 2HF
e-mail: amandafrendcasting@hotmail.co.uk

**FRISBY Jane CASTING**
*Contact: By Post*
*Accepts Showreels/Voicereels only on request*
*Commercials. Film. Theatre*
51 Ridge Road, London N8 9LJ        Tel: 020-8341 4747
e-mail: jane.frisby@tiscali.co.uk

**FUNNELL Caroline**
(CDG Member)
25 Rattray Road
London SW2 1AZ        Tel: 020-7326 4417

**GALLAGHER Juliet CASTING**
Website: www.julietgallagher.com
e-mail: julietgallagher@hotmail.com

**GILLHAM Tracey**
(CDG Member)
*Comedy. Entertainment*
BBC Television Centre, Room 4018
Wood Lane, London W12 7RJ
Fax: 020-8576 4414        Tel: 020-8225 8648

**GILLON Tamara CASTING**
26 Carson Road, London SE21 8HU
e-mail: tamaragillon@yahoo.co.uk
Fax: 020-8265 6330        Tel: 020-8766 0099

**GING Thyrza CASTING**
First Floor
18 Dame Court, Dublin 2        Tel: 00 35 31 63 39 090
Website: www.castingireland.ie
e-mail: thyrzaging@gmail.com

**GLOBAL7**
PO Box 56232
London N4 4XP
Website: www.global7casting.com
e-mail: global7castings@gmail.com
Mobile: 07956 956652        Tel/Fax: 020-7281 7679

**GOLD Nina**
(CDG Member)
117 Chevening Road
London NW6 6DU
e-mail: info@ninagold.co.uk
Fax: 020-8968 6777        Tel: 020-8960 6099

**GOOCH Miranda CASTING**
*Contact: By Post/e-mail*
*Accepts Showreels/Voicereels*
*Film. Television. Theatre*
102 Leighton Gardens, London NW10 3PR
e-mail: mirandagooch@gmail.com
Fax: 020-8962 9579     Tel: 020-8962 9578

**GREEN Jill CASTING**
(CDG Member)
PO Box 56927, London N10 3UR     Tel: 0845 4786343

**GREENE Francesca CASTING**
79 Ashworth Mansions
London W9 1LN     Tel: 020-7286 5957
Website: www.francescagreenecasting.com
e-mail: francesca@francescagreene.co.uk

**GRESHAM Marcia**
(CDG Member)
3 Langthorne Street
London SW6 6JT     Tel: 020-7381 2876

**GROSVENOR Angela**
(CDG Member)
*(Head of Casting)*
Talkback Thames Studios
Talkback Thames
1 Deer Park Road, London SW19 3TL
Fax: 020-8543 2794     Tel: 020-8540 0600

**GUISH Michelle**
See CASTING COMPANY (UK) The

**HALL David CASTING**
2 The Shrubbery
2 Lavender Gardens
London SW11 1DL     Tel: 020-7223 4382

**HALL Janet**
3 Shaw Road, Littleborough, Oldham OL15 9LG
e-mail: stage@hall257.fsbusiness.co.uk
Mobile: 07956 822773     Tel: 01706 377900

**HALL Pippa**
*Children. Teenagers*
Rosebank, High Street
Blockley, Glos GL56 9EX
e-mail: pippa@pippahallcasting.com

**HAMMOND Louis**
6 Brewer Street, London W1F 0SD     Tel: 020-7734 1880
e-mail: louis.hammond@virgin.net

**HAMPSON Janet CASTING**
Fourways House
57 Hilton Street, Manchester M1 2EJ
Website: www.janethampson.co.uk
e-mail: janet@janethampson.co.uk
Mobile: 07931 513223     Tel: 0161-408 2037

**HANCOCK Gemma**
(CDG Member)
*Contact: By e-mail*
North Lodge, Weald Chase
Staplefield Road, Cuckfield
West Sussex RH17 5HY
e-mail: gemma@hancockstevenson.com

**HARKIN Julie**
(CDG Member)
22 Clonbrock Road, London N16 8RR     Tel: 020-7241 0728
e-mail: julieharkincasting@gmail.com

**HARRIS Lisa**
290 Coulsdon Road
Old Coulsdon, Surrey CR5 1EB     Mobile: 07956 561247

**HAWSER Gillian CASTING**
24 Cloncurry Street
London SW6 6DS
e-mail: gillianhawser@btinternet.com
Fax: 020-7731 0738     Tel: 020-7731 5988

**HAYFIELD Judi**
(CDG Member)
6 Richmond Hill Road, Gatley
Cheadle, Stockport SK8 1QG     Mobile: 07919 221873
e-mail: judi.hayfield@hotmail.co.uk

**HILL Serena**
Sydney Theatre Company
Pier 4, Hickson Road, Walsh Bay
NSW 2000, Australia     Tel: 00 612 925 01727
e-mail: shill@sydneytheatre.com.au

**HOOTKINS Polly**
(CDG Member)
PO Box 52480, London NW3 9DH     Tel: 020-7692 1184
e-mail: phootkins@clara.net

**HORAN Julia**
(CDG Member)
26 Falkland Road, London NW5 2PX     Tel: 020-7267 5261

**HOWE Gary CASTING**
34 Orbit Street, Roath,
Cardiff CF24 0JX     Tel/Fax: 029-2045 3883

**HUBBARD CASTING**
*Contact: Dan Hubbard* (CDG Member), *Amy Hubbard,*
*Ros Hubbard, John Hubbard*
*No Showreels*
14 Rathbone Place, London W1T 1HT
e-mail: info@hubbardcasting.com
Fax: 020-7636 7117     Tel: 020-7631 4944

**HUGHES Sarah**
(CDG Member)
BBC Television Centre, Wood Lane
London W12 7RJ     Tel: 020-8225 8610
e-mail: sarah.hughes@bbc.co.uk

**HUGHES Sylvia**
Casting Suite, The Deanwater
Wilmslow Road, Woodford
Cheshire SK7 1RJ     Mobile: 07770 520007
e-mail: sylviahughes@hotmail.co.uk

**JACKSON Sue**
(CDG Member)
53 Moseley Wood Walk
Leeds LS16 7HQ     Tel: 0113-267 0819

**JAFFA Janis CASTING**
(CDG Member)
*Contact: By Post. Accepts Showreels*
67 Starfield Road
London W12 9SN     Tel: 020-7565 2877
e-mail: janis@janisjaffacasting.co.uk

**JAFFREY Jennifer**
*Contact: By Post*
The Double Lodge, Pinewood Studios
Pinewood Road, Iver Heath, Bucks SL0 0NH
e-mail: mail@jaffreyactors.co.uk
Fax: 01753 785163     Tel: 01753 785162

# jack ladenburg
## photographer

julian rhind-tutt

victoria kruger

## 07932 053 743

www.jackladenburg.co.uk

info@jackladenburg.co.uk

**JAY Jina CASTING**
(CDG Member)
Office 2, Sound Centre
Twickenham Film Studios
The Barons, St Margarets
Twickenham, Middlesex TW1 2AW
Fax: 020-8607 8982          Tel: 020-8607 8888

**JELOWICKI Ilenka**
(Mad Dog Casting Ltd)
*Contact: By Post/e-mail*
*Accepts Showreels/Voicereels. Children. Real People*
*Street Casting*
15 Leighton Place, London NW5 2QL
e-mail: ilenka@maddogcasting.com
Fax: 020-7284 2689          Tel: 020-7482 4703

**JENKINS Lucy**
(CDG Member)
*Contact: By Post/e-mail*
*Accepts Showreels/Voicereels*
*Commercials. Film. Television. Theatre*
74 High Street, Hampton Wick
Kingston on Thames KT1 4DQ          Tel: 020-8943 5328
e-mail: lucy.jenkins@blueyonder.co.uk

**JN PRODUCTION**
16-24 Underwood Street, London N1 7JQ
e-mail: james@jnproduction.net
Fax: 020-7608 1876          Tel: 020-7278 8800

**JOHN Priscilla**
(CDG Member)
PO Box 22477, London W6 0GT
Fax: 020-8741 4005          Tel: 020-8741 4212

**JOHNSON Alex CASTING**
15 McGregor Road, London W11 1DE
e-mail: alex@alexjohnsoncasting.com
Fax: 020-7229 1665          Tel: 020-7229 8779

**JOHNSON Marilyn**
(CDG Member)
1st Floor, 11 Goodwins Court, London WC2N 4LL
e-mail: casting@marilynjohnsoncasting.com
Fax: 020-7497 5530          Tel: 020-7497 5552

**JONES Doreen**
(CDG Member)
PO Box 22478, London W6 0WJ
Fax: 020-8748 8533          Tel: 020-8746 3782

**JONES Lenka**
Coach House, Pinewood Road, Iver Heath
Buckinghamshire SL0 0NH          Mobile: 07921 182055
e-mail: lenki13@yahoo.co.uk

**JONES Sue**
(CDG Member)
e-mail: info@suejones.net

**KATE & LOU CASTING**
The Basement, Museum House
25 Museum Street, London WC1A 1JT
Website: www.kateandloucasting.com
e-mail: cast@kateandloucasting.com
Mobile: 07976 252531          Mobile: 07885 763429

**KENNEDY Anna CASTING**
8 Rydal Road
London SW16 1QN          Tel: 020-8677 6710
e-mail: anna@kennedycasting.com

**KEOGH Beverley CASTING Ltd**
29 Ardwick Green North
Ardwick Green, Manchester M12 6DL
e-mail: beverley@beverleykeogh.tv
Fax: 0161-273 4401
Tel: 0161-273 4400

**KESTER Gaby**
e-mail: casting@gabykester.com

**KIBBEY Leoni CASTING**
Website: www.leonikibbey.com
e-mail: casting@leonikibbey.com
Mobile: 07855 313552
Tel: 01727 375166

**KLIMEK Nana CASTING**
Unit 4, 2nd Floor, 18 Kingsland Road
Shoreditch, London E2 8DA
Website: www.nanaklimek.com
e-mail: casting@nanaklimek.com
Tel: 020-7502 9478

**KNIGHT-SMITH Jerry**
(CDG Member)
Royal Exchange Theatre Company
St Ann's Square, Manchester M2 7DH
Fax: 0161-615 6691
Tel: 0161-615 6761

**KOREL Suzy**
(CDG Member)
20 Blenheim Road, London NW8 0LX
e-mail: suzy@korel.org
Fax: 020-7372 3964
Tel: 020-7624 6435

**KRUGER Beatrice**
(FBI Casting S.r.l.)
46 via della Pelliccia, 00153 Roma, Italy
Website: www.fbicasting.com
e-mail: beatrice.kruger@fbicasting.it
Fax: 00 39 06 23328203
Tel: 00 39 06 58332747

**KYLE CASTING**
*Contact: Greg Kyle*
71B North Worple Way
Mortlake, London SW14 8PR
e-mail: kylecasting@btinternet.com
Tel: 020-8876 6763

**LARCA Ltd**
*(Welsh Language/English) Commercials. Film. Stage
Television*
Ynyslas Uchaf Farm, Blackmill, Bridgend CF35 6DW
Website: www.leigh-annregancasting.co.uk
Fax: 01656 841815
Mobile: 07779 321954

**LAYTON Claudie CASTING**
Unit 308, Canalot Studios
222 Kensal Road, London W10 5BN
e-mail: casting@claudielayton.com
Fax: 020-8968 1330
Tel: 020-8964 2055

**LEVENE Jon**
Website: www.jonlevenecasting.com
e-mail: jonlevene@mac.com
Mobile: 07977 570899
Tel: 020-7792 8501

**LEVINSON Sharon**
30 Stratford Villas, London NW1 9SG
e-mail: sharonlev@blueyonder.co.uk
Tel: 020-7485 2057

**LIHUK CASTING**
28 Meir Yaari, Tel Aviv 69371
Website: www.lihuk.co.il
e-mail: info@lihuk.co.il
Tel: +972 77 7675006

**LINDSAY-STEWART Karen**
(CDG Member)
PO Box 2301, London W1A 1PT
Fax: 020-7439 0548
Tel: 020-7439 0544

**LIP SERVICE CASTING Ltd**
*Contact: By Post
Accepts Voicereels. Voice Overs only*
60-66 Wardour Street, London W1F 0TA
Website: www.lipservice.co.uk
e-mail: bookings@lipservice.co.uk
Fax: 020-7734 3373
Tel: 020-7734 3393

**LUNN Maggie**
(CDG Member)
Unit HG14, Aberdeen Centre
22-24 Highbury Grove
London N5 2EA
e-mail: maggie@maggielunn.co.uk
Tel: 020-7226 7502

**MAGSON Kay**
(CDG Member)
*Contact: By e-mail. Theatre*
PO Box 175, Pudsey, Leeds LS28 7WY
e-mail: kay.magson@btinternet.com
Tel: 0113-236 0251

**MANN Andrew**
Studio 125, 77 Beak Street, London W1F 9DB
Website: www.castinguk.com
e-mail: drew@castinguk.com
Tel: 020-7993 5165

**MANNING John**
4 Holmbury Gardens
Hayes, Middlesex UB3 2LU
Tel: 020-8573 5463

**MARCH Heather CASTING**
*Contact: By e-mail. Commercials. Idents
Photographic. Pop Promos*
Bow Wharf
221 Grove Road, London E3 5SN
Website: www.heathermarchcasting.com
e-mail: hm@heathermarchcasting.com
Tel: 020-8981 4184

**McCANN Joan**
(CDG Member)
26 Hereford Road, London W3 9JW
Fax: 020-8992 8715
Tel: 020-8993 1747

**McLEOD Carolyn**
*Contact: By e-mail
Commercials. Film. Television*
10 Courtmead Close, London SE24 9HW
Website: www.cmcasting.co.uk
e-mail: info@cmcasting.co.uk
Tel: 020-7274 4981

**McLEOD Thea**
e-mail: mcleodcasting@hotmail.com
Mobile: 07941 541314
Tel: 020-8888 8993

**McMURRICH Chrissie**
*Contact: By Post
Accepts Showreels*
16 Spring Vale Avenue
Brentford, Middlesex TW8 9QH
Tel: 020-8568 0137

**McSHANE Sooki**
(CDG Member)
8A Piermont Road,
East Dulwich, London SE22 0LN
Tel: 020-8693 7411

**McWILLIAMS Debbie**
e-mail: debbie@debbiemcwilliamscasting.com
Mobile: 07785 575805
Tel: 020-7450 0529

**MEULENBERG Thea**
Keizersgracht 116, 1015 CW
Amsterdam, The Netherlands
Website: www.theameulenberg.com
e-mail: info@theameulenberg.com
Fax: 00 31 20 622 9894
Tel: 00 31 20 626 5846

### KATHERINE JAMES PHOTOGRAPHY

M: 07734 680543     info@katherine-james.com          www.katherine-james.com

**MILLER Hannah**
(CDG Member)
(See ROYAL SHAKESPEARE COMPANY)

**MOISELLE Frank**
7 Corrig Avenue
Dun Laoghaire
Co. Dublin, Ireland
Fax: 00 353 1 2803277          Tel: 00 353 1 2802857

**MOISELLE Nuala**
7 Corrig Avenue, Dun Laoghaire
Co. Dublin, Ireland
Fax: 00 353 1 2803277          Tel: 00 353 1 2802857

**MOORE Stephen**
BBC DRAMA SERIES CASTING
BBC Elstree, Room N222
Neptune House, Clarendon Road
Borehamwood, Herts WD6 1JF
Fax: 020-8228 8311          Tel: 020-8228 7109

**MORGAN Andy CASTING**
Coach House
114 Palace Road, London SW2 3JZ          Tel: 020-8674 5375

**MORRISON Melika**
Contact: By Post
Accepts Showreels. Film. Radio. Television
12A Rosebank, Holyport Road
London SW6 6LG          Tel/Fax: 020-7381 1571

**MUGSHOTS**
Contact: Becky Kidd
153 Buckhurst Avenue, Carshalton, Surrey SM5 1PD
e-mail: becky@mugshots.co.uk
Fax: 020-8296 8056          Mobile: 07880 896911

**NATIONAL THEATRE CASTING DEPARTMENT**
Contact: Wendy Spon, Head of Casting (CDG Member)
Alastair Coomer, Deputy Head of Casting (CDG Member),
Juliet Horsley, Casting Assistant.
By Post
Upper Ground, South Bank, London SE1 9PX
Website: www.nationaltheatre.org.uk
Fax: 020-7452 3340          Tel: 020-7452 3336

**NEEDLEMAN Sue**
19 Stanhope Gardens, London NW7 2JD
Fax: 020-8959 0225          Tel: 020-8959 1550

 # SPOTLIGHT
## Casting from start to finish

## Spotlight Database

- Browse over 35,000 actors, actresses, presenters, stunt artists, children and dancers
- View performer CVs, photos, showreels, portfolios and contact details
- Know that every Spotlight performer has professional training or experience

## Spotlight Website

- Email casting calls to hundreds of UK agents and performers, and receive responses in minutes
- Find exactly the right performer for the part, with our award-winning search engine

## Spotlight Rooms & Studios

- Six meeting rooms and three state-of-the-art casting studios
- Hold your auditions in the heart of central London
- Post DVD quality audition clips online in minutes

www.spotlight.com    020 7437 7631    casting@spotlight.com

**NORCLIFFE Belinda**
*Contact: Belinda Norcliffe, Matt Selby*
23 Brougham Road, London W3 6JD
e-mail: belinda@bncasting.co.uk
Fax: 020-8992 5533                    Tel: 020-8992 1333

**O'BRIEN Debbie**
72 High Street, Ashwell
Nr Baldock, Herts SG7 5NS
Fax: 01462 743110                     Tel: 01462 742919

**O'CONNOR Orla**
The Out of The Blue Drill Hall
36 Dalmeny Street
Edinburgh EH6 8RG                     Tel: 0131-553 0559
e-mail: orlaoconnor@live.co.uk

**O'DONNELL Rory**
178A Adelaide Avenue, London SE4 1JN
e-mail: tyrconnellpictures@hotmail.com
Fax: 020-8690 8005           Mobile: 07940 073165

**ORANGE James CASTING**
PO Box 51130
London SE13 7ZW                      Tel: 020-8297 0524
e-mail: casting@jamesorange.com

**PALMER Helena**
(CDG Member)
(See ROYAL SHAKESPEARE COMPANY)

**PARRISS Susie CASTING**
(CDG Member)
PO Box 40, Morden SM4 4WJ
Fax: 020-8543 3327                    Tel: 020-8543 3326

**PERRYMENT Mandy CASTING**
e-mail: mail@mandyperryment.com    Mobile: 07790 605191

**PETTS Tree CASTING**
125 Hendon Way
London NW2 2NA                       Tel: 020-8458 8898
e-mail: casting@treepetts.co.uk

**PLANTIN Kate**
4 Riverside
Lower Hampton Road
Sunbury on Thames TW16 5PW
e-mail: kateplantin@hotmail.com
Fax: 01932 783235                    Tel: 01932 782350

**POLENTARUTTI Tania CASTING**
(CDG Member)
*Contact: By e-mail*
e-mail: tania@filmtvcasting.com
Mobile: 07720 299635                 Tel: 020-8555 3163

**POOLE Gilly**
(CDG Member)
(See CROWLEY POOLE CASTING)

**PROCTOR Carl**
(CDG Member)
3rd Floor, 76 Neal Street
Covent Garden, London WC2H 9PL
Website: www.carlproctor.com
e-mail: carlproctor@btconnect.com
Mobile: 07956 283340                 Tel: 020-7379 6200

**PRYOR Andy**
(CDG Member)
Suite 3, 15 Broad Court
London WC2B 5QN
Fax: 020-7836 8299                   Tel: 020-7836 8298

**PURO CASTING**
91 Bellenden Road, London SE15 4QL
Website: www.purocasting.com
e-mail: office@purocasting.com
Fax: 07006 056678                    Tel: 020-7207 9155

**REICH Liora**
25 Manor Park Road, London N2 0SN   Tel: 020-8444 1686

**REYNOLDS Gillian CASTING**
25 St Kevin's Parade
Dublin 8, Ireland            Tel: 00 353 1 4546309
Website: www.gillianreynoldscasting.com
e-mail: gillianreynoldscasting@gmail.com

**REYNOLDS Simone**
(CDG Member)
60 Hebdon Road, London SW17 7NN     Tel: 020-8672 5443

**RHODES JAMES Kate**
(CDG Member)
Suite 6, 135 High Street
Teddington TW11 8HH                  Tel: 020-8977 1191
e-mail: office@krjcasting.com

**RIPLEY Jane**
e-mail: jane@janeripleycasting.co.uk   Tel: 020-8342 8216

**ROBERTSON Sasha CASTING Ltd**
*Contact: Sasha Robertson (CDG Member)*
*Maddy Hinton, Associate*
19 Wendell Road, London W12 9RS
e-mail: casting@sasharobertson.com
Fax: 020-8740 1396                   Tel: 020-8740 0817

**ROFFE Danielle**
(CDG Member)
e-mail: danielle@danielleroffe.com   Mobile: 07939 225791

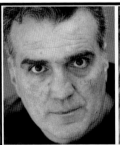

**ROSE Dionne**
78 York Street
London W1H 1DP                    Mobile: 07500 554813
e-mail: mail@drbentertainment.co.uk

**ROWAN Amy CASTING**
PO Box 10247, Blackrock
Co. Dublin, Ireland
Fax: 00 353 1 2802005             Tel: 00 353 1 2140514

**ROYAL SHAKESPEARE COMPANY**
*Contact: Hannah Miller, Head of Casting (CDG Member)*
*Helena Palmer (CDG Member), Janine Snape, Jim Arnold*
Casting Department
1 Earlham Street, London WC2H 9LL
Website: www.rsc.org.uk
Fax: 020-7845 0505                Tel: 020-7845 0530

**RYCROFT CASTING**
*Contact: Amy Rycroft*
17 Bow Connection
London E3 2QF                     Tel: 0844 3510205
Website: www.rycroftcasting.co.uk
e-mail: amy@rycroftcasting.co.uk

**SALBERG Jane**
86 Stade Street, Hythe, Kent CT21 6DY
e-mail: janesalberg@aol.com
Mobile: 07931 932103             Tel: 01303 239277

**SCHILLER Ginny**
53 Clapton Common
London E5 9AA                     Tel: 020-8806 5383
e-mail: ginny.schiller@virgin.net

**SCHOFIELD Gilly**
(CDG Member)
G S CASTING Ltd
e-mail: gillyschofield1@btinternet.com

**SCHWARTZ Marie Claude**
13 Av de Fouilleuse
Saint Cloud, 92210, France        Tel: 00 33 146 02 99 09
Website: www.assorda.com
e-mail: mc.schwartz@assorda.com

**SCOTT Laura**
(CDG Member)
56 Rowena Crescent
London SW11 2PT
Website: www.thecdg.co.uk
e-mail: laurascottcasting@mac.com
Fax: 020-7924 1907               Tel: 020-7978 6336

**SEARCHERS The**
70 Sylvia Court
Cavendish Street, London N1 7PG
e-mail: waynesearcher@mac.com
Fax: 020-7684 5763               Mobile: 07958 922829

**SEECOOMAR Nadira**
PO Box 167, Twickenham TW1 2UP    Tel: 020-8892 8478

**SELECT CASTING Ltd**
PO Box 748, London NW4 1TT
Website: www.selectcasting.co.uk
e-mail: info@selectcasting.co.uk
Fax: 020-8203 2007               Mobile: 07956 131494

**SHAW David**
(See KEOGH Beverley CASTING Ltd)

**SHAW Phil**
Suite 476, 2 Old Brompton Road
South Kensington, London SW7 3DQ  Tel: 020-8715 8943
e-mail: shawcastlond@aol.com

**SHEPHERD Debbie CASTING**
Suite 16, 63 St Martin's Lane
London WC2N 4JS                  Tel: 020-7240 0400
e-mail: debbie@debbieshepherd.com

**SID PRODUCTIONS**
110 Sandringham Flats
Charing Cross Road, London WC2H 0BP  Tel: 01932 863194
Website: www.sidproductions.co.uk
e-mail: casting@sidproductions.co.uk

**SIMPSON Georgia**
The Gate House
20 Killaire Road
Bangor, Co. Down
Northern Ireland BT19 1EY        Tel: 028-9147 0800
Website: www.georgiasimpson.com
e-mail: georgia@georgiasimpson.com

**SINGER Sandra ASSOCIATES**
*Contact: By e-mail*
21 Cotswold Road
Westcliff-on-Sea, Essex SS0 8AA
Website: www.sandrasinger.com
e-mail: sandrasingeruk@aol.com
Fax: 01702 339393                Tel: 01702 331616

**SMITH Michelle**
(CDG Member)
*Contact: By Post*
*Accepts Showreels/Voicereels*
*Animation. Commercials. Corporate. Film. Television*
220 Church Lane, Stockport SK7 1PQ
Fax: 0161-439 0622               Tel: 0161-439 6825

**SMITH Suzanne**
(CDG Member)
33 Fitzroy Street, London W1T 6DU
e-mail: zan@dircon.co.uk
Fax: 020-7436 9690               Tel: 020-7436 9255

**SNAPE Janine**
(See ROYAL SHAKESPEARE COMPANY)

**SOLOMON Alison**
Birmingham Repertory Theatre
Centenary Square, Broad Street
Birmingham B1 2EP                Tel: 0121-245 2023

## ROUND ISLAND

HEADSHOTS BY LAURA MILLER

### £130

www.roundisland.net
email: photos@roundisland.net

"A breath of fresh air.
Relaxed. Friendly. Fantastic shots."
Pauline Whitaker

LILLIE COLLIER

TRISTAM SUMMERS

**STAFFORD Emma CASTING**
The Royal Exchange
St Ann's Square, Manchester M2 7BR
Website: www.emmastafford.tv
e-mail: info@emmastafford.tv
Fax: 0161-833 4264
Tel: 0161-833 4263

**STAFFORD Helen**
14 Park Avenue
Enfield, Middlesex EN1 2HP
e-mail: helen.stafford@blueyonder.co.uk
Fax: 020-8372 0611
Tel: 020-8360 6329

**STARK CASTING**
e-mail: stark.casting@virgin.net
Mobile: 07956 150689
Tel: 020-8800 0060

**STEVENS Gail CASTING**
(CDG Member)
Greenhill House
90-93 Cowcross Street, London EC1M 6BF
Fax: 020-7253 6574
Tel: 020-7253 6532

**STEVENS MILLEFIORINI Danny**
Via Sillaro 14, Cerveteri
Rome, Italy 00052
Tel: 0039 389 435 22 00
e-mail: dannystevens62@gmail.com

**STEVENSON Sam**
(CDG Member)
e-mail: sam@hancockstevenson.com

**STEWART Amanda CASTING**
Apartment 1, 35 Fortess Road
London NW5 1AD
Tel: 020-7485 7973

**STOLL Liz**
BBC DRAMA SERIES CASTING
BBC Elstree, Room N223
Neptune House
Clarendon Road
Borehamwood, Herts WD6 1JF
Fax: 020-8228 8311
Tel: 020-8228 8285

**STYLE Emma**
(CDG Member)
1 Overton Cottages, Kings Lane
Cookham, Maidenhead SL6 9BA
Tel: 01628 483740

**SUMMERS Mark CASTING**
(Formerly CASTING UNLIMITED)
1 Beaumont Avenue
West Kensington
London W14 9LP
Website: www.marksummers.com
e-mail: mark@marksummers.com
Tel: 020-7229 8413

**SYERS Michael**
(See CASTING CONNECTION The)

**SYSON GRAINGER CASTING**
Contact: Lucinda Syson (CDG Member)
Elaine Grainger (CDG Member)
1st Floor, 33 Old Compton Street
London W1D 5JT
e-mail: office@lucindasysoncasting.com
Fax: 020-7287 3629
Tel: 020-7287 5327

**TABAK Amanda (CDG Member)**
(See CANDID CASTING)

 **NICHOLAS DAWKES** ☎ 07787 111 997 WWW.NICHOLASDAWKESPHOTOGRAPHY.CO.UK

**TEECE Shirley CASTING**
Contact: By e-mail
106 North View Road, London N8 7LP    Tel: 020-8347 9241
e-mail: shirlteece@btinternet.com

**TOPPING Nicci**
The Media Centre
7 Northumberland Street HD1 1RL
Website: www.toppscasting.co.uk
e-mail: info@toppscasting.co.uk
Mobile: 07802 684256    Tel: 01484 511988

**TRAMONTANO Luisa CASTING**
Wild Farm, Harper Lane, Radlett
Herts WD7 9HJ    Mobile: 07767 438787
Website: www.luisatcasting.co.uk
e-mail: luisa@luisatcasting.co.uk

**TREVELLICK Jill**
(CDG Member)
92 Priory Road, London N8 7EY    Tel: 020-8340 2734
e-mail: jill@jilltrevellick.com

**TREVIS Sarah**
(CDG Member)
PO Box 47170, London W6 6BA
e-mail: info@sarahtrevis.com
Fax: 020-7602 8110    Tel: 020-7602 5552

**TWIST & FLIC CASTING**
Contact: Penny Burrows
1A Carlton Avenue
Dulwich Village, London SE21 7DE
Website: www.sportsmodels.com
e-mail: info@sportsmodels.com
Mobile: 07973 863263    Tel: 020-8299 8800

**VAN OST & MILLINGTON CASTING**
Contact: Valerie Van Ost, Andrew Millington
PO Box 115
Petersfield GU31 5BB    Tel: 01730 821530

**VAUGHAN Sally**
(CDG Member)
Contact: By Post.
Accepts Showreels. Theatre
2 Kennington Park Place
London SE11 4AS    Tel: 020-7735 6539
e-mail: svaughan12@btinternet.com

**VITAL PRODUCTIONS**
e-mail: mail@vital-productions.co.uk    Mobile: 07957 284709

**VOSSER Anne CASTING**
(CDG Member)
PO Box 408
Aldershot GU11 9DS
e-mail: anne@vosser-casting.co.uk
Mobile: 07968 868712    Tel: 01252 404716

**WEIR Fiona**
(CDG Member)
2nd Floor
138 Portobello Road
London W11 2DZ    Tel: 020-7727 5600

**WEST June**
(CDG Member)
Granada Television, Quay Street
Manchester M60 9EA
Fax: 0161-827 2853    Tel: 0161-952 1000

**WESTERN Matt CASTING**
Contact: By Post/e-mail
Accepts Showreels
Children. Commercials. Film. Television
150 Blythe Road
London W14 0HD    Tel: 020-7602 6646
Website: www.mattwestern.co.uk
e-mail: matt@mattwestern.co.uk

**WHALE Toby**
(CDG Member)
80 Shakespeare Road
London W3 6SN
Website: www.whalecasting.com
e-mail: toby@whalecasting.com
Fax: 020-8993 8096    Tel: 020-8993 2821

**WHITTINGHAM Ian Zachary CASTING**
77 Brick Lane
Liverpool Street
London E1 6QL
Website: www.ipc.co.uk
e-mail: zachwhittingham@ymail.com
Fax: 020-3246 0081    Tel: 020-3246 0088

**WICKSTEED Rose CASTING**
39 Sinclair Mansions, Richmond Way
London W12 8LN    Tel: 020-8743 0193
Website: www.rosewicksteed.com
e-mail: casting@rosewicksteed.com

**WILDMANHALL CASTING**
Contact: Vicky Wildman, Buffy Hall
1 Child's Place, London SW5 9RX    Tel: 020-7373 2036
e-mail: wildmanhall@mac.com

**WILLIS Catherine**
Contact: By e-mail
e-mail: catherine@cwcasting.co.uk    Tel: 020-7697 4482

**YOUNGSTAR CASTING**
Children & Teenagers only
5 Union Castle House
Canute Road SO14 3FJ    Tel: 023-8047 7717
Website: www.youngstar.tv
e-mail: info@youngstar.tv

**ZIMMERMANN Jeremy CASTING**
36 Marshall Street
London W1F 7EY
Fax: 020-7437 4747    Tel: 020-7478 5161

**ACADEMY OF PERSONAL TRAINING Ltd**
(APT Ltd)
West Acre, Hurst Lane
Egham, Surrey TW20 8QJ     Mobile: 07776 304511
e-mail: alan@academypt.org

**ACE FEATURE FILM**
Contact: Margaret Cooper (Executive Producer)
(Sourcing Investors, Product Placement, Cast & Crew)
75/1 Old College Street
Sliema SLM03, Malta
Website: www.maggiessite.multiply.com
e-mail: acefilm1@yahoo.com
Mobile: 07765 927008     Tel: 00 3 56 99 09 71 79

**ACTING BUDDY**
Website: www.actingbuddy.com
e-mail: info@actingbuddy.com     Tel: 020-7558 8020

**ACTOR'S ONE-STOP SHOP The**
(Showreels for Performing Artists)
First Floor, Above The Gate Pub
Station Road, London N22 7SS     Tel: 020-8888 7006
Website: www.actorsonestopshop.com
e-mail: info@actorsonestopshop.com

**AGENTFILE**
(Software for Agents)
Website: www.agentfile.com
e-mail: admin@agentfile.com     Mobile: 07050 683662

**AKA PRODUCTIONS**
(Advertising, Design, Sales, Promotions & Marketing)
1st Floor
115 Shaftesbury Avenue
Cambridge Circus, London WC2H 8AF
Website: www.akauk.com
e-mail: aka@akauk.com
Fax: 020-7836 8787     Tel: 020-7836 4747

**ARIAS Enrique**
(Subtitles, Translations & Voice Overs)
Website: www.nwlondon.com/eag
e-mail: enriqueag@gmail.com     Mobile: 07956 261568

**ARTS VA The**
Contact: Bronwyn Robertson
(Experienced PA and Admin Support)
PO Box 2911 CV37 1WU     Tel: 01789 552559
Website: www.theartsva.com
e-mail: bronwyn@theartsva.com

**AUDIO DESCRIPTION (THEATRE DESCRIPTION)**
(West End & on Tour)
e-mail: info@theatredescription.com     Mobile: 07747 655215

**BARTERCARD**
Lakeside House
1 Furzeground Way
Stockley Park East
Uxbridge UB11 1BD     Tel: 0845 2197000
Website: www.bartercard.co.uk
e-mail: info@bartercard.co.uk

**BIG PICTURE**
(Casual Work in IT Field Marketing)
13 Netherwood Road
London W14 0BL     Tel: 020-7371 4455
Website: www.ebigpicture.co.uk
e-mail: info@ebigpicture.co.uk

**BRITISH ASSOCIATION OF DRAMATHERAPISTS**
Waverley
Battledown Approach
Cheltenham, Glos GL52 6RE     Tel/Fax: 01242 235515
Website: www.badth.org.uk
e-mail: enquiries@badth.org.uk

**BUTCHER Litz**
(Psychic Medium)
Cromer Mansions
Cheam Road, Sutton SM1 2SR     Tel: 020-8401 6234
e-mail: litz@litzbutcher.co.uk

**BYFORD Simon PRODUCTION MANAGEMENT SERVICES**
(Production & Event Management)
22 Freshfield Place
Brighton
East Sussex BN2 0BN
e-mail: simon@simonbyfordpms.com
Fax: 01273 606402     Tel: 01273 623972

**BYRNE John**
(One-to-one Advice from The Stage's Career Advisor)
Website: www.showbusiness-success.com
e-mail: johnbyrnecontact@gmail.com     Tel: 0845 3969972

**CAP PRODUCTION SOLUTIONS Ltd**
(Technical Production Services)
116 Wigmore Road
Carshalton, Surrey SM5 1RQ
e-mail: leigh@leighporter.com
Fax: 07970 763480     Mobile: 07973 432576

**CASTLE MAGICAL SERVICES**
Contact: Michael Shepherd (Magical Effect Consultants)
Broompark
131 Tadcaster Road
Dringhouses, York YO24 1QJ  Tel/Fax: 01904 709500
e-mail: info@castlemagicalservices.co.uk

**CAULKETT Robin Dip SM, MIIRSM**
(Abseiling, Rope Work)
3 Churchill Way
Mitchell Dean, Glos GL17 0AZ  Mobile: 07970 442003

**CELEBRITIES WORLDWIDE Ltd**
(Celebrity Contacts & Booking)
39-41 New Oxford Street
London WC1A 1BN
Website: www.celebritiesworldwide.com
e-mail: info@celebritiesworldwide.com
Fax: 020-7836 7701  Tel: 020-7836 7702

**CHAPERONE AGENCY The**
Website: www.chaperoneagency.com  Mobile: 07960 075928
e-mail: chaperoneagency@hotmail.co.uk

**CHRISALYS CIRCUS**
(Circus Casting & Consultancy Service)
31 Abbess Close, London SW2 3BP  Mobile: 07809 832008
Website: www.chrisalys-circus.com
e-mail: chrisbab@hotmail.com

**CIRCUS MANIACS**
(Circus, Theatre, Dance, Choreography, Extreme Sports)
Office 8A
The Kingswood Foundation
Britannia Road, Kingswood, Bristol BS15 8DB
Website: www.circusmaniacsagency.com
e-mail: agency@circusmaniacs.com
Mobile: 07977 247287  Tel/Fax: 0117-947 7042

**CLASS - CARLINE LUNDON ASSOCIATES**
25 Falkner Square
Liverpool L8 7NZ  Mobile: 07853 248957
e-mail: carline.lundon@ukonline.co.uk

**COBO MEDIA Ltd**
(Performing Arts, Entertainment & Leisure Marketing)
43A Garthorne Road, London SE23 1EP
Website: www.cobomedia.com
e-mail: admin@cobomedia.com
Fax: 020-8291 4969  Tel: 020-8291 7079

**COLCLOUGH John**
(Practical Independent Guidance for Actors and Actresses)
Website: www.johncolclough.co.uk  Tel: 020-8873 1763
e-mail: john@johncolclough.org.uk

**CREATIVE CULTURE**
5 Denmark Street
London WC2H 8LP  Tel: 020-7193 3076
Website: www.creativecultureint.com
e-mail: m.chevalier@creativecultureint.com

**CREATIVE INDUSTRIES DEVELOPMENT AGENCY (CIDA)**
(Professional Development & Business Support for Artists
& Creative Businesses)
Media Centre, Huddersfield
West Yorkshire HD1 1RL
Website: www.cida.org
e-mail: info@cida.org
Fax: 01484 483150  Tel: 01484 483140

**CROFTS Andrew**
(Book Writing Services)
Westlands Grange
West Grinstead
Horsham, West Sussex RH13 8LZ  Tel/Fax: 01403 864518
Website: www.andrewcrofts.com

**CS SPORTS PROMOTIONS Ltd**
(Production Advisors, Sport, Stunts, Safety)
PO Box 878
Crystal Palace National Sports Centre
London SE19 2BH
e-mail: irene@sportspromotions.co.uk
Fax: 020-8776 7772  Tel: 020-8659 4561

**EARLE Kenneth PERSONAL MANAGEMENT**
214 Brixton Road
London SW9 6AP
e-mail: kennethearle@agents-uk.com
Fax: 020-7274 9529  Tel: 020-7274 1219

**EQUIP**
11 Balmoral Road, Gidea Park
Romford, Essex RM2 5XD  Tel: 01708 479898
Website: www.equip-u.com
e-mail: sales@equip-u.com

**ES GROUP Ltd**
Bell Lane
North Woolwich Road
London E16 2AB
Website: www.esgroup-uk.com
e-mail: info@esgroup-uk.com
Fax: 020-7055 7201  Tel: 020-7055 7200

**EVENT-SAFE**
(Matt-LX Ltd)
Gunnery House
9 Gunnery Terrace, London SE18 6SW
Website: www.mattlx.com
e-mail: eventsafe@mattlx.com
Fax: 020-8301 8149  Tel: 020-8301 8692

**EXCELLENT VIRTUAL ASSISTANCE Ltd**
N21 2HY
Website: www.excellentvirtualassistance.com
e-mail: info@excellentvirtualassistance.com
Mobile: 07787 186478  Tel: 0844 3309719

**FACADE**
(Creation & Production of Musicals)
43A Garthorne Road
London SE23 1EP
e-mail: facade@cobomedia.com
Fax: 020-8291 4969  Tel: 020-8291 7079

**FERRIS ENTERTAINMENT MUSIC**
(London, Cardiff, Belfast. Music for Film & Television)
Number 8
132 Charing Cross Road
London WC2H 0LA  Tel: 0845 4724725
Website: www.ferrisentertainment.com
e-mail: info@ferrisentertainment.com

**FIGHT CHOREOGRAPHER & ACTION DIRECTOR**
Contact: Nic Main (Professional Actor, Film Fighting
Choreographer)
South East  Mobile: 07739 184418
Website: www.nicmain.com
e-mail: nicmain@nicmain.com

# Magus Lynius Shadeè
## 'King of all Witches'
### Psychic ~ International ~ Occult Investigator & Consultant

**Specialist in**

*Psychic Research* ✳ *Paranormal Phenomena* ✳ *Practical Ritual Workings* ✳ *Hauntings*
*Physical Mediumship* ✳ *Materialisations* ✳ *Direct Voice Communications* ✳ *Exorcisms*
✳ *Transcendental Magic* ✳ *Witchcraft* ✳ *White & Black Magic* ✳ *The Occult*

**Suite 362  10 Great Russell Street  London WC1B 3BC  Tel: 020 8378 6844  Mob: 07740 043156**
email: maguslyniusshadee@hotmail.com  www.occultcentre.com  www.lifeafterdeath.net

**102 Rue de Normandy  53250  Neuilly Le Vendin  France**
**Tel: (00) (33) 2430395  www.barackobama4u.com  www.infantjesus.com**

---

**FISHER Judy Associates**
(Recruitment Consultants)
7 Swallow Street, London W1B 4DE
Website: www.judyfisher.co.uk
e-mail: david@judyfisher.co.uk
Fax: 020-7494 4595          Tel: 020-7437 2277

**FLAMES MARTIAL ARTS ACADEMY**
Contact: Adam Richards
Unit 2, 128 Milton Road Business Park
Gravesend, Kent DA12 2PG          Mobile: 07950 396389
Website: www.kuentao.com
e-mail: stunts@adamrichardsstunts.co.uk

**FOUR SEASONS RECRUITMENT**
(Recruitment Company)
Landmark House, Hammersmith Bridge Road
London W6 9EJ
Website: www.fsrl.co.uk
e-mail: lizi@fsrl.co.uk
Fax: 020-8237 8999          Tel: 020-8237 8900

**FULL EFFECT The**
(Live Event Producers including Choreographers)
Exchange Building
16 St Cuthbert's Street
Bedford MK40 3JG
Website: www.thefulleffect.co.uk
e-mail: mark.harrison@tfe.co.uk
Fax: 01234 214445          Tel: 01234 269099

**GHOSTWRITER/AUTHOR**
Contact: John Parker
Dove Cottage
The Street, Ickham CT3 1QP          Tel: 01227 721071
e-mail: parkerwrite@aol.com

**GILMOUR Rev/Prof/Dr Glenn, MscD, SHsc.D, NFH, BCMA.Reg**
(Fully Qualified/International Medium. Clairvoyant, Healer & Holistic Therapist. Consultant Paranormal/Metaphysics/Occult for Radio/TV)
Website: www.drglenngilmour.com          Tel: 0114-231 6500
e-mail: drglenngilmour@yahoo.com

**GOLDIELLE PROMOTIONS**
(Events)
68 Lynton Drive, Hillside
Southport, Merseyside PR8 4QQ          Tel: 01704 566604
Website: www.goldiellepromotions.com
e-mail: goldielle@yahoo.co.uk

**HANDS UP PUPPETS**
Contact: Marcus Clarke
7 Cavendish Vale
Nottingham NG5 4DS          Mobile: 07909 824630
Website: www.handsuppuppets.com
e-mail: enquiries@handsuppuppets.com

**HARLEY PRODUCTIONS**
68 New Cavendish Street
London W1G 8TE
e-mail: harleyprods@aol.com
Fax: 020-8202 8863          Tel: 020-7580 3247

**HAYES Susan**
(Choreographer)
46 Warrington Crescent
London W9 1EP          Mobile: 07721 927714
e-mail: susan22@btinternet.com

**HERITAGE RAILWAY ASSOCIATION**
10 Hurdeswell
Long Hanborough
Witney
Oxfordshire OX29 8DH          Tel: 01993 883384
Website: www.heritagerailways.com

**HGV BRAND IDENTITY DESIGN CONSULTANTS**
2-6 Northburgh Street
London EC1V 0AY
Website: www.hgv.co.uk
e-mail: pierre@hgv.co.uk
Fax: 020-7336 6345          Tel: 020-7336 6336

**IMAGE DIGGERS**
(Slide/Stills/Audio/Video Library & Theme Research)
618B Finchley Road
London NW11 7RR          Tel: 020-8455 4564
Website: www.imagediggers.netfirms.com
e-mail: lambhorn@gmail.com

**IMPACT AGENCY The**
(Public Relations)
3 Bloomsbury Place
London WC1A 2QL
e-mail: mail@impactagency.co.uk
Fax: 020-7580 7200          Tel: 020-7580 1770

**I R A - INDEPENDENT REVIEWS ARTS SERVICES**
(Stories from the Art World)          Mobile: 07956 212916
e-mail: critic@independentradioarts.com

**JACKSON Kim**
(Forum Theatre Practitioner)
Transforum, Studio B402
LCB Depot
31 Rutland Street
Leicester LE1 1RW      Tel: 0116-253 3429
e-mail: kim@transforum.co.uk

**JENKINS Andrew Ltd**
(General Management & Accountancy)
63 Kidbrooke Park Road
London SE3 0EE
Website: www.andrewjenkinsltd.com
e-mail: info@andrewjenkinsltd.com
Fax: 020-8856 7106      Tel: 020-8319 3657

**JFL SEARCH & SELECTION**
(Recruitment Consultants)
27 Beak Street
London W1F 9RU
Website: www.jflrecruit.com
Fax: 020-7734 6501      Tel: 020-7009 3500

**JOHNSON Gareth Ltd**
Plas Hafren, Eglwyswrw
Crymych
Pembrokeshire SA41 3UL      Tel: 01239 891368
e-mail: gjltd@mac.com

**JORDAN Richard PRODUCTIONS Ltd**
(General Management, UK and International Productions,
Festivals, Production Consultancy)
Mews Studios
16 Vernon Yard
London W11 2DX
e-mail: richard.jordan@virgin.net
Fax: 020-7313 9667      Tel: 020-7243 9001

**JOSHI CLINIC The**
57 Wimpole Street
London W1G 8YW
Website: www.joshiclinic.co.uk
e-mail: info@joshiclinic.co.uk
Fax: 020-7486 9622      Tel: 020-7487 5456

**KEAN LANYON Ltd**
(Graphic Designers, PR & Marketing Consultants)
Rose Cottage
Aberdeen Centre
22 Highbury Grove
London N5 2EA
Website: www.keanlanyon.com
e-mail: iain@keanlanyon.com
Fax: 020-7359 0199      Tel: 020-7354 3362

**KELLER Don**
(Marketing Consultancy & Project Management)
65 Glenwood Road
Harringay
London N15 3JS      Tel: 020-8800 4882
e-mail: info@dakam.org.uk

**KIEVE Paul**
(Magical Effects for Theatre & Film)
2 St Philip's Road
London E8 3BP      Tel/Fax: 020-7502 2213
Website: www.stageillusion.com
e-mail: mail@stageillusion.com

**LAMBOLLE Robert**
(Script Evaluation/Editing)
618B Finchley Road
London NW11 7RR      Tel: 020-8455 4564
Website: www.readingandrighting.netfirms.com
e-mail: lambhorn@gmail.com

**LEEP MARKETING & PR**
(Marketing, Press and Publicity)
5 Nassau House
122 Shaftesbury Avenue, London W1D 5ER
e-mail: philip@leep.biz
Fax: 020-7439 8833      Tel: 020-7439 9777

**LEO MEDIA & ENTERTAINMENT GROUP The**
(Television & Literary Consultancy, Legal Work, Executive
Production)
150 Minories, London EC3N 1LS
Website: www.leomediagroup.com
e-mail: info@leomediagroup.com
Fax: 07006 057893      Tel: 020-7183 3177

**LOCATION TUTORS NATIONWIDE**
(Fully Qualified/Experienced Teachers working with
Children on Film Sets and Covering all Key Stages of
National Curriculum)
16 Poplar Walk
Herne Hill, London SE24 0BU
Website: www.locationtutors.co.uk
e-mail: locationtutorsnationwide@hotmail.com
Fax: 020-7207 8794      Tel: 020-7978 8898

**LOVE Billie HISTORICAL PHOTOGRAPHS**
(Picture Research. Formerly 'Amanda' Theatrical
Portraiture)
3 Winton Street, Ryde, Isle of Wight PO33 2BX
Fax: 01983 616565      Tel: 01983 812572

**LUXFACTOR GROUP (UK) The**
Fleet Place
12 Nelson Drive
Petersfield, Hampshire GU31 4SJ
Website: www.luxfactor.co.uk
e-mail: info@luxfactor.co.uk
Fax: 0845 3700588      Tel: 0845 3700589

**MAGICIANS.CO.UK**
(Entertainers and Magic Consultants)
Regent House
291 Kirkdale, London SE26 4QD
e-mail: mail@magicians.co.uk
Fax: 0845 0062443      Tel: 0845 0062442

**MAIN Nic**
(Experienced Stage, TV & Film Action & Fight Director &
Actor)
62 Kingsway, Blackwater
Camberley, Surrey GU17 0JB      Mobile: 07739 184418
Website: www.nicmain.com
e-mail: nicmain@nicmain.com

**MAYS Lorraine**
(Children's Licensed Chaperone)
Park View, Stanley Avenue
Chesham, Bucks HP5 2JF
e-mail: laneatrainbows@aol.com
Mobile: 07778 106552      Tel: 01494 771029

## Minimal Risk Consultancy
Security Consultancy ■ Security Services ■ Security Recruitment
www.minimalrisk.co.uk ■ london@minimalrisk.co.uk ■ www.minimalriskrecruitment.com

We are a family owned business who cater for the needs of specialist organisations & individuals; including those in the arts & entertainment. From overseas travel advice to location security & personal protection using former military personnel. Tailored & affordable care for both one-off & longer-term requirements. Call us in confidence on **020 7340 8565**.

**McKENNA Deborah Ltd**
(Celebrity Chefs & Lifestyle Presenters)
64-66 Glentham Road
Barnes, London SW13 9PP
Website: www.deborahmckenna.com
e-mail: info@deborahmckenna.com
Fax: 020-8846 0967     Tel: 020-8846 0966

**MEDIA LEGAL**
(Education Services)
West End House
83 Clarendon Road
Sevenoaks, Kent TN13 1ET     Tel: 01732 460592

**MILDENBERG Vanessa**
(Director, Choreographer, Movement Director)
Flat 6
Cameford Court
New Park Road
London SW2 4LH     Mobile: 07796 264828

**MILITARY ADVISORY & INSTRUCTION SPECIALISTS**
Contact: John Sessions (Advice on Weapons, Drill, Period to Present. Ex-Army Instructors)
38 Kempton Close
Strensall
York YO32 5ZF     Tel: 01904 491198
e-mail: johnmusic1@hotmail.com

**MINIMAL RISK**
(Security Consultancy)
3rd Floor
111 Buckingham Palace Road
London SW1W 0SR     Tel: 01432 360643
Website: www.minimalrisk.co.uk
e-mail: london@minimalrisk.co.uk

**MINISTRY OF FUN The**
(Entertainment/Promotions/PR Marketing Campaigns)
Unit 1
Suffolk Studios
127-129 Great Suffolk Street
London SE1 1PP
Website: www.ministryoffun.net
e-mail: james@ministryoffun.net
Fax: 020-7407 5763     Tel: 020-7407 6077

**MORGAN Jane ASSOCIATES (JMA)**
(Marketing & Media)
8 Heathville Road
London N19 3AJ
e-mail: jma@janemorganassociates.com
Fax: 020-7263 9877     Tel: 020-7263 9867

**MULLEN Julie**
(Improvisors/Comedy Consultancy)
The Impro Lab
34 Watts Lane
Teddington Lock TW11 8HQ     Mobile: 07956 877839

**MUSIC SOLUTIONS Ltd**
Garden Studios
11-15 Betterton Street
London WC2H 9BP     Tel: 020-7866 8160
e-mail: mail@musicsolutions.ltd.uk

**NEATE Rodger PRODUCTION MANAGEMENT**
15 Soutcote Road
London N19 5BJ     Tel: 020-7609 9538
e-mail: rneate@dircon.co.uk

**NEXTSTOPLAX**
(Relocation of Entertainment Industry Professionals)
Next Stop House
3450 Cahuenga Blvd
Unit 304, Los Angeles CA 90068
Website: www.nextstoplax.com
e-mail: info@nextstoplax.com
Tel: (323) 798-5102     Tel: (323) 798-5103

**ORANGE TREE STUDIO Ltd & MUSIC SERVICES**
(Original Music/Composition & Production, Saxophonist & Brass Section For Hire)
PO Box 99
Kings Langley WD4 8FB
Website: www.orangetreestudio.com
e-mail: richard@orangetreestudio.com
Mobile: 07768 146200     Tel: 01923 440550

**PB PRODUCTIVE**
(Photographers' Agent. Shoot, Production & Event Management)
Ubbeston Lodge, Ubbeston
Halesworth, Suffolk IP19 0EY     Mobile: 07957 424776
Website: www.pbproductive.com
e-mail: info@pbproductive.com

**PENROSE Scott**
(Magic for TV, Film & Theatre)
17 Berkeley Drive, Billericay
Essex CM12 0YP     Mobile: 07767 336882
Website: www.stagemagician.com
e-mail: mail@stagemagician.com

**PINEWOOD NET**
(Networking Group)
86 Hurst Farm Road
East Grinstead
West Sussex RH19 4DH     Mobile: 07882 794583
Website: www.pinewoodnet.net
e-mail: katy@pinewoodnet.net

**POLICE ACTION**
(Police Personnel & Tactical Arms Group Inc./Riot Police with Shields)
39 Gregson Close
Borehamwood WD6 5RW
e-mail: police-action@hotmail.co.uk
Mobile: 07920 421347     Mobile: 07005 993434

**PRODUCTIONS & PROMOTIONS Ltd**
Apsley Mills Cottage
London Road
Hemel Hempstead
Herts HP3 9QU     Mobile: 07885 811757
Website: www.prodmotions.com
e-mail: reception@prodmotions.com

**PSYCHOLOGY GROUP The**
(Expert Opinion, Assessments, Psychotherapy &
Counselling, Presentation. Nationwide Service)
Website: www.psychologygroup.co.uk
e-mail: info@psychologygroup.co.uk
Fax: 0845 2805243     Tel: 0870 6092445

**PUPPET CENTRE TRUST**
(Development & Advocacy Agency for Puppetry & Related
Theatre)
BAC Lavender Hill
London SW11 5TN     Tel: 020-7228 5335
Website: www.puppetcentre.org.uk
e-mail: pct@puppetcentre.org.uk

**RB & Co Ltd**
Park View
Stanley Avenue
Chesham, Bucks HP5 2JF     Tel: 01494 771029
Website: www.childrensentertainmenttraining.co.uk
e-mail: laneatrainbows@aol.com

**RICHARDS Adam**
(Fight Director)
Unit 2
128 Milton Road Business Park
Gravesend
Kent DA12 2PG     Mobile: 07950 396389
Website: www.kuentao.com
e-mail: stunts@adamrichardsstunts.co.uk

**RIPLEY-DUGGAN PARTNERSHIP The**
(Tour Booking)
26 Goodge Street
London W1T 2QG     Tel: 020-7436 1392
e-mail: info@ripleyduggan.com

**SHAW Jennifer EVENTS**
(Event Management & Promotions)
15 Ladyhouse Lane
Milnrow OL16 4EH     Tel: 0845 1309517
Website: www.jennifershawevents.co.uk
e-mail: jennifer@jennifershawevents.co.uk

**SHOWBIZ FRIENDS**
(Community Website for all Showbiz People)
Website: www.showbizfriends.com

**SINCLAIR Andy**
(Mime)
Website: www.andyjsinclair.co.uk
e-mail: andynebular@hotmail.com     Mobile: 07831 196675

**SPENCER Ivor SCHOOL FOR BUTLERS The**
12 Little Bornes
Dulwich
London SE21 8SE
Website: www.ivorspencer.com
Fax: 020-8670 0055     Tel: 020-8670 5585

**STAGE CRICKET CLUB**
(Cricketers & Cricket Grounds)
39-41 Hanover Steps
St George's Fields
Albion Street, London W2 2YG
Website: www.stagecc.co.uk
e-mail: brianjfilm@aol.com
Fax: 020-7262 5736     Tel: 020-7402 7543

**STUDIO143**
(Events & Entertainment)
143 Talgarth Road
Barons Court, London W14 9DA     Mobile: 07976 294604
Website: www.emmaboardman.net
e-mail: ideas@emmaboardman.net

**STUNT ACTION SPECIALISTS (S.A.S.)**
(Corporate & TV Stunt Work)
110 Trafalgar Road
Portslade
East Sussex BN41 1GS
Website: www.stuntactionspecialists.com
e-mail: wayne@stuntactionspecialists.co.uk
Fax: 01273 708699     Tel: 01273 230214

**STYLES John - MAGICAL MART**
(Magic, Ventriloquism & Punch & Judy Consultant)
42 Christchurch Road
Sidcup, Kent DA15 7HQ     Tel/Fax: 020-8300 3579
Website: www.johnstylesentertainer.co.uk

**TALENT SCOUT The**
(Referral Service, Agents & Managers)
19 Edge Road, Thornhill
Dewsbury
West Yorkshire WF12 0QA     Tel: 01924 464049
e-mail: connect@thetalentscout.org

**THEATRE PROJECTS CONSULTANTS**
4 Apollo Studios
Charlton Kings Road
London NW5 2SW
Website: www.tpcworld.com
e-mail: info@theatreprojects.com
Fax: 020-7284 0636     Tel: 020-7482 4224

**THERAPEDIA LONDON BRIGHTON**
93 Gloucester Place
London W1U 6JQ     Mobile: 07941 300871
Website: www.gregmadison.net
e-mail: info@gregmadison.net

**TIGERLILIES**
(Promotions & Events)
66 Cambie Crescent
Colchester
Essex CO4 5DW     Mobile: 07985 763518
Website: www.tigerliliesevents.piczo.com
e-mail: tigerlilies.info@yahoo.co.uk

**TODD Carole**
(Director/Choreographer)
c/o Chris Davis Management Ltd
Tenbury House
36 Teme Street
Tenbury Wells, Worcs WR15 8AA
e-mail: cdavis@cdm-ltd.com
Fax: 01584 819076     Tel: 01584 819005

**TWINS The**
(Magical Special Effects for Film, Stage & Television
Productions)
30 Westmill Crescent
Wareham
Dorset BH20 4BW                    Mobile: 07971 589186
Website: www.theillusionists.com
e-mail: info@thetwins.co.uk

**UK THEATRE AVAILABILITY**
(Bookings Service for Theatre Producers)
1 Hogarth Hill, London NW11 6AY      Tel: 020-8455 3278
Website: www.uktheatreavailability.co.uk
e-mail: info@uktheatreavailability.co.uk

**UNITED KINGDOM COPYRIGHT BUREAU**
(Script Services)
110 Trafalgar Road
Portslade, East Sussex BN41 1GS      Tel: 01273 277333
Website: www.copyrightbureau.co.uk
e-mail: info@copyrightbureau.co.uk

**VERNON Doremy**
(Author 'Tiller Girls'/Archivist/Dance Routines Tiller Girl
Style)
16 Ouseley Road
London SW12 8EF                Tel/Fax: 020-8767 6944

**VOCALEYES**
(Audio Description "Describing The Arts")
1st Floor
54 Commercial Street, London E1 0LT    Tel: 020-7375 1043
Website: www.vocaleyes.co.uk
e-mail: enquiries@vocaleyes.co.uk

**VOICEATWORK**
5 Anhalt Road, London SW11 4NZ      Mobile: 07973 871479
Website: www.voiceatwork.co.uk
e-mail: kateterris@voiceatwork.co.uk

**WELBOURNE Jacqueline**
(Circus Trainer, Choreographer, Consultant)
c/o Circus Maniacs Agency
Office 8A, The Kingswood Foundation
Britannia Road, Kingswood, Bristol BS15 8DB
e-mail: jackie@circusmaniacs.com
Mobile: 07977 247287          Tel/Fax: 0117-947 7042

**WEST END WORKSHOPS**
(Audition Coaching/Arts Workshops)
Website: www.westendworkshops.co.uk
e-mail: info@westendworkshops.co.uk    Tel: 01202 526667

**WHITE Leonard**
(Production & Script Consultant)
Highlands, 40 Hill Crest Road, Newhaven, Brighton
East Sussex BN9 9EG              Tel: 01273 514473
e-mail: leoguy.white@virgin.net

**WILKINSON Gavin**
(Children's Director. Arts Consultant)
Website: www.westendworkshops.co.uk
e-mail: info@westendworkshops.co.uk    Tel: 01202 526667

**WISE MONKEY FINANCIAL COACHING**
Contact: Simonne Gnessen
14 Eastern Terrace Mews
Brighton BN2 1EP                Tel: 01273 691223
Website: www.financial-coaching.co.uk
e-mail: simonne@financial-coaching.co.uk

**WWW.EYENNCEE.COM**
(Networking Site)
I.N.C. Space, 9-13 Grape Street
Covent Garden, London WC2H 8ED
Website: www.eyenncee.com
e-mail: chris@internationalcollective.com
Fax: 020-7557 6656              Tel: 020-7557 6650

**YOUNGBLOOD Ltd**
(Fight Direction)
Website: www.youngblood.co.uk
e-mail: info@youngblood.co.uk      Tel: 020-7193 3207

## Rosemarie Swinfield
m a k e - u p   d e s i g n e r

**Rosie's Make-up Box**
m: 07976-965520
e: rosemarie@rosiesmake-up.co.uk
www.rosiesmake-up.co.uk

Author of:
* Stage Make-Up Step By Step
* Period Make-Up For The Stage
* Hair And Wigs For The Stage

Also
**Courses, Workshops & Seminars**

Samaurai Warrior, photo shoot

Richard Walters - Burton

**ACADEMY COSTUMES**
50 Rushworth Street, London SE1 0RB
Website: www.academycostumes.com
e-mail: info@academycostumes.com
Fax: 020-7928 6287     Tel: 020-7620 0771

**AJ COSTUMES Ltd**
(Theatrical Costume Hire, Design & Making)
Sullom Lodge, Sullom Side Lane
Barnacre, Garstang PR3 1GH
Website: www.trendsgroup.co.uk
e-mail: info@trendsgroup.co.uk
Fax: 01253 407715     Tel: 0871 2003343

**ALL-SEWN-UP**
Mechanics Institute
7 Church Street, Heptonstall, West Yorks HX7 7NS
Website: www.allsewnup.org.uk
e-mail: nwheeler_allsewnup@hotmail.com
Fax: 01422 845070     Tel: 01422 843407

**AND SEW TO DANCE**
Unit 11, Cornwallis House, Howard Chase, Basildon
Essex SS14 3BB     Tel: 01268 285050
e-mail: andsewtodance@blueyonder.co.uk

**ANELLO & DAVIDE**
(Handmade Shoes)
15 St Albans Grove
London W8 5BP     Tel: 020-7938 2255

**ANGELS**
(Fancy Dress & Revue)
119 Shaftesbury Avenue, London WC2H 8AE
Website: www.fancydress.com
e-mail: party@fancydress.com
Fax: 020-7240 9527     Tel: 020-7836 5678

**ANGELS THE COSTUMIERS**
1 Garrick Road, London NW9 6AA
Website: www.angels.uk.com
e-mail: angels@angels.uk.com
Fax: 020-8202 1820     Tel: 020-8202 2244

**ANGELS WIGS**
(Wig Hire/Makers, Facial Hair Suppliers)
1 Garrick Road, London NW9 6AA
Website: www.angels.uk.com
e-mail: wigs@angels.uk.com
Fax: 020-8202 1820     Tel: 020-8202 2244

**ANTOINETTE COSTUME HIRE**
(Stage, Screen and Fancy Dress)
High Street Buildings, 134 Kirkdale
London SE26 4BB     Tel: 020-8699 1913
Website: www.costumehirelondon.com
e-mail: antoinettehire@aol.com

**ARMS & ARCHERY**
(Armour, Weaponry, Chainmail, Warrior Costumes,
Medieval Tents, Banners)
Thrift Lane, off London Road, Ware
Herts SG12 9QS     Tel: 01920 460335
e-mail: armsandarchery@btconnect.com

**ATTLE COSTUMIERS**
Contact: Jamie Attle (Designs, Makes & Hires Costumes)
4 Toynbee Road, Wimbledon
London SW20 8SS     Tel/Fax: 020-8540 3044
e-mail: aalexiscolby@aol.com

**BAHADLY R**
(Hair & Make-up Artist, incl. Bald Caps, Ageing & Casualty)
47 Ploughmans Way
Macclesfield, Cheshire SK10 2UN
e-mail: rosienico@hotmail.co.uk
Mobile: 07973 553073     Tel: 01625 615878

**BERTRAND Henry**
(London Stockhouse for Silk)
52 Holmes Road
London NW5 3AB
Website: www.henrybertrand.co.uk
e-mail: sales@henrybertrand.co.uk
Fax: 020-7424 7001     Tel: 020-7424 7000

**BIRMINGHAM COSTUME HIRE**
Suites 209-210
Jubilee Centre, 130 Pershore Street
Birmingham B5 6ND
e-mail: info@birminghamcostumehire.co.uk
Fax: 0121-622 2758     Tel: 0121-622 3158

**BISHOP Kerry**
(Hair & Make-up Artist)
Flat 4, 49 Upper Rock Gardens
Brighton, East Sussex BN2 1QF
e-mail: kerrybishop@email.com     Mobile: 07759 704394

**BRIGGS Ron DESIGN**
(Costume Making, Costume Design)
1 Bedford Mews
London N2 9DF     Tel: 020-8444 8801
e-mail: costumes@ronbriggs.com

**BRODY Shirley**
14 Jenner House
London WC1N 1BL     Mobile: 07717 855684
e-mail: s.brody@blueyonder.co.uk

**BURLINGTONS**
(Hairdressers)
14 John Princes Street
London W1G 0JS     Tel: 0870 8701299
Website: www.burlingtonsuk.com

**CALICO FABRICS**
(Suppliers of Unbleached Calico & other Fabrics for Stage,
Costumes, Backdrops etc)
3 Ram Passage, High Street
Kingston-upon-Thames, Surrey KT1 1HH
Website: www.calicofabrics.co.uk
e-mail: sales@calicofabrics.co.uk
Fax: 020-8546 7755     Tel: 020-8541 5274

**CAPEZIO**
(Dance Products)
95 Whiffler Road, Norwich, Norfolk NR3 2AW
Website: www.capeziodance.com
e-mail: eusales@balletmakers.com
Fax: 0870 3500074     Tel: 0870 3500073

**CHRISANNE Ltd**
(Specialist Fabrics & Accessories)
Chrisanne House
110-112 Morden Road
Mitcham, Surrey CR4 4XB
Website: www.chrisanne.com
e-mail: sales@chrisanne.com
Fax: 020-8640 2106     Tel: 020-8640 5921

**COLTMAN Mike**
(See COSTUME CONSTRUCTION)

**COOK Sheila TEXTILES**
(Vintage Textiles, Costumes & Accessories for Sale/Hire)
26 Addison Place
London W11 4RJ     Tel: 020-7603 3003
Website: www.sheilacook.co.uk
e-mail: sheilacook@sheilacook.co.uk

**COSPROP Ltd**
(Costumes & Accessories)
469-475 Holloway Road, London N7 6LE
Website: www.cosprop.com
e-mail: enquiries@cosprop.com
Fax: 020-7561 7310     Tel: 020-7561 7300

**COSTUME BOUTIQUE**
(Bespoke Costume Hire)
37 Great Western Studios
Great Western Road, London W9 3NY
Website: www.costumeboutique.co.uk
e-mail: costumeboutique@me.com
Mobile: 07973 794450     Tel: 020-8968 4606

**COSTUME CONSTRUCTION**
(Costumes, Masks, Props, Puppets)
Studio 1, Croft Street
Cheltenham GL53 0EE     Tel/Fax: 01242 581847
Website: www.costumeconstruction.co.uk

**COSTUME CREATIONS**
10 Olinthus Avenue
Wolverhampton WV11 3DE     Tel: 01902 738282
e-mail: yourcostume@googlemail.com

**COSTUMEGENIE.CO.UK**
102 Raphael Drive, Shoeburyness
Southend-On-Sea SS3 9UX     Tel: 01702 290704
Website: www.costumegenie.co.uk
e-mail: costume-genie@hotmail.com

**COSTUME GUIDE The**
(Products & Suppliers Directory)
e-mail: tp@tessap.plus.com     Tel: 020-7602 2857

**COSTUME SOLUTIONS**
43 Rowan Road, London W6 7DT     Tel: 020-7603 9035
Website: www.costumesolutions.co.uk
e-mail: karen@costumesolutions.co.uk

**COSTUME STORE Ltd The**
(Costume Accessories)
16 Station Street, Lewes, East Sussex BN7 2DB
Website: www.thecostumestore.co.uk
e-mail: enquiries@thecostumestore.co.uk
Fax: 01273 477191                    Tel: 01273 479727

**COSTUME STUDIO Ltd**
(Costumes & Wigs)
Montgomery House
159-161 Balls Pond Road, London N1 4BG
Website: www.costumestudio.co.uk
e-mail: costume.studio@btconnect.com
Tel/Fax: 020-7923 9065              Tel: 020-7275 9614

**COSTUMIA**
Unit 9, Hockley Goods Yard, Pitsford Street, Hockley
Birmingham B18 6PT          Tel: 0121-551 2710
Website: www.costumia.co.uk
e-mail: info@costumia.co.uk

**COUTURE BEADING & EMBELLISHMENT**
6 Milton Road, London E17 4SR        Tel: 020-8677 0810
e-mail: dianavernon@mac.com

**CRAZY CLOTHES CONNECTION**
(1920's-1970's for Sale or Hire)
134 Lancaster Road
Ladbroke Grove, London W11 1QU        Tel: 020-7221 3989
Website: www.crazy-clothes.co.uk
e-mail: info@crazy-clothes.co.uk

**DANCIA INTERNATIONAL**
168 Drury Lane, London WC2B 5QA    Tel/Fax: 020-7831 9483
Website: www.dancia.co.uk
e-mail: dancialondon@btconnect.com

**DAVIES Bryan Philip COSTUMES**
(Lavish Pantomime, Musical Shows, Opera)
68 Court Road, Lewes, East Sussex BN7 2SA
Website: www.bpdcostumes.co.uk
e-mail: bryan@bpdcostumes.force9.co.uk
Mobile: 07931 249097                Tel: 01273 481004

**DELAMAR ACADEMY**
(Make-up Training)
Ealing Studios, Building D, 2nd Floor, Ealing Green
London W5 5EP              Tel/Fax: 020-8579 9511
Website: www.delamaracademy.co.uk
e-mail: info@delamaracademy.co.uk

**DESIGNER ALTERATIONS**
(Restyling & Remodelling of Clothes & Costumes)
220A Queenstown Road, Battersea, London SW8 4LP
Website: www.designeralterations.com
e-mail: info@designalterations.com
Fax: 020-7622 4148                  Tel: 020-7498 4360

**DR. BOO**
22 North Cross Road
East Dulwich, London SE22 9EU        Tel: 020-8693 4823
Website: www.drboo.co.uk
e-mail: info.boo@virgin.net

**EASTON Derek**
(Wigs For Theatre, Film & TV)
1 Dorothy Avenue, Peacehaven, East Sussex BN10 8LP
Website: www.derekeastonwigs.co.uk
e-mail: wigs@derekeastonwigs.co.uk
Mobile: 07768 166733              Tel/Fax: 01273 588262

**EIA MILLINERY DESIGN**
1620 W. Nelson Street
Chicago, Illinois 60657          Tel: 001 77 39 75 59 59
e-mail: info@eiahatart.com

**EVOLUTION SETS & COSTUMES Ltd**
(Set & Costume Hire)
Langdon Abbey, West Langdon
Dover, Kent CT15 5HJ
e-mail: emily@evolution-productions.co.uk
Fax: 01304 615353                  Tel: 01304 615333

**FOX Charles H. Ltd**
(Professional Make-up & Wigs)
22 Tavistock Street, London WC2E 7PY
Website: www.charlesfox.co.uk
e-mail: makeup@charlesfox.co.uk
Fax: 0870 2001369                  Tel: 0870 2000369

**FOXTROT PRODUCTIONS Ltd**
(Armoury Services, Firearms, Weapons & Costume Hire)
Unit 46 Canalot Production Studios
222 Kensal Road
London W10 5BN                  Tel: 020-8964 3555
Website: www.foxtrot-productions.co.uk
e-mail: mail@foxtrot-productions.co.uk

**FRANK Lina B.**
(London & Scandinavia) (Design & Workshops)
Website: www.scenography.co.uk/linabfrank
e-mail: linabfrank@gmail.com
Mobile: 07951 596078              Tel: +46 07 61 38 28 29

**FREED OF LONDON**
(Dancewear & Dance Shoes)
94 St Martin's Lane, London WC2N 4AT
Website: www.freedoflondon.com
e-mail: shop@freed.co.uk
Fax: 020-7240 3061                Tel: 020-7240 0432

**FUNN Ltd**
(Silk, Cotton Wool Stockings, Opaque Opera Tights & 40's
Rayon Stockings)
PO Box 102, Steyning, West Sussex BN44 3EB
e-mail: funn.biz@lycos.com
Fax: 0870 8794450                Tel: 01403 257116

**GAMBA THEATRICAL**
(See THEATRICAL FOOTWEAR COMPANY Ltd The)

**GAV NICOLA THEATRICAL FOOTWEAR**
West Wick, Marshes
Burnham-on-Crouch, Essex CM0 8NE
Website: www.theatricalshoes.com
e-mail: gavnicola@yahoo.com
Mobile: 07961 974278              Tel/Fax: 01621 785623

**GILLHAM Felicite**
(Wig Makers for Theatre, Opera & Film)
12 Sheeplands Lane, Sherborne, Dorset DT9 4BP
e-mail: felicite@gillywigs.co.uk
Mobile: 07802 955908          Tel: 01935 814328

**GREASEPAINT**
143 Northfield Avenue, Ealing, London W13 9QT
Website: www.greasepaint.co.uk
e-mail: info@greasepaint.co.uk
Fax: 020-8840 3983          Tel: 020-8840 6000

**GROVE Sue DESIGNS**
(Costume Designers & Makers. Historical Specialist)
12 Ampthill Road, Shirley
Southampton, Hants SO15 8LP          Tel: 023-8078 6849
e-mail: sue.grove1@tiscali.co.uk

**HAIRAISERS**
(Wigs)
9-11 Sunbeam Road, Park Royal, London NW10 6JP
Website: www.hairaisers.com
e-mail: info@hairaisers.com
Fax: 020-8963 1600          Tel: 020-8965 2500

**HAND & LOCK**
86 Margaret Street, London W1W 8TE
Website: www.handembroidery.com
e-mail: enquiries@handembroidery.com
Fax: 020-7580 7499          Tel: 020-7580 7488

**HARVEYS OF HOVE**
(Theatrical Costumes & Military Specialists)
110 Trafalgar Road, Portslade, Sussex BN41 1GS
Website: www.harveysofhove.co.uk
e-mail: harveys.costume@ntlworld.com
Fax: 01273 708699          Tel: 01273 430323

**HENRY Lewis Ltd**
(Dress Makers)
111-113 Great Portland Street
London W1W 6QQ          Tel: 020-7636 6683

**HERALD & HEART Ltd**
(Men's & Women's Hats & Headdresses - Period & Modern)
102 High Street, Rye
East Sussex TN31 7JN          Tel: 01797 225261
Website: www.heraldandheart.com
e-mail: heraldandheart2@mac.com

**HIREARCHY**
(Classic & Contemporary Costume)
45-47 Palmerston Road, Boscombe
Bournemouth, Dorset BH1 4HW          Tel: 01202 394465
Website: www.hirearchy.co.uk
e-mail: hirearchy1@aol.com

**HODIN Annabel**
(Costume Designer/Stylist)
12 Eton Avenue, London NW3 3EH
e-mail: annabelhodin@aol.com
Mobile: 07836 754079          Tel: 020-7431 8761

**HOPKINS Trisha**
6 Willow Grove, Formby L37 3NX          Tel: 01704 873055
e-mail: trisha_hopkins@hotmail.co.uk

**INCE Katie**
(Wig Maker & Make-up Artist)
15 Birchwood Gardens
Idle Park, Bradford BD10 9EW          Tel: 07900 250853
e-mail: katie.hunt@katieswigs.com

**INTERNATIONAL COLLECTIVE (CREATIVE)**
9-13 Grape Street, Covent Garden, London WC2H 8ED
Website: www.inccreative.co.uk
e-mail: enquiries@internationalcollective.co.uk
Fax: 020-7557 6656          Tel: 020-7557 6650

**INTERNATIONAL DANCE SUPPLIES/GRISHKO UK Ltd**
(Importer & Distributor of Dance Shoes and Dancewear)
64 Butt Lane, Milton, Cambridge CB24 6DG
Website: www.grishko.co.uk
e-mail: info@grishko.co.uk
Fax: 01223 280388                    Tel: 01223 861425

**JULIETTE DESIGNS**
(Diamante Jewellery Manufacturers)
90 Yerbury Road, London N19 4RS
Website: www.stagejewellery.com
e-mail: juliettedesigns@hotmail.com
Fax: 020-7281 7326                   Tel: 020-7263 7878

**KIDD Ella J.**
(Bespoke Millinery, Wigs & Head-dresses for Theatre,
Film & TV)
Website: www.ellajkidd.co.uk          Tel: 020-8539 2786

**LARGER THAN LIFE STAGEWEAR**
(Theatrical Costumes for Hire)
2 Sundridge Parade
Bromley, Kent BR1 4DT             Tel/Fax: 020-8466 9010
Website: www.largerthanlifestagewear.co.uk
e-mail: info@largerthanlifestagewear.co.uk

**LECOMTE Virginie**
36 Rue Simart, 75018 Paris           Tel: 06 61 75 18 65
Website: www.lilane.net
e-mail: lilane@hotmail.fr

**MADDERMARKET THEATRE COSTUME HIRE**
(Period Clothing, Costume Hire & Wig Hire)
St John's Alley, Norwich NR2 1DR
Website: www.maddermarket.co.uk
e-mail: mmtheatre@btconnect.com
Fax: 01603 661357                    Tel: 01603 626292

**MAKE-UP ON THE MOVE**
17 Henley Road, Wolverhampton
West Midlands WV10 6UY            Mobile: 07949 943688
e-mail: info@makeuponthemove.co.uk

**MARSDEN Chloe COSTUMES & MILLINERY**
1st Floor, 61-63 Coldharbour Lane, London SE5 9NS
Website: www.chloemarsden.co.uk
e-mail: mail@chloemarsden.co.uk     Mobile: 07786 427386

**MASK Kim**
(Costume & Make-up Protection Masks)
Website: www.kimmask.com
e-mail: info@kimmask.com               Tel: 0845 0568482

**MASQUERADE COSTUMES BRIGHTON Ltd**
(Superior Fancy Dress, Film & Theatre Costume, Styling for
Shows/Events)
38 Preston Road, Brighton BN1 4QF    Tel: 01273 673381
Website: www.masqueradecostumes.co.uk
e-mail: masqueradecostumes@googlemail.com

**MASTER CLEANERS The**
(Dry Cleaning of Theatrical Costumes & Antique Garments)
189 Haverstock Hill
London NW3 4QG                      Tel: 020-7431 3725
e-mail: info@themastercleaners.com

**MEANANDGREEN.COM**
17 Lichfield Street
Wolverhampton WV1 1EA               Tel: 0845 8991133
Website: www.meanandgreen.com
e-mail: custserv@meanandgreen.com

**MIDNIGHT**
Costume Design & Wardrobe Services
(Music, Theatre, Film, Tours)       Mobile: 07722 882847
e-mail: midnight_wardrobe@hotmail.com

**MORCOM Roo**
Mia Make Up, 67 High Street
Old Amersham, Bucks HP7 0DT         Mobile: 07956 035657
Website: www.miamakeup.com
e-mail: roo@miamakeup.com

**MORRIS Heather**
(Wigs)
c/o The Hair Clinic at JBC, 50-54 Wigmore Street
London W1U 2AU                      Tel: 020-7935 9200
Website: www.fortysevenhair.co.uk
e-mail: heather.morris@btconnect.com

**NATIONAL THEATRE**
(Costume, Furniture & Props Hire)
Chichester House
Kennington Park Estate
1-3 Brixton Road, London SW9 6DE
e-mail: costume_hire@nationaltheatre.org.uk
Tel: 020-7735 4774 (Costume)   Tel: 020-7820 1358 (Props)

**NEW ID**
(Makeover & Photographic Studios)
2 Lacemaker Court, London Road
Old Amersham HP7 0HS                Tel: 0870 8701299
Website: www.newidstudios.com
e-mail: bookings@newidstudios.co.uk

**NORMAN Sam**
(Hair & Make-up)
Website: www.samnorman.co.uk
e-mail: sam@samnorman.co.uk         Mobile: 07932 397465

**ORIGINAL KNITWEAR**
Contact: Gina Pinnick (Inc. Fake Fur)
Avalon, Tregoney Hill
Mevagissey, Cornwall PL26 6RG
Website: www.originalknitwear.co.uk
e-mail: okgina@btinternet.com
Mobile: 07957 376855                Tel: 01726 844807

**PATEY (LONDON) Ltd**
Unit 1, 9 Gowlett Road, London SE15 4HX
Website: www.pateyhats.com
e-mail: trevor@pateyhats.com
Fax: 020-7732 9538                  Tel: 020-7635 0030

**PEARCE Kate**
(Costume Maker)
Thistledown, Wellfield Road
Marshfield, Near Newport CF3 2UB    Mobile: 07749 283802
e-mail: kpearce55@hotmail.com

**PINK POINTES DANCEWEAR**
1A Suttons Lane
Hornchurch, Essex RM12 6RD          Tel/Fax: 01708 438584
e-mail: pink.pointes@btconnect.com

**POLAND DENTAL STUDIO**
(Film/Stage Dentistry)
1 Devonshire Place, London W1G 6HH
e-mail: robpoland@btconnect.com
Fax: 020-7486 3952                  Tel: 020-7935 6919

# Derek Easton *Wigs*
## for Theatre, Film and Television

www.derekeastonwigs.co.uk
wigs@derekeastonwigs.co.uk
T/F: 01273 588262   M: 07768 166733

1 Dorothy Avenue  East Sussex  Peacehaven BN10 8LP

**PORSELLI**
4 Frensham Road, Sweet Briar Ind Estate, Norwich NR3 2BT
Website: www.dancewear.co.uk
e-mail: porselliuk@aol.com
Fax: 01603 406676                          Tel: 0845 0170817

**PROBLOOD**
11 Mount Pleasant
Framlingham, Suffolk IP13 9HQ          Tel/Fax: 01728 723865

**RAINBOW PRODUCTIONS Ltd**
(Manufacture & Handling of Costume Characters)
Unit 3, Green Lea Park
Prince George's Road, London SW19 2JD
Website: www.rainbowproductions.co.uk
e-mail: info@rainbowproductions.co.uk
Fax: 020-8254 5306                          Tel: 020-8254 5300

**REPLICA WAREHOUSE**
(Costumiers & Props)
200 Main Road, Goostrey
Cheshire CW4 8PD                          Tel/Fax: 01477 534075
Website: www.replicawarehouse.co.uk
e-mail: lesleyedwards@replicawarehouse.co.uk

**ROBBINS Sheila**
(Wig Hire)
Broombarn, 7 Ivy Cottages
Hinksey Hill, Oxford OX1 5BQ            Tel/Fax: 01865 735524

**ROLANDI Gianluca**
(Hair & Make-up)
83 Deroy Lodge, Wicklow Street, London WC1X 3LF
Website: www.gluca.co.uk
e-mail: gluca@gluca.co.uk                Mobile: 07990 637299

**ROSE Eda MILLINERY**
(Ladies' Model Hat Design & Manufacture)
Lalique, Mongewell, Wallingford, Oxon OX10 8BP
Website: www.hatsbyedarose.co.uk
e-mail: edarose.lawson@btconnect.com
Fax: 01491 835909                          Tel: 01491 837174

**ROUSSINOV Sarah**
20 Isabella Place
Kingston Upon Thames KT2 5PB        Mobile: 07747 777493
Website: www.sarahroussinov.co.uk
e-mail: sarahroussinov@aol.com

**ROYAL EXCHANGE THEATRE COSTUME HIRE**
(Period Costumes & Accessories)
47-53 Swan Street
Manchester M4 5JY                          Tel/Fax: 0161-819 6660
Website: www.royalexchange.co.uk
e-mail: costume.hire@royalexchange.co.uk

**ROYER Hugo INTERNATIONAL Ltd**
(Hair & Wig Materials)
10 Lakeside Business Park, Swan Lane
Sandhurst, Berkshire GU47 9DN
Website: www.hugoroyer.com
e-mail: enquiries@royer.co.uk
Fax: 01252 878852                          Tel: 01252 878811

**RSC COSTUME HIRE**
28 Timothy's Bridge Road
Stratford Enterprise Park, Stratford-upon-Avon
Warwickshire CV37 9UY                    Tel/Fax: 01789 205920
e-mail: costume.hire@rsc.org.uk

**RUMBLE Jane**
(Masks, Millinery, Helmets Made to Order)
121 Elmstead Avenue
Wembley, Middlesex HA9 8NT            Tel: 020-8904 6462

**SEXTON Sally Ann**
(Hair & Make-up Designer)
c/o The Harris Agency Ltd
71 The Avenue
Watford, Herts WD17 4NU
e-mail: theharrisagency@btconnect.com
Mobile: 07973 802842                      Tel: 01923 211644

**SIDE EFFECTS**
(Custom-made Character/FX Costumes)
92 Fentiman Road, London SW8 1LA
e-mail: sfx@lineone.net
Fax: 020-7207 0062                          Tel: 020-7587 1116

**SINGER Sandra ASSOCIATES**
(Fashion Stylists for TV & Theatre, Costume/Designer)
21 Cotswold Road
Westcliff-on-Sea, Essex SS0 8AA
Website: www.sandrasinger.com
e-mail: sandrasingeruk@aol.com
Fax: 01702 339393                          Tel: 01702 331616

**SLEIMAN Hilary**
(Specialist & Period Knitwear)
72 Godwin Road, London E7 0LG
e-mail: hilary.sleiman@ntlworld.com
Mobile: 07940 555663          Tel: 020-8555 6176

**SOFT PROPS**
(Costume & Model Makers)
92 Fentiman Road, London SW8 1LA
e-mail: jackie@softprops.co.uk
Fax: 020-7207 0062          Tel: 020-7587 1116

**SOLAK Shenay**
51 Drury House, London SW8 4JL          Mobile: 07771 921931
e-mail: shenays@yahoo.de

**STAGEWORKS WORLDWIDE PRODUCTIONS**
(Largest Costume Wardrobe in North)
525 Ocean Boulevard, Blackpool FY4 1EZ
Website: www.stageworkswwp.com
e-mail: simon.george@stageworkswwp.com
Fax: 01253 342702          Tel: 01253 342426

**STRIBLING Joan**
(London/Southwest Based. Film & Television Make-up &
Hair Designer. BAFTA Craft, Design & Art Director's Awards)
Website: www.joanstribling.com
e-mail: joanstribling@hotmail.com
Mobile: 07791 758480          Tel: 0845 4266169

**SWINFIELD Rosemarie**
(Rosie's Make-up Box) (Make-up Design & Training)
Website: www.rosiesmake-up.co.uk    Mobile: 07976 965520
e-mail: rosemarie@rosiesmake-up.co.uk

**TALK TO THE HAND PUPPETS**
(Custom Puppets for Film, Television & Theatre)
Studio 277, Wimbledon Art Studios
Riverside Yard, Riverside Road
Earlsfield, London SW17 0BB
Website: www.talktothehandpuppets.com
e-mail: info@talktothehandpuppets.com
Mobile: 07813 682293          Mobile: 07855 421454

**THEATREKNITS**
102C Belgravia Workshops
157-163 Marlborough Road
London N19 4NF          Tel/Fax: 020-7561 0044
e-mail: theatreknits@yahoo.co.uk

**THEATRICAL FOOTWEAR COMPANY Ltd The**
(Trading as GAMBA Theatrical)
Unit 14, Chingford Industrial Centre
Hall Lane, Chingford, London E4 8DJ
e-mail: gambatheatrical1@btconnect.com
Fax: 020-8529 7995          Tel: 020-8529 9195

**THEATRICAL SHOEMAKERS Ltd**
(Footwear)
Unit 7A
Thames Road Industrial Estate
Thames Road
Silvertown, London E16 2EZ
Website: www.shoemaking.co.uk
e-mail: ts@shoemaking.co.uk
Fax: 020-7476 5220          Tel: 020-7474 0500

**THORNE Sarah Kate**
(Based in Berkshire)
Website: www.sarahkatethorne.co.uk
e-mail: sarah@sarahkatethorne.co.uk          Tel: 07776 196733

**TRYFONOS Mary MASKS**
(Designer & Maker of Masks & Costume Properties)
59 Shaftesbury Road
London N19 4QW
e-mail: marytryfonos@aol.com
Mobile: 07764 587433          Tel: 020-7561 9880

**TUTU-TOPIA**
Lincoln LN1          Mobile: 07999 553021
Website: www.tutu-topia.co.uk
e-mail: sales@tutu-topia.co.uk

**VINTAGE SHIRT COMPANY The**
2 Mount Place, Lewes
East Sussex BN7 1YH          Tel/Fax: 01273 477699
Website: www.vintageshirt.co.uk
e-mail: info@vintageshirt.co.uk

**WALKER Fran**
(Wardrobe Stylist & Costumes for Film, TV & Theatre)
9 Winchester Way
Peterborough PE3 6HL          Mobile: 07545 499254
e-mail: wfran@live.co.uk

**WEST YORKSHIRE FABRICS Ltd**
(Venetian, Crepe, Suiting, Barathea Stretch Fabrics, Linen,
Cut Lengths)
Unit 5 Milestone Court
Stanningley, Leeds LS28 6HE          Tel/Fax: 0113-225 6550
e-mail: neil@wyfabrics.com

**WIG EXPECTATIONS**
3 Northernhay Walk
Morden
Surrey SM4 4BS          Tel: 020-8540 5667
Website: www.wigexpectations.com
e-mail: wigexpectations@aol.com

**WIG ROOM The**
22 Coronation Road, Basingstoke
Hants RG21 4HA          Tel: 01256 415737
e-mail: darren@wigroom.co.uk

**WIG SPECIALITIES Ltd**
(Hand Made Wigs & Facial Hair, Hair Extensions etc)
First Floor
173 Seymour Place
London W1H 4PW
Website: www.wigspecialities.co.uk
e-mail: wigspecialities@btconnect.com
Fax: 020-7723 1566          Tel: 020-7262 6565

**WILLIAMS Emma**
(Costume Designer & Stylist - Film, TV & Theatre)
e-mail: emmacoz@dsl.pipex.com          Mobile: 07710 130345

**WRIGHT Fay**
(Freelance Make-up Artist)
37 Veryan, Woking
Surrey GU21 3LL          Mobile: 07816 128575
e-mail: faylin_wright@hotmail.com

**DAILY EXPRESS**  Tel: 0871 4341010
Northern Shell Building
10 Lower Thames Street
London EC3R 6EN
Films: Alan Hunter
Television: Matt Baylis

**DAILY MAIL**  Tel: 020-7938 6000
Northcliffe House
2 Derry Street, Kensington
London W8 5TT
Theatre: Quentin Letts
Films: Chris Tookey

**DAILY STAR**  Tel: 0871 4341010
Northern Shell Building
10 Lower Thames Street
London EC3R 6EN
Show Business & Television: Nigel Pauley, Amy Watts,
Charli Morgan
Films & Video: Alan Frank

**DAILY TELEGRAPH**  Tel: 020-7931 2000
111 Buckingham Palace Road
London SW1W 0DT
Theatre: Charles Spencer, Dominic Cavendish
Films: Sukhdev Sandhu, Tim Robey
Radio: Gillian Reynolds  Art: Richard Dorment
Dance: Sarah Crompton, Mark Monahan
Music: Geoffrey Norris, Ivan Hewitt

**FINANCIAL TIMES**  Tel: 020-7873 3000
1 Southwark Bridge
London SE1 9HL
Theatre: Sarah Hemmings, Ian Shuttleworth
Films: Nigel Andrews, Karl French
Television: Martin Hoyle, John Lloyd

**GUARDIAN**  Tel: 020-3353 2000
King's Place
90 York Way, London N1 9GU
Theatre: Michael Billington
Television: Nancy Banks-Smith

**INDEPENDENT**  Tel: 020-7005 2000
2 Derry Street
London W8 5HF
Television: Gerard Gilbert

**LONDON EVENING STANDARD**  Tel: 020-7938 6000
Northcliffe House
2 Derry Street, Kensington
London W8 5EE
Theatre: Nicholas de Jongh, Fiona Mountford,
Kieron Quirke
Films: Derek Malcolm  Opera: Fiona Maddocks
Television: Ceri Thomas
Classical Music: Barry Millington

**MAIL ON SUNDAY**  Tel: 020-7938 6000
(Review Section)
Northcliffe House
2 Derry Street, London W8 5TS
Theatre: Georgina Brown
Films: Jason Solomons, Matthew Bond
Radio: Simon Garfield

**MIRROR**  Tel: 020-7510 3000
Mirror Group Newspapers Ltd
1 Canada Square
Canary Wharf, London E14 5AP
Films: Dave Edwards
Television: James Simon, Jim Shelley

**MORNING STAR**  Tel: 020-8510 0815
William Rust House
52 Beachy Road, London E3 2NS
Theatre & Films: Katie Lambert

**NEWS OF THE WORLD**  Tel: 020-7782 4000
News International Plc
1 Virginia Street, London E98 1NW
Show Business: Rav Singh
Films: Robbie Collin

**OBSERVER**  Tel: 020-3353 2000
King's Place
90 York Way, London N1 9GU
Theatre: Susanna Clapp
Films: Philip French, Akin Ojumu
Radio: Miranda Sawyer

**PEOPLE**  Tel: 020-7293 3000
1 Canada Square
Canary Wharf, London E14 5AP
Television & Radio: John Wise
Films: Conor Nolan
Show Business: Katie Hind
Features: Caroline Waterson

**SPORT**  Tel: 0161-236 4466
Sport Newspapers Ltd
19 Great Ancoats Street, Manchester M60 4BT
Showbusiness/Features: Neil Goodwin

**SUN**  Tel: 020-7782 4000
News International Plc
1 Virginia Street, Wapping, London E98 1SN
Television: Ally Ross
Films: Grant Rollings

**SUNDAY EXPRESS**  Tel: 0871 4341010
Northern Shell Building
10 Lower Thames Street, London EC3R 6EN
Theatre: Mark Shenton
Films: Henry Fitzherbert
Television: David Stephenson
Radio & Arts: Clare Heal

**SUNDAY MIRROR**  Tel: 020-7510 3000
Mirror Group
1 Canada Square, Canary Wharf, London E14 5AP
Theatre & Television: Kevin O'Sullivan
Films: Mark Adams
Showbiz: Dean Piper

**SUNDAY TELEGRAPH**  Tel: 020-7931 2000
111 Buckingham Palace Road
London SW1W 0DT
Theatre: Tim Walker
Films: Jenny McCartney
Television: John Preston

**SUNDAY TIMES**  Tel: 020-7782 5000
News International Plc
1 Pennington Street, London E98 1ST
Theatre: Christopher Hart
Films: Cosmo Landesman
Television: A. A. Gill
Radio: Paul Donovan

**TIMES**  Tel: 020-7782 5000
News International Plc
1 Pennington Street, London E98 1TT
Theatre: Benedict Nightingale
Films: James Christopher
Television: James Jackson
Video: Ed Potton  Radio: Chris Campling

**D**

Dance Companies & Organisations
Dance Training & Professional Classes
Drama Schools (Conference of)
Drama Training, Schools & Coaches

**AKADEMI SOUTH ASIAN DANCE UK**
213 Haverstock Hill
Hampstead Town Hall
Haverstock Hill, London NW3 4QP
Website: www.akademi.co.uk
e-mail: info@akademi.co.uk
Fax: 020-7691 3211     Tel: 020-7691 3210

**ANJALI DANCE COMPANY**
The Mill Arts Centre
Spiceball Park, Banbury
Oxford OX16 5QE     Tel: 01295 251909
Website: www.anjali.co.uk
e-mail: info@anjali.co.uk

**BALLROOM, LONDON THEATRE OF**
(Artistic Director: Paul Harris®)
24 Montana Gardens
Sutton, Surrey SM1 4FP
Website: www.londontheatreofballroom.com
e-mail: office@londontheatreofballroom.com
Mobile: 07958 784462     Tel/Fax: 020-8722 8798

**BEDLAM DANCE COMPANY**
Contact: By Post/e-mail
18 St Augustine's Road, London NW1 9RN
Website: www.bedlamdance.com
e-mail: info@bedlamdance.com

**BIRMINGHAM ROYAL BALLET**
Thorp Street, Birmingham B5 4AU
Website: www.brb.org.uk
e-mail: administrator@brb.org.uk
Fax: 0121-245 3570     Tel: 0121-245 3500

**BODY OF PEOPLE**
(BOP Jazz Theatre Company)
10 Stayton Road
Sutton, Surrey SM1 1RB     Tel: 020-8641 6959
Website: www.bop.org.uk
e-mail: info@bop.org.uk

**BOLLYWOOD GROOVES DANCE COMPANY**
6 Balmoral Court
20 Queens Terrace
London NW8 6DQ     Mobile: 07875 023744
Website: www.bollywoodgrooves.com
e-mail: info@bollywoodgrooves.com

**BROWN Carole DANCES**
Contact: Gwen Van Spijk
PO Box 563, Banbury OX16 6AQ     Tel: 01869 338458
Website: www.cueperformance.com
e-mail: gwen@cueperformance.com

**CANDOCO DANCE COMPANY**
2T Leroy House
436 Essex Road, London N1 3QP
Website: www.candoco.co.uk
e-mail: info@candoco.co.uk
Fax: 020-7704 1645     Tel: 020-7704 6845

**CHOLMONDELEYS & FEATHERSTONEHAUGHS The**
LF1.1 Lafone House
The Leathermarket
11-13 Leathermarket Street, London SE1 3HN
Website: www.thecholmondeleys.org
e-mail: admin@thecholmondeleys.org
Fax: 020-7378 8810     Tel: 020-7378 8800

**[ CONTACTS 2010 ]**

**COMPANY OF CRANKS**
1st Floor, 62 Northfield House
Frensham Street, London SE15 6TN
Website: www.mimeworks.com
e-mail: mimetic16@yahoo.com          Mobile: 07963 617981

**DANCE SOUTH WEST**
PO Box 5457
Bournemouth, Dorset BH1 1WU          Tel: 01202 554131
Website: www.dancesouthwest.org.uk
e-mail: info@dancesouthwest.org.uk

**DAVIES Siobhan DANCE**
85 St George's Road
London SE1 6ER
Website: www.siobhandavies.com
e-mail: info@siobhandavies.com
Fax: 020-7091 9669                   Tel: 020-7091 9650

**DV8 PHYSICAL THEATRE**
Arts Admin, Toynbee Studios
28 Commercial Street
London E1 6AB
Website: www.dv8.co.uk
e-mail: dv8@artsadmin.co.uk
Fax: 020-7247 5103                   Tel: 020-7655 0977

**ENGLISH NATIONAL BALLET Ltd**
Markova House
39 Jay Mews, London SW7 2ES
Website: www.ballet.org.uk
e-mail: comments@ballet.org.uk
Fax: 020-7225 0827                   Tel: 020-7581 1245

**ENGLISH YOUTH BALLET**
Appledowne, The Hillside
Orpington, Kent BR6 7SD
Website: www.englishyouthballet.co.uk
e-mail: misslewis@englishyouthballet.co.uk
Mobile: 07732 383600                 Tel: 01689 856747

**GREEN CANDLE DANCE COMPANY**
Oxford House
Derbyshire Street
Bethnal Green, London E2 6HG
Website: www.greencandledance.com
e-mail: info@greencandledance.com
Fax: 020-7739 7731                   Tel: 020-7739 7722

**IJAD DANCE COMPANY**
22 Allison Road
London N8 0AT                        Mobile: 07930 378639
Website: www.ijad.freeserve.co.uk
e-mail: info@ijad.freeserve.co.uk

**INDEPENDENT BALLET WALES**
30 Glasllwch Crescent
Newport
South Wales NP20 3SE
Website: www.welshballet.co.uk
e-mail: dariusjames@welshballet.co.uk
Fax: 01633 221690                    Tel: 01633 253985

**JEYASINGH Shobana DANCE COMPANY**
Moving Arts Base
134 Liverpool Road
Islington, London N1 1LA            Tel: 020-7697 4444
Website: www.shobanajeyasingh.co.uk
e-mail: admin@shobanajeyasingh.co.uk

**KHAN Akram COMPANY**
Unit 232A
35A Britannia Row, London N1 8QH
Website: www.akramkhancompany.net
e-mail: office@akramkhancompany.net
Fax: 020-7354 5554                   Tel: 020-7354 4333

**KOSH The**
(Physical Theatre)
59 Stapleton Hall Road
London N4 3QF                        Tel/Fax: 020-8374 0407
e-mail: info@thekosh.com

**LUDUS DANCE**
Assembly Rooms
King Street, Lancaster LA1 1RE
Website: www.ludusdance.org
e-mail: info@ludusdance.org
Fax: 01524 847744                    Tel: 01524 35936

**NEIGHBOURHOOD PRODUCTIONS**
9 Weavers Terrace
Fulham
London SW6 1QE                       Mobile: 07958 377595
e-mail: info@creativekidzandco.co.uk

**NEW ADVENTURES**
Sadler's Wells, Rosebery Avenue
London EC1R 4TN
Website: www.new-adventures.net
e-mail: info@new-adventures.net      Tel/Fax: 020-7713 6766

**NORTHERN BALLET THEATRE**
West Park Centre
Spen Lane, Leeds LS16 5BE
e-mail: administration@northernballettheatre.co.uk
Fax: 0113-274 5381                   Tel: 0113-274 5355

**OGUIKE Henri DANCE COMPANY**
Laban, The Cottages
Office No 2
Creekside, London SE8 3DZ
Website: www.henrioguikedance.co.uk
e-mail: info@henrioguikedance.co.uk
Fax: 020-8694 3669                   Tel: 020-8694 7444

**PHOENIX DANCE THEATRE**
3 St Peter's Buildings
St Peter's Square,Leeds LS9 8AH
Website: www.phoenixdancetheatre.co.uk
e-mail: info@phoenixdancetheatre.co.uk
Fax: 0113-244 4736                   Tel: 0113-242 3486

# infopage

## How do I become a professional dancer?

Full-time vocational training can start from as young as ten years old. A good starting point for researching the different schools and courses available is CDET (Council for Dance Education & Training) www.cdet.org.uk. There are over sixteen dance colleges offering professional training accredited by CDET, and nearly three hundred university courses which include some form of dance training. It is estimated that over one thousand dancers graduate from vocational training schools or university courses every year, so it is a highly competitive career. Therefore anyone wanting to be a professional dancer must obtain as many years of training and experience as possible, plus go to see plenty of performances spanning different types and genres of dance. If you require further information on vocational dance schools, applying to accredited dance courses, auditions and funding, contact CDET's information line 'Answers for Dancers' on 020-7240 5703 or see their article on page 186.

## What are dance companies?

There are more than two hundred dance companies in the UK, spanning a variety of dance styles including ballet, contemporary, hip hop and African. A dance company will either be resident in a venue, be a touring company, or a combination of both. Many have websites which you can visit for full information. Most dance companies employ ensemble dancers on short to medium contracts, who may then work on a number of different productions for the same company over a number of months. In addition, the company will also employ principal/leading dancers on a role-by-role basis.

## What are dance organisations?

There are numerous organisations which exist to support professional dancers, covering important areas including health and safety, career development, networking and legal and financial aspects. Other organisations (e.g. Regional / National Dance Agencies) exist to promote dance within the wider community.

## I have already trained to be a dancer. Why do I need further training?

Dance training should not cease as soon as you get your first job or complete a course. Throughout your career you should continuously strive to maintain your fitness levels, enhance and develop your existing skills and keep learning new ones in order to retain a competitive edge. You must also be prepared to continuously learn new dance styles and routines for specific roles. Ongoing training and classes can help you stay fit and active, and if you go through a period of unemployment you can keep your mind and body occupied, ready to take on your next job.

## How should I use these listings?

The following pages will supply you with up-to-date contact details for a wide range of dance companies and organisations, followed by listings for dance training and professional classes. Always research schools and classes thoroughly, obtaining copies of prospectuses where available. Most vocational schools offer two and three year full-time training programmes, many also offer excellent degree programmes. Foundation Courses offer a sound introduction to the profession, but they can never replace a full-time vocational course. Many schools, organisations and studios also offer part-time / evening classes which offer a general understanding of dance and complementary technique or the opportunity to refresh specific dance skills; they will not, however, enable a student to become a professional dancer.

## How else can I find work as a dancer?

Dance also plays a role in commercial theatre, musicals, opera, film, television, live music and video, corporate events and many other industries. Dancers may also want to be represented by an agent. Agents have many more contacts within the industry than an individual dancer can have, and can offer advice and negotiate contracts on your behalf as well as submit you for jobs. A number of specialist dance agencies are listed in the 'Agents - Dance' section towards the front of this book.

## What is Spotlight Dancers?

Dancers wishing to promote themselves to these types of job opportunities should consider joining Spotlight's specialist casting directory for dancers. This is a central directory of dancers published annually which is used by dance employers throughout the UK to locate dancers and send out casting or audition information. Members receive a page in the directory containing a headshot and body shot, agency contact details and selected credits as well as an online CV. Dancers who attend CDET accredited schools receive a discount when applying in their graduating year. Please see www.spotlight.com/dancers for more information.

## What other careers are available in dance?

Opportunities also exist to work as a teacher, choreographer, technician or manager. Dance UK www.danceuk.org is a valuable source of information for anyone considering this type of work.

## What should I do to avoid injury?

An injury is more likely to occur if you are inflexible and unprepared for sudden physical exertion. The last thing you want to do is to pick up an injury, however minor, and be prevented from working, so continuous training during both employment and unemployment will help you to minimise the risk of an injury during a performance or rehearsal. If you do sustain an injury you will want to make sure it does not get any worse by getting treatment with a specialist. The British Association for Performing Arts Medicine (BAPAM) provides specialist health support for performers, free health assessment clinics and a directory of performing arts health practitioners and specialists. Visit their website www.bapam.org.uk for more information. You may also find the advice preceding the 'Health & Wellbeing' section of Contacts useful.

## I'm not a professional dancer but I enjoy dancing. Why should I use these listings?

People don't just dance to perform, teach or advise within the industry. Dance can be pursued for fun, recreation, social reasons and for health. Training and professional advice should still be pursued to ensure that you do not injure yourself while dancing and prevent yourself from working. You can also use the 'Dance Training & Professional Classes' listings to find suitable dance lessons in your area, which you could attend to make friends, keep fit and stay occupied.

## Where can I find more information?

For further advice about the dance industry, you could try contacting CDET (www.cdet.org.uk) for training information, Dance UK (www.danceuk.org) regarding the importance and needs of dance and dancers, or BAPAM (www.bapam.org.uk) for health issues. You may want to get involved with Move It - the UK's biggest dance exhibition which takes place every year in March. Visit www.dance-london.co.uk for more information. If you are looking for a dance agent to promote you to job opportunities, please see the 'Agents - Dance' section of Contacts.

# infopage

**The Council for Dance Education and Training (CDET) is the accrediting body of the dance and musical theatre industry. It is the first point of contact for students wishing to work professionally in dance and musical theatre, students wanting to take dance or dance teaching qualifications and those who want to dance simply because it's there.**

CDET runs a free information service - *Answers for Dancers (AfD)* - on all aspects of dance and musical theatre education and publishes the annual UK Handbook of Accredited Courses in Dance and Musical Theatre. The Handbook, sponsored by Spotlight, is the country's most comprehensive dance and musical theatre guide and is available free of charge from www.samuelfrench-london.co.uk. *Answers for Dancers* information sheets can be found on the CDET website and personal advice is also available by telephone. *AfD* addresses thousands of enquiries a year from students, parents, dancers and musical theatre artists. Here are some *Answers for Dancers...*

### How do I become a professional dancer, dance teacher or musical theatre artist?

Whether you want to dance for leisure or professionally it is vitally important you get teaching of the highest quality in studios properly equipped to ensure you are safe and secure. Injury is an occupational hazard of the dancer and it is essential you are taught by professionals who understand the effect of hard, physical work on the body, that you dance on floors designed to minimise the risk of stress and strain and that you work in a space big enough to let you move freely and safely. Whether you dance professionally or as a serious hobby, injury means you have to stop until you have recovered. For professionals it might mean losing the next job.

### Where can I find professional teachers who work to standards approved by the industry?

At a CDET accredited vocational dance or musical theatre school or college and at a CDET accredited Dance Awarding Body.

### What makes CDET accredited education and training so special?

Every CDET accredited institution has been inspected by trained panels of dance and musical theatre professionals to ensure it meets the needs of both the industry and the student. Council inspection reports are used by the government, Ofsted, charitable foundations and trusts when making funding decisions. If a school or college fails to maintain its standards, it can lose its accreditation.

### What is a CDET accredited vocational dance or musical theatre school?

A CDET accredited vocational school is a school or college offering performance or teaching courses for students over the age of 16 (Further Education) or 18 (Higher Education).

### What is a CDET accredited Dance Awarding Body?

A CDET accredited Dance Awarding Body (and Dance Teaching Society) is an organisation offering qualifications by means of examinations and other forms of assessment.

### What is a CDET Recognised pre-vocational School?

A CDET Recognised pre-vocational School (RS) is a dance or musical theatre school working with students under the age of 16. Schools awarded RS have confirmed in writing to the Council that they meet all nine requirements of the award, full details of which can be found in the pre-vocational dance section of the Council's website. The award is run in association with Dancing Times and The Stage.

Students applying to a vocational dance or musical theatre school, taking the qualifications of a Dance Awarding Body or attending a pre- or non-vocational dance or musical theatre school are strongly advised to ensure it holds CDET approval.

Competition for places at CDET accredited dance and musical theatre schools and colleges is fierce and you may be considering an offer from a vocational school not accredited by the Council. If so, make sure you are confident you will receive the quality of training you expect, that studio facilities and medical resources are suitable for the teaching of dance or musical theatre and that you request a written explanation as to why the school does not hold CDET accreditation.

Whatever your query regarding dance or musical theatre education and training visit the Council website at www.cdet.org.uk or telephone the Council on 020 7240 5703.

**PIPER George DANCES**
Sadler's Wells, Rosebery Avenue
Islington, London EC1R 4TN
Website: www.gpdances.com
e-mail: contact@gpdances.com
Fax: 020-7278 5684                    Tel: 020-7278 5508

**PLACE The**
Robin Howard Dance Theatre
17 Duke's Road, London WC1H 9PY
Website: www.theplace.org.uk
e-mail: info@theplace.org.uk
Fax: 020-7121 1142                    Tel: 020-7121 1000

**PMB PRESENTATIONS Ltd**
Vicarage House
58-60 Kensington Church Street
London W8 4DB
Website: www.pmbpresentations.co.uk
e-mail: p@triciamurraybett.com
Fax: 020-7368 3338                    Tel: 020-7368 3337

**RAMBERT DANCE COMPANY**
94 Chiswick High Road, London W4 1SH
Website: www.rambert.org.uk
e-mail: rdc@rambert.org.uk
Fax: 020-8747 8323                    Tel: 020-8630 0600

**ROTIE Marie-Gabrielle PRODUCTIONS**
7 Trinity Rise, London SW2 2QP        Tel: 020-8674 1518
Website: www.rotieproductions.com
e-mail: rotiemanager@aol.com

**ROYAL BALLET The**
Royal Opera House
Covent Garden, London WC2E 9DD
e-mail: balletcompnay@roh.org.uk
Fax: 020-7212 9121          Tel: 020-7240 1200 ext 712

**RUSS Claire ENSEMBLE**
(Choreography, Contemporary/Commercial/Corporate)
4 Heatham Park
Twickenham TW2 7SF              Mobile: 07932 680224
Website: www.clairerussensemble.com
e-mail: info@clairerussensemble.com

**SCOTTISH BALLET**
Tramway, 25 Albert Drive
Glasgow G41 2PE                    Tel: 0141-331 2931
Website: www.scottishballet.co.uk
e-mail: sb@scottishballet.co.uk

**SCOTTISH DANCE THEATRE**
Dundee Repertory Theatre
Tay Square
Dundee DD1 1PB
Website: www.scottishdancetheatre.com
e-mail: achinn@dundeereptheatre.co.uk
Fax: 01382 228609                    Tel: 01382 342600

**SKY BLUE PINK**
Website: www.skybluepinkproductions.com
e-mail: info@skybluepinkproductions.com
Mobile: 07779 866439                Tel: 020-8715 5007

**SLOVAK DANCE THEATRE**
Holicska 50, Bratislava
Slovakia 851 05          Tel/Fax: 00 42 12 54 64 58 11
Website: www.sdt.sk
e-mail: sdt@sdt.sk

**SPLITZ THEATRE ARTZ**
5 Cow Lane
Fulbourn
Cambridge CB21 5HB                  Tel: 01223 880389
Website: www.splitz-ta.co.uk
e-mail: splitz-ta@btopenworld.com

**SPRINGS DANCE COMPANY**
99 Tressillian Road
London SE4 1XZ
Website: www.springsdancecompany.org.uk
e-mail: info@springsdancecompany.org.uk
Mobile: 07775 628442                Tel: 01634 817523

**TRANSITIONS DANCE COMPANY**
Creekside, London SE8 3DZ            Tel: 020-8691 8600
e-mail: info@laban.org

**TWITCH EVENT CHOREOGRAPHY**
5 Breakspears Mews
Brockley, London SE4 1PY
Website: www.twitch.uk.com
e-mail: info@twitch.uk.com
Mobile: 07932 656358            Mobile: 07747 770816

**UNION DANCE**
Top Floor
6 Charing Cross Road
London WC2H 0HG
Website: www.uniondance.co.uk
e-mail: info@uniondance.co.uk
Fax: 020-7836 7847                  Tel: 020-7836 7837

**ACCELERATE Ltd**
374 Ley Street, Ilford IG1 4AE          Mobile: 07782 199181
Website: www.accelerate-productions.co.uk
e-mail: info@accelerate-productions.co.uk

**AKADEMI SOUTH ASIAN DANCE UK**
Hampstead Town Hall
213 Haverstock Hill, London NW3 4QP
Website: www.akademi.co.uk
e-mail: info@akademi.co.uk
Fax: 020-7691 3211          Tel: 020-7691 3210

**ALLIED DANCING ASSOCIATION**
137 Greenhill Road
Mossley Hill
Liverpool L18 7HQ          Tel: 0151-724 1829

**ASSOCIATION OF DANCE OF THE AFRICAN DIASPORA**
Urdang, The Old Finsbury Town Hall
Rosebery Avenue, London EC1R 4QT
Website: www.adad.org.uk
e-mail: info@adad.org.uk
Fax: 020-7833 2363          Tel: 020-7841 7357

**BENESH INSTITUTE The**
36 Battersea Square, London SW11 3RA
Website: www.benesh.org
e-mail: beneshinstitute@rad.org.uk
Tel: 020-7326 8031          Tel: 020-7326 8035

**BLUE EYED SOUL DANCE COMPANY**
The Lantern, Meadow Farm Drive
Shrewsbury SY1 4NG          Tel: 01743 210830
Website: www.blueeyedsouldance.com
e-mail: admin@blueeyedsouldance.com

**BRITISH ARTS The**
12 Deveron Way, Rise Park
Romford RM1 4UL          Tel: 01708 756263
Website: www.britisharts.org

**BRITISH ASSOCIATION OF TEACHERS OF DANCING**
Pavilion, 8 Upper Level
Watermark Business Park
315 Govan Road
Glasgow G51 2SE          Tel: 0141-427 3699
Website: www.batd.co.uk
e-mail: enquiries@batd.co.uk

**BRITISH BALLET ORGANISATION**
(Dance Examining Society & Teacher Training)
Woolborough House
39 Lonsdale Road, Barnes
London SW13 9JP          Tel: 020-8748 1241
Website: www.bbo.org.uk
e-mail: info@bbo.org.uk

**BRITISH THEATRE DANCE ASSOCIATION**
Garden Street, Leicester LE1 3UA
Website: www.btda.org.uk
e-mail: info@btda.org.uk
Fax: 0845 1662189          Tel: 0845 1662179

**CHISENHALE DANCE SPACE**
64-84 Chisenhale Road
Bow, London E3 5QZ
Website: www.chisenhaledancespace.co.uk
e-mail: mail@chisenhaledancespace.co.uk
Fax: 020-8980 9323          Tel: 020-8981 6617

**COUNCIL FOR DANCE EDUCATION & TRAINING**
Old Brewer's Yard
17-19 Neal Street
Covent Garden
London WC2H 9UY
Website: www.cdet.org.uk
e-mail: info@cdet.org.uk
Fax: 020-7240 2547          Tel: 020-7240 5703

**DANCE 4**
(National Dance Agency)
3-9 Hockley
Nottingham NG1 1FH
Website: www.dance4.co.uk
e-mail: info@dance4.co.uk
Fax: 0115-941 0776          Tel: 0115-941 0773

**DANCE BASE NATIONAL CENTRE FOR DANCE**
14-16 Grassmarket
Edinburgh EH1 2JU
Website: www.dancebase.co.uk
e-mail: dance@dancebase.co.uk
Fax: 0131-225 5234          Tel: 0131-225 5525

**DANCE CITY**
(National Dance Agency)
Temple Street
Newcastle-upon-Tyne NE1 4BR          Tel: 0191-261 0505
Website: www.dancecity.co.uk
e-mail: info@dancecity.co.uk

**DANCE DIGITAL**
2 Bond Street
Chelmsford
Essex CM1 1GH          Tel: 01245 346036
Website: www.dancedigital.org.uk
e-mail: admin@dancedigital.org.uk

**DANCE EAST**
(National Dance Agency)
Northgate Arts Centre
Sidegate Lane West
Ipswich IP4 3DF
Website: www.danceeast.co.uk
e-mail: info@danceeast.co.uk
Fax: 01473 639236          Tel: 01473 639230

**DANCE HOUSE**
20 St Andrew's Street
Glasgow G1 5PD          Tel: 0141-552 2442
Website: www.dancehouse.org
e-mail: info@dancehouse.org

**DANCE IN DEVON**
(County Dance Development Agency)
Exeter Phoenix
Bradnich Place
Gandy Street, Exeter EX4 3LS          Tel: 01392 667050
Website: www.danceindevon.org.uk
e-mail: info@danceindevon.org.uk

**DANCE INITIATIVE GREATER MANCHESTER**
Zion Arts Centre
Stretford Road
Hulme, Manchester M15 5ZA
Website: www.digm.org
e-mail: info@digm.org.uk
Fax: 0161-232 7483          Tel: 0161-232 7179

**DANCERS' CAREER DEVELOPMENT**
Plouviez House
19-20 Hatton Place
London EC1N 8RU
Website: www.thedcd.org.uk
e-mail: admin@thedcd.org.uk
Fax: 020-7242 1462
Tel: 020-7831 1449

**DANCE SOUTH WEST**
PO Box 5457
Bournemouth
Dorset BH1 1WU
Tel/Fax: 01202 554131
Website: www.dancesouthwest.org.uk
e-mail: info@dancesouthwest.org.uk

**DANCE UK**
(Including the Healthier Dancer Programme)
The Urdang
The Old Finsbury Town Hall
Rosebery Avenue
London EC1R 4QT
Website: www.danceuk.org
e-mail: info@danceuk.org
Fax: 020-7833 2363
Tel: 020-7713 0730

**DANCE UMBRELLA**
20 Chancellors Street
London W6 9RN
Website: www.danceumbrella.co.uk
e-mail: mail@danceumbrella.co.uk
Fax: 020-8741 7902
Tel: 020-8741 4040

**DANCEXCHANGE**
(National Dance Agency)
Birmingham Hippodrome
Thorp Street
Birmingham B5 4TB
Tel: 0121-689 3170
Website: www.dancexchange.org.uk
e-mail: info@dancexchange.org.uk

**DAVIES Siobhan DANCE**
(Professional Development for Dance Artists & Education)
85 St George's Road
London SE1 6ER
Website: www.siobhandavies.com
e-mail: info@siobhandavies.com
Fax: 020-7091 9669
Tel: 020-7091 9650

**EAST LONDON DANCE**
Stratford Circus
Theatre Square
London E15 1BX
Website: www.eastlondondance.org
e-mail: office@eastlondondance.org
Fax: 020-8279 1054
Tel: 020-8279 1050

**FOUNDATION FOR COMMUNITY DANCE**
LCB Depot
31 Rutland Street
Leicester LE1 1RE
Website: www.communitydance.org.uk
e-mail: info@communitydance.org.uk
Fax: 0116-261 6801
Tel: 0116-253 3453

**COUNCIL** *for* **DANCE**
EDUCATION AND TRAINING

**The Council for Dance Education and Training** is the national standards body of the professional dance industry. It accredits programmes of training in vocational dance schools and holds the Register of Dance Awarding Bodies - the directory of teaching societies whose syllabuses have been inspected and approved by the Council. It is the body of advocacy of the dance education and training communities and offers a free and comprehensive information service - *Answers for Dancers* - on all aspects of vocational dance provision to students, parents, teachers, dance artists and employers.

**The Conference of Professional Dance Schools (CPDS)** is a committee of the Council and provides a forum in which representatives from vocational dance training institutions may discuss policy and recommend action in relation to vocational dance training.

**CDET Accredited Schools**
- **ArtsEd London • Bird College • Cambridge Performing Arts • Elmhurst School for Dance**
- **Hammond School • Italia Conti Academy of Theatre Arts Ltd • Laine Theatre Arts**
- **Liverpool Theatre School and College • London Studio Centre**
- **Merseyside Dance and Drama Centre • Midlands Academy of Dance and Drama**
- **Northern Ballet School • Performers College • Stella Mann College**
- **Tring Park School for The Performing Arts • Urdang Academy**

**For more info on the CPDS and CDET contact:**
**Council for Dance Education & Training**
Old Brewer's Yard   17-19 Neal Street   Covent Garden   London WC2H 9UY
**Tel: 020 7240 5703   Email: info@cdet.org.uk   Website: www.cdet.org.uk**

**GREENWICH DANCE AGENCY**
The Borough Hall
Royal Hill
London SE10 8RE                           Tel: 020-8293 9741
Website: www.greenwichdance.org.uk
e-mail: info@greenwichdance.org.uk

**IDTA (INTERNATIONAL DANCE TEACHERS'
ASSOCIATION)**
International House
76 Bennett Road
Brighton, East Sussex BN2 5JL
Website: www.idta.co.uk
e-mail: info@idta.co.uk
Fax: 01273 674388                         Tel: 01273 685652

**LANGUAGE OF DANCE CENTRE**
4th Floor, Charles House
375 Kensington High Street
London W14 8QH                            Tel: 020-7603 8500
Website: www.lodc.org
e-mail: info@lodc.org

**LONDON CONTEMPORARY DANCE SCHOOL**
16 Flaxman Terrace, London WC1H 9AT
Website: www.theplace.org.uk
e-mail: lcds@theplace.org.uk
Fax: 020-7121 1142                         Tel: 020-7121 1111

**LUDUS DANCE**
The Assembly Rooms
King Street, Lancaster LA1 1RE
Website: www.ludusdance.org
e-mail: info@ludusdance.org
Fax: 01524 847744                         Tel: 01524 35936

**MERSEYSIDE DANCE INITIATIVE**
(National Dance Agency)
24 Hope Street
Liverpool L1 9BX                          Tel: 0151-708 8810
Website: www.merseysidedance.co.uk
e-mail: info@mdi.org.uk

**MIDLAND INTERNATIONAL DANCE ARTS ASSOCIATION**
29A Sycamore Road
Birmingham B23 5QP
Website: www.midaa.co.uk
e-mail: midaa.hq@hotmail.com
Fax: 0121-694 0013                        Tel: 0121-694 0012

**NATIONAL RESOURCE CENTRE FOR DANCE**
University of Surrey
Guildford GU2 7XH
Website: www.surrey.ac.uk/nrcd
e-mail: nrcd@surrey.ac.uk
Fax: 01483 689500                         Tel: 01483 689316

**PLACE The**
(National Dance Agency)
Robin Howard Dance Theatre
17 Duke's Road, London WC1H 9BY
Website: www.theplace.org.uk
e-mail: info@theplace.org.uk
Fax: 020-7121 1142                         Tel: 020-7121 1000

**PROFESSIONAL TEACHERS OF DANCING**
Quay West Business Centre
Quay Lane, Gosport
Hants PO12 4LJ                            Tel: 023-9260 4285
Website: www.ptdance.com
e-mail: ptdenquiries@msn.com

**SOUTH EAST DANCE**
(National Dance Agency)
28 Kensington Street, Brighton BN1 4AJ
Website: www.southeastdance.org.uk
e-mail: info@southeastdance.org.uk
Fax: 01273 697212                         Tel: 01273 696844

**SWINDON DANCE**
(National Dance Agency)
Town Hall Studios
Regent Circus, Swindon SN1 1QF            Tel: 01793 601700
Website: www.swindondance.org.uk
e-mail: info@swindondance.org.uk

**TURTLE KEY ARTS**
Ladbroke Hall
79 Barlby Road
London W10 6AZ
Website: www.turtlekeyarts.org.uk
e-mail: shaun@turtlekeyarts.org.uk
Fax: 020-8964 4080                         Tel: 020-8964 5060

**TWITCH EVENT CHOREOGRAPHY**
5 Breakspears Mews
Brockley, London SE4 1PY
Website: www.twitch.uk.com
e-mail: info@twitch.uk.com
Mobile: 07932 656358                      Mobile: 07747 770816

**WELSH INDEPENDENT DANCE**
Chapter
Market Road
Canton, Cardiff CF5 1QE                   Tel: 029-2038 7314
Website: www.welshindance.co.uk
e-mail: info@welshindance.co.uk

**YORKSHIRE DANCE**
(National Dance Agency)
3 St Peters Buildings
St Peters Square
Leeds LS9 8AH
Website: www.yorkshiredance.com
e-mail: admin@yorkshiredance.com
Fax: 0113-259 5700                         Tel: 0113-243 9867

# PAUL HARRIS® 07958-784462 www.paulharris.uk.com

**Choreographer: "The Other Boleyn Girl" "Harry Potter 5" (Wand Combat)**
Choreography and Coaching in Period and Contemporary Social Dance
**\* Swing \* Waltz \* Salsa \* Tango \* Charleston \* Quadrille** *etc.*

**AIRCRAFT CIRCUS**
Unit 7A, Melish House
Harrington Way
London SE18 5NR                  Tel: 020-8317 8401
Website: www.aircraftcircus.com
e-mail: moira@aircraftcircus.com

**ARTS EDUCATIONAL SCHOOLS, LONDON**
Cone Ripman House
14 Bath Road, Chiswick
London W4 1LY                    Tel: 020-8987 6666
Website: www.artsed.co.uk
e-mail: reception@artsed.co.uk

**AVIV DANCE STUDIOS**
Wren House, 1st Floor
19-23 Exchange Road
Watford WD18 0JD             Tel/Fax: 01923 250000
Website: www.avivdance.com
e-mail: nikkiavron@btconnect.com

**BALLROOM, LONDON THEATRE OF**
(Artistic Director: Paul Harris®, Mentor "Faking It")
24 Montana Gardens
Sutton, Surrey SM1 4FP
Website: www.londontheatreofballroom.com
e-mail: office@londontheatreofballroom.com
Mobile: 07958 784462            Tel: 020-8722 8798

**BHAVAN CENTRE**
4A Castletown Road
London W14 9HE                   Tel: 020-7381 3086
Website: www.bhavan.net
e-mail: info@bhavan.net

**BIRD COLLEGE DANCE MUSIC & THEATRE
PERFORMANCE**
(Dance & Theatre Performance HE & FE Programmes)
Birkbeck Centre, Birkbeck Road
Sidcup, Kent DA14 4DE
Website: www.birdcollege.co.uk
e-mail: admin@birdcollege.co.uk
Fax: 020-8308 1370               Tel: 020-8300 6004

**BODENS STUDIOS**
(Performing Arts Classes)
Bodens Studios & Agency
99 East Barnet Road
New Barnet, Herts EN4 8RF
Website: www.bodenstudios.com
e-mail: info@bodenstudios.com
Mobile: 07545 696888            Tel: 020-8449 0982

**BRIGHTON DANCE DIVERSION**
93 Sea Lane
Rustington
West Sussex BN16 2RS             Tel: 01903 770304
Website: www.brightondancediversion.com
e-mail: info@brightondancediversion.com

**CAMBRIDGE PERFORMING ARTS AT BODYWORK**
Bodywork Company Dance Studios
25-29 Glisson Road
Cambridge CB1 2HA                Tel: 01223 314461
Website: www.bodywork-dance.co.uk
e-mail: admin@bodyworkds.co.uk

**CANDOCO DANCE COMPANY**
2T Leroy House, 436 Essex Road
London N1 3QP                    Tel: 020-7704 6845
Website: www.candoco.co.uk
e-mail: info@candoco.co.uk

**CENTRAL SCHOOL OF BALLET**
(Full Time Vocational Training, Open Classes
Beginner/Professional Level)
10 Herbal Hill, Clerkenwell Road, London EC1R 5EG
Website: www.centralschoolofballet.co.uk
e-mail: info@csbschool.co.uk
Fax: 020-7833 5571               Tel: 020-7837 6332

**CENTRE - PERFORMING ARTS COLLEGE The**
Building 62, Level 4, 37 Bowater Road
Charlton, London SE18 5TF
Website: www.thecentrepac.com
e-mail: dance@thecentrepac.com
Fax: 020-8855 6662               Tel: 020-8855 6661

**COLLECTIVE DANCE & DRAMA**
The Studio, Rectory Lane
Rickmansworth, Herts WD3 1FD    Tel/Fax: 020-8428 0037
Website: www.collectivedance.co.uk
e-mail: info@collectivedance.co.uk

**CONTI Italia ACADEMY OF THEATRE ARTS**
(Full-time 3 year & 1 year Musical Theatre Courses, Dance
Teacher Training with Performing Arts Course)
Italia Conti House, 23 Goswell Road, London EC1M 7AJ
Website: www.italiaconti.com
e-mail: admin@italiaconti.co.uk
Fax: 020-7253 1430               Tel: 020-7608 0044

| **THE CENTRE** | Performing Arts College | Building 62, Level 4, 37 Bowater Road, Charlton. |
| | Agency | London SE18 5TF |
| | | T: +44 (0)20 8855 6661 |
| Principal: Karen King FISTD, ARAD, Cert. Ed. | Theatre School | F: +44 (0)20 8855 6662 |
| | | E: dance@thecentrepac.com |
| | | W: www.thecentrepac.com |

**COUNCIL FOR DANCE EDUCATION & TRAINING (CDET) The**
Old Brewer's Yard
17-19 Neal Street, Covent Garden
London WC2H 9UY
Website: www.cdet.org.uk
e-mail: info@cdet.org.uk
Fax: 020-7240 2547                     Tel: 020-7240 5703

**CPA COLLEGE**
The Studios
219B North Street, Romford RM1 4QA
Website: www.colinsperformingarts.co.uk
e-mail: agency@colinsperformingarts.co.uk
Fax: 01708 766077                     Tel: 01708 766007

**D & B SCHOOL OF PERFORMING ARTS**
Central Studios
470 Bromley Road
Bromley, Kent BR1 4PN
Website: www.dandbperformingarts.co.uk
e-mail: bonnie@dandbmanagement.com
Fax: 020-8697 8100                     Tel: 020-8698 8880

**DANCE BASE NATIONAL CENTRE FOR DANCE**
14-16 Grassmarket
Edinburgh EH1 2JU
Website: www.dancebase.co.uk
e-mail: dance@dancebase.co.uk
Fax: 0131-225 5234                     Tel: 0131-225 5525

**DANCE HOUSE**
20 St Andrew's Street
Glasgow G1 5PD                       Tel: 0141-552 2442
Website: www.dancehouse.org
e-mail: info@dancehouse.org

**DANCE RESEARCH COMMITTEE - IMPERIAL SOCIETY OF TEACHERS OF DANCING**
(Training in Historical Dance)
c/o Ludwell House, Charing, Kent TN27 0LS
Website: www.istd.org
e-mail: n.gainesarmitage@tiscali.co.uk
Fax: 01233 712768                     Tel: 01233 712469

**DANCEWORKS**
(Also Fitness, Yoga & Martial Arts Classes)
16 Balderton Street
London W1K 6TN                       Tel: 020-7629 6183
Website: www.danceworks.net
e-mail: info@danceworks.net

**DAVIES Siobhan STUDIOS**
(Daily Professional Classes, open dance & body conditioning classes for wider community)
85 St George's Road, London SE1 6ER
Website: www.siobhandavies.com
e-mail: info@siobhandavies.com
Fax: 020-7091 9669                     Tel: 020-7091 9650

**DIRECTIONS THEATRE ARTS CHESTERFIELD Ltd**
1A-2A Sheffield Road
Chesterfield, Derbyshire S41 7LL     Tel/Fax: 01246 854455
Website: www.directionstheatrearts.org
e-mail: julie.cox5@btconnect.com

**D M AGENCY The**
The Studios, Briggate, Shipley
Bradford, West Yorks BD17 7BT
Website: www.dmacademy.co.uk
e-mail: info@dmacademy.co.uk
Fax: 01274 592502                     Tel: 01274 585317

**DUFFILL Drusilla THEATRE SCHOOL**
Grove Lodge
Oakwood Road
Burgess Hill, West Sussex RH15 0HZ
Website: www.drusilladuffilltheatreschool.co.uk
e-mail: drusilladschool@btclick.com
Fax: 01444 232680                     Tel: 01444 232672

**EAST LONDON DANCE**
Stratford Circus
Theatre Square, London E15 1BX
Website: www.eastlondondance.org
e-mail: office@eastlondondance.org
Fax: 020-8279 1054                     Tel: 020-8279 1050

**EDINBURGH'S TELFORD COLLEGE**
350 West Granton Road, Edinburgh EH5 1QE
Website: www.ed-coll.ac.uk
e-mail: mail@ed-coll.ac.uk
Fax: 0131-559 4111                     Tel: 0131-559 4000

**ELIE Mark DANCE FOUNDATION**
Portobello Dance School
The Tabernacle, Powis Square
London W11 2AY                       Mobile: 07947 484021
Website: www.portobellodance.org.uk
e-mail: markeliedancefoundation@uk2.net

**ELMHURST SCHOOL FOR DANCE**
249 Bristol Road
Edgbaston, Birmingham B5 7UH
Website: www.elmhurstdance.co.uk
e-mail: enquiries@elmhurstdance.co.uk
Fax: 0121-472 6654                     Tel: 0121-472 6655

**ENGLISH NATIONAL BALLET SCHOOL**
Carlyle Building
Hortensia Road, London SW10 0QS
Website: www.enbschool.org.uk
e-mail: info@enbschool.org.uk
Fax: 020-7376 3404                     Tel: 020-7376 7076

**EXCEL SCHOOL OF PERFORMING ARTS**
KT Summit House, 100 Hanger Lane
Ealing, London W5 1EZ                 Tel: 020-8799 6168
Website: www.ktioe-excel.org
e-mail: excel@kt.org

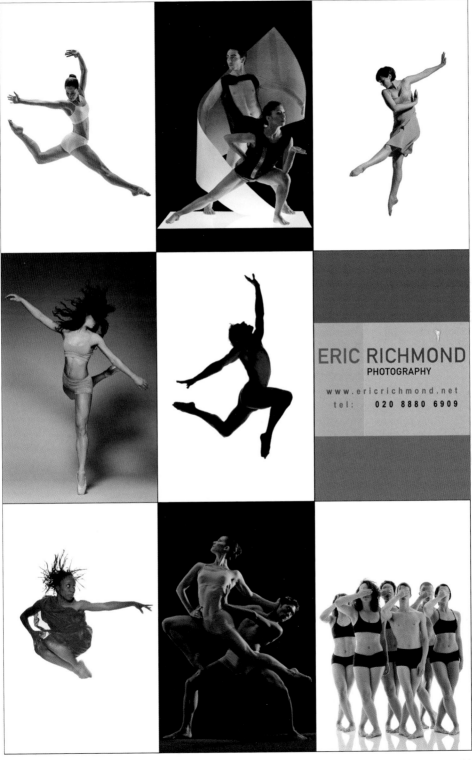

ERIC RICHMOND
PHOTOGRAPHY

www.ericrichmond.net
tel: **020 8880 6909**

**EXPRESSIONS ACADEMY OF PERFORMING ARTS**
3 Newgate Lane, Mansfield, Nottingham NG18 2LB
Website: www.expressionsperformingarts.co.uk
e-mail: expressions-uk@btconnect.com
Fax: 01623 647337                Tel: 01623 424334

**FANTASY FEET DANCE & MUSICAL THEATRE ACADEMY**
16 Llwyn Yr Eos Grove
Penyard, Merthyr Tydfil
Mid Glamorgan, Wales CF47 0GD
Website: www.fantasyfeetdance.co.uk
e-mail: fantasyfeetdanceacademy@yahoo.co.uk
Mobile: 07894 164104            Mobile: 07947 345434

**GEORGIE SCHOOL OF THEATRE DANCE**
101 Lane Head Road, Shepley
Huddersfield
West Yorkshire HD8 8DB          Tel/Fax: 01484 606994
e-mail: donna.george@virgin.net

**GREASEPAINT ANONYMOUS**
4 Gallus Close, Winchmore Hill
London N21 1JR
e-mail: info@greasepaintanonymous.co.uk
Fax: 020-8882 9189              Tel: 020-8886 2263

**HAMMOND SCHOOL The**
Hoole Bank, Mannings Lane, Chester CH2 4ES
Website: www.thehammondschool.co.uk
e-mail: info@thehammondschool.co.uk
Fax: 01244 305351               Tel: 01244 305350

**HARRIS Paul**
Contact: Paul Harris® (Movement for Actors,
Choreography, Tuition in Period & Contemporary Social
Dance)
24 Montana Gardens, Sutton, Surrey SM1 4FP
Website: www.paulharris.uk.com
e-mail: office@paulharris.uk.com
Mobile: 07958 784462            Tel: 020-8722 8798

**ISLINGTON ARTS FACTORY**
2 Parkhurst Road, London N7 0SF
e-mail: iaf@islingtonartsfactory.fsnet.co.uk
Fax: 020-7700 7229              Tel: 020-7607 0561

**LABAN**
Creekside, London SE8 3DZ
Website: www.laban.org
e-mail: info@laban.org
Fax: 020-8691 8400              Tel: 020-8691 8600

**LAINE THEATRE ARTS**
The Studios, East Street
Epsom, Surrey KT17 1HH
Website: www.laine-theatre-arts.co.uk
e-mail: webmaster@laine-theatre-arts.co.uk
Fax: 01372 723775               Tel: 01372 724648

**LEARN SALSA, CHA CHA CHA & MERENGUE WITH PATRICE**
The Hendon Methodist Church
The Burroughs, Hendon Central Station
London NW4                     Mobile: 07748 676670
Website: www.myspace.com/salsaisback
e-mail: salsawithpatrice@gmail.com

**LEE Lynn THEATRE SCHOOL The**
(Office)
126 Church Road, Benfleet
Essex SS7 4EP                   Tel: 01268 795863
e-mail: lynn@leetheatre.fsnet.co.uk

**LIVERPOOL THEATRE SCHOOL**
(Musical Theatre & Professional Classes)
19 Aigburth Road, Liverpool
Merseyside L17 4JR
Website: www.liverpooltheatreschool.co.uk
e-mail: info@liverpooltheatreschool.co.uk
Fax: 0151-728 9582             Tel: 0151-728 7800

**LONDON CONTEMPORARY DANCE SCHOOL**
(Full-time Vocational Training at Degree & Postgraduate
Level)
16 Flaxman Terrace, London WC1H 9AT
Website: www.theplace.org.uk
e-mail: lcds@theplace.org.uk
Fax: 020-7121 1145             Tel: 020-7121 1111

**LONDON STUDIO CENTRE**
42-50 York Way, London N1 9AB
Website: www.london-studio-centre.co.uk
e-mail: info@london-studio-centre.co.uk
Fax: 020-7837 3248            Tel: 020-7837 7741

**MANN Stella COLLEGE OF PERFORMING ARTS Ltd**
(Professional Training Course for Performers & Teachers)
10 Linden Road, Bedford
Bedfordshire MK40 2DA
Website: www.stellamanncollege.co.uk
e-mail: info@stellamanncollege.co.uk
Fax: 01234 217284            Tel: 01234 213331

**MGA STAGE ACADEMIES**
11/4 Abbey Street
Edinburgh EH7 5XN             Tel: 0131-466 9392
Website: www.themgacompany.com
e-mail: info@themgacompany.com

**MIDLANDS ACADEMY OF DANCE & DRAMA**
Century House, Building B
428 Carlton Hill
Nottingham NG4 1QA            Tel/Fax: 0115-911 0401
Website: www.maddcollege.co.uk
e-mail: admin@maddcollege.supanet.com

**MILLENNIUM PERFORMING ARTS Ltd**
29 Thomas Street, Woolwich
London SE18 6HU               Tel: 020-8301 8744
Website: www.md2000.co.uk
e-mail: info@md2000.co.uk

Stella Mann College has been invited to offer places under the Government's Dance and Drama Awards scheme.

This College offers the opportunity to study for the National Diploma in either Professional Dance or Professional Musical Theatre, both validated by Trinity College, London.

Course accredited by the Council for Dance Education and Training.

Photo by Peter Teigen

Stella Mann College promotes individuality and difference and welcomes applications from people from under-represented groups.

10 Linden Road, Bedford, Bedfordshire, MK40 2DA.    Tel: 01234 213331  Fax: 01234 217284
e-mail: info@stellamanncollege.co.uk   www.stellamanncollege.co.uk

**...stretch yourself to the max!**

**NEW LONDON PERFORMING ARTS CENTRE**
(Performing Arts Classes 3-19 years/All Dance Styles, GCSE
Course, RAD & ISTD Exams)
76 St James Lane, Muswell Hill, London N10 3DF
Website: www.nlpac.co.uk
e-mail: nlpac@aol.com
Fax: 020-8444 4040                    Tel: 020-8444 4544

**NORTH LONDON DANCE STUDIO**
843-845 Green Lanes, Winchmore Hill, London N21 2RX
e-mail: thedancestudio@btopenworld.com
Fax: 020-8364 2009                    Tel: 020-8360 5700

**NORTHERN ACADEMY OF PERFORMING ARTS**
Anlaby Road, Hull HU1 2PD
Website: www.northernacademy.org.uk
e-mail: napa@northernacademy.org.uk
Fax: 01482 212280                    Tel: 01482 310690

**NORTHERN BALLET SCHOOL**
The Dancehouse, 10 Oxford Road, Manchester M1 5QA
Website: www.northernballetschool.co.uk
e-mail: enquiries@northernballetschool.co.uk
Fax: 0161-237 1408                    Tel: 0161-237 1406

**NORTHERN SCHOOL OF CONTEMPORARY DANCE The**
98 Chapeltown Road
Leeds LS7 4BH                    Tel: 0113-219 3000
Website: www.nscd.ac.uk
e-mail: info@nscd.ac.uk

**PAUL'S THEATRE SCHOOL**
Ardleigh House
42 Ardleigh Green Road, Hornchurch
Essex RM11 2LG                    Tel: 01708 447123
Website: www.paulstheatreschool.com
e-mail: info@paulstheatreschool.com

**PERFORMERS COLLEGE**
Southend Road, Corringham, Essex SS17 8JT
Website: www.performerscollege.co.uk
e-mail: pdc@dircon.co.uk
Fax: 01375 672353                    Tel: 01375 672053

**PINEAPPLE DANCE STUDIOS**
7 Langley Street, London WC2H 9JA
Website: www.pineapple.uk.com
e-mail: studios@pineapple.uk.com
Fax: 020-7836 0803                    Tel: 020-7836 4004

**PLACE The**
Robin Howard Dance Theatre
17 Duke's Road, London WC1H 9BY
Website: www.theplace.org.uk
e-mail: info@theplace.org.uk
Fax: 020-7121 1142                    Tel: 020-7121 1000

**PROFESSIONAL TEACHERS OF DANCING**
Quay West Business Centre
Quay Lane, Gosport
Hants PO12 4LJ                    Tel: 023-9260 4285
Website: www.ptdance.com
e-mail: ptdenquiries@msn.com

**RAMBERT SCHOOL OF BALLET & CONTEMPORARY DANCE**
Clifton Lodge, St Margaret's Drive
Twickenham, Middlesex TW1 1QN
Website: www.rambertschool.org.uk
e-mail: info@rambertschool.org.uk
Fax: 020-8892 8090                    Tel: 020-8892 9960

**RIDGEWAY STUDIOS PERFORMING ARTS COLLEGE**
Fairley House, Andrews Lane
Cheshunt, Herts EN7 6LB
Website: www.ridgewaystudios.co.uk
e-mail: info@ridgewaystudios.co.uk
Fax: 01992 633844                    Tel: 01992 633775

**RIVERSIDE REFLECTIONS BATON TWIRLING TEAM**
34 Knowle Avenue
Bexleyheath, Kent DA7 5LX
Website: www.riverside-reflections.piczo.co.uk
e-mail: c.johnson717@ntlworld.com
Mobile: 07958 617976                    Tel/Fax: 01322 410003

**ROEBUCK Gavin**
(Classical Ballet)
51 Earls Court Square
London SW5 9DG                    Tel: 020-7370 7324
e-mail: info@gavinroebuck.com

**ROJO Y NEGRO**
(Argentine Tango School of Dance)
52 Lloyd Baker Street, Clerkenwell
London WC1X 9AA                    Tel: 020-8520 2726
Website: www.rojoynegroclub.com
e-mail: info@rojoynegroclub.com

**ROYAL ACADEMY OF DANCE**
36 Battersea Square, London SW11 3RA
Website: www.rad.org.uk
e-mail: info@rad.org.uk
Fax: 020-7924 2311                    Tel: 020-7326 8000

**SAFREY ACADEMY OF PERFORMING ARTS**
10 St Julians Close, London SW16 2RY
Website: www.safreyarts.co.uk
e-mail: mbkdance@msn.com
Fax: 020-8488 9121                    Tel: 020-8664 6676

**TIFFANY THEATRE COLLEGE**
969-973 London Road, Leigh on Sea
Essex SS9 3LB                    Tel: 01702 710069
Website: www.tiffanytheatrecollege.com
e-mail: info@tiffanytheatrecollege.com

**URDANG ACADEMY The**
Finsbury Town Hall
Rosebery Avenue
London EC1R 4RP
Website: www.theurdangacademy.com
e-mail: info@theurdangacademy.com
Fax: 020-7278 6727                    Tel: 020-7713 7710

**VALLÉ ACADEMY OF PERFORMING ARTS**
The Vallé Academy Studios
Wilton House, Delamare Road
Cheshunt, Herts EN8 9SG
Website: www.valleacademy.co.uk
e-mail: enquiries@valleacademy.co.uk
Fax: 01992 622868                    Tel: 01992 622862

**WHITEHALL PERFORMING ARTS CENTRE**
Rayleigh Road, Leigh-on-Sea
Essex SS9 5UU                    Tel/Fax: 01702 529290

**YOUNG Sylvia THEATRE SCHOOL**
Rossmore Road, Marylebone, London NW1 6NJ
Website: www.sylviayoungtheatreschool.co.uk
e-mail: sylvia@sylviayoungtheatreschool.co.uk
Fax: 020-7723 1040                    Tel: 020-7402 0673

**ALRA (ACADEMY OF LIVE AND RECORDED ARTS)**
Studio One
The Royal Victoria Patriotic Building
John Archer Way, London SW18 3SX
Website: www.alra.co.uk
e-mail: info@alra.co.uk
Fax: 020-8875 0789                    Tel: 020-8870 6475

**ARTS EDUCATIONAL SCHOOLS LONDON**
14 Bath Road, London W4 1LY
Website: www.artsed.co.uk
e-mail: drama@artsed.co.uk
Fax: 020-8987 6699                    Tel: 020-8987 6666

**BIRMINGHAM SCHOOL OF ACTING**
Level 0, Millennium Point
Curzon Street, Birmingham B4 7XG
Website: www.bsa.bcu.ac.uk
e-mail: info@bsa.bcu.ac.uk
Fax: 0121-331 7221                    Tel: 0121-331 7220

**BRISTOL OLD VIC THEATRE SCHOOL**
1-2 Downside Road, Clifton, Bristol BS8 2XF
Website: www.oldvic.ac.uk
e-mail: enquiries@oldvic.ac.uk
Fax: 0117-923 9371                    Tel: 0117-973 3535

**CENTRAL SCHOOL OF SPEECH & DRAMA The**
Embassy Theatre, 64 Eton Avenue
Swiss Cottage, London NW3 3H          Tel: 020-7722 8183
Website: www.cssd.ac.uk
e-mail: enquiries@cssd.ac.uk

**CONTI Italia ACADEMY OF THEATRE ARTS**
Avondale, 72 Landor Road
London SW9 9PH
Website: www.italiaconti-acting.co.uk
e-mail: acting@lsbu.ac.uk
Fax: 020-7737 2728                    Tel: 020-7733 3210

**CYGNET TRAINING THEATRE**
New Theatre, Friars Gate
Exeter, Devon EX2 4AZ         Tel/Fax: 01392 277189
Website: www.cygnetnewtheatre.com
e-mail: cygnetarts@btconnect.com

**DRAMA CENTRE LONDON**
Central Saint Martins College of Art & Design
10 Back Hill, London EC1R 5EN
Website: www.csm.arts.ac.uk/drama
e-mail: drama@arts.ac.uk
Fax: 020-7514 8777                    Tel: 020-7514 8778

**DRAMA STUDIO LONDON**
Grange Court, 1 Grange Road, London W5 5QN
Website: www.dramastudiolondon.co.uk
e-mail: admin@dramastudiolondon.co.uk
Fax: 020-8566 2035                    Tel: 020-8579 3897

**EAST 15 ACTING SCHOOL**
Hatfields, Rectory Lane
Loughton IG10 3RY
Website: www.east15.ac.uk
e-mail: east15@essex.ac.uk
Fax: 020-8508 7521                    Tel: 020-8508 5983

**GSA, GUILDFORD SCHOOL OF ACTING**
Millmead Terrace, Guildford
Surrey GU2 4YT                        Tel: 01483 560701
*From 1st June 2010:*
University of Surrey, Stag Hill Campus
Guildford, Surrey GU2 7XH
Website: www.gsauk.org
e-mail: enquiries@gsauk.org

**GUILDHALL SCHOOL OF MUSIC & DRAMA**
Silk Street, Barbican
London EC2Y 8DT
Website: www.gsmd.ac.uk
e-mail: info@gsmd.ac.uk
Fax: 020-7256 9438                    Tel: 020-7628 2571

**LAMDA**
155 Talgarth Road, London W14 9DA
Website: www.lamda.org.uk
e-mail: enquiries@lamda.org.uk
Fax: 020-8834 0501                    Tel: 020-8834 0500

**LIVERPOOL INSTITUTE FOR PERFORMING ARTS The**
Mount Street, Liverpool L1 9HF
Website: www.lipa.ac.uk
e-mail: reception@lipa.ac.uk
Fax: 0151-330 3131                    Tel: 0151-330 3000

**MANCHESTER SCHOOL OF THEATRE AT MANCHESTER METROPOLITAN UNIVERSITY**
The Mabel Tylecote Building
Cavendish Street
Manchester M15 6BG                    Tel: 0161-247 1305
Website: www.theatre.mmu.ac.uk

**MOUNTVIEW**
Academy of Theatre Arts
Ralph Richardson Memorial Studios
1 Kingfisher Place
Clarendon Road, London N22 6XF
Website: www.mountview.org.uk
e-mail: enquiries@mountview.org.uk
Fax: 020-8829 0034                    Tel: 020-8881 2201

**OXFORD SCHOOL OF DRAMA The**
Sansomes Farm Studios
Woodstock, Oxford OX20 1ER
Website: www.oxforddrama.ac.uk
e-mail: info@oxforddrama.ac.uk
Fax: 01993 811220                     Tel: 01993 812883

**QUEEN MARGARET UNIVERSITY, EDINBURGH**
Queen Margaret University Drive
Musselburgh, East Lothian EH21 6UU
Website: www.qmu.ac.uk
e-mail: admissions@qmu.ac.uk
Fax: 0131-474 0001                    Tel: 0131-474 0000

**ROSE BRUFORD COLLEGE**
Lamorbey Park, Burnt Oak Lane
Sidcup, Kent DA15 9DF
Website: www.bruford.ac.uk
e-mail: enquiries@bruford.ac.uk
Fax: 020-8308 0542                    Tel: 020-8308 2600

**ROYAL ACADEMY OF DRAMATIC ART**
62-64 Gower Street, London WC1E 6ED
Website: www.rada.org
e-mail: enquiries@rada.ac.uk
Fax: 020-7323 3865                    Tel: 020-7636 7076

**ROYAL SCOTTISH ACADEMY OF MUSIC & DRAMA**
100 Renfrew Street
Glasgow G2 3DB                        Tel: 0141-332 4101
Website: www.rsamd.ac.uk
e-mail: registry@rsamd.ac.uk

**ROYAL WELSH COLLEGE OF MUSIC & DRAMA**
Drama Department, Castle Grounds
Cathays Park, Cardiff CF10 3ER
Website: www.rwcmd.ac.uk
e-mail: drama.admissions@rwcmd.ac.uk
Fax: 029-2039 1302                    Tel: 029-2039 1327

# THE CONFERENCE OF DRAMA SCHOOLS

The Conference of Drama Schools comprises Britain's 22 leading Drama Schools. CDS exists to set and maintain the highest standards of training within the vocational drama sector and to make it easier for prospective students to understand the range of courses on offer and the application process. CDS member schools offer courses in Acting, Musical Theatre, Directing and Technical Theatre training.

**CDS members offer courses which are:**
**Professional** – you will be trained to work in the theatre by staff with professional experience and by visiting professionals.
**Intensive** – courses are full-time
**Work Orientated** – you are being trained to do a job – these courses are practical training for work.

CDS publishes *The Conference of Drama Schools – Guide to Professional Training in Drama and* *Technical Theatre 2010* and *The CDS Guide to Careers Backstage*.

For links to CDS schools please visit the website at **www.drama.ac.uk**

The full texts of both guides are available on the website – if you would like a hard copy please contact French's Theatre Bookshop, by phone on 020 7255 4300 or by emailing **theatre@samuelfrench-london.co.uk** or by visiting the shop at 52 Fitzroy Street, London, W1T 5JR. Single copies will be sent free of charge to UK addresses.
To contact CDS please visit the website or write to the Executive Secretary, CDS Ltd, P.O. Box 34252, London NW5 1XJ.

in association with

**A B ACADEMY THEATRE SCHOOL**
Act Out Ltd
22 Greek Street
Stockport, Cheshire SK3 8AB       Tel/Fax: 0161-429 7413
e-mail: ab22actout@aol.com

**ABOMELI TUTORING**
Contact: Charles Abomeli BA LLAM. Stage & Screen Acting
Technique. Characterisation Coach
Website: www.charlesabomeli.com
e-mail: charlesabm@aol.co.uk       Mobile: 07960 954904

**ACADEMY ARTS Ltd The**
PO Box 54435
London E10 7AY
Website: www.academyarts.co.uk
e-mail: info@academyarts.co.uk     Tel: 020-8539 1151

**ACADEMY OF CREATIVE TRAINING**
8-10 Rock Place, Brighton, East Sussex BN2 1PF
Website: www.actbrighton.org
e-mail: info@actbrighton.org        Tel: 01273 818266

**ACADEMY OF THE SCIENCE OF ACTING AND DIRECTING The**
9-15 Elthorne Road, London N19 4AJ
Website: www.asad.org.uk
e-mail: info@asad.org.uk
Fax: 020-7272 0026                  Tel: 020-7272 0027

**ACADEMY SCHOOL OF PERFORMING ARTS The**
Dance. Drama. Singing
Website: www.academy-sopa.co.uk
e-mail: theacademy@ntlworld.com
Mobile: 07983 981186                Tel: 0161-287 9700

# infopage

### Why do I need drama training?

The entertainment industry is an extremely competitive one, with thousands of performers competing for a small number of jobs. In such a crowded market, professional training will increase an actor's chances of success, and professionally trained artists are also more likely to be represented by agencies. Drama training can begin at any age and should continue throughout an actor's career.

### I have already trained to be an actor. Why do I need further training?

Drama training should not cease as soon as you graduate or get your first job. Throughout your career you should strive to enhance your existing skills and keep up-to-date with the techniques new actors are being taught, even straight after drama school, in order to retain a competitive edge. You must also be prepared to learn new skills for specific roles if required. Ongoing drama training and classes can help you stay fit and active, and if you go through a period of unemployment you can keep your mind and body occupied, ready to take on your next job.

### What kind of training is available?

For the under 18's, stage schools provide specialist training in acting, singing and dancing. They offer a variety of full and part-time courses. After 18, students can attend drama school. The standard route is to take a three-year, full-time course, in the same way you would take a university degree. Some schools also offer one or two-year courses.

### What is the Conference of Drama Schools (CDS)?

The Conference of Drama Schools was founded in 1969 and comprises Britain's twenty two leading Drama Schools. It exists in order to strengthen the voice of the member schools, to set and maintain the highest standards of training within the vocational drama sector, and to make it easier for prospective students to understand the range of courses on offer and the application process. The twenty two member schools listed in the section 'Drama Schools (Conference Of)' offer courses in Acting, Musical Theatre, Directing and Technical Theatre training. For more information you can visit their website www.drama.ac.uk

### What is NCDT?

The National Council for Drama Training was established in 1976 and is a unique collaborative partnership of employers in the theatre, broadcast and media industry, employee representatives and training providers. Its aim is to champion and support professional drama training and education working to safeguard the highest standards and quality assurance through accreditation for vocational drama courses in the UK. This provides students with the confidence that the courses they choose are recognised by the drama profession as being relevant to the purposes of their employment. For more information please see www.ncdt.co.uk

### How should I use these listings?

The following listings provide up-to-date contact details for a wide range of performance courses, classes and coaches. Every company listed is done so by written request to us. Some companies have provided contact names, areas of specialisation and a selection of courses on offer.

### I want to apply to join a full-time drama course. Where do I start?

Your first step should be to research as many different courses as possible. Have a look on each school's website and request a prospectus. Ask around to find out where other people have trained or are training now and who they recommend. You would be advised to begin your search by considering CDS courses. Please refer to the *CDS Guide to Professional Training in Drama & Technical Theatre* for a description of each school, its policy and the courses it offers together with information about funding, available from www.drama.ac.uk

### What types of courses are available?

Drama training courses generally involve three-year degree or diploma courses or one-year postgraduate courses if you have already attended university or can demonstrate a certain amount of previous experience. Alternatively, short-term or part-time foundation courses are available, which can serve as an introduction to acting but are not a substitute for a full-time drama course.

# infopage

## When should I apply?

Deadlines for applications to drama courses vary between schools so make sure you check each school's individual deadlines. Most courses start in September. If the school you are considering requires you to apply via UCAS, you must submit your application between mid-September 2009 and 15th January 2010 to guarantee that your application will be considered for a course beginning in 2010. You can apply after that until 30th June, but the school is then under no obligation to consider your application.

See www.ucas.ac.uk/students/startapplication/whentoapply or contact the individual school for more details.

## What funding is available to me?

Drama courses are unavoidably expensive. Most students have to fund their own course fees and other expenses, whether from savings, part-time work or a student loan. However, if you are from a low-income household you may qualify for a maintenance grant from the government to cover some of the costs. Some NCDT accredited courses offer a limited number of students Dance and Drama Awards (DaDA) scholarships, introduced to increase access to dance, drama and stage management training for talented students. These scholarships include help with both course fees and living expenses. Find out what each school offers in terms of potential financial support before applying. See www.ncdt.co.uk/acourse.asp for details of accredited courses and funding options.

Another possibility is to raise funds from a charity, trust or foundation. As with applying to agents and casting professionals for representation and work, do your research first and target your letters to explain how your needs meet each organisation's objectives, rather than sending a generalised letter to everyone. You are much more likely to be considered if you demonstrate that you know the background of the organisation and what they can offer performers. You will find further advice and a list of charities and foundations you could approach www.ncdt.co.uk under 'Funding'.

## How can my child become an actor?

If your child is interested in becoming an actor, they should try to get as much practical experience as possible. They could also join a stage school or sign with an agent. Please see the 'Agents - Children's & Teenagers'' section for more information, or 'Drama Training, Schools & Coaches' for stage school listings.

## What about other forms of training?

Building on your initial acting course is essential for both new and more experienced actors. There are so many new skills you can learn - you could take stage fighting classes, hire a vocal coach, attend singing and dance lessons, and many more. These will enhance your CV and will give you a competitive edge. It is also extremely useful to take occasional 'refresher' courses on audition skills, different acting techniques and so on in various forms such as one-to-one lessons, one-off workshops or evening classes, to make sure you are not rusty when your next audition comes along.

## Where can I find more information?

The Actors Centre runs approximately 1700 classes and workshops a year to encourage performers to develop their talent throughout their career in a supportive environment. They also run introductory classes for people who are interested in becoming actors but currently have no training or experience. Visit their website www.actorscentre.co.uk for more information. You may also want to refer to the 'Dance Training & Professional Classes' to add additional skills to your CV as well as keep fit. If you are interested in a career behind rather than in front of the camera or stage, please see the *CDS Guide to Careers Backstage*, available from www.drama.ac.uk

# infopage

Peter Barlow is the Chair of the CDS (Conference of Drama Schools) and Director of Guildford School of Acting. For further information on CDS and its member schools please visit www.drama.ac.uk. Please contact individual schools (listed on page 197) for a prospectus and course details.

These days instant access and instant success are a part of our psyche. If we want to find out about something, we google it. If we want to get rich we play the lottery or bingo or hope that someone will die and leave us money. If we want to be famous we know you can become a celebrity by being 'yourself' on reality TV. Every day the papers are full of role models who have 'succeeded', become wealthy or achieved notoriety not through any skill or effort, but merely by being slightly quirky because they are lewd, crude or selfish.

In the western world we now have 'everything' and our entertainment has started to spiral into the depths of voyeurism because we are losing the talent of invention. Invention requires many ingredients: one is imagination; another is skill; and another is that ingredient which we all find difficult to define - talent. In the world of performing arts I believe true talent to be a subtle combination of instinct for storytelling and an ability to set aside one's own ego. Talent alone is not enough because it has no basis in knowledge or skill and that is why talent shows ultimately fail to produce sustainable and credible actors or performers.

CDS schools take talented individuals and turn them into credible performers because their courses require deep exploration of the craft of acting. It is not possible to find out 'how to act' on the internet in any meaningful way. Learning this craft requires hours of practice and dedication to studying the human condition, plus one's own ability to engage with all aspects of it. It is simply not possible to do this solely by reading books, theories and critical academic study. There are many people who think that acting is easy and if you have the ability to walk, talk and learn lines from a play you can easily grace the stage and show off your skills. This is why there are so many amateur theatre companies and so few amateur classical ballet companies. You owe it to yourself and to your art and craft to ensure that you are at the very peak of mental and physical fitness for your vocation. An Olympic athlete recognises and responds to the hours of dedication needed to perform in the most prestigious events of the sporting calendar and whilst one celebrates the achievements of the one-time marathon participator there is no comparison between him/her and the medal-winning professional.

The Conference of Drama Schools, through its member schools, celebrates the very best in professional preparation for the performing arts world and our graduates are ensuring that Britain continues to provide the most highly skilled artists and craftsmen and women in the world. If you are thinking of joining this highly competitive, precarious, passionate, dangerous, rewarding, lonely, engaging, soul-destroying yet magical profession then please do your research properly by visiting theatres; finding out about actors, technicians, dancers, directors, designers and everyone else involved in the industry; watch TV and films; read books (any books); go to art galleries; dance when you can; sing anywhere you can and play always.

*Members of the Conference of Drama Schools offer their students the highest quality training in the industry. Graduates from these schools are in a strong position to advise anyone thinking of following in their path. We have asked two recent graduates from CDS schools to share their thoughts on the benefits of drama training.*

**Lauren O'Neil recently graduated from The Guildhall School of Music & Drama where she achieved a BA in Acting. She is a Spotlight Prize Winner and was awarded Best Female Actor for 2009.**

I have always been very passionate about literature and the study of words so I took English at university. I auditioned for a drama society production of Tom Stoppard's *Arcadia* and got the part of Hannah Jarvis. I had the time of my life working on it and, when it was over, I couldn't wait to get involved in the next one. The following year I started to think about applying for drama schools.

I didn't know what to expect at a drama school audition, what the standard would be like or how they would react to what I thought was a severe lack of experience. I met a lot of applicants who had been acting since they were children so I felt completely under-qualified, but my auditions went well. They always say at Guildhall that you are auditioning the school as much as they you and I think that is true. The Director of Drama auditioned me and his passion for acting was incredibly encouraging and infectious.

The training has been so rewarding. We have worked with a range of directors and I have played a wide range of parts, both classical and modern. I was very lucky and signed with a fantastic agency before graduating and started to audition for professional jobs. There are, of course, no guarantees in this industry, but Guildhall has set me in good stead both as an artist and as a professional. It is a new experience moving into the world of casting directors, meeting lots of people and doing auditions for all kinds of different things, but I am gaining a great deal of experience and crossing my fingers for a job to come along soon!

**John McKeever recently graduated from East 15 Acting School where he studied for a BA in Acting & Contemporary Theatre, achieving a First Class Honours degree. He is a Spotlight Prize Winner and was awarded Best Male Actor for 2009.**

The most important piece of advice I can give to you is to be completely honest with yourself and others. Embrace your weaknesses and celebrate your strengths shamelessly.

Straight out of sixth form, I joined the foundation course at East 15. I had a year to weigh up my options, whilst doing some amazing theatre and having a fantastic time. If anyone is considering drama school and has the time to 'test the waters', a foundation course should be your first port of call. For me it meant that my decision to apply for East 15's Contemporary Theatre course was based entirely on direct experience as opposed to reputation alone, so in that way I was extremely lucky. I knew that by the end of the three years I would be riddled with new skills; a rounded, competent actor; and able to make work if there's none around.

The highlights of my training would have to be taking part in the Sam Wanamaker Festival in April 2009 and, as an ever-lasting gem, the "theatrical clown" project in my second year - a fundamental concept to an actor.

Since graduating, I have performed in two plays at the 2009 Edinburgh Fringe Festival: Zoo Lodge and Snarl Up. I've also been involved in bits and pieces here and there, including a play reading with Yellow Earth theatre company and workshop facilitation for the University of Essex.

How have I found the transition between drama school and the real world? Hectic, terrifying and infinitely exciting. Just what I wanted!

**ACKERLEY STUDIOS OF SPEECH, DRAMA & PUBLIC SPEAKING**
Contact: Margaret Christina Parsons (Principal)
Speech. Drama
5th Floor, Hanover House
Hanover Street, Liverpool L1 3DZ          Tel: 0151-709 5995

**ACT ONE DRAMA STUDIO**
PO Box 4483
Sheffield S10 9DX          Tel: 0114-266 7209
Website: www.actonedrama.co.uk
e-mail: actonedramastudio@mypostoffice.co.uk

**ACT UP**
Acting Classes for Everyone. Acting Workshops. Audition Technique. Pre-Drama School (18+ yrs). Public Speaking Vocal Coaching
Unit 88, Battersea Business Centre
99-109 Lavender Hill
London SW11 5QL
Website: www.act-up.co.uk
e-mail: info@act-up.co.uk
Fax: 020-7924 6606          Tel: 020-7924 7701

**ACTING AUDITION SUCCESS**
Contact: Philip Rosch, Association of Guildhall Teachers FVCM, LGSM, LALAM, ATCL, ANEA, BA (Hons). Audition Speeches/Effective Auditioning. Sight Reading & Expert Career Advice. RADA Acting Exams
53 West Heath Court, North End Road, London NW11 7RG
Website: www.philiprosch.com
e-mail: philiprosch@hotmail.com          Tel: 020-8731 6686

**ACTING BUDDY**
Website: www.actingbuddy.com
e-mail: info@actingbuddy.com          Tel: 020-7558 8020

**ACTION LAB**
Contact: Miranda French, Peter Irving. Part-time Acting Courses. Private Coaching
18 Lansdowne Road, London W11 3LL
e-mail: miranda@mirandafrench.com
Mobile: 07979 623987          Tel: 020-7727 3474

**ACTOR WORKS The**
Contact: Daniel Brennan, Wendy Smith. Courses: 1 Year Intensive, 1 Year Foundation, 2 Year Full-time Evening, Part-time. Drama School (Over 18s)
1 Knighten Street, Wapping, London E1W 1PH
Website: www.theactorworks.co.uk
e-mail: info@theactorworks.co.uk          Tel: 020-7702 0909

**ACTORS CENTRE The**
Accent/Dialect Coaching. Acting for Camera. Audition Technique. Beginners & Professional Workshops. Meisner Shakespeare. Singing. TV Presenting
1A Tower Street, London WC2H 9NP          Tel: 020-7632 8003
Website: www.actorscentre.co.uk
e-mail: members@actorscentre.co.uk

**ACTORS STUDIO**
Accompanist. Acting Workshops. Audition Technique Dialect/Accent Coaching. Elocution. Improvisation Language Tutoring. Private Acting Classes. Public Speaking. Singing. Stage School for Children Vocal Coaching
Pinewood Film Studios
Pinewood Road, Iver Heath, Bucks SL0 0NH
Website: www.actorsstudio.co.uk
e-mail: info@actorsstudio.co.uk
Fax: 01753 655622          Tel: 01753 650951

Unit 10, 21 Wren Street, London WC1X 0HF

**ACTOR'S TEMPLE The**
13-14 Warren Street, London W1T 5LG
Website: www.actorstemple.com
e-mail: info@actorstemple.com
Mobile: 07771 734670          Tel: 020-3004 4537

**ACTORS' THEATRE SCHOOL**
Foundation Course
32 Exeter Road, London NW2 4SB
Website: www.theactorstheatreschool.co.uk
e-mail: info@theactorstheatreschool.co.uk
Fax: 020-8450 1057          Tel: 020-8450 0371

**ACTORSPACE.CO.UK**
Auditions. Voice & Text
6 Chandos Court, The Green
Southgate, London N14 7AA          Tel: 020-8886 8870
Website: www.actorspace.co.uk
e-mail: drama@london.com

---

# RICK LIPTON DIALECT, DIALOGUE AND VOICE COACH

- American Accent Coaching from an American in London
- Digital Recordings of your sessions provided
- Film, Television, Theatre, Auditions, Private Lessons
- 10+ years experience, 1000+ actors trained and coached

**07961445247**

**RL@RICKLIPTON.COM**

---

**ACTS**
Ayres-Clark Theatre School
12 Gatward Close, Winchmore Hill
London N21 1AS
e-mail: actsn21@talktalk.net          Tel: 020-8360 0352

**ALEXANDER Helen**
Audition Technique, Drama School Entry
14 Chestnut Road
Raynes Park, London SW20 8EB
e-mail: helenalexander@fsmail.com     Tel: 020-8543 4085

**ALLSORTS - DRAMA**
Part-time Courses & Drama Training. Kensington,
Notting Hill, Hampstead, Fulham, Putney (3-18 yrs)
34 Pember Road
London NW10 5LS          Tel/Fax: 020-8969 3249
Website: www.allsortsdrama.com
e-mail: info@allsortsdrama.com

**ALRA (ACADEMY OF LIVE & RECORDED ARTS)**
See DRAMA SCHOOLS (Conference of)

**AMERICAN VOICES**
Contact: Lynn Bains. American Accent/Dialect Coach
Acting Teacher & Director
20 Craighall Crescent
Edinburgh EH6 4RZ          Mobile: 07875 148755
e-mail: mail@lynnbains.com

**AMERSHAM & WYCOMBE COLLEGE**
Dual Campuses: Amersham & Chesham
Website: www.amersham.ac.uk
e-mail: info@amersham.ac.uk          Tel: 0800 614016

**AND ALL THAT JAZZ**
Contact: Eileen Hughes. Accompanist. Vocal Coaching
165 Gunnersbury Lane, Acton Town
London W3 8LJ          Tel: 020-8993 2111

**ARABESQUE SCHOOL OF PERFORMING ARTS**
Quarry Lane
Chichester PO19 8NY          Tel/Fax: 01243 531144
Website: www.aspauk.com
e-mail: arabesqueschool@aol.com

**ARDEN SCHOOL OF THEATRE The**
Contact: Victoria Muir (Administrator). Professional Stage
Practice in Acting Studies & Musical Theatre. HNC in Drama
FD in Theatre Practice. PGDip in Writing for Performance
The Arden, 3 Universal Square
Devonshire Street North, Manchester M12 6JH
e-mail: ast@ccm.ac.uk
Fax: 0161-279 7199          Tel: 0161-279 7257

**ARTEMIS SCHOOL OF SPEECH & DRAMA**
Peredur Centre of The Arts
West Hoathly Road
East Grinstead
West Sussex RH19 4NF          Tel/Fax: 01342 321330
Website: www.artemisspeechanddrama.org.uk
e-mail: office@artemisspeechanddrama.org.uk

**ARTEMIS STUDIOS**
30 Charles Square, Bracknell
Berkshire RG12 1AY          Tel: 01344 429403
Website: http://agency.artemis-studios.co.uk
e-mail: info@artemis-studios.co.uk

**ARTS EDUCATIONAL SCHOOLS LONDON**
See DRAMA SCHOOLS (Conference of)

**ASHCROFT ACADEMY OF DRAMATIC ART The**
Drama LAMDA, Dance ISTD, Singing (4-18 yrs)
Malcolm Primary School
Malcolm Road
Penge, London SE20 8RH
Website: www.ashcroftacademy.com
e-mail: geraldi.gillma@btconnect.com
Mobile: 07799 791586          Tel/Fax: 0844 8005328

**ASHFORD Clare BSc, PGCE, LLAM, ALAM (Recital),
ALAM (Acting)**
20 The Chase, Coulsdon
Surrey CR5 2EG          Tel: 020-8660 9609
e-mail: clareashford@handbag.com

**AUDITION COACH**
Contact: Martin Harris. Acting Workshops. Audition
Techniques. Private Acting Classes. Group Evening Classes
32 Baxter Road
Sale, Manchester M33 3AL
Website: www.auditioncoach.co.uk
e-mail: martin@auditioncoach.co.uk
Mobile: 07788 723570          Tel: 0161-969 1444

**AVERY-CLARK Kenneth**
Musical Theatre. Voice Coach
32 Brookfield Road
London E9 5AH          Tel: 020-8525 0111

**BAC**
(Battersea Arts Centre) Young People's Theatre Workshops
& Performance Projects (12-25 yrs)
Lavender Hill, London SW11 5TN
Website: www.bac.org.uk
e-mail: bacypt@bac.org.uk
Fax: 020-7978 5207          Tel: 020-7223 6557

---

# TESS DIGNAN MA
## VOICE AND ACTING COACH
Audition Preparation Assisted

- RADA
- RSC
- FILM

- LAMDA
- RNT
- TV

- CSSD
- WEST END
- RADIO

All Enquiries Welcome **t:** 07946 088 719   **e:** tessdignan60@tiscali.co.uk

**ARTS EDUCATIONAL SCHOOLS LONDON**

CELEBRATING **90** years

**MUSICAL THEATRE & ACTING DEGREES**

**INDEPENDENT VOCATIONAL DAY SCHOOL 11-18YRS**

**PART TIME COURSES**

**WWW.ARTSED.CO.UK**

# DIALECT COACH

## LINDA JAMES R.A.M. Dip. Ed., I.P.D. (Lon Univ), L.R.A.M.

### FILMS, T.V., STAGE & PRIVATE COACHING, ERADICATION OF ACCENT

## 020 8568 2390

**BATE Richard MA (Theatre) LGSM (TD), PGCE (FE), Equity**
Audition Technique. Vocal & Acting Training
Drama School Entry
Apt 1, Broom Hall, High Street
Broom, Biggleswade
Bedfordshire SG18 9ND                    Mobile: 07940 589295
e-mail: rich.bate@yahoo.co.uk

**BATES Esme CSSD STSD**
LAMDA Exam Specialist. TIE Facilitator
Youth Theatre Director
2 Barons Court, Western Elmes Avenue
Reading, Berks RG30 2BP
e-mail: esmebates@btinternet.com
Mobile: 07941 700941                    Tel: 0118-958 9330

**BENCH Paul MEd, LGSM, ALAM, FRSA, LJBA (Hons), PGCE, ACP (Lings) (Hons), MASC (Ph), MIFA (Reg)**
Corporate Vocal Presentation. Audition Technique. LAMDA
Exams, Grades to Diploma Level. Private Acting Classes
Public Speaking. Stress Management. Vocal Coaching
1 Whitehall Terrace, Shrewsbury
Shropshire SY2 5AA                    Tel/Fax: 01743 233164
Website: www.paulbench.co.uk
e-mail: pfbench@aol.com

**BENSKIN Eileen**
Dialect Coach                    Tel: 020-8455 9750

**BERKERY Barbara**
Dialogue/Dialect Coach for
Film & Television                    Tel: 020-7281 3139

**BEST THEATRE ARTS**
PO Box 749, St Albans AL1 4YW        Tel: 01727 759634
Website: www.besttheatrearts.com
e-mail: bestarts@aol.com

**BIG ACT The**
Unit 1FA, Gate C
Knorr-Bremse Business Park
Douglas Road, Bristol BS15 8HJ        Tel: 0870 8810367
Website: www.thebigact.com
e-mail: info@thebigact.com

**BIG ACT THEATRE SCHOOL The**
90 Chapel Way, Epsom Downs
Epsom, Surrey KT18 5SY
Website: www.bigacttheatre.co.uk
e-mail: lucy@bigacttheatre.co.uk
Mobile: 07816 524066                    Tel: 01737 211541

**BIG LITTLE THEATRE SCHOOL**
Acting Workshops. Dancing. Improvisation. ISTD Modern &
Tap. Musical Theatre. Performance Dance. Professional
Development Programme. RAD Ballet. Singing Technique
Vocal Coaching. Youth Theatres
305 Maycrete Road, Aviation Business Park
Bournemouth International Airport
Christchurch BH23 6NW                    Tel: 01202 574422
Website: www.biglittle.biz
e-mail: info@biglittle.biz

**BIRD COLLEGE**
Drama/Musical Theatre College
Birkbeck Centre, Birkbeck Road, Sidcup, Kent DA14 4DE
Website: www.birdcollege.co.uk
e-mail: admin@birdcollege.co.uk
Fax: 020-8308 1370                    Tel: 020-8300 6004

**BIRMINGHAM SCHOOL OF ACTING**
See DRAMA SCHOOLS (Conference of)

**BIRMINGHAM THEATRE SCHOOL The**
The Old Rep Theatre
Station Street
Birmingham B5 4DY                    Tel: 0121-643 3300
Website: www.birminghamtheatreschool.co.uk
e-mail: info@birminghamtheatreschool.co.uk

**BODENS STUDIOS**
Contact: Adam Boden. Acting Workshops. Audition
Technique. Dancing. Improvisation. Part-time Performing
Arts Classes. Singing
Bodens Studio & Agency, 99 East Barnet Road
New Barnet, Herts EN4 8RF
Website: www.bodenstudios.com
e-mail: info@bodenstudios.com
Fax: 020-8449 5212                    Tel: 020-8449 0982

# CYGNET TRAINING THEATRE Patron Peter Brook

*The Tempest*

## PROFESSIONAL ACTING TRAINING

CYGNET students train and tour as a company playing at a wide variety of venues. The training gives high priority to voice technique, musical skills and the acting methods of Stanislavsky and Michael Chekhov.

ENTRY (over 18) by audition workshop and interview
Apply (with SAE) to: New Theatre, Friars Gate, Exeter EX2 4AZ
Member of The Conference of Drama Schools     Registered Charity No. 1081824

 CYGNET

# PAUL GREGORY ACTOR / DRAMA COACH

EX RSC & RNT ACTOR. RECENTLY - DEMOCRACY & EMBERS.
Recent Film Sir Jack Crawford in SISTERHOOD (Comedy Feature).
Also HENRY V & FRANKENSTEIN with Kenneth Branagh.
Acted with & Directed by Sir Laurence Olivier, Robert De Niro, Anthony Hopkins,
Leonard Rossiter, Sir John Mills, Sir Anthony Sher, Jeremy Irons etc.

My students include: Louie Batley - HOLLYOAKS 2 Years
Stephanie Blacker - I WANT CANDY, Feature Film with Carmen Electra
Avtar Kaul - SHOOT ON SIGHT, Feature with Brian Cox
Kieran Leonard - HUSTLE, BBC TV with Robert Vaughn
Lauren Owen - LEND ME A TENOR, CBS New York
Peter Peralta - SUMMER, Short Feature, Berlin Film Festival & UK
Adrian Sharp - THE CLUB, Feature
Morgan Thrift - Bristol Old Vic Rep. Co., 1 Year
Scott Ryan Vickers - EMMERDALE
Sargon Yelda - MIDNIGHT MAN, ITV with James Nesbitt & SADDAM'S TRIBE, Channel 4

*I have known Paul Gregory for many years and cannot recommend him highly enough, both personally and professionally. I am a huge admirer of his talent and for his work with drama students. His enthusiasm is infectious and his students are inspired by it. He is much respected and admired in the acting profession for his professionalism and dedication.*

**Judi Dench**

**Private Coaching for Professionals and Students.**
Successful applicants including Scholarships to ALL MAJOR DRAMA SCHOOLS
**Many of my students also now represented by Top Agents.**

Contact: **(LA) Mob: 001 323 533 3675**   *or*   **(LA) T:** 001 323 798 5102
email: pgregory789@yahoo.co.uk

## SHARRONE COMBER
BA (HONS) ACTING/ MA VOICE STUDIES (CSSD) PGCE D E Sp (Teacher-London Drama Schools)
## VOICE AND SPEECH COACH
Technical Voice & Text Work, Speech, Dialect, Elocution, Audition Coaching, Presentation Skills, Private Tuition.
### 07752 029 422 / sharronecomber@hotmail.com

**BOWDEN ACADEMY OF DRAMATIC ARTS The**
The Annex, Merley House
Merley House Lane
Wimborne, Dorset BH21 3AA       Mobile: 07902 253499
Website: www.bowdenacademy.co.uk
e-mail: admin@bowdenacademy.co.uk

**BOWES Sara**
Child Acting Coach for Film & Commercials
23 John Aird Court, London W2 1UY
e-mail: sara@sarabowes.com
Mobile: 07830 375389       Tel: 020-7262 3543

**BOYD Beth**
Private Acting Classes
10 Prospect Road, Long Ditton
Surbiton, Surrey KT6 5PY       Tel: 020-8398 6768

**BRADSHAW Irene**
Private Coach. Voice & Audition Preparation
Flat F, Welbeck Mansions, Inglewood Road
West Hampstead, London NW6 1QX
Website: www.voice-power-works.co.uk
e-mail: irene@irenebradshaw.fsnet.co.uk
Mobile: 07949 552915       Tel: 020-7794 5721

**BRAITHWAITE'S ACROBATIC SCHOOL**
8 Brookshill Avenue
Harrow Weald, Middlesex       Tel: 020-8954 5638

**BRANSTON Dale**
Audition Technique. Singing Teacher
Ground Floor Flat, 16 Fernwood Avenue
Streatham, London SW16 1RD
e-mail: branpickle@yahoo.co.uk
Mobile: 07767 261713       Tel: 020-8696 9958

**BRIDGE THEATRE TRAINING COMPANY The**
Cecil Sharp House, 2 Regent's Park Road, London NW1 7AY
Website: www.thebridge-ttc.org
e-mail: admin@thebridge-ttc.org
Fax: 020-7424 9118       Tel: 020-7424 0860

**BRIGHTON PERFORMERZONE**
Contact: William Pool (ARCM). Singing. Tuition. Workshops
33A Osmond Road, Hove
East Sussex BN3 1TD       Mobile: 07973 518643
Website: www.performerzone.co.uk
e-mail: info@performerzone.co.uk

**BRIGHTON SCHOOL OF MUSIC & DRAMA**
96 Claremont Road, Seaford
East Sussex BN25 2QA       Tel: 01323 492918

**BRISTOL ACADEMY OF PERFORMING ARTS**
The Academy Theatre, Market Place, Shepton Mallet
Somerset BA4 5AZ       Tel: 01749 347984
Website: www.bapa.co.uk
e-mail: lucy@bapa.co.uk

**BRISTOL OLD VIC THEATRE SCHOOL**
See DRAMA SCHOOLS (Conference of)

**BRITISH AMERICAN DRAMA ACADEMY**
14 Gloucester Gate, Regent's Park, London NW1 4HG
Website: www.badaonline.com
Fax: 020-7487 0731       Tel: 020-7487 0730

**B.R.I.T. SCHOOL FOR PERFORMING ARTS & TECHNOLOGY The**
60 The Crescent, Croydon CR0 2HN
Website: www.brit.croydon.sch.uk
e-mail: admin@brit.croydon.sch.uk
Fax: 020-8665 8676       Tel: 020-8665 5242

**BSA ACTOR TRAINING Ltd**
Acting Workshops. Private Acting Classes. One Year Stage &
Screen Part Time Course. 10 Week Courses Including
Screen-Acting, Meisner Technique & Foundation
Admin Only:
First Floor, 75 Brownlow Road
London N11 2BN       Tel: 020-3240 1064
Website: www.bsa-actortraining.co.uk
e-mail: info@bsa-actortraining.co.uk

**CALE Bart TRAINING**
Bristol       Tel: 0117-969 2224
e-mail: bart.cale@virgin.net

**CAMERON BROWN Jo PGDVS**
Dialect. Dialogue. Voice Coaching for Films,
TV, Theatre & Auditions       Mobile: 07970 026621
e-mail: jocameronbrown@hotmail.com

**CAMPBELL Jon**
36 Fentiman Road
London SW8 1LF       Mobile: 07854 697971
Website: www.joncampbell.co.uk
e-mail: joncampbell36@yahoo.co.uk

**CAMPBELL Kenneth**
Parkhills, 6 Clevelands Park
Northam, Bideford
North Devon EX39 3QH       Tel: 01237 425217
e-mail: campbell870@btinternet.com

**CAMPBELL Ross ARCM, Dip RCM (Perf)**
Head of Singing & Music, GSA Professor, Royal Academy of
Music. Singing Coach, Accompanist & Music Director
17 Oldwood Chase
Farnborough, Hants GU14 0QS
e-mail: rosscampbell@ntlworld.com
Mobile: 07956 465165       Tel: 01252 510228

**CAPITAL ARTS THEATRE SCHOOL**
Contact: Kathleen Shanks
Wyllyotts Centre
Darkes Lane
Potters Bar, Herts EN6 2HN
e-mail: capitalarts@btconnect.com
Mobile: 07885 232414       Tel/Fax: 020-8449 2342

**CARAVANSERAI PRODUCTIONS & ACTING STUDIO**
Unit 30, Grand Union Centre
West Row, London W10 5AS       Tel: 020-8968 3769
Website: www.caravanseraiproductions.com
e-mail: info@caravanseraiproductions.com

**CARSHALTON COLLEGE**
Nightingale Road
Carshalton, Surrey SM5 2EJ
Website: www.carshalton.ac.uk
e-mail: cs@carshalton.ac.uk
Fax: 020-8544 4440       Tel: 020-8544 4444

# 1 Year Acting Course

Accredited by NCDT
Validated by Trinity College London
Member of the Conference of Drama Schools
Dance and Drama Awards Scheme

# 2 Year Acting Course

Intensive training for the
acting profession, for postgraduate
and mature students

The teaching is passionate, personal
and always relevant

We teach you not just how to act,
but how to be an actor

also

## 1 Year Directing Course
## 4 Week Summer Acting Course

### DRAMA STUDIO LONDON

Grange Court, 1 Grange Road, London, W5 5QN

### 020 8579 3897

**admin@dramastudiolondon.co.uk**
**www.dramastudiolondon.co.uk**

*ACTING*
*CHARACTERISATION*
*STAGECRAFT*
*TV AND SCREEN*
*RADIO*
*TEXT ANALYSIS*
*MOVEMENT*
*IMPROVISATION*
*PHYSICAL THEATRE*
*VOICE AND ACCENTS*
*SINGING*
*WORK & AUDITIONS*

**DRAMA STUDIO LONDON**

**CELEBRATION THEATRE COMPANY FOR THE YOUNG**
Contact: Neville Wortman. Summer Week Intensive Course
Acting Workshops. Audition Technique. Dialect/Accent
Coaching. Drama School (over 18s). Elocution
Improvisation. Language Tutoring. Private Acting Classes
Public Speaking
48 Chiswick Staithe, London W4 3TP
Website: www.speakwell.co.uk
e-mail: neville@speakwell.co.uk
Mobile: 07976 805976                    Tel: 020-8994 8886

**CELEBRITY TALENT ACADEMY**
2A Tileyard Studios, Tileyard Road
Kings Cross, London N7 9AH          Tel: 0845 1162355
Website: www.celebritytalentacademy.com
e-mail: celebritytalentacademy@gmail.com

**CENTRAL SCHOOL OF SPEECH & DRAMA The**
See DRAMA SCHOOLS (Conference of)

**CENTRE STAGE SCHOOL OF PERFORMING ARTS**
Students (4-18 yrs). North London
The Croft, 7 Cannon Road
Southgate, London N14 7HE
Website: www.centrestageuk.com
e-mail: carole@centrestageuk.com
Fax: 020-8886 7555                    Tel: 020-8886 4264

**CENTRESTAGE SCHOOL OF PERFORMING ARTS**
All Day Saturday Classes, Summer Courses, Private
Coaching for Professionals & Drama School Auditions
Centrestage House
117 Canfield Gardens
London NW6 3DY                    Tel: 020-7328 0788
Website: www.centrestageschool.co.uk
e-mail: vickiwoolf@centrestageschool.co.uk

Holy Trinity School, Trinity Walk
London NW3 5SQ                    Tel: 020-7328 0788

# COURT
**Theatre Training Company**

*Train for a life
in the theatre
by working in
the theatre...*

### BA (Hons) Acting
validated by Thames Valley University

### MA Script Writing
subject to validation

## Various weekend workshops in
## Drama School entry
## & Foundation courses

**address:** Court Theatre Training Company, The Courtyard Theatre, Bowling Green Walk, 40 Pitfield St, London N1 6EU

**phone/fax:** 020 7251 6018          **email:** info@thecourtyard.org.uk          **web:** www.thecourtyard.org.uk

**CHARD Verona LRAM, Dip RAM (Musical Theatre)**
Teacher at Central School of Speech & Drama
Singing Tutor
Ealing House, 33 Hanger Lane
London W5 3HJ                         Tel: 020-8997 3355
e-mail: veronachardmusic@aol.com

**CHARRINGTON Tim**
Dialect/Accent Coaching
54 Topmast Point
Strafford Street, London E14 8SN
e-mail: tim.charrington@googlemail.com
Mobile: 07967 418236                  Tel: 020-7987 3028

**CHASE Stephan PRODUCTIONS Ltd**
Private Coach for Acting Auditions & Public Speaking
Dialect/Accent Coaching. Language Tutoring. Managing
Authentic Presence
The Studio, 22 York Avenue
London SW14 7LG                       Tel: 020-8878 9112
Website: www.stephanchase.com
e-mail: stephan@stephanchase.com

**CHEKHOV Michael CENTRE**
Acting Workshops. Audition/Casting Technique. Film/TV
Acting. Private Acting sessions. Vocal Training. Group
Training: The Awakening, The Deepening
Website: www.michaelchekhov.org.uk
e-mail: admin@michaelchekhov.org.uk

**CHRISKA STAGE SCHOOL**
37-39 Whitby Road,
Ellesmere Port, Cheshire L64 8AA
Website: www.chriska.co.uk             Tel: 01928 739166

**CHRYSTEL ARTS THEATRE SCHOOL**
Part-time classes for Children, Teenagers & Young Adults in
Dance, Drama & Musical Theatre. ISTD & LAMDA
Examinations
Edgware Parish Hall
Rectory Lane
Edgware, Middlesex HA8 7LG
e-mail: chrystelarts@waitrose.com
Tel/Fax: 020-8952 6010                Tel/Fax: 01494 785589

**CHURCHER Mel MA**
Acting & Vocal Coach
Website: www.melchurcher.com
e-mail: melchurcher@hotmail.com       Mobile: 07778 773019

**CHURCHER Teresa (MASC)**
Acting, Audition & Career & Life Coach
One to One & Groups
London & Northampton
Website: www.teresachurcher.co.uk
e-mail: info@teresachurcher.co.uk     Mobile: 01908 542166

**CIRCOMEDIA**
Centre for Contemporary Circus & Physical Performance
Britannia Road, Kingswood
Bristol BS15 8DB                      Tel/Fax: 0117-947 7288
Website: www.circomedia.com
e-mail: info@circomedia.com

**CIRCUS MANIACS SCHOOL OF CIRCUS ARTS**
Full & Part-time Courses, One-to-One Act Development &
Production Support
43 Kingsway Avenue, Kingswood, Bristol BS15 8AN
Website: www.circusmaniacs.com
e-mail: info@circusmaniacs.com
Mobile: 07977 247287                  Tel/Fax: 0117-947 7042

**CITY LIT The**
Accredited & Non-Accredited Part-time & Full-time Day &
Evening Courses. Acting Workshops. Audition Technique
Bi-Media. Camera Training. Dancing. Dialect/Accent
Coaching. Directing. Elocution Coaching. Improvisation
Presenting. Professional Preparation. Public Speaking
Role-play Training. Singing. Story Telling
Keeley Street, Covent Garden
London WC2B 4BA                       Tel: 020-7492 2542
Website: www.citylit.ac.uk
e-mail: drama@citylit.ac.uk

**CLEMENTS Anne MA, LGSM, FRSA**
Audition Technique. Back to Basics for Professional Actors
Dialect/Accent Coaching. Preparation for Drama School
Entry. Vocal Coaching
Hampstead                             Mobile: 07963 818845
e-mail: woodlandcreature10@hotmail.com

**COLDIRON M J**
Audition Preparation & Presentation Skills
Private Coaching
54 Millfields Road, London E5 0SB     Tel: 020-8533 1506
Website: www.web.me.com/mcoldiron
e-mail: jiggs@blueyonder.co.uk

**COLGAN Valerie**
Audition Technique & Voice Production
The Green, 17 Herbert Street
London NW5 4HA                        Tel: 020-7267 2153

**COMBER Sharrone BA (Hons) MAVS (CSSD) PGCE**
Audition Technique. Dialect/Accent Coaching. Elocution
Presentation Skills. Private Acting Classes. Public Speaking
Vocal Coaching
8 Pinelands Close, St John's Park
Blackheath, London SE3 7TF            Mobile: 07752 029422
e-mail: sharronecomber@hotmail.com

**COMEDY COACH**
Contact: Jack Milner
43 Church Street, Chesham
Buckinghamshire HP5 1HU               Tel: 01494 772908
Website: www.jackmilner.com
e-mail: jack@jackmilner.com

**COMPLETE WORKS CREATIVE COMPANY Ltd The**
The Old Truman Brewery
91 Brick Lane, London E1 6QL
Website: www.tcw.org.uk
e-mail: theatre@tcw.org.uk
Fax: 020-7247 7405                    Tel: 020-7377 7280

**CONTI Italia ACADEMY OF THEATRE ARTS**
See DRAMA SCHOOLS (Conference of)

**CONTI Italia ACADEMY OF THEATRE ARTS**
Italia Conti House, 23 Goswell Road, London EC1M 7AJ
Website: www.italiaconti-acting.co.uk
e-mail: info@italiaconti.co.uk
Fax: 020-7253 1430          Tel: 020-7608 0044

**CORNER Clive AGSM LRAM**
Qualified Teacher, Private Coaching & Audition Training
'The Belenes', 60 Wakeham, Portland DT5 1HN
e-mail: cornerassociates@aol.com          Tel: 01305 860267

**COURT THEATRE TRAINING COMPANY**
The Courtyard Theatre, Bowling Green Walk
40 Pitfield Street, London N1 6EU      Tel/Fax: 020-7251 6018
Website: www.thecourtyard.org.uk
e-mail: info@thecourtyard.org.uk

**COX Gregory**
Audition Coaching. Drama Coaching
Sight Reading Skills. Voice Work
South West London          Mobile: 07931 370135
e-mail: gregoryedcox@hotmail.com

**COX Jerry MA PGCE BA (Hons)**
Acting Coach. Audition Technique. Preparation/Entry for
Drama School. Private Acting Classes
Flat 16 Aldermen Court
London N11 3GW          Mobile: 07957 654027
e-mail: jerrymarwood@hotmail.com

**CPA COLLEGE**
Full-time 3 yr Performing Arts College
The Studios, 219B North Street
Romford, Essex RM1 4QA
Website: www.colinsperformingarts.co.uk
e-mail: college@colinsperformingarts.co.uk
Fax: 01708 766077          Tel: 01708 766007

**CREATIVE PERFORMANCE**
Mobile Workshop in Circus Skills & Drama TIE. Events
Management for Communities
20 Pembroke Road, North Wembley
Middlesex HA9 7PD          Tel/Fax: 020-8908 0502
e-mail: creative.performance@yahoo.co.uk

## JON CAMPBELL SUCCESSFUL DRAMA COACH

www.joncampbell.co.uk    07854 697971    Personal tuition • Competitive rates

Central School trained actor/director offers confidence building,
audition speeches, presentation skills. All levels.

*Realise your potential*

**CROWE Ben**
Acting/Audition Tuition, Accent Coach
23 John Aird Court, London W2 1UY
e-mail: bencrowe@hotmail.co.uk
Mobile: 07952 784911          Tel: 020-7262 3543

**CYGNET TRAINING THEATRE**
See DRAMA SCHOOLS (Conference of)

**D & B SCHOOL OF PERFORMING ARTS**
Central Studios, 470 Bromley Road, Bromley BR1 4PN
Website: www.dandbperformingarts.co.uk
e-mail: bonnie@dandbmanagement.com
Fax: 020-8697 8100          Tel: 020-8698 8880

**DALLA VECCHIA Sara**
Italian Teacher
13 Fauconberg Road
London W4 3JZ          Mobile: 07877 404743

**DAVIDSON Clare**
30 Highgate West Hill, London N6 6NP    Tel: 020-8348 0132
Website: www.claredavidson.co.uk
e-mail: clare@claredavidson.co.uk

**DE BURGH Luan BA (Hons), MA, MA Dip**
Accent Softening. Elocution Coaching. Improvisation
Presentation Skills. Public Speaking. Vocal Coaching
22 Newton Avenue, London W3 8AL
Website: www.luandeburgh.com
e-mail: luan@luandeburgh.com        Mobile: 07976 809693

**DEBUT THEATRE SCHOOL OF PERFORMING ARTS**
14 Titania Close, Cottingley
Bingley, West Yorkshire BD16 1WE
Website: www.debuttheatreschool.co.uk
Fax: 01274 565548          Tel: 01274 564448

**DE COURCY Bridget**
Singing Teacher
19 Muswell Road, London N10          Tel: 020-8883 8397

**De FLOREZ Jane LGSM PG Dip**
Singing Teacher - Auditions. Musical Theatre. Jazz
Classical
70 Ipsden Buildings , Windmill Walk
Waterloo, London SE1 8LT          Tel: 020-7803 0835
Website: www.singingteacherlondon.com
e-mail: janedeflorez@fsmail.net

**DIGNAN Tess PDVS**
Audition, Text & Voice Coach
004 Oregon Building, Deals Gateway
Lewisham SE13 7RR          Tel: 020-8691 4275
e-mail: tessdignan60@tiscali.co.uk

**DI LACCIO Gabriela**
Singing Teacher & Coach
165 Gunnersbury Lane, London W3 8LJ    Tel: 020-8993 2111

**DIRECTIONS THEATRE ARTS (CHESTERFIELD) Ltd**
Musical Theatre School & College
Studios: 1A/2A Sheffield Road, Chesterfield, Derby S41 7LL
Website: www.directionstheatrearts.org
e-mail: geoffrey.cox@btconnect.com
Mobile: 07973 768201          Tel/Fax: 01246 854455

**DOGGETT Antonia**
Flat 2/2, 131 Queen Margaret Drive
Glasgow G20 8PD          Mobile: 07814 155090
e-mail: antonia.doggett@googlemail.com

**DONNELLY Elaine**
Children's Acting Coach
Sangwin Associates
8-30 Galena Road
Hammersmith, London W6 0LT          Tel: 020-8748 8698

**DRAGON DRAMA**
Drama for Children
347 Hanworth Road
Hampton TW12 3EJ          Tel/Fax: 020-8255 8356
Website: www.dragondrama.co.uk
e-mail: info@dragondrama.co.uk

**DRAMA ASSOCIATION OF WALES**
Summer Courses for Amateur Actors & Directors
The Old Library
Singleton Road
Splott, Cardiff CF24 2ET          Tel: 029-2045 2200
e-mail: gary@dramawales.org.uk

**DRAMA CENTRE LONDON**
See DRAMA SCHOOLS (Conference of)

**DRAMA STUDIO EDINBURGH The**
Children's Weekly Drama Workshops
19 Belmont Road
Edinburgh EH14 5DZ          Tel: 0131-453 3284
Website: www.thedramastudio.com
e-mail: info@thedramastudio.com

**DRAMA STUDIO LONDON**
See DRAMA SCHOOL (Conference of)

**DREAM FACTORY The**
Accredited Professional Creative Arts Training Facility
Located within a UK Prison - Open to Offenders
Ex-offenders & the Wider Community
PO Box 31855
London SE17 3XP          Tel: 020-7793 9755
Website: www.londonshakespeare.org.uk
e-mail: londonswo@hotmail.com

**DULIEU John**
Acting Coach. Audition & Role Preparation
16 Fernwood Avenue
Streatham, London SW16 1RD
e-mail: john_dulieu@yahoo.com
Mobile: 07803 289599          Tel: 020-8696 9958

**DUNMORE Simon**
Acting & Audition Tuition
Website: www.simon.dunmore.btinternet.co.uk
e-mail: simon.dunmore@btinternet.com

**DURRENT Peter**
Audition & Rehearsal Pianist, Vocal Coach
Blacksmiths Cottage
Bures Road
Little Cornard, Sudbury
Suffolk CO10 0NR          Tel: 01787 373483

# GUILDFORD SCHOOL OF ACTING

## Courses for 2010–11 entry

### Undergraduate:

- BA (Hons) Acting or Musical Theatre [3 years]
- National Diploma in Professional Acting or Musical Theatre [3 years]*
- BA (Hons) Professional Production Skills [3 years]
- National Diploma Professional Production Skills [2 years]*
- BA (Hons) Theatre Conversion Course [1 year FT Distance Learning or PT up to 4 yrs]
- BA (Hons) Professional Production Skills [1 year APL extension to 2 yr Diploma]

### Postgraduate:

- MA Acting [1 year]
- MA Musical Theatre [1 year]
- MA Practice of Voice and Singing [1 year]

Leading learning and skills

\* Diploma courses validated by Trinity College London
  Fully funded places available from Dance and Drama Awards for Trinity Diplomas
  (option to top up to BA [Hons] with extra fee) and Higher Education Funding Council
  for England on 3 year courses
  All vocational courses accredited by the National Council for Drama Training

Member of CDS

## Just 35 minutes from the 'West End'

**Guildford School of Acting** University of Surrey,
Stag Hill Campus, Guildford, Surrey GU2 7XH

t: 01483 560701 | f: 01483 535431 | admissions@gsauk.org

## VOICE CONSULTANT & COACH

**Tel: 020-7359 7848    Mobile: 079-4019 3631**
Basic vocal technique - text and acting -
Consultancy in all areas of voice use.

---

**DYSON Kate LRAM**
Audition Technique Coaching. Drama
39 Arundel Street, Kemptown BN2 5TH
e-mail: kate.dyson@talktalk.net
Mobile: 07812 949875                 Tel: 01273 607490

**EARNSHAW Susi THEATRE SCHOOL**
The Bull Theatre, 68 High Street, Barnet, Herts EN5 5SJ
Website: www.susiearnshaw.co.uk
e-mail: info@sets.org.uk
Fax: 020-8364 9618                 Tel: 020-8441 5010

**EAST 15 ACTING SCHOOL**
See DRAMA SCHOOLS (Conference of)

**EASTON Helena BPSA MA ATC (CSSD)**
Acting Coach
103 Red Square
Carysfort Road, London N16 9AG        Mobile: 07985 931473
e-mail: helena.easton@gmail.com

**ECOLE INTERNATIONALE DE THEATRE JACQUES LECOQ**
Contact: Rita Leys. Acting Workshops. Drama School (over
21 yrs). Mime. Movement & Creative Theatre. Play Writing
57 rue du Faubourg Saint-Denis, 75010 Paris
Website: www.ecole-jacqueslecoq.com
e-mail: contact@ecole-jacqueslecoq.com
Fax: 00 331 45 23 40 14           Tel: 00 331 47 70 44 78

**ELLIOTT CLARKE THEATRE SCHOOL & COLLEGE**
Full-time Vocational & Evening classes
132 Bold Street
Liverpool L1 4EZ                 Tel: 0151-709 3323
e-mail: contact@elliottclarke.co.uk

**EUROPEAN SCHOOL FOR YOUNG PERFORMERS**
County Hall, Riverside Building
London SE1 7PB
Website: www.themovieum.com/esyp
e-mail: marcus@themovieum.com        Tel: 020-7202 7044

**EXCEL SCHOOL OF PERFORMING ARTS**
KT Summit House, 100 Hanger Lane, Ealing W5 1EZ
Website: www.ktioe-excel.org
e-mail: excel@kt.org                 Tel: 020-8799 6168

**EXPRESSIONS ACADEMY OF PERFORMING ARTS**
3 Newgate Lane, Mansfield, Notts NG18 2LB
Website: www.expressionsperformingarts.co.uk
e-mail: expressions-uk@btconnect.com
Fax: 01623 647337                 Tel: 01623 424334

**FAIRBROTHER Victoria MA, CSSD, LAMDA Dip**
Audition Technique. Improvisation. Private Acting Classes
Public Speaking. Vocal Coaching
15A Devenport Road, Shepherd's Bush, London W12 8NZ
e-mail: victoriafairbrother1@hotmail.com
Mobile: 07877 228990                 Tel: 020-8749 1253

**FAITH Gordon BA, IPA Dip, REM Sp, MCHC (UK), LRAM**
Speech
1 Wavel Mews, Priory Road
London NW6 3AB                 Tel: 020-7328 0446
Website: www.gordonfaith.co.uk/voice.htm

**FBI AGENCY Ltd**
Acting Classes for Everyone
PO Box 250, Leeds LS1 2AZ          Tel/Fax: 07050 222747
Website: www.fbi-agency.co.uk
e-mail: j.spencer@fbi-agency.co.uk

**FERRIS Anna MA (Voice Studies, CSSD)**
Audition Technique. Private Acting Classes. Vocal Coaching
Gil'cup Leaze, Hilton, Blandford Forum
Dorset DT11 0DB                 Tel: 01258 881098

**FERRIS ENTERTAINMENT PERFORMING ARTS**
London, Belfast & Cardiff
Number 8, 132 Charing Cross Road
London WC2H 0LA                 Tel: 0845 4724725
Website: www.ferrisentertainment.com
e-mail: info@ferrisentertainment.com

**FINBURGH Nina**
Sight Reading Specialist (Masterclasses & Individuals)
Audition Technique (Equity Members Only)
1 Buckingham Mansions
West End Lane, London NW6 1LR        Tel: 020-7435 9484
e-mail: ninafinburgh@aol.com

**FOOTSTEPS THEATRE SCHOOL**
Dance, Drama & Singing Training
1st Floor, Morrisons Enterprise
5 Bradford Road, Bradford
West Yorkshire BD10 8EW          Tel/Fax: 01274 616535
e-mail: helen@footsteps.fslife.co.uk

**FORD Carole Ann ADVS**
Acting Coach & Communication Skills
N10 2AL                 Tel: 020-8815 1832
e-mail: emko2000@aol.com

**FORREST Dee**
Deputy Head of Voice, Mountview. Audition Technique
Dialect/Accent Coaching for Film & Television. Elocution
Confidence Building/NLP. Public Speaking. Vocal Coaching
20 Landseer Road, Hove BN3 7AF
Website: www.projecturvoice.com
e-mail: dee_forrest@yahoo.com
Mobile: 07957 211065                 Tel: 01273 204779

**FOX Betty STAGE SCHOOL**
Slade Road, Erdington, Birmingham B23 7PX
e-mail: bettyfox.school@virgin.net
Mobile: 07703 436045             Tel/Fax: 0121-327 1020

**FRANKLIN Michael**
Meisner Technique
Correspondence: c/o Spotlight, 7 Leicester Place
London WC2H 7RJ              Tel/Fax: 020-8979 9185

**FRANKLYN Susan**
Audition Speeches. Confidence. Interview Technique
Presentation. Sight Readings
Mobile: 07780 742891                 Tel: 01306 884913

**FRIEZE Sandra**
English & Foreign Actors
London Area NW3/NW6              Mobile: 07802 865305

# MOUNTVIEW
## ACADEMY OF THEATRE ARTS

Ralph Richardson Memorial Studios, Kingfisher Place,
Clarendon Road, Wood Green, London N22 6XF

Musical
Theatre

Acting

Technical
Theatre

Stage Management · Lighting · Sound · Design · Construction

Undergraduate &
Postgraduate Courses
Plus an exciting programme of
Part-time and Summer Courses

Tel: 020 8881 2201
Fax: 020 8829 0034
enquiries@mountview.org.uk
www.mountview.org.uk

CDS MEMBER

*Mountview is committed to equal opportunities.*

…

## CLARE DAVIDSON, MFA
### VOICE and ACTING COACH    FILM, TV and THEATRE
### 020-8348-0132
davidson_clare@hotmail.com  www.claredavidson.co.uk

**FURNESS Simon**
Contact: Simon Furness. Actor Training (Sanford Meisner Technique). Acting Workshops. Audition Preparation & Technique. Drama School (over 18s). Private Acting Classes
c/o The Actors' Temple
13-14 Warren Street
London W1T 5LG                          Mobile: 07702 619665
e-mail: simonfurness@googlemail.com

**GLASGOW ACTING ACADEMY**
Contact: Maureen Cairns, Allan Jones, Hugh Hastie
2nd Floor, 34 Argyle Arcade Chambers
Buchanan Street, Glasgow G2 8BD        Tel: 0141-222 2942
e-mail: info@glasgowactingacademy.com

**GLYNNE Frances THEATRE STUDENTS**
Flat 9, Elmwood, 6 The Avenue
Hatch End
Middlesex HA5 4EP                      Mobile: 07950 918355

**GMA TELEVISION PRESENTER TRAINING**
Presenting for Television, Radio, Live Events. Autocue Talkback. Scriptwriting. Improvisation. Vocal Coaching
86 Beverley Gardens, Maidenhead, Berks SL6 6SW
e-mail: geoff@gma-training.co.uk
Mobile: 07769 598625                   Tel: 01628 673078

**GRAYSON John**
Acting Workshops. Audition Technique. Improvisation Private Acting Classes. Public Speaking. Singing Vocal Coaching
2 Jubilee Road, St Johns
Worcester WR2 4LY                      Mobile: 07702 188031
e-mail: jgbizzybee@btinternet.com

**GRAYSTONS**
843-845 Green Lanes, Winchmore Hill, London N21 2RX
e-mail: graystons@btinternet.com
Fax: 020-8364 2009                     Tel: 020-8360 5700

**GREASEPAINT ANONYMOUS**
(Youth Theatre & Training Company) Part-time Theatre Workshops Run Weekly through School Term Time. Holiday Courses at Easter & Summer. Acting Workshops. Dancing Singing (Age 4-30)
4 Gallus Close, Winchmore Hill, London N21 1JR
e-mail: info@greasepaintanonymous.co.uk
Fax: 020-8882 9189                     Tel: 020-8886 2263

**GREGORY Lynda SCHOOL OF SPEECH & DRAMA**
Speech and Drama Classes, All Ages
23 High Ash Avenue
Leeds LS17 8RS                         Tel: 0113-268 4519
e-mail: lyndagregory@hotmail.co.uk

**GREGORY Paul**
RSC & RNT Actor/Drama Coach
133 Kenilworth Court
Lower Richmond Road
Putney, London SW15 1HB
e-mail: pgregory789@yahoo.co.uk
Mobile: 001 323 533 3675               Tel: 001 323 798 5102

**GREVILLE Jeannine THEATRE SCHOOL**
Melody House, Gillott's Corner
Henley-on-Thames, Oxon RG9 1QU         Tel: 01491 572000
Website: www.jgdance.co.uk
e-mail: info@jgdance.co.uk

**GROUT Philip**
Theatre Director. Drama Coaching. Tuition for Students & Professionals
81 Clarence Road
London N22 8PG                         Tel: 020-8881 1800
e-mail: philipgrout@hotmail.com

**GSA, GUILDFORD SCHOOL OF ACTING**
See DRAMA SCHOOLS (Conference of)

**GUILDHALL SCHOOL OF MUSIC & DRAMA**
See DRAMA SCHOOLS (Conference of)

**HANCOCK Allison LLAM**
Acting. Audition Coach. Dramatic Art. Elocution Speech Correction. Voice
38 Eve Road, Isleworth
Middlesex TW7 7HS                      Tel/Fax: 020-8891 1073

**HARLEQUIN STUDIOS PERFORMING ARTS SCHOOL**
Drama & Dance Training
122A Phyllis Avenue, Peacehaven
East Sussex BN10 7RQ                   Tel: 01273 581742

**HARRIS Sharon NCSD, LRAM, LAM, STSD, IPA Dip DA (London Univ)**
Speech & Drama Specialist Teacher. Private Acting Coach for Screen and Stage. Training for RADA, LAMDA and ESB Exams. Audition Technique. Drama School and National Youth Theatre Audition Preparation
71 The Avenue
Watford, Herts WD17 4NU
e-mail: theharrisagency@btconnect.com
Mobile: 07956 388716                    Tel: 01923 211644

**HARRISON Abigail**
Audition & Acting Coach
e-mail: creativeacting@hotmail.co.uk  Mobile: 07847 420882

**HARRISON Lucie MA Voice Studies, BA (Hons) Drama**
Voice Teacher & Acting Coach
25 Shortlands Road
Kingston
Surrey KT2                    Mobile: 07773 798440
Website: www.lucieharrison.co.uk
e-mail: info@lucieharrison.co.uk

**HASS Leona**
Vocal Coach
12 Silverton Road, London W6 9NY    Mobile: 07801 270745
Website: www.apstudios.co.uk
e-mail: info@apstudios.co.uk

**HEALING VOICES**
Contact: Felicitas Ste. Croix. Singing & Voice Coach
London, Paris
Los Angeles, Athens                    Mobile: 07939 143721
e-mail: healing.voices@yahoo.com

**HESTER John LLCM (TD)**
(Member of The Society of Teachers of Speech & Drama)
Acting Courses for All Ages. Acting Workshops. Audition Technique. Dialect/Accent Coaching. Drama School Auditions (over 18s). Elocution Coaching. Private Acting Classes. Public Speaking. Stage School for Children
Vocal Coaching
105 Stoneleigh Park Road
Epsom, Surrey KT19 0RF          Tel: 020-8393 5705
e-mail: hjohnhester@aol.com

**HIGGS Jessica**
Voice
41A Barnsbury Street
London N1 1PW
Mobile: 07940 193631          Tel: 020-7359 7848

**H. J. A. (HERBERT JUSTICE ACADEMY)**
PO Box 253
Beckenham
Kent BR3 3WH
Website: www.hjaworld.com
e-mail: mail@hjaworld.com
Fax: 020-8249 2616          Tel: 020-8249 3299

**HOFFMANN-GILL Daniel**
Acting & Audition Tuition
e-mail: danielhg@gmail.com
Mobile: 07946 433903          Tel: 020-8888 6045

**HONEYBORNE Jack**
Accompanist & Coach
The Studio, 165 Gunnersbury Lane
London W3 8LJ          Tel: 020-8993 2111

## BARBARA HOUSEMAN VOICE, TEXT, ACTING COACH
### Author: Finding Your Voice & Tackling Text [and subtext]
### RSC, WEST END, TV, FILM
barbarahouseman@hotmail.com   www.barbarahouseman.com

**HOPE STREET Ltd**
Physical & Multi-Media Perfomance. Training for Actors,
Designers, Directors & Participatory Arts Workers
13A Hope Street, Liverpool L1 9BQ
Website: www.hope-street.org
e-mail: peter@hope-street.org
Fax: 0151-709 3242                    Tel: 0151-708 8007

**HOPNER Ernest LLAM**
Elocution. Public Speaking. Vocal Coaching
70 Banks Road, West Kirby CH48 ORD    Tel: 0151-625 5641

**HOUSEMAN Barbara**
Ex-RSC Voice Dept, Associate Director Young Vic. Acting
Confidence. Text. Voice         Mobile: 07767 843737
Website: www.barbarahouseman.com
e-mail: barbarahouseman@hotmail.com

**HOWARD Ashley BA MA**
Voice Coach
87 Waddington Street, Norwich
Norfolk NR2 4JX              Mobile: 07821 213752
Website: www.ashleyhoward.sythasite.com
e-mail: ashley.howard@cssd.ac.uk

**HUGHES-D'AETH Charlie**
Acting Workshops. Audition Techniques. Dialect/Accent
Coaching. Elocution. Private Acting Classes. Public
Speaking. Singing. Vocal Coaching
22 Osborne Road
Brighton BN1 6LQ              Mobile: 07811 010963
e-mail: chdaeth@aol.com

**HUGHES Dewi**
Accents. Auditions. Bodywork. Text. Voice
Flat 2, 4 Fielding Road
London W14 OLL               Mobile: 07836 545717
e-mail: dewi.hughes@gmail.com

**IMPULSE COMPANY The**
Meisner-Based Core Training
PO Box 158, Twickenham TW1 3WG    Tel/Fax: 07525 264173
e-mail: info@impulsecompany.co.uk

**INDEPENDENT THEATRE WORKSHOP The**
2 Mornington Road, Ranelagh
Dublin 6, Ireland            Tel/Fax: 00 353 1 4968808
Website: www.independent-theatre-workshop.com
e-mail: info@independent-theatre-workshop.com

**INTERACT**
Contact: Lauren Bigby (LGSM). Acting Workshops. Audition
Technique. Elocution Coaching. Private Acting Classes
Public Speaking
19 Raven Lane, Billericay
Essex CM12 OJB               Mobile: 07961 982198
Website: www.laurenbigby.me.uk
e-mail: renbigby@hotmail.com

**INTERNATIONAL SCHOOL OF SCREEN ACTING**
3 Mills Studios, Unit 3, 24 Sugar House Lane
London E15 2QS               Tel: 020-8555 5775
Website: www.screenacting.co.uk
e-mail: office@screenacting.co.uk

**JACK Andrew**
Dialect Coach
Vrouwe Johanna
24 The Moorings, Willows Riverside
Windsor, Berks SL4 5TG        Mobile: 07836 615839
Website: www.andrewjack.com

**JACK Paula**
Dialect Coach & Language Specialist
Vrouwe Johanna
24 The Moorings, Willows Riverside
Windsor, Berks SL4 5TG        Mobile: 07836 615839
Website: www.paulajack.com

**JACOBSEN Anja**
German Language and Accent Tuition
Acting in German, Translation
54 Higham Hill Road, London E17 6ER
Mobile: 07501 467825          Tel: 020-8523 4950

**JAMES Linda RAM Dip Ed, IPD, LRAM**
Dialect & Speech Coach
25 Clifden Road, Brentford
Middlesex TW8 OPB             Tel: 020-8568 2390

**JAM THEATRE COMPANY**
21 Beechtree Avenue
Marlow, Bucks SL7 3NH         Tel: 01628 487773
Website: www.jamtheatre.co.uk
e-mail: office@jamtheatre.co.uk

**JAQUARELLO Roland BA**
Audition, Drama School Entrance, Radio Coaching
41 Parfrey Street
London W6 9EW                Tel/Fax: 020-8741 2446
Website: www.rolandjaquarello.com
e-mail: roland@jaquarellofulham.freeserve.co.uk

**JIGSAW PERFORMING ARTS SCHOOLS**
Head Office, 64-66 High Street
Barnet, Herts EN5 5SJ         Tel: 020-8447 4530
e-mail: admin@jigsaw-arts.co.uk

**JINGLES Jo**
1 Boismore Road
Chesham, Bucks HP5 1SH        Tel: 01494 778989
Website: www.jojingles.com
e-mail: headoffice@jojingles.co.uk

**JONES Desmond**
Courses in Dynamic Acting, The Total Actor. Introduction to
Mime & Physical Theatre. Physical Story Telling for the
Theatre. Private Classes & Consultant - Freelance
Choreography. Director. Teacher. Coach
20 Thornton Avenue
London W4 1QG                Tel/Fax: 020-8747 3537
Website: www.desmondjones.com
e-mail: enquiries@desmondjones.com

**JUDE'S DRAMA ACADEMY & MANAGEMENT**
Manor House, Oldham Road
Springhead, Oldham OL4 4QJ    Tel: 0161-624 5378
Website: www.judesdrama.co.uk
e-mail: judesdrama@yahoo.co.uk

## KENT YOUTH THEATRE
(Stage & Screen Academy) Contact: Richard Andrews
Courses in Drama, Dance, Musical Theatre, Singing, Film
Acting/Making. Improvisation. Private Acting Classes. Stage
School for Children
Office: Mulberry Croft, Mulberry Hill, Chilham CT4 8AJ
Website: www.kentyouththeatre.co.uk
e-mail: richard@kentyouththeatre.co.uk
Mobile: 07967 580213       Tel/Fax: 01227 730177

## KERR Louise
Voice Coach
20A Rectory Road, London E17 3BQ
Website: www.resonancevoice.com
e-mail: louise@louisekerr.com
Mobile: 07780 708102       Tel: 020-8509 2767

## KIRKLEES COLLEGE
Courses in Acting, Dance & Musical Theatre
(BTec, GCSE & HNC)
Highfields Annexe, New North Road
Huddersfield HD1 5NN       Tel: 01484 437047
e-mail: info@kirkleescollege.ac.uk

## KNYVETTE Sally
Drama School Preparation. Drama Tuition. All Levels
52 Burnfoot Avenue
London SW6 5EA       Tel/Fax: 020-7731 0639
e-mail: salkny@aol.co.uk

## KRIMPAS Titania
One-to-one Tuition. Audition Technique. Drama School
(over 18s)
The Garden Flat, 23 Lambolle Road
London NW3 4HS       Mobile: 07957 303958
e-mail: titania@krimpas.freeserve.co.uk

## LAINE THEATRE ARTS
Contact: Betty Laine
The Studios, East Street, Epsom, Surrey KT17 1HH
Website: www.laine-theatre-arts.co.uk
e-mail: info@laine-theatre-arts.co.uk
Fax: 01372 723775       Tel: 01372 724648

## LAMDA
See DRAMA SCHOOLS (Conference of)

## LAMONT DRAMA SCHOOL & CASTING AGENCY
Contact: Diane Lamont. Part-time Lessons. Acting Skills
Audition Technique. Coaching
2 Harewood Avenue, Ainsdale
Merseyside PR8 2PH       Mobile: 07736 387543
Website: www.lamontcasting.co.uk
e-mail: diane@lamontcasting.co.uk

## LAURIE Rona
Coach for Auditions & Voice and Speech Technique
Flat 1, 21 New Quebec Street
London W1H 7SA       Tel: 020-7262 4909

## LEAN David Lawson BA Hons, PGCE
Acting Tuition for Children, LAMDA Exams, Licensed
Chaperone
72 Shaw Drive, Walton-on-Thames
Surrey KT12 2LS       Tel: 01932 230273
Website: www.davidlawsonlean.com
e-mail: dlawsonlean@aol.com

## LEE THEATRE SCHOOL The
Office:
126 Church Road
Benfleet, Essex SS7 4EP       Tel: 01268 795863
Website: www.lynnlee.co.uk
e-mail: lynn@leetheatre.fsnet.co.uk

**LESLIE Maeve**
Classical & Musicals. Presentations. Singing
Voice Production
60 Warwick Square, London SW1V 2AL     Tel: 020-7834 4912

**LEVENTON Patricia BA Hons**
Audition & Dialect Coach
113 Broadhurst Gardens
West Hampstead, London NW6 3BJ
e-mail: patricia@lites2000.com
Mobile: 07703 341062     Tel: 020-7624 5661

**LINCOLN ACADEMY OF DRAMATIC ARTS**
(6-18 yrs)
Sparkhouse Studios, Rope Walk
Lincoln, Lincs LN6 7DQ
Website: www.lada.org.uk/academy
e-mail: info@lada.org.uk
Fax: 01522 837201     Tel: 01522 837242

**LIPTON Rick**
Dialect/Accent Coaching
14 Lock Road, Richmond
Surrey TW10 7LH     Mobile: 07961 445247
e-mail: ricklipton@gmail.com

**LIVERPOOL INSTITUTE FOR PERFORMING ARTS The**
See DRAMA SCHOOLS (Conference of)

**LIVINGSTON Dione LRAM, FETC**
Audition Technique. Dialect/Accent Coaching. Elocution
Coaching. Improvisation. Language Tutoring. Private Acting
Classes. Public Speaking. Vocal Coaching
7 St Luke's Street
Cambridge CB4 3DA     Tel: 01223 365970

**LLOYD Gabrielle**
Audition Technique. Drama School Entrance. LAMDA Exams
Private Acting Classes. Public Speaking. Vocal Coaching
90B Melbury Gardens
London SW20 0DN     Tel: 020-8946 4042
e-mail: gubilloyd@hotmail.com

**LOCATION TUTORS NATIONWIDE**
Fully Qualified/Experienced Teachers Working with Children
on Film Sets & Covering all Key Stages of National
Curriculum
16 Poplar Walk, Herne Hill SE24 0BU
Website: www.locationtutors.co.uk
e-mail: locationtutorsnationwide@hotmail.com
Fax: 020-7207 8794     Tel: 020-7978 8898

**LONDON ACTORS WORKSHOP**
29B Battersea Rise
London SW11 1HG     Mobile: 07748 846294
Website: www.londonactorsworkshop.co.uk
e-mail: info@londonactorsworkshop.co.uk

**LONDON DRAMA SCHOOL**
Acting. Singing. Speech Training
30 Brondesbury Park, London NW6 7DN
Website: www.london-drama-school.co.uk
e-mail: enquiries@startek-uk.com
Fax: 020-8830 4992     Tel: 020-8830 0074

**LONDON INTERNATIONAL SCHOOL OF PERFORMING
ARTS**
The Old Lab, 3 Mills Studios
Three Mill Lane, London E3 3DU
Website: www.lispa.co.uk
e-mail: welcome@lispa.co.uk
Fax: 020-8215 3392     Tel: 020-8215 3390

**LONDON REPERTORY COMPANY ACADEMY**
27 Old Gloucester Street
London WC1N 3XX     Tel/Fax: 020-7258 1944
Website: www.londonrepertorycompany.com/academy
e-mail: academy@londonrepertorycompany.com

**LONDON SCHOOL OF DRAMATIC ART**
Foundation & Advanced Diplomas in Acting
(Full & Part-time). Drama School (over 18s)
4 Bute Street, South Kensington
London SW7 3EX     Tel: 020-7581 6100
Website: www.lsda-acting.com
e-mail: enquiries@lsda-acting.com

**LONDON SCHOOL OF MUSICAL THEATRE**
83 Borough Road
London SE1 1DN     Tel/Fax: 020-7407 4455
e-mail: enquiries@lsmt.co.uk

**LONDON STUDIO CENTRE**
Courses in Theatre Dance (3 yrs), Full-time, BA, FdA. 1 Year
Professional Diploma. Summer Course
Evening & Saturday Classes
42-50 York Way, London N1 9AB
Website: www.london-studio-centre.co.uk
e-mail: info@london-studio-centre.co.uk
Fax: 020-7837 3248     Tel: 020-7837 7741

**LONG OVERDUE THEATRE SCHOOL The**
2 Reculver Way
Andover, Hants SP10 4EH     Mobile: 07875 309868
Website: www.longoverdue.co.uk
e-mail: school@longoverdue.co.uk

**MACKINNON Alison**
Voice & Accent Auditions
London SE6     Mobile: 07973 562132
e-mail: alison.mackinnon@bruford.ac.uk

**MADDERMARKET THEATRE**
Contact: Education Officer
Education Department
St John's Alley, Norwich NR2 1DR
Website: www.maddermarket.co.uk
e-mail: mmtedu@btconnect.com
Fax: 01603 661357     Tel: 01603 628600

**MANCHESTER SCHOOL OF THEATRE AT MANCHESTER
METROPOLITAN UNIVERSITY**
See DRAMA SCHOOLS (Conference of)

**MANCHESTER SCHOOL OF ACTING**
29 Ardwick Green North
Manchester M12 6DL     Tel/Fax: 0161-273 4738
Website: www.manchesterschoolofacting.co.uk
e-mail: actorclass@aol.com

**MARLOW Chris**
Voice & Speech Coach
RDDC, 52 Bridleway, Waterfoot, Rossendale, Lancs BB4 9DS
Website: www.rddc.co.uk
e-mail: rddc@btinternet.com          Mobile: 07792 309992

**MARLOW Jean LGSM**
32 Exeter Road, London NW2 4SB          Tel: 020-8450 0371

**MARTIN Liza GRSM, GRSM (Recital), ARMCM (Singing & Piano)**
Singing Tuition & Piano Accompanist    Tel: 020-8348 0346

**MARTIN Mandi SINGING TECHNIQUE**
Currently Coaching at Millennium Dance 2000 & Bodywork
at Cambridge Performing Arts
90 School Lane, Bushey
Hertfordshire WD23 1BX               Mobile: 07811 758656
e-mail: mandi.martin@sky.com

**MASTERS PERFORMING ARTS COLLEGE Ltd**
Musical Theatre/Dance Course
Arterial Road, Rayleigh
Essex SS6 7UQ                        Tel: 01268 777351
e-mail: info@mastersperformingarts.co.uk

**MAVERICK YOUTH ACADEMY**
12 Lydney Grove, Northfield
Birmingham B31 1RB                   Mobile: 07531 138248
Website: www.mavericktheatre.co.uk
e-mail: academy@mavericktheatre.co.uk

**MAY Maggie DRAMA**
The Epsom Playhouse
Ashley Avenue
Epsom, Surrey KT18 5AL               Mobile: 07984 745323
Website: www.maggiemayltd.com
e-mail: office@maggiemayltd.com

**McDAID Marj**
1 Chesholm Road, Stoke Newington, London N16 0DP
Website: www.voicings.co.uk
e-mail: marj@voicings.co.uk
Mobile: 07815 993203                     Tel: 020-7923 4929

**McDONAGH Melanie ACADEMY OF PERFORMING ARTS & CASTING AGENCY The**
(Northwest)
14 Apple Tree Way, Oswaldtwistle
Accrington, Lancashire BB5 0FB
Website: www.mcdonaghmanagement.co.uk
e-mail: mcdonaghmgt@aol.com
Mobile: 07909 831409                     Tel: 01254 392560

**McKEAND Ian**
Audition Technique. Drama School Entry
12 Linnet Close, Birchwood
Lincoln LN6 0JQ                          Tel: 01522 805966
Website: http://homepage.ntlworld.com/ian.mckeand1
e-mail: ian.mckeand@ntlworld.com

**McKELLAN Martin**
Acting Workshops. Dialect/Accent Coaching. Private Acting Classes. Vocal Coaching
62A Neal Street, London WC2H 9PA        Tel: 020-7240 0145
e-mail: martinmckellan@yahoo.co.uk

**MEAD Alison**
Website: www.dramatraininguk.co.uk
e-mail: info@dramatraininguk.co.uk      Tel: 020-8402 7858

**MELLECK Lydia**
Pianist & Coach for Auditions & Repertoire - RADA Workshops on Sondheim. Accompanist. Singing for Beginners. Vocal Coaching
10 Burgess Park Mansions
London NW6 1DP                           Tel: 020-7794 8845
e-mail: lyd.muse@yahoo.co.uk

**MGA PART TIME THEATRE SCHOOL**
11/4 Abbey Street
Edinburgh EH7 5XN                        Tel/Fax: 0131-466 9392
Website: www.themgacompany.com
e-mail: info@themgacompany.com

**MICHEL Hilary ARCM**
Accompanist. Audition Songs. Diction & Languages for Songs. Piano. Recorders. Singing Teacher. Technique Theory. Vocal Coach
82 Greenway, Totteridge, London N20 8EJ
e-mail: hilarymich@hotmail.com
Mobile: 07775 780182                     Tel: 020-8343 7243

**MILLER Christie**
Acting & Life Coach
32 Brookfield Road, London E9 5AH        Tel: 020-8525 0111
Website: www.christiemillercoaching.com
e-mail: christie.miller@btinternet.com

**MILLER Robin**
South West London                        Mobile: 07957 627677
e-mail: robinjenni@hotmail.com

**MONTAGE THEATRE ARTS**
Contact: Judy Gordon (Artistic Director). Dance. Drama Singing. Children & Adults
The Albany, Douglas Way
London SE8 4AG                           Tel: 020-8692 7007
Website: www.montagetheatre.com
e-mail: office@montagetheatre.com

**MOORE Stefanie BA Hons LLAM**
Audition Preparation, Public Speaking, Voice and Text
119 Francis Road, London E10 6PL        Mobile: 07751 564223
Website: www.tinbobbin.com
e-mail: stef@tinbobbin.com

**MORGAN Katie BA (Hons) PG dip, PGCE**
Private Acting Coach. Audition Preparation/ Drama School Entry
London                                   Mobile: 07956 344255
e-mail: katie080@hotmail.com

**MORLEY ADULT EDUCATION COLLEGE**
Day & Evening LOCN Accredited, Acting School Programme
61 Westminster Bridge Road
London SE1 7HT                           Tel: 020-7450 1925
Website: www.morleycollege.ac.uk
e-mail: dominic.grant@morleycollege.ac.uk

**MORRISON Elspeth**
Accent & Dialect Coach                   Mobile: 07790 919870
e-mail: elsp.morrison@talk21.com

**MORRISON Stuart MA Voice Studies (CSSD), FVCM (Hons), PGCE (Drama)**
Voice & Speech Coach
24 Deans Walk, Coulsdon
Surrey CR5 1HR                           Mobile: 07867 808648
e-mail: stuartvoicecoach@yahoo.co.uk

**MOUNTVIEW**
See DRAMA SCHOOLS (Conference of)

**MRS WORTHINGTON'S WORKSHOPS**
Part-time Performing Arts for Children (6-16 yrs)
16 Ouseley Road, London SW12 8EF        Tel: 020-8767 6944

# Eileen Benskin
### *Dialect/Dialogue Coach*
R.A.D.A. dip., C.P.E.P. University College London

## FILMS • TELEVISION • THEATRE
*Specialist in Standard British English (R.P.)*
*and American, British & Foreign Accents & Dialects*
**Tel/Fax: 020-8455 9750  or  Spotlight 020-7437 7631   Mobile 07785 791715**

**MTA**
Musical Theatre Academy
The Drill Hall, 16 Chenies Street
London WC1E 7EX                    Tel: 020-8882 8181
Website: www.thetma.co.uk
e-mail: info@themta.co.uk

**MURRAY Barbara LGSM, LALAM**
129 Northwood Way
Northwood
Middlesex HA6 1RF                  Tel: 01923 823182

**MUSICAL KIDZ THEATRE COMPANY The**
Spires Meade
4 Bridleways
Wendover, Bucks HP22 6DN
Website: www.themusicalkidz.co.uk
e-mail: themusicalkidz@aol.com
Fax: 01296 623696              Mobile: 07989 353673

**NATHENSON Zoe**
Audition Technique. Film Acting. Sight Reading
Group Classes
55 St James's Lane
London N10 3DA                 Mobile: 07956 833850
Website: www.zoenathenson.com
e-mail: zoe.act@btinternet.com

**NEIL Andrew**
Audition Technique. Private Acting Classes. Public Speaking
2 Howley Place
London W2 1XA
e-mail: andrewneil@talktalk.net
Mobile: 07979 843984           Tel/Fax: 020-7262 9521

**NEW LONDON PERFORMING ARTS CENTRE**
Courses in Performing Arts (3-19 yrs). Dance. Drama. GCSE
Courses, LAMDA, ISTD & RAD
76 St James Lane, Muswell Hill, London N10 3DF
Website: www.nlpac.co.uk
e-mail: nlpac@aol.com
Fax: 020-8444 4040                 Tel: 020-8444 4544

**NEWNHAM Caryll**
Singing Teacher
35 Selwyn Crescent, Hatfield, Herts AL10 9NL
e-mail: caryll@ntlworld.com
Mobile: 07976 635745               Tel: 01707 267700

**NOBLE Penny PSYCHOTHERAPY**
8 Shaftesbury Gardens
Victoria Road, North Acton
London NW10 6LJ                Mobile: 07506 579895
Website: www.pennynoblepsychotherapy.com
e-mail: penny.noble@virgin.net

**NORTHERN ACADEMY OF PERFORMING ARTS**
Anlaby Road, Hull HU1 2PD
Website: www.northernacademy.org.uk
e-mail: napa@northernacademy.org.uk
Fax: 01482 212280                  Tel: 01482 310690

**NORTHERN FILM & DRAMA**
Acting Workshops. Audition Technique. Dancing. Drama
School (over 18s). Film & Television Training. Improvisation
Private Acting Classes. Stage School for Children
PO Box 76, Leeds LS25 9AG          Tel/Fax: 01977 681949
Website: www.northernfilmanddrama.com
e-mail: info@northernfilmanddrama.com

**Sam Rumbelow**
t: 020 7622 9742
m: 07764 680 232
www.methodacting.co.uk
**Acting Classes & Coaching**

**method Acting**

**To develop & strengthen your work**

**NPAS @ THE STUDIOS**
Docklands, Dublin 1, Ireland      Tel/Fax: 00 353 1 8944660
Website: www.npas.ie
e-mail: info@npas.ie

**O'FARRELL STAGE & THEATRE SCHOOL**
Dance. Drama. Singing
36 Shirley Street, Canning Town
London E16 1HU      Tel/Fax: 020-7511 9444
e-mail: linda@ofarrells.wanadoo.co.uk

**OLLERENSHAW Maggie BA (Hons), Dip Ed**
Acting Workshops. Audition Technique. Career Guidance
Private Acting. Television & Theatre Coaching
151D Shirland Road, London W9 2EP      Tel: 020-7286 1126
e-mail: maggieoll@aol.com

**OLSON Lise**
American Accents. Practical Voice. Vocal Coaching
Working with Text
Midlands Based, c/o Birmingham School of Acting
Millennium Point, Curzon Street
Birmingham B4 7XG      Mobile: 07790 877145
e-mail: lise.olson@bcv.ac.uk

**OMOBONI Lino**
Private Acting Classes
2nd Floor, 12 Weltje Road, London W6 9TG
e-mail: bluewand@btinternet.com
Mobile: 07525 187468      Tel/Fax: 020-8741 2038

**OPEN VOICE**
Contact: Catherine Owen. Auditions. Consultancy
Personal Presentations
9 Bellsmains, Gorebridge
Near Edinburgh EH23 4QD      Tel: 01875 820175

**OPPOSITE LEG Ltd**
Contact: David Windle. Acting Workshops. Classroom
Presence for Teachers. Corporate Voice & Body Training
Improvisation. Presentation Skills Training. Private Acting
Classes. Public Speaking. Teenage Drama Workshops
Vocal Coaching
132 Bethwin Road, London SE5 0YY      Mobile: 07950 824123
Website: www.oppositeleg.co.uk
e-mail: david@oppositeleg.co.uk

**ORAM Daron**
Audition Preparation. Dialect/Accent Coaching. Voice
Coaching. Senior Voice Teacher ArtsEd Musical Theatre
School
North Greenwich      Mobile: 07905 332497
e-mail: darono@yahoo.com

**OSBORNE HUGHES John**
Spiritual Psychology of Acting
Miracle Tree Productions Training Department
51 Church Road, London SE19 2TE
Website: www.spiritualpsychologyofacting.com
e-mail: johughes@miracletreeproductions.com
Mobile: 07801 950916      Tel: 020-8653 7735

**OSCARS COLLEGE OF PERFORMANCE ARTS Ltd**
Contact: Paula Danholm
Oscars Management, Spring Bank House
1 Spring Bank, New North Road
Huddersfield, West Yorkshire HD1 5NR      Tel: 01484 545519
e-mail: oscars.college@virgin.net

**OVERSBY William**
Singing & Vocal Projection
Petersfield, Hants
e-mail: billo363@msn.com
Mobile: 07811 946663      Tel: 01420 538549

**OXFORD SCHOOL OF DRAMA The**
See DRAMA SCHOOLS (Conference of)

**PALMER Jackie STAGE SCHOOL**
30 Daws Hill Lane, High Wycombe, Bucks HP11 1PW
Website: www.jackiepalmer.co.uk
e-mail: jackie.palmer@btinternet.com
Fax: 01494 510479      Tel: 01494 510597

**PARKES Frances MA, AGSM**
Contact: Frances Parkes, Sarah Upson. Clarity
Dialect/Accent Coaching. Interview Skills for Castings
Private Acting Classes. Public Speaking. R.P. English for
Actors with English as a Second Language. Vocal Coaching
11 Jasmine Court, 102 Alexandra Road
London SW19 7JY      Tel/Fax: 020-8542 2777
Agent: Upson Edwards      01782 827222
Website: www.maxyourvoice.com
e-mail: frances@maxyourvoice.com

**PAUL'S THEATRE SCHOOL**
Ardleigh House, 42 Ardleigh Green Road
Hornchurch, Essex RM11 2LG
Website: www.paulstheatreschool.com
e-mail: info@paulstheatreschool.com
Tel: 01708 446167      Tel: 01708 447123

**PERFORMANCE BUSINESS The**
78 Oatlands Drive
Weybridge, Surrey KT13 9HT      Tel: 01932 888885
Website: www.theperformance.biz
e-mail: michael@theperformance.biz

**PERFORMERS COLLEGE**
Contact: Brian Rogers, Susan Stephens
Southend Road
Corringham, Essex SS17 8JT
Website: www.performerscollege.co.uk
e-mail: pdc@dircon.co.uk
Fax: 01375 672353　　　　　Tel: 01375 672053

**PERFORMERS THEATRE SCHOOL**
Hope Street, Liverpool L18 4QJ
& Royal Victoria Patriotic Buildings, London L18 4QJ
Website: www.performerstheatre.co.uk
e-mail: info@performerstheatre.co.uk
Tel: 0151-708 4000　　　　　Tel: 020-8479 3000

**PILATES INTERNATIONAL Ltd**
Pilates Teacher Training (NVQ3 - Cert). Physical Coaching
Unit 1, Broadbent Close, 20-22 Highgate High Street
London N6 5JG　　　　　Tel/Fax: 020-8348 1442
Website: www.pilatesinternational.co.uk
e-mail: pilates@pilatesinternational.co.uk

**PLAIN SPEAKING**
Also Available in London
64 Ferry Road, Sudbourne
Woodbridge, Suffolk IP12 2BJ　　　　Tel/Fax: 01394 450265
Website: www.plainspeaking.co.uk
e-mail: enquiries@plainspeaking.co.uk

**POLLYANNA CHILDREN'S TRAINING THEATRE**
1 Knighten Street, Wapping, London E1W 1PH
Website: www.pollyannatheatre.org
e-mail: pollyanna_mgmt@btinternet.com
Fax: 020-7480 6761　　　　　Tel: 020-7481 1911

**POLYDOROU Anna**
147C Fernhead Road, Maida Hill
Queens Park W9 3ED　　　　　Mobile: 07833 545292
e-mail: annahebe@yahoo.co.uk

**POOR SCHOOL**
242 Pentonville Road
London N1 9JY　　　　　Tel: 020-7837 6030
Website: www.thepoorschool.com
e-mail: acting@thepoorschool.com

**PRECINCT THEATRE The**
Units 2/3 The Precinct
Packington Square, London N1 7UP
Website: www.breakalegman.com
e-mail: theatre@breakalegman.com
Fax: 020-7359 3660　　　　　Tel: 020-7359 3594

**QUEEN MARGARET UNIVERSITY, EDINBURGH**
See DRAMA SCHOOLS (Conference of)

**QUESTORS THEATRE EALING The**
12 Mattock Lane
London W5 5BQ
Website: www.questors.org.uk
e-mail: jane@questors.org.uk
Fax: 020-8567 2275　　　　　Admin: 020-8567 0011

**RAVENSCOURT THEATRE SCHOOL Ltd**
8-30 Galena Road
Hammersmith, London W6 0LT
Website: www.ravenscourt.net
e-mail: info@ravenscourt.net
Fax: 020-8741 1786　　　　　Tel: 020-8741 0707

# TIM CHARRINGTON

Dip. C.S.S.D., A.D.V.S., ACTOR & TEACHER

## ACCENT & DIALECTS   T: 020 7987 3028   M: 07967 418 236

---

**RAW TALENT PRODUCTIONS & THE ACTORS CENTRE SCOTLAND**
Contact: Helen Raw. Courses in Acting for Film, TV & Theatre (2 Days). Cold Reading & Audition Technique Monologue & Character Development. Improvisation & Scene Study. After School Drama Classes
1 St Colme Street
Edinburgh EH3 6AA                          Tel: 0131-220 8304
Website: www.rawtalentproductions.co.uk
e-mail: info@rawtalentproductions.co.uk

**RAZZAMATAZ THEATRE SCHOOLS**
2nd Floor, Atlas Works
Nelson Street
Denton Holme
Carlisle CA2 5NB                           Tel: 01228 550129
Website: www.razzamataz.co.uk
e-mail: franchise@razzamataz.co.uk

**RC-ANNIE Ltd**
For Dramatic Fight Services & Theatrical Blood Supplies
34 Pullman Place
London SE9 6EG                             Tel: 020-8123 5936
Website: www.rc-annie.com
e-mail: info@rc-annie.com

**REBEL SCHOOL OF THEATRE ARTS AND CASTING AGENCY Ltd**
Based in Leeds
PO Box 169
Huddersfield HD8 1BE                       Mobile: 07808 803637
e-mail: suerebeltheatre@aol.com

**RED ONION PERFORMING ARTS CENTRE**
Dance. Drama. Vocal Training (8 yrs - Adult)
26-28 Hatherley Mews
London E17 4QP                             Tel: 020-8520 3975
Website: www.redonion.uk.com
e-mail: info@redonion.uk.com

**REDROOFS THEATRE SCHOOL**
Littlewick Green
Maidenhead, Berks SL6 3QY
Website: www.redroofs.co.uk
e-mail: sam@redroofs.co.uk
Fax: 01628 822461
                                           Tel: 01628 822982

**REFLECTIONS AGENCY**
34 Knowle Avenue
Bexleyheath, Kent DA7 5LX
Website: www.reflectionsperfarts.tripod.com
e-mail: c.johnson717@ntlworld.com
Mobile: 07958 617976                       Tel/Fax: 01322 410003

**REP COLLEGE The**
17 St Mary's Avenue
Purley on Thames
Berks RG8 8BJ                              Tel: 0118-942 1144
Website: www.repcollege.co.uk
e-mail: tudor@repcollege.co.uk

**RICHARDSON ASSOCIATES**
The Mill House, 3 Clough Mill
Walsden, West Yorkshire OL14 7QX           Tel: 01706 812420
Website: www.russrichardson.co.uk
e-mail: russell@richardsonassoc.co.uk

**RICHMOND DRAMA SCHOOL**
1 Year Course
Richmond Adult College
Parkshot, Richmond
Surrey TW9 2RE
e-mail: mark.woolgar@racc.ac.uk           Tel: 020-8439 8944

**RIDGEWAY STUDIOS PERFORMING ARTS COLLEGE**
Fairley House, Andrews Lane
Cheshunt, Herts EN7 6LB
Website: www.ridgewaystudios.co.uk
e-mail: info@ridgewaystudios.co.uk
Fax: 01992 633844                          Tel: 01992 633775

**RISING STARS DRAMA SCHOOL**
PO Box 6281, Dorchester
Dorset DT1 9BB                             Tel: 0845 2570127
Website: www.risingstarsdramaschool.co.uk
e-mail: info@risingstarsdramaschool.co.uk

**ROFFE Danielle**
Acting Workshops. Audition Technique. Dialect/Accent Coaching. Drama School (over 18s). Elocution. Private Acting Classes. Public Speaking. Vocal Coaching
e-mail: danielle@danielleroffe.com        Mobile: 07939 225791

**ROSCH Philip**
Association of Guildhall Teachers, FVCM, LALAM, ATCL, LGSM, ANEA, BA Hons. Auditions for Top UK Drama Schools Audition Speeches. Effective Sight-reading. Commercial Castings. Expert Career Guidance. Private Acting Classes RADA Acting Exams
53 West Heath Court
London NW11 7RG                            Tel: 020-8731 6686
Website: www.philiprosch.com

**ROSE BRUFORD COLLEGE**
See DRAMA SCHOOLS (Conference of)

**ROSS David ACTING ACADEMY**
8 Farrier Close, Sale
Cheshire M33 2ZL                          Mobile: 07957 862317
Website: www.davidrossacting.com
e-mail: info@davidrossacting.com

**ROSSENDALE DANCE & DRAMA CENTRE**
Contact: Chris Marlow. LAMDA, LCM, TCL Grade & Diploma Courses & Exams. Acting Workshops. Audition Technique Dancing. Dialect/Accent Coaching. Drama School (over 18s) Elocution. Improvisation. Private Acting Classes. Public Speaking. Stage School for Children. Vocal Coaching
52 Bridleway
Waterfoot, Rossendale
Lancs BB4 9DS                             Tel: 01706 211161
e-mail: rddc@btinternet.com

## VOICEPOWERWORKS *training tomorrow's actors today*

**Irene Bradshaw**    t: 020 7794 5721    e: irene@irenebradshaw.fsnet.co.uk    www.voice-power-works.co.uk

· voice coaching    · audition preparation    · public speaking    · presentations

---

**ROYAL ACADEMY OF DRAMATIC ART**
See DRAMA SCHOOLS (Conference of)

**ROYAL ACADEMY OF MUSIC**
Musical Theatre Department
Marylebone Road
London NW1 5HT     Tel: 020-7873 7483
Website: www.ram.ac.uk
e-mail: mth@ram.ac.uk

**ROYAL SCOTTISH ACADEMY OF MUSIC & DRAMA**
See DRAMA SCHOOLS (Conference of)

**ROYAL WELSH COLLEGE OF MUSIC & DRAMA**
See DRAMA SCHOOLS (Conference of)

**RUMBELOW Sam**
Acting & Method Acting Coach
84 Union Road
London SW4 6JU     Tel: 020-7622 9742
Website: www.methodacting.co.uk
e-mail: samson@methodacting.co.uk

**RYDER Richard**
Voice & Accent Coach
9 Kamen House
17-21 Magdalen Street
London SE1 2RH     Mobile: 07967 352551
e-mail: richard_j_ryder@hotmail.com

**SALES Stephanie**
61 Brookfield Road, Chiswick
London W4 1DF     Tel: 020-8995 9127
Website: www.stephaniesales.co.uk/dramacoaching
e-mail: steph@stephaniesales.co.uk

**SAMUELS Marianne**
Voice Coach, Accents, Text & Business Voice
Ealing
West London     Mobile: 07974 203001
e-mail: mariannemicallef@hotmail.com

**SCALA SCHOOL OF PERFORMING ARTS**
Audition Technique. Dancing. Dialect/Accent Coaching
Improvisation. Singing. Stage School for Children
Vocal Training
Office: 42 Rufford Avenue
Yeadon, Leeds LS19 7QR
Website: www.scalakids.com
e-mail: office@scalkids.com
Fax: 0113-250 8806     Tel: 0113-250 6823

**SEMARK Rebecca LLAM**
Audition Technique. Drama School Entry. Speech Faults
Voice & Speech Coach
11 Charles Street, Epping
Essex CM16 7AU     Mobile: 07956 850330
Website: www.semark.biz
e-mail: rebecca@semark.biz

**SHAW Phil**
Actors' Consultancy Service. Audition Technique/
Voice Coaching
Suite #476, 2 Old Brompton Road
South Kensington, London SW7 3DQ     Tel: 020-8715 8943
e-mail: shawcastlond@aol.com

**SHENEL Helena**
Singing Teacher
80 Falkirk House, 165 Maida Vale, London W9 1QX
Tel: 020-7328 2921     Tel: 020-7724 8793

**SHOWSONG ACCOMPANIST**
165 Gunnersbury Lane, London W3 8LJ     Tel: 020-8993 2111

**SIMMONS Jacki BA (Hons) PGCE MA (CSSD)**
Audition Technique. Private Acting Classes
16 Tower Terrace
London N22 6SX     Mobile: 07989 389183
e-mail: jacki_@hotmail.com

**SIMMONS Ros MA**
Auditions. Dialects/Accents. Presentations. Voice
The Real Speaking Company
120 Hillfield Avenue, Crouch End, London N8 7DN
Website: www.realspeaking.co.uk
e-mail: info@realspeaking.co.uk
Mobile: 07957 320572     Tel: 020-8347 8089

**SIMPKIN Heather**
Morriston, Fairmile
Henley-on-Thames, Oxon RG9 2JX     Tel: 01491 574349
e-mail: heathersimpkin@btinternet.com

**SINGER Sandra ASSOCIATES**
LAMDA & ISTD Exams. Acting Workshops. Audition
Technique. Dancing. Dialect/Accent Coaching. Part-time
Drama School (over 18s). Improvisation. Private Acting
Classes. Singing. Stage School for Children. Vocal Coaching
21 Cotswold Road, Westcliff-on-Sea, Essex SS0 8AA
Website: www.sandrasinger.com
e-mail: sandrasingeruk@aol.com
Fax: 01702 339393     Tel: 01702 331616

---

## Michael Vivian   Actor ▍ Director ▍ Writer

Productions at Arts Ed., Mountview, Guildford & Central
Also QDOS, UK Productions & various reps.
Voice Speech & Drama, Audition Coaching, Private Tuition
### Tel: 020-8876 2073   Mob: 07958-903911

**SINGER STAGE SCHOOL**
Part-time Vocational Stage School & Summer School. Adult
Classes (16+ yrs) for Singing, Acting & Tap. Acting
Workshops. Audition Technique. Dancing. Dialect/Accent
Coaching. Drama School (over 18s). Improvisation. ISTD
Private Acting Classes. Singing. Stage School for Children
Vocal Coaching
Office: 21 Cotswold Road
Westcliff-on-Sea
Essex SS0 8AA
Website: www.sandrasinger.com
e-mail: sandrasingeruk@aol.com
Fax: 01702 339393                    Tel: 01702 331616

**SOCIETY OF TEACHERS OF SPEECH & DRAMA The**
The Registered Office:
73 Berry Hill Road, Mansfield
Notts NG18 4RU                       Tel: 01623 627636
Website: www.stsd.org.uk
e-mail: ann.k.jones@btinternet.com

**SPEAK EASILY**
142 Buckingham Palace Road
London SW1W 9TR                      Tel: 020-7717 9649
Website: www.speak-easily.com
e-mail: info@speak-easily.com

**SPEAKE Barbara STAGE SCHOOL**
East Acton Lane
London W3 7EG                        Tel/Fax: 020-8743 1306
e-mail: speakekids3@aol.com

**SPEED Anne-Marie Hon ARAM, MA (Voice Studies),
CSSD, ADVS, BA**
Accents. Auditions. Coaching. Vocal Technique - Speaking &
Singing. Vanguard Estill Practitioner
Website: www.thevoiceexplained.com
e-mail: anne-marie.speed@virgin.net   Mobile: 07957 272554

**SPIRITUAL PSYCHOLOGY OF ACTING The**
51 Church Road
London SE19 2TE                      Tel: 020-8653 7735
Website: www.spiritualpsychologyofacting.com
e-mail: info@spiritualpsychologyofacting.com

**SPONTANEITY SHOP The**
85-87 Bayham Street
London NW1 0AG                       Tel: 020-7788 4080
Website: www.the-spontaneity-shop.com
e-mail: info@the-spontaneity-shop.com

**STAGE2 YOUTH THEATRE**
12 Valentine Road
Kings Heath
Birmingham, West Midlands B14 7AN
Website: www.stage2.org
e-mail: liz.light@stage2.org
Mobile: 07961 018841                 Tel: 0121-444 6524

**STAGE 84 YORKSHIRE SCHOOL OF PERFORMING ARTS**
Evening & Weekend Classes & Summer Schools
Old Bell Chapel, Town Lane, Idle, West Yorks BD10 8PR
e-mail: valeriejackson@stage84.com
Mobile: 07785 244984                 Tel: 01274 569197

**STAGE CENTRAL THEATRE ARTS**
St John Fisher High School
Harrogate, North Yorkshire HG2 8PT
Website: www.stagecentral.co.uk
e-mail: darren@stagecentral.co.uk
Mobile: 07940 014448                 Tel: 01423 331478

**STAGECOACH TRAINING CENTRES FOR THE
PERFORMING ARTS**
The Courthouse, Elm Grove
Walton-on-Thames, Surrey KT12 1LZ
Website: www.stagecoach.co.uk
e-mail: mail@stagecoach.co.uk
Fax: 01932 222894                    Tel: 01932 254333

**STAGEFIGHT**
138 Wilden Lane, Stourport-on-Severn
Worcestershire DY13 9LP              Mobile: 07813 308672
Website: www.stagefight.co.uk
e-mail: raph@stagefight.co.uk

**STAR-BRIGHT DRAMA WORKSHOPS**
Royal Exchange, St Ann's Square
Manchester M2 7BR
Website: www.emmastafford.tv
e-mail: workshops@emmastafford.tv
Fax: 0161-833 4264                   Tel: 0161-833 4263

**S.T.A.R.S.**
(Stageworks Theatre Arts School)
32 Brookfield Road
London E9 5AH                        Tel: 020-8525 0111
Website: www.stageworkstraining.co.uk

**STE. CROIX Felicitas**
Former Assistant to Jack Waltzer. Audition Preparation
Meisner. Meyerhold. Chekhov. Sense Memories
London & Los Angeles                 Mobile: 07939 143721
e-mail: felicitasstecroix@yahoo.com

**STEPHENSON Sarah**
Accompanist. Vocal Coach
8A Edgington Road, Streatham, London SW16 5BS
e-mail: s.stephenson@ntlworld.com
Mobile: 07957 477642                 Tel: 020-8425 1225

**STEWART Carola LRAM NCSD LUD**
Audition Technique. CV Advice. Dialect/Accent Coaching
Elocution. Interview Technique. LAMDA Exams
Private Acting Classes. Public Speaking
13 Church Lane, East Finchley
London N2 8DX                        Tel: 020-8444 5994
e-mail: carolastewart@msn.com

## SCREEN ACTING
# STEFAN GRYFF (DGGB) (LLB)
*"I believe that for film and TV an actors quality is more important than their level of talent."*

**I will provide:**
- ⭘ Individual or group tuition in camera acting
- ⭘ Preparation of show reels for Casting Directors and Agents
- ⭘ Special training for beginners and artists unused to camera acting
- ⭘ Rehearsal & workshops for experienced actors currently employed in TV or film

### MARBLE ARCH STUDIO  TEL: 020 7723-8181

**STIRLING ACADEMY**
Contact: Glen Mortimer. Acting Workshops. Audition Techniques. Audition Training for Camera. Drama School (over 18s). Improvisation. Private Acting Classes. Showreels
Falcon Court, 490A Halliwell Road, Bolton, Lancs BL1 8AN
Website: www.stirlingacademy.co.uk
e-mail: admin@stirlingacademy.co.uk
Fax: 0844 4128689                    Tel: 0845 0176500

**STOCKTON RIVERSIDE COLLEGE**
Education & Training
Harvard Avenue, Thornaby
Stockton TS17 6FB                    Tel: 01642 865400
Website: www.stockton.ac.uk

**STOMP! THE SCHOOL OF PERFORMING ARTS**
Stage School for Children. Street Dance. Acting & Singing Classes (6-19 yrs). Evenings & Weekends. Mill Hill & Finchley Areas
c/o Suite 5, Lyndhurst House, 120 Bunns Lane, Mill Hill
London NW7 2AR                    Tel/Fax: 020-8959 5353
Website: www.stompschool.com
e-mail: stompschoolnw7@aol.com

**STREETON Jane**
Singing Teacher - RADA
24 Richmond Road, Leytonstone
London E11 4BA                    Tel: 020-8556 9297

**STUDIOS The**
Office:
47 Furze Platt Road
Maidenhead SL6 7NF                    Tel: 01628 777853
e-mail: julie.fox@virgin.net

**SUPPORT ACT SERVICES**
Contact: Ian McCracken. Services for Actors including Stage Combat Instruction
243A Lynmouth Avenue
Morden, Surrey SM4 4RX                    Tel: 0845 0940796
Website: www.supportact.co.uk
e-mail: info@supportact.co.uk

**SWINFIELD Rosemarie**
Make-Up Design & Training
Rosie's Make-Up Box, London          Mobile: 07976 965520
Website: www.rosiesmake-up.co.uk
e-mail: rosemarie@rosiesmake-up.co.uk

**TALENTED KIDS PERFORMING ARTS SCHOOL & AGENCY**
Contact: Maureen V. Ward. Acting Workshops. Audition Technique. Dance. Drama School (over 18s). Elocution Improvisation. Musical Theatre. Singing. Stage School for Children. Vocal Coaching
23 Burrow Manor, Calverstown
Kilcullen, Co. Kildare, Ireland
Website: www.talentedkidsireland.com
e-mail: talentedkids@hotmail.com
Mobile: 00 353 872480348          Tel/Fax: 00 353 45 485464

**TALENT TIME THEATRE SCHOOL**
Show Company
252 Mutton Lane, Potters Bar, Herts EN6 2AU
Website: www.talenttimetheatre.com
e-mail: talenttimeyouth@aol.com
Mobile: 07930 400647          Mobile: 07904 771980

**TEAM ACTIVATE**
Auditions & Presentation Skills
Activity-based Workshops
Website: www.teamactivate.com
e-mail: teamactivate@fastmail.fm          Mobile: 07837 712323

**THAT'S A WRAP PERFORMING ARTS SCHOOL**
Accompanist. Acting Workshops. Audition Technique Dialect & Accent Coaching. Elocution. Improvisation. Private Acting Classes. Singing. Stage School for Children
The Actors Studio, Pinewood Studios, Pinewood Road
Iver Heath
Bucks SL0 0NH                    Tel: 01753 650951
Website: www.actorsstudio.co.uk
e-mail: info@actorsstudio.co.uk
Unit 10, 21 Wren Street
London WC1X 0HF

**THEATRETRAIN**
Annual West End Productions Involving all Pupils (6-18 yrs)
PO Box 10343
Epping CM16 9DG                          Tel: 01992 577977
Website: www.theatretrain.co.uk
e-mail: admin@theatretrain.co.uk

**TIP TOE STAGE SCHOOL**
Dance, Drama, Singing & Performing Arts Part-time Training
For correspondence only:
45 Viola Close, South Ockendon
Essex RM15 6JF                           Mobile: 07914 899438
Website: www.tiptoestageschool1.piczo.com
e-mail: julieecarter@aol.com

**TLC COACHING**
Contact: Teresa Churcher. Acting & Audition Coach. Career
& Life Coach (MASC). Public Speaking. Talks to Graduating
Students
Herne Hill, London SE24                  Tel: 01908 524166
Website: www.teresachurcher.co.uk
e-mail: info@teresachurcher.co.uk

**TO BE OR NOT TO BE**
Contact: Anthony Barnett. LAMDA Exams. Showreels
Theatre/Audition Pieces. TV/Film Acting Technique
40 Gayton Road
King's Lynn, Norfolk PE30 4EL
Website: www.showreels.org.uk
e-mail: tony@tobeornottobe.org.uk
Mobile: 07958 996227                     Tel/Fax: 01553 776995

**TODD Paul**
Audition Technique. Improvisation. Vocal Coaching
3 Rosehart Mews
London W11 3JN                           Tel: 020-7229 9776
e-mail: paultodd@talk21.com

**TOMORROW'S TALENT THEATRE ARTS**
Theatre Training for students (6-18+ yrs)
Website: www.tomorrowstalent.co.uk
e-mail: info@tomorrowstalent.co.uk       Tel: 01202 526667

**TOP HAT STAGE SCHOOL**
Part-time Theatre Arts Training in Hertforshire (4-17 yrs)
Schools in Potters Bar
Welwyn, Stevenage
St Albans & Hertford
PO Box 860, St Albans
Herts AL1 9BR                            Tel/Fax: 01727 812666
Website: www.tophatstageschool.co.uk
e-mail: admin@tophatstageschool.co.uk

**TOP TV ACADEMY**
Presenter Training. Researcher Workshop
Elstree Film & TV Studios
Shenley Road, Herts WD6 1JG              Mobile: 07971 284958
Website: www.toptvacademy.co.uk
e-mail: liz@toptvacademy.co.uk

**TRING PARK SCHOOL FOR THE PERFORMING ARTS**
Dance, Drama & Musical Theatre Training School (8-19 yrs)
Tring Park, Tring, Herts HP23 5LX        Tel: 01442 824255
Website: www.tringpark.com
e-mail: info@tringpark.com

**TROLLOPE Ann**
Voice/Acting Coach
Harpsford, St. Peters Lane
Solihull B92 0DR                         Mobile: 07943 816276
e-mail: ann-t@uwclub.net

**TROTTER William BA, MA, PGDVS**
25 Thanet Lodge, Mapesbury Road
London NW2 4JA                           Tel/Fax: 020-8459 7594
Website: www.ukspeech.co.uk
e-mail: william.trotter@ukspeech.co.uk

**TUCKER John**
Accents. Audition/Role Preparation. Singing Lessons
Voice Coaching
503 Mountjoy House
Barbican, London EC2Y 8BP                Mobile: 07903 269409
Website: www.john-tucker.com
e-mail: mail@john-tucker.com

**TURNBALL Mark**
96 Knyngtoon Drive
Sunbury, Middlesex TW16 7RZ              Tel: 01932 770495
e-mail: sharon.turnball2@btopenworld.com

**TV ACTING CLASSES**
Contact: Elisabeth Charbonneau
e-mail: ejcharbonneau@aol.com            Mobile: 07885 621061

**TWICKENHAM THEATRE WORKSHOP FOR CHILDREN**
29 Campbell Road, Twickenham
Middlesex TW2 5BY                        Tel: 020-8898 5882

**UK DRAMA EDUCATION**
Contact: Esme Bates CSSD STSD. LAMDA Associate
Youth Theatre Director. TIE Facilitator
2 Barons Court, Western Elms Avenue
Reading, Berks RG30 2BP
e-mail: esmebates@btinternet.com
Mobile: 07941 700941                     Tel: 0118-958 9330

**URQUHART Moray**
Private Coaching for Auditions, Schools, Showbiz, etc
61 Parkview Court
London SW6 3LL                Tel: 020-7731 3604
e-mail: nmuphelps@yahoo.co.uk

**VALLÉ ACADEMY OF PERFORMING ARTS**
The Vallé Academy Studios
Wilton House, Delamare Road
Cheshunt, Herts EN8 9SG
Website: www.valleacademy.co.uk
e-mail: enquiries@valleacademy.co.uk
Fax: 01992 622868                Tel: 01992 622862

**VERRALL Charles**
19 Matilda Street
London N1 0LA                Tel: 020-7833 1971
Website: www.learntoact.co.uk
e-mail: info@charlesverrall.com

**VISUAL NOISE ARTS CENTRE & WHITE NOISE CASTING**
Performing Arts Centre
19 Preston Old Road
Blackpool, Lancs FY3 9PR
e-mail: info@visualnoiseuk.com                Tel: 01253 696990

**VIVIAN Michael**
Acting Workshops. Audition Technique. Improvisation
Private Acting Classes. Public Speaking
15 Meredyth Road, Barnes, London SW13 0DS
e-mail: vivcalling@aol.com
Mobile: 07958 903911                Tel: 020-8876 2073

**VOCAL CONFIDENCE**
Contact: Alix Longman. Audition Preparation. Presentation
Singing. Speech
Website: www.vocalconfidence.com
e-mail: alix@vocalconfidence.com                Mobile: 07958 450382

**VOICE & ACCENT COACHING**
7 Dodcott Grange Barns
Lodmore Lane, Burleydam
Cheshire SY13 4QB                Mobile: 07723 620728
Website: www.carohetherington.co.uk
e-mail: voice@carohetherington.co,uk

**VOICE MASTER**
Specialized Training for Voice-Overs & TV Presenters
88 Erskine Hill, London NW11 6HR                Tel: 020-8455 2211
Website: www.voicemaster.co.uk
e-mail: stevehudson@voicemaster.co.uk

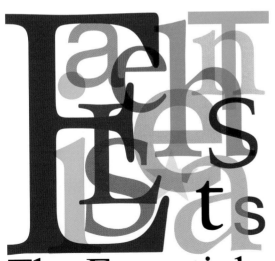 

**VOICES AND PERFORMANCE**
Contact: Julia Gaunt ALCM, TD-Musical Theatre
116 Nottingham Road
Selston
Nottinghamshire                    Mobile: 07712 624083
Website: www.joolsmusicbiz.com
e-mail: joolsmusicbiz@aol.com

**VOICES LONDON**
Vocal Coaching. Technique. Auditions
36 Wigmore Street
London W1U 2BP
Website: www.voicesvocal.co.uk
e-mail: info@voicesvocal.co.uk
Mobile: 07775 810572              Tel: 01279 655542

**VOICE TAPE SERVICES INTERNATIONAL**
Professional Management/Voice-Over Direction & CDs
80 Netherlands Road
New Barnet
Herts EN5 1BS
Website: www.vtsint.co.uk
e-mail: info@vtsint.co.uk
Fax: 020-8441 4828               Tel: 020-8440 4848

**VOXTRAINING Ltd**
Voice-Over Training & Demo CDs
20 Old Compton Street
London W1D 4TW                   Tel: 020-7434 4404
Website: www.voxtraining.com
e-mail: info@voxtraining.com

**WALLACE Elaine BA**
Voice
249 Goldhurst Terrace
London NW6 3EP                   Tel: 020-7625 4049
e-mail: im@voicebiz.biz

**WALSH Anne**
Accents. Dialect. Speech
45B Windsor Road
Willesden Green, London NW2 5DT
Mobile: 07932 440043             Tel: 020-8459 8071

**WALSH Genevieve**
Acting Tuition. Audition Coaching
37 Kelvedon House
Guildford Road, Stockwell
London SW8 2DN                   Tel: 020-7627 0024

**WALTZER Jack**
Professional Acting Workshops
5 Minetta Street Apt 2B
New York NY 10012
Website: www.jackwaltzer.com
e-mail: jackwaltzer@hotmail.com
Tel: 001 (212) 840-1234        Mobile: 07847 126318 (London)

**WEAKLIAM Brendan PGDip Mus Perf, BA Hons Mus Perf, DipABRSM, LCTS**
Acting Tuition. Audition Preparation. Singing
Vocal Coaching
23 Alders Close
Wanstead, London E11 3RZ        Mobile: 07724 558955
e-mail: brenweakliam@hotmail.com

**WEBB Bruce**
Audition Technique. Singing
Abbots Manor
Kirby Cane, Bungay
Suffolk NR35 2HP                Tel: 01508 518703

**WELBOURNE Jacqueline**
Circus Trainer, Choreographer, Consultant
c/o Circus Maniacs Agency
Office 8A, Britannia Road
The Kingswood Foundation
Kingswood
Bristol BS15 8DB
Website: www.circusmaniacs.com
e-mail: jackie@circusmaniacs.com
Mobile: 07977 247287            Tel/Fax: 0117-947 7042

**WEST END WORKSHOPS**
Arts Workshops. Audition Coaching
Website: www.westendworkshops.co.uk
e-mail: info@westworkshops.co.uk    Tel: 01202 526667

## MARK TURNBULL MA Theatre and Performance (Rose Bruford) Dip Acting (Webber Douglas Academy)

**ACTING & VOCAL COACHING:**
Method of Physical Action, Practical Aesthetics
Audition techniques, sight reading
Voice, Speech, RP, Singing technique for musical theatre, rock and pop

**ACTOR:**
(ex West End: Les Miserables, Rocky Horror Show)
Tutor London Drama Schools

**01932 770495 or 07742070122 or markturnbull14@btinternet.com**

---

**WESTMINSTER KINGSWAY COLLEGE**
Performing Arts
Regent's Park Centre
Longford Street, London NW1 3HB
Website: www.westking.ac.uk
e-mail: courseinfo@westking.ac.uk
Fax: 020-7391 6400      Tel: 0870 0609800

**WHITE Chris**
Head of Acting Rose Bruford, BSA, Italia Conti
e-mail: chrisjohnwhite40@aol.com    Mobile: 07971 234829

**WHITE Susan**
BA TEFL LGSM MA Voice Studies Distinction. Coach of
Spoken Voice & Personal Presence and Reflective
Practioner.
Central London      Tel: 020-7244 0402
Website: www.per-sona.com
e-mail: susan@per-sona.com

**WHITEHALL PERFORMING ARTS CENTRE**
Rayleigh Road
Leigh-on-Sea
Essex SS9 5UU      Tel: 01702 529290
e-mail: info@whitehallcollege.co.uk

**WHITWORTH Geoffrey LRAM, MA**
Piano Accompanist
789 Finchley Road
London NW11 8DP      Tel: 020-8458 4281

**WILDER Andrea**
23 Cambrian Drive
Colwyn Bay
Conwy LL28 4SL
Website: www.awagency.co.uk
e-mail: andrea@awagency.co.uk
Fax: 07092 249314      Mobile: 07919 202401

**WILSON Holly**
3 Worple Street, Mortlake
London SW14 8HE      Tel: 020-8878 0015

**WIMBUSH Martin Dip GSMD**
Audition Technique. Drama School (over 18s). Elocution
Public Speaking. Vocal Coaching
Flat 4, 289 Trinity Road
Wandsworth Common
London SW18 3SN      Tel: 020-8877 0086
Website: www.martinwimbush.com
e-mail: martinwimbush@btinternet.com

---

# PETER ZANDER

*Old Pro, will help you with your*
*acting, voice, speech, improvisation,*
*mime, audition, career.*

**Ring/email/text/write:**
**22 Romilly Street London W1D 5AG**
**00 44 (0) 20 7437 4767**
**UK Mobile: 00 44 (0) 79 20 12 55 09**
**peterzan.berlin@virgin.net**

**WINDSOR Judith Ph. D**
American Accents/Dialects
Woodbine, Victoria Road, Deal, Kent CT14 7AS
e-mail: sarah.upson@voicecoach.tv
Fax: 01782 728004                     Tel: 01782 827222

**WOOD Tessa Teach Cert AGSM, CSSD, PGDVS**
Voice Coach
43 Woodhurst Road, London W3 6SS     Tel: 020-8896 2659
e-mail: tessaroswood@aol.com

**WOODHOUSE Alan AGSM ADVS**
Acting Coach. Acting Workshops. Elocution. Private Acting
Classes. Public Speaking. Voice Coach
33 Burton Road, Kingston upon Thames
Surrey KT2 5TG                        Mobile: 07748 904227
Website: www.woodhousevoice.co.uk
e-mail: alanwoodhouse50@hotmail.com

**WOODHOUSE Nan (Playwright & Honorary F.L.A.M.)**
LGSM (Hons Medal) LLAM,
LLCM (TD), ALCM                       Mobile: 07812 921625

**WORTMAN Neville**
Voice Training & Speech Coach
11 Mandeville Place, London W1U 3AJ
Website: www.speakwell.co.uk
e-mail: wortman.speakwell@btinternet.com
Mobile: 07976 805976                  Tel: 020-8994 8886

**WYNN Madeleine**
Acting Workshops. Audition Technique. Directing & Acting
Coach. Drama School (over 18s). LAMDA Exams. Private
Acting Classes. Public Speaking
40 Barrie House
Hawksley Court
Albion Road, London N16 0TX          Tel: 01394 450265
e-mail: madeleine@onetel.com

**WYTHENSHAWE YOUTH THEATRE**
17 Kennett Road
Newall Green, Wythenshawe
Manchester M23 2XS                    Tel: 0161-493 9160
Website: www.wythenshaweyouththeatre.piczo.com
e-mail: wythyyouththeatre@btinternet.com

**YOUNG ACTORS THEATRE**
70-72 Barnsbury Road
London N1 0ES
Website: www.yati.org.uk
e-mail: info@yati.org.uk
Fax: 020-7833 9467                    Tel: 020-7278 2101

**YOUNG Sylvia THEATRE SCHOOL**
Acting Workshops. Audition Technique. Dancing
Improvisation. Singing. Stage School for Children. Summer
Schools. Vocal Coaching
Rossmore Road
Marylebone, London NW1 6NJ
Website: www.sylviayoungtheatreschool.co.uk
e-mail: info@sylviayoungtheatreschool.co.uk
Fax: 020-7723 1040                    Tel: 020-7402 0673

**YOUNG VICTORIA The**
Drama Training. Singing
Correspondence:
35 Thorpes Crescent
Skelmanthorpe
Huddersfield HD8 9DH                  Tel: 01484 866401
e-mail: tsaml@btconnect.com

**YOUNGSTAR TELEVISION & FILM ACTING SCHOOL**
Part-time Schools across the UK (8-20 yrs)
Head Office, 5 Union Castle House
Canute Road, Southampton SO14 3FJ
Website: www.youngstar.tv
e-mail: info@youngstar.tv
Fax: 023-8045 5816                    Tel: 023-8047 7717

**YOUNGSTARS THEATRE SCHOOL & AGENCY**
Contact: Coralyn Canfor-Dumas. Dancing. Drama
Part-time Children's Theatre School (2-16 yrs). Singing
Voice Overs
4 Haydon Dell
Bushey, Herts WD23 1DD
e-mail: coralyncd@gmail.com
Mobile: 07966 176756                  Tel: 020-8950 5782

**ZANDER Peter**
Acting on Stage, Screen & Opera. Breathing. German
Speech. Improvisation. Mime. Movement. Posture
Relaxation. Speech. Voice
22 Romilly Street
London W1D 5AG
e-mail: peterzan.berlin@virgin.net
Mobile: 07920 125509                  Tel: 020-7437 4767

### 24:7 THEATRE FESTIVAL
(26 July - 1 August 2010)
PO Box 247
Manchester M60 2ZT — Tel: 0845 4084101
Website: www.247theatrefestival.co.uk
e-mail: info@247theatrefestival.co.uk

### ACTOR EXPO TRADESHOW The
(June, Scotland/October, London 2010)
Suite 2
B106 Faircharm Trading Estate
8-12 Creekside, London SE8 3DX — Tel: 020-8320 2111
Website: www.actorexpo.co.uk
e-mail: info@actorexpo.co.uk

### ALDEBURGH FESTIVAL OF MUSIC AND THE ARTS
(11-27 June 2010)
Aldeburgh Music
Snape Maltings Concert Hall
Snape Bridge
Nr Saxmundham, Suffolk IP17 1SP
Website: www.aldeburgh.co.uk
e-mail: enquiries@aldeburgh.co.uk
Fax: 01728 687120
BO: 01728 687110 — Admin: 01728 687100

### BARBICAN INTERNATIONAL THEATRE EVENT (BITE)
(Year-Round Festival)
Barbican Theatre
Silk Street
London EC2Y 8DS
Website: www.barbican.org.uk
e-mail: theatre@barbican.org.uk
Fax: 020-7382 7377 — Tel: 020-7382 7372

### BATH INTERNATIONAL MUSIC FESTIVAL
(28 May - 12 June 2010)
Bath Festivals
Abbey Chambers
Kingston Buildings
Bath BA1 1NT
Website: www.bathmusicfest.org.uk
e-mail: info@bathfestivals.org.uk
Fax: 01225 445551
BO: 01225 463362 — Tel: 01225 462231

### BATH LITERATURE FESTIVAL
(27 February - 7 March 2010)
Bath Festivals
Abbey Chambers
Kingston Buildings, Bath BA1 1LY
Website: www.bathlitfest.org.uk
e-mail: info@bathfestivals.org.uk
Fax: 01225 445551
BO: 01225 463362 — Tel: 01225 462231

### BRIGHTON DOME & FESTIVAL Ltd
(1-23 May 2010)
12A Pavilion Buildings
Castle Square
Brighton BN1 1EE
Chief Executive: Andrew Comben
Website: www.brightonfestival.org
e-mail: info@brightonfestival.org
BO: 01273 709709 — Admin: 01273 700747

# infopage

## What do I need to know about the listed festivals?

The festivals listed in this section are all dedicated to creative and performing arts. Festivals are an opportunity for like-minded people to gather together to appreciate and learn from both well-established and new and up-and-coming acts and performers.

## Why should I get involved?

Being a spectator at a festival is a chance to see others in action and to see a variety of shows that are not necessarily mainstream. This is an opportunity to see talent in its rawest form, which is exactly why casting directors often attend drama festivals: they may spot someone who is just what they are looking for, who would otherwise have gone unnoticed in a pile of CVs.

Taking part in festivals will be something else to add to your CV and will help develop your skills. This not only means performance skills but social skills as well: you will meet hundreds of new faces with the same passion for their work as you, so this is a great opportunity to make friends and useful contacts in the industry.

## What do I need to bear in mind?

Before committing to performing at a festival, there are a number of issues to take into consideration. You will usually be unpaid and you will have to set aside enough money to fund the time spent rehearsing for and performing at the festival, not to mention travel, accommodation and food expenses. Not only that, you must also consider that you will be putting yourself out of the running for any paid work offered to you during this time. Make sure you let your agent know the dates you will be unavailable for work.

You may be required to not just perform but help out with any odd jobs involved with your show, such as setting up the stage and handing out flyers. If you are considering taking your own show to a festival, you will have to think well in advance about entrance fees, choosing and hiring a suitable venue, publicising your show, casting if necessary, finding technicians, buying or hiring props, costumes, sets, and so on. You must weigh up the financial outlays and potential headaches with the learning and networking opportunities that come with being involved in festivals.

## How can I get involved?

If you are a performer at a festival, casting professionals could be there looking for you! Let them know that you will be performing and where and when. Send them a covering letter giving details and enclose your CV and headshot if you have not already done so in previous correspondence. You could do the same with agents if you are currently searching for new representation.

Spotlight members performing at the Edinburgh Fringe Festival can access a number of free services including a free workshop, free one-on-one advice sessions, and casting seminars. Visit www.spotlight.com/edinburgh for more details and check for updated information each year during July and August.

Most festivals have websites which you can browse for further information on what to expect and how to get involved. Even if you simply go as a spectator to a festival, you will learn a lot and will have the opportunity to network. If you are performing in or organising a show, make sure you know exactly what you are letting yourself in for and make the most of your time there!

**David Jubb and David Micklem are Joint Artistic Directors of Battersea Arts Centre (BAC). The mission of BAC is "to invent the future of theatre" supporting the development of artists and their work in Battersea's Town Hall.**

Imagine it's Friday night. You're exploring your options. Pub...click...film...click...club...click...show...click. You can't decide. Maybe you opt for an evening in front of the telly with a takeaway...click. Be honest, on how many Friday nights do you do something you've never done before?...risk being exhilarated or bored to within an inch of your life?...experience something you might never again before you die? Now imagine another Friday night. This time you're in a strange city and your senses are alive to difference all around you. You're at a festival. The streets and parks and buildings are bursting with light, colour, aroma and live music. What do you choose to do? Dive in and take a risk? Or run home and switch on your computer?

When it comes to festivals, there's something in our bones that encourages us to take risks, to be more adventurous and to be playful. The diversity of the festival experience is staggering, matching the depth and breadth of human imagination. You could be cramming in eight shows a day at the Edinburgh Fringe, rolling down a Gloucestershire hill impersonating a piece of cheese or at Glastonbury with one hundred and fifty thousand other people up to your knees in mud. You could be dodging splashes of hot tar in Ottery St. Mary on bonfire night or coming over all literary at Hay-on-Wye. Just a boat journey away you could be chased through the streets of Pamplona by a bull, covered in tomatoes in Valencia or seeing shows from every corner of the globe in Avignon.

Even a single festival creates a rich variety of experience for audiences. Take last Friday. It was a warm evening at Latitude: one of the UK's most exciting new arts festivals. Grace Jones was playing on the main stage. In a tiny cabaret tent two performers from Uninvited Guests played love dedications for audience members in a tribute to the thing that makes the world go round. A few minutes walk away another tent was crammed with hundreds of people poised in silence hanging on every word of poet Polar Bear. At a bar created entirely from scrap wood there were people discussing the visit of climate minister Ed Milliband and the forthcoming Copenhagen summit. Everywhere people were talking, eating and dancing to live music. Despite the presence of the big names from the music industry, our hunger for the unknown, the unexpected and left field is insatiable. We crave things we didn't know we wanted: rich and diverse cultural experiences underscored by genuine ambition.

Not everything comes with a cast-iron guarantee of quality. At the Edinburgh Fringe for example, much of the work feels either desperate or derivative. Or both! Some shows are half-baked ideas, others misjudged. But sometimes you will find a gem in the most unexpected of places. An impromptu performance in the queue at the box office, a fifteen minute work-in-progress showing in the bar or a mini opera when maybe you thought you didn't even like opera.

At Battersea Arts Centre we talk a lot about the festival experience. Not just as part of the festivals we programme each year, but as a central component of any visit to our Town Hall home. We aim to engender audiences every evening with the same desire to take risks, to embark on adventures and encounter the unexpected. We are on a journey towards creating a programme that offers audiences a festival experience every night across our 70-room home. We are seeking the essence of those fantastic festival experiences with evenings chock-full of new ideas, experiments and unexpected journeys. Next Friday, move beyond the click, find a festival experience, hang out and see what happens. If you don't find something you're looking for, then come and talk to us about your ideas for a life-changing festival experience in Battersea.

Please visit www.bac.org.uk for further information.

SPOTLIGHT

www.spotlight.com

The industry's leading casting resource

Spotlight
7 Leicester Place
London WC2H 7RJ
t 020 7437 7631
e questions@spotlight.com

**BUXTON FESTIVAL**
(8-25 July 2010)
3 The Square, Buxton
Derbyshire SK17 6AZ
Website: www.buxtonfestival.co.uk
e-mail: info@buxtonfestival.co.uk
BO: 0845 1272190                    Admin: 01298 70395

**CHESTER SUMMER MUSIC FESTIVAL**
(1-9 July 2010)
Chester Festivals Ltd
Chester Railway Station
1st Floor, West Wing Offices
Station Road, Chester CH1 3NT
Contact: Kate Sawallisch
Website: www.chesterfestivals.co.uk/site/music
e-mail: k.sawallisch@chesterfestivals.co.uk
BO: 0845 2417868                    Admin: 01244 3405631

**CHICHESTER FESTIVITIES (Not Chichester Festival Theatre)**
(25 June - 11 July 2010)
Canon Gate House, South Street
Chichester, West Sussex PO19 1PU
Website: www.chifest.org.uk
e-mail: info@chifest.org.uk
Fax: 01243 528356                    Tel: 01243 785718

**DANCE UMBRELLA**
(6 October - 7 November 2010)
Annual Contemporary Dance Festival
20 Chancellors Street
London W6 9RN
Website: www.danceumbrella.co.uk
e-mail: mail@danceumbrella.co.uk
Fax: 020-8741 7902                    Tel: 020-8741 4040

**EDINBURGH FESTIVAL FRINGE**
(6 - 30 August 2010)
Festival Fringe Society Ltd
180 High Street, Edinburgh EH1 1QS
Website: www.edfringe.com
e-mail: admin@edfringe.com
Fax: 0131-226 0016
Tel: 0131-226 0013                    BO: 0131-226 0000

**EDINBURGH INTERNATIONAL FESTIVAL**
(13 August - 5 September 2010)
The Hub, Castlehill, Edinburgh EH1 2NE
Website: www.eif.co.uk
e-mail: eif@eif.co.uk
BO: 0131-473 2000                    Admin: 0131-473 2099

**HARROGATE INTERNATIONAL FESTIVAL**
(16 - 31 July 2010)
Raglan House, Raglan Street
Harrogate, North Yorkshire HG1 1LE
Website: www.harrogate-festival.org.uk
e-mail: info@harrogate-festival.org.uk
Fax: 01423 521264                    Tel: 01423 562303

**KING'S LYNN FESTIVAL**
(18 - 31 July 2010)
5 Thoresby College
Queen Street, King's Lynn, Norfolk PE30 1HX
Website: www.kingslynnfestival.org.uk
Fax: 01553 767688                    Tel: 01553 767557

## LIFT
(Annual Festival)
19-20 Great Sutton Street
London EC1V 0DR
Website: www.liftfestival.com
e-mail: info@liftfest.org.uk
Fax: 020-7490 3976                     Tel: 020-7490 3964

## LLANDOVERY THEATRE ARTS FESTIVAL
(Autumn 2010)
Llandovery Theatre
Stone Street, Llandovery
Carmarthenshire SA20 0DQ               Tel: 01550 720113
Director: Jacqueline Harrison
Website: www.llandoverytheatre.com

## LUDLOW FESTIVAL SOCIETY Ltd
(19 June - 3 July 2010)
Festival Office, Castle Square
Ludlow, Shropshire SY8 1AY
Website: www.ludlowfestival.co.uk
e-mail: admin@ludlowfestival.co.uk
Fax: 01584 877673                      Admin: 01584 875070

## RE VAMP - READY MADE STREET FESTIVALS
Ealing House, 33 Hanger Lane
London W5 3HJ                          Tel: 020-8997 3355
e-mail: verona.chard@vampevents.com

## TAIWAN CINEFEST LONDON
(17-21 March 2010)
c/o Arkwright Studios
1st Floor, Albion Mills
London E1 8DN                          Mobile: 07932 364665
Website: www.taiwancinefest.com
e-mail: s.flynn@taiwancinefest.com

## THE SUNDAY TIMES NATIONAL STUDENT DRAMA FESTIVAL
(27 March - 2 April 2010)
AH107 Aberdeen Centre
22-24 Highbury Grove
London N5 2DQ                          Tel: 020-7354 8070
Director: Holly Kendrick
Website: www.nsdf.org.uk
e-mail: admin@nsdf.org.uk

## ULSTER BANK BELFAST FESTIVAL AT QUEEN'S
(15-30 October 2010)
8 Fitzwilliam Street, Belfast BT9 6AW
Website: www.belfastfestival.com
e-mail: festivalservice@qub.ac.uk
Fax: 028-9097 1336                     Tel: 028-9097 1034

## ULSTER BANK DUBLIN THEATRE FESTIVAL
(24 September - 11 October 2010)
44 East Essex Street, Temple Bar
Dublin 2, Ireland
Contact: Jessica Hilliard
Website: www.dublintheatrefestival.com
e-mail: info@dublintheatrefestival.com
Fax: 00 353 1 6797709                  Tel: 00 353 1 6778439

## WINCHESTER HAT FAIR, FESTIVAL OF STREET THEATRE
(2-5 July 2010)
5A Jewry Street, Winchester
Hampshire SO23 8RZ                     Tel: 01962 849841
Website: www.hatfair.co.uk
e-mail: info@hatfair.co.uk

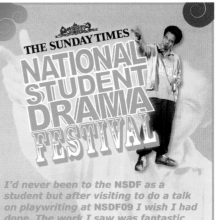

**ACTOR'S ONE-STOP SHOP The**
(Showreels for Performing Artists)
First Floor
Above The Gate Pub
Station Road, London N22 7SS    Tel: 020-8888 7006
Website: www.actorsonestopshop.com
e-mail: info@actorsonestopshop.com

**ALBANY The**
Douglas Way, London SE8 4AG
Website: www.thealbany.org.uk
e-mail: hires@thealbany.org.uk
Fax: 020-8469 2253    Tel: 020-8692 4446

**ANVIL POST PRODUCTION**
Contact: Mike Anscombe (Studio Manager)
Perivale Park
Horsenden Lane South
Perivale UB6 7RL    Tel: 020-8799 0555
Website: www.technicolor.com
e-mail: mike.anscombe@technicolor.com

**ARRI MEDIA**
3 Highbridge, Oxford Road
Uxbridge, Middlesex UB8 1LX
Website: www.arrimedia.com
e-mail: info@arrimedia.com
Fax: 01895 457101    Tel: 01895 457100

**ASCENT MEDIA Ltd**
(Post-Production Facilities)
Film House, 142 Wardour Street
London W1F 8DD
Website: www.ascentmedia.co.uk
Fax: 020-7878 7800    Tel: 020-7878 0000

**AXIS FILMS**
(Film Equipment Rental)
Shepperton Studios
Studios Road
Middlesex TW17 0QD
Website: www.axisfilms.co.uk
e-mail: info@axisfilms.co.uk
Fax: 01932 592246    Tel: 01932 592244

**CENTRAL FILM FACILITIES**
(Camera Tracking Specialists)
c/o Myddle Cottage, Plaish
Church Stretton
Shropshire SY6 7HX    Mobile: 07966 421877
Website: www.centralfilmfacilities.com

**CENTRELINE VIDEO Ltd**
138 Westwood Road, Tilehurst
Reading RG31 6LL    Tel: 0118-941 0033
Website: www.centrelinevideo.com

**CHANNEL 2020 Ltd**
2020 House, 26-28 Talbot Lane
Leicester LE1 4LR
Website: www.channel2020.co.uk
e-mail: info@channel2020.co.uk
Fax: 0116-222 1113    Tel: 0844 8402020

The Clerkenwell Workshops
27/31 Clerkenwell Close
London EC1R 0AT    Tel: 0844 8402020

**CINE TO VIDEO & FOREIGN TAPE CONVERSION & DUPLICATING**
(Peter J Snell Enterprises)
Amp House
Grove Road
Rochester, Kent ME2 4BX
e-mail: pjstv@blueyonder.co.uk
Fax: 01634 726000    Tel: 01634 723838

**CLICKS**
Media Studios, Grove Road
Rochester
Kent ME2 4BX
e-mail: info@clicksstudios.co.uk
Fax: 01634 726000    Tel: 01634 723838

**CLUB The**
35 Bedfordbury, Covent Garden
London WC2N 4DU
Website: www.theclub.co.uk
e-mail: kabir@theclub.co.uk
Fax: 020-7379 5210    Tel: 020-7759 7100

**CRYSTAL MEDIA**
28 Castle Street, Edinburgh EH2 3HT
Website: www.crystal-media.co.uk
e-mail: hello@crystal-media.co.uk
Fax: 0131-240 0989    Tel: 0131-240 0988

**DE LANE LEA**
(Film & TV Sound Dubbing & Editing Suite)
75 Dean Street
London W1D 3PU
Website: www.delanelea.com
e-mail: solutions@delanelea.com
Fax: 020-7432 3838    Tel: 020-7432 3800

**DENMAN PRODUCTIONS**
(3D Computer Animation, Film/Video CD Business Card Showreels)
60 Mallard Place
Strawberry Vale
Twickenham TW1 4SR    Tel: 020-8891 3461
Website: www.denman.co.uk
e-mail: info@denman.co.uk

**DIVERSE PRODUCTION Ltd**
(Pre & Post-Production)
6-12 Gorleston Street
London W14 8XS
Website: www.diverse.tv
e-mail: reception@diverse.tv
Fax: 020-7603 2148    Tel: 020-7603 4567

**EXECUTIVE AUDIO VISUAL**
(Showreels for Actors & TV Presenters, DVD Duplication)
80 York Street
London W1H 1QW    Tel: 020-7723 4488

**FARM DIGITAL POST PRODUCTION The**
27 Upper Mount Street
Dublin 2, Ireland
Website: www.thefarm.ie
e-mail: info@thefarm.ie
Fax: 00 353 1 676 8816    Tel: 00 353 1 676 8812

**FROME SILK MILL STUDIOS**
Westbrook House
33 Vicarage Street, Frome BA11 1PU
e-mail: damonmoore@macace.net
Mobile: 07811 440584    Tel: 01373 473246

**GREENPARK PRODUCTIONS Ltd**
(Film Archives)
Illand, Launceston, Cornwall PL15 7LS
Website: www.greenparkimages.co.uk
e-mail: info@greenparkimages.co.uk
Fax: 01566 782127    Tel: 01566 782107

**HARLEQUIN PRODUCTIONS**
Suite 5, Woodville Court
31 Sylvan Road, London SE19 2SG    Tel: 020-8653 2333
Website: www.harlequinproductions.co.uk
e-mail: neill@harlequinproductions.co.uk

**HARVEY HOUSE FILMS Ltd**
(Full Pre/Post Production, Showreels, Animation &
Graphics)
71 Southfield Road
London W4 1BB    Mobile: 07968 830536
Website: www.harveyhousefilms.co.uk
e-mail: chris@harveyhousefilms.co.uk

**HUNKY DORY PRODUCTIONS Ltd**
(Facilities & Crew, Also Editing: Non-Linear)
57 Alan Drive, Barnet
Herts EN5 2PW    Tel: 020-8440 0820
Website: www.hunkydory.tv

**MPC (THE MOVING PICTURE COMPANY)**
(Post-Production)
127 Wardour Street
London W1F 0NL
Website: www.moving-picture.com
e-mail: mailbox@moving-picture.com
Fax: 020-7287 5187    Tel: 020-7434 3100

**OCEAN OPTICS**
(Underwater Camera Sales & Operator Rental)
Archer Fields
Burnt Mills Industrial Estate
Basildon, Essex SS13 1DL
Website: www.oceanoptics.co.uk
e-mail: optics@oceanoptics.co.uk
Fax: 01268 523795    Tel: 01268 523786

**PANAVISION UK**
The Metropolitan Centre
Bristol Road, Greenford
Middlesex UB6 8GD
Website: www.panavision.co.uk
Fax: 020-8839 7300    Tel: 020-8839 7333

**PEDIGREE PUNKS**
(Shooting Crews, Editing, Compositing, Encoding, Mastering
to all formats)
49 Woolstone Road
Forest Hill, London SE23 2TR
Website: www.pedigree-punks.com
e-mail: video@pedigree-punks.com
Fax: 020-8291 5801    Tel: 020-8314 4580

**PLACE The**
Robin Howard Dance Theatre
17 Duke's Road, London WC1H 9PY
Website: www.theplace.org.uk
e-mail: info@theplace.org.uk
Fax: 020-7121 1142    Tel: 020-7121 1000

**PRO-LINK RADIO SYSTEMS Ltd**
(Radio Microphones & Communications)
5, B Block
Saxon Business Park
Hanbury Road, Bromsgrove
Worcestershire B60 4AD
Website: www.prolink-radio.com
e-mail: service@prolink-radio.com
Fax: 01527 577757    Tel: 01527 577788

**RICH VIDEO Ltd**
Houldsworth Mill
Houldsworth Street
Reddish, Stockport
Cheshire SK5 6DA    Tel: 0161-975 6207
Website: www.richvideo.co.uk
e-mail: sales@richvideo.co.uk

**SALON Ltd**
(Post-Production & Editing Equipment Hire)
12 Swainson Road
London W3 7XB    Tel: 020-8746 7611
Website: www.salonrentals.com
e-mail: hire@salonrentals.com

**SOUNDHOUSE The**
10th Floor
Astley House
Quay Street
Manchester M3 4AE
Website: www.thesoundhouse.tv
e-mail: mail@thesoundhouse.com
Fax: 0161-832 7266    Tel: 0161-832 7299

**VIDEO INN PRODUCTION**
(AV Equipment Hire)
Glebe Farm
Wooton Road, Quinton
Northampton NN7 2EE    Tel: 01604 864868
Website: www.videoinn.co.uk
e-mail: post@videoinn.co.uk

**VSI - VOICE & SCRIPT INTERNATIONAL**
(Dubbing, Subtitling, Voice Overs, Editing, DVD Encoding &
Authoring Facilities)
132 Cleveland Street, London W1T 6AB
Website: www.vsi.tv
e-mail: info@vsi.tv
Fax: 020-7692 7711    Tel: 020-7692 7700

**W6 STUDIO**
(Video Production, Editing Facilities & Photography)
359 Lillie Road
Fulham
London SW6 7PA
Website: www.w6studio.co.uk
Fax: 020-7381 5252    Tel: 020-7385 2272

**30 BIRD PRODUCTIONS**
17 Emery Street
Cambridge CB1 2AX     Mobile: 07970 960995
Website: www.30birdproductions.org
e-mail: info@30birdproductions.org

**303 PRODUCTIONS**
11 D'Arblay Street, London W1T 8DT
e-mail: lucy@303productions.co.uk
Fax: 020-7434 1955     Tel: 020-7494 0955

**ACADEMY**
16 West Central Street, London WC1A 1JJ
Website: www.academyfilms.com
e-mail: post@academyfilms.com
Fax: 020-7240 0355     Tel: 020-7395 4155

**ACTAEON FILMS Ltd**
*Contact: Daniel Cormack. By Post/e-mail. Comedy & Light
Entertainment. Documentaries. Drama. Feature Films
Films. Television*
50 Gracefield Gardens, London SW16 2ST
Website: www.actaeonfilms.com
e-mail: info@actaeonfilms.com
Fax: 0870 1347980     Tel: 020-8769 3339

**AGILE FILMS**
Unit 1, 68-72 Redchurch Street
London E2 7DD     Tel: 020-7000 2882
Website: www.agilefilms.com
e-mail: info@agilefilms.com

**ALGERNON Ltd**
24B Cleveleys Road, London E5 9JN
Website: www.algernonproductions.com
e-mail: info@algernonproductions.com
Fax: 0870 1388516     Mobile: 07092 805026

**AN ACQUIRED TASTE TV CORP**
51 Croham Road, South Croydon CR2 7HD
e-mail: cbennetttv@aol.com
Fax: 020-8686 5928     Tel: 020-8686 1188

**APTN**
The Interchange, Oval Road
Camden Lock, London NW1 7DZ
Fax: 020-7413 8312     Tel: 020-7482 7400

**ARIEL PRODUCTIONS Ltd**
46 Melcombe Regis Court, 59 Weymouth Street
London W1G 8NT     Tel/Fax: 020-7935 6636

**ARLINGTON PRODUCTIONS Ltd**
Cippenham Court, Cippenham Lane
Cippenham, Nr Slough, Berkshire SL1 5AU
Fax: 01753 691785     Tel: 01753 516767

**ASCENT 142**
Film House, 142 Wardour Street, London W1F 8DD
Website: www.ascentmedia.co.uk
Fax: 020-7878 7870     Tel: 020-7878 0000

**ASF PRODUCTIONS Ltd**
*Contact: Alan Spencer, Malcolm Bubb. Commercials.
Corporate Videos. Documentaries, Feature Films. Films*
38 Clunbury Court, Manor Street
Berkhamsted, Herts HP4 2FF
e-mail: info@asfproductions.co.uk
Fax: 01442 872536     Mobile: 07770 277637

**ASHFORD ENTERTAINMENT CORPORATION Ltd The**
*Contact: Frazer Ashford. By e-mail. Documentaries. Drama
Feature Films. Films. Television*
20 The Chase, Coulsdon
Surrey CR5 2EG     Tel: 0844 3576393
Website: www.ashford-entertainment.co.uk
e-mail: info@ashford-entertainment.co.uk

**ATTICUS TELEVISION Ltd**
5 Clare Lawn, London SW14 8BH
e-mail: attwiz@aol.com
Fax: 020-8878 3821     Tel: 020-8487 1173

**AVALON TELEVISION Ltd**
4A Exmoor Street, London W10 6BD
Fax: 020-7598 7313     Tel: 020-7598 8000

**BAILEY Catherine Ltd**
110 Gloucester Avenue, Primrose Hill
London NW1 8JA     Tel: 020-7483 3330
Website: www.cbltd.net

**BANANA PARK Ltd**
*Animation Production Company*
Banana Park, 6 Cranleigh Mews, London SW11 2QL
Website: www.bananapark.co.uk
e-mail: studio@bananapark.co.uk
Fax: 020-7738 1887     Tel: 020-7228 7136

**BARFORD PRODUCTIONS**
35 Bedfordbury, London WC2N 4DU
Website: www.barford.co.uk
e-mail: info@barford.co.uk
Fax: 020-7379 5210     Tel: 020-7240 4188

**BARRATT Michael**
9 Andrews Reach, Bourne End
Bucks SL8 5EA     Tel: 01628 530895
e-mail: michael@mbarratt.co.uk

**BBC WORLDWIDE Ltd**
Media Centre, Media Village
201 Wood Lane W12 7TQ     Tel: 020-8433 2000
Website: www.bbcworldwide.com

**BLACKBIRD PRODUCTIONS**
6 Molasses Row, Plantation Wharf
Battersea, London SW11 3UX     Tel: 020-7924 6440
e-mail: enquiries@blackbirdproductions.co.uk

**BLUE FISH MEDIA**
39 Ratby Close, Lower Earley
Reading RG6 4ER     Tel: 0118-975 0272
Website: www.bfmedia.co.uk
e-mail: ideas@bfmedia.co.uk

**BRUNSWICK FILMS Ltd**
*Formula One Motor Racing Archive*
Brunswick House, 26 Macroom Road
Maida Vale, London W9 3HY
Website: www.brunswickfilms.com
e-mail: info@brunswickfilms.com
Fax: 020-8960 4997     Tel: 020-8960 0066

**BRYANT WHITTLE Ltd**
49 Federation Road, Abbey Wood
London SE2 0JT     Tel: 020-8311 8752
Website: www.bryantwhittle.com
e-mail: administrator@bryantwhittle.com

**BUCKMARK PRODUCTIONS**
Commer House, Station Road
Tadcaster, North Yorkshire LS24 9JF
Website: www.buckmark.com
e-mail: info@buckmark.com
Fax: 01937 835901     Tel: 01937 835900

**BUENA VISTA PRODUCTIONS**
3 Queen Caroline Street, Hammersmith, London W6 9PE
Fax: 020-8222 2795     Tel: 020-8222 1000

**BURDER FILMS**
37 Braidley Road, Meyrick Park
Bournemouth BH2 6JY     Tel: 01202 295395
Website: www.johnburder.co.uk
e-mail: burderfilms@aol.com

**CALDERDALE TELEVISION**
Dean Clough, Halifax HX3 5AX   Tel: 01422 253100
e-mail: ctv@calderdaletv.co.uk

**CARDINAL BROADCAST**
Room 14, NP Building, Pinewood Studios
Iver Heath, Bucks SL0 0NH   Tel: 01753 639210

**CARNIVAL FILM & TELEVISION Ltd**
47 Marylebone Lane, London W1U 2NT
Website: www.carnivalfilms.co.uk
e-mail: info@carnivalfilms.co.uk
Fax: 020-7317 1380   Tel: 020-7317 1370

**CELTIC FILMS ENTERTAINMENT Ltd**
Lodge House, 69 Beaufort Street
London SW3 5AH
Website: www.celticfilms.co.uk
e-mail: info@celticfilms.co.uk
Fax: 020-7351 4139   Tel: 020-7351 0909

**CENTRAL OFFICE OF INFORMATION**
Television
Hercules House, Hercules Road, London SE1 7DU
Website: www.coi.gov.uk
e-mail: eileen.newton@coi.gsi.gov.uk
Fax: 020-7261 8776   Tel: 020-7261 8220

**CENTRE SCREEN PRODUCTIONS**
Eastgate, Castle Street
Castlefield, Manchester M3 4LZ
Website: www.centrescreen.co.uk
e-mail: info@centrescreen.co.uk
Fax: 0161-832 8934   Tel: 0161-832 7151

**CHANNEL 2020 Ltd**
2020 House, 26-28 Talbot Lane
Leicester LE1 4LR
Website: www.channel2020.co.uk
e-mail: info@channel2020.co.uk
Fax: 0116-222 1113   Tel: 0844 8402020

**CHANNEL TELEVISION PRODUCTION**
The Television Centre, La Pouquelaye
St Helier, Jersey JE1 3ZD
e-mail: production@channeltv.co.uk
Fax: 01534 816889   Tel: 01534 816816

**CHANNEL X Ltd**
4 Candover Street, London W1W 7DJ
e-mail: firstname.lastname@channelx.co.uk
Fax: 020-7580 8016   Tel: 08459 002940

**CHILDREN'S FILM & TELEVISION FOUNDATION Ltd**
e-mail: annahome@cftf.org.uk   Mobile: 07887 573479

**CINEMANX Ltd**
3rd Floor, 12 Great Portland Street
London W1W 8QN
Fax: 020-7636 5481   Tel: 020-7637 2612

**CLASSIC MEDIA**
Colet Court, 100 Hammersmith Road, London W6 7JP
e-mail: enquiries@classicmedia.tv
Fax: 020-8762 6299   Tel: 020-8762 6200

**CLASSIC MEDIA GROUP**
Shepperton Studios, Studios Road
Shepperton, Middlesex TW17 0QD
e-mail: lyn.beardsall@classic-media-group.com
Fax: 01932 592046   Tel: 01932 592016

**CLAW FILMS Ltd**
11-15 Betterton Street, London WC2H 9BP
Website: www.clawfilms.com
e-mail: info@clawfilms.com
Fax: 020-7470 8810   Tel: 020-7470 8809

**COLLINGWOOD O'HARE PRODUCTIONS Ltd**
10-14 Crown Street
Acton, London W3 8SB
e-mail: info@crownstreet.co.uk
Fax: 020-8993 9595   Tel: 020-8993 3666

**COMMERCIAL BREAKS**
Anglia House
Norwich NR1 3JG
Website: www.commercialbreaks.co.uk
e-mail: commercialbreaks@itv.com
Fax: 0844 8816790   Tel: 0844 8816789

**COMMUNICATOR Ltd**
Omnibus Business Centre
39-41 North Road, London N7 9DP   Tel: 020-7700 0777
e-mail: info@communicator.ltd.uk

**COMPLETE WORKS The**
The Old Truman Brewery
91 Brick Lane, London E1 6QL
Website: www.tcw.org.uk
e-mail: film@tcw.org.uk
Fax: 020-7247 7405   Tel: 020-7377 0280

**COMTEC Ltd**
Unit 19, Tait Road
Croydon, Surrey CR0 2DP
Website: www.comtecav.co.uk
e-mail: info@comtecav.co.uk
Fax: 020-8684 6947   Tel: 020-8684 6615

**COURTYARD PRODUCTIONS**
*TV Production Company*
Little Postlings Farmhouse
Four Elms, Kent TN8 6NA   Tel: 01732 700324
e-mail: courtyard@mac.com

**CPL PRODUCTIONS Ltd**
38 Long Acre, London WC2E 9JT
e-mail: info@cplproductions.co.uk
Fax: 020-7836 9633                    Tel: 020-7240 8101

**CREATIVE PARTNERSHIP The**
13 Bateman Street, London W1D 3AF
Website: www.creativepartnership.co.uk
Fax: 020-7437 1467                    Tel: 020-7439 7762

**CROFT TELEVISION**
Croft House, Progress Business Centre
Whittle Parkway, Slough, Berkshire SL1 6DQ
e-mail: nick@croft-tv.com
Fax: 01628 668791                    Tel: 01628 668735

**CROSSROADS FILMS**
2nd Floor, 83 Long Acre, London WC2E 9NG
Website: www.crossroadsfilms.co.uk
e-mail: info@crossroadsfilms.co.uk
Fax: 020-7395 4849                    Tel: 020-7395 4848

**CROWS NEST FILMS**
3 Wains Cottages, High Street
Buxton SK17 6EZ                      Tel: 01298 72250
Website: www.crowsnestfilms.com
e-mail: cjt@crowsnestfilms.com

**CUPSOGUE PICTURES**
40 Hayway, Irthlingborough
Wellingborough NN9 5QP               Tel: 020-3011 5244
Website: www.cupsoguepictures.com
e-mail: enquiries@cupsoguepictures.com

**CUTHBERT Tony PRODUCTIONS**
Suite 14, 7 Dials Court, 3 Shorts Gardens
London WC2H 9AT                      Tel: 020-7836 3432
Website: www.tonycuthbert.com
e-mail: tonycuthbert@btconnect.com

**DALTON FILMS Ltd**
127 Hamilton Terrace
London NW8 9QR                       Tel: 020-7328 6169
e-mail: dalton@robdal.demon.co.uk

**DARLOW SMITHSON PRODUCTIONS Ltd**
Highgate Studios
53-79 Highgate Road, London NW5 1TL
Website: www.darlowsmithson.com
e-mail: mail@darlowsmithson.com
Fax: 020-7482 7039                   Tel: 020-7482 7027

**DIALOGICS**
249-251 Kensal Road
London W10 5DB                       Tel: 020-8960 6069
e-mail: dialogue@dialogics.com

**DLT ENTERTAINMENT UK Ltd**
10 Bedford Square, London WC1B 3RA
Fax: 020-7636 4571                   Tel: 020-7631 1184

**DON PRODUCTIONS Ltd**
2 Soskett Mews, Shacklewell Lane, London E8 2BZ
Website: www.donproductions.com
e-mail: info@donproductions.com
Fax: 07092 273283                    Tel: 020-7254 0044

**DRAMATIS PERSONAE Ltd**
*Contact: Nathan Silver, Nicolas Kent*
19 Regency Street, London SW1P 4BY   Tel: 020-7834 9300
e-mail: ns@nathansilver.com

**DREAMING WILL INITIATIVE The**
PO Box 38155
London SE17 3XP                      Tel/Fax: 020-7793 9755
Website: www.lswproductions.co.uk
e-mail: londonswo@hotmail.com

**DVA**
8 Campbell Court, Bramley, Hampshire RG26 5EG
Website: www.dva.co.uk
e-mail: barrieg@dva.co.uk
Fax: 01256 882024                    Tel: 01256 882032

**ECOSSE FILMS Ltd**
Brigade House, 8 Parsons Green, London SW6 4TN
Website: www.ecossefilms.com
e-mail: info@ecossefilms.com
Fax: 020-7736 3436                   Tel: 020-7371 0290

**EDGE PICTURE COMPANY Ltd The**
7 Langley Street, London WC2H 9JA
Website: www.edgepicture.com
e-mail: ask.us@edgepicture.com
Fax: 020-7836 6949                   Tel: 020-7836 6262

**EFFINGEE PRODUCTIONS Ltd**
*Contact: Lesley Kiernan. By e-mail. Television*
13 Colquhoun Avenue
Hillington Park, Glasgow G52 4BN
Website: www.effingee.com
e-mail: info@effingee.com
Fax: 0141-882 5003                   Tel: 0141-443 9301

**ENDEMOL UK Plc**
(Including Endemol UK Productions, Initial, Brighter
Pictures & Victoria Real)
Shepherds Building Central
Charecroft Way, Shepherd's Bush
London W14 0EE
Fax: 0870 3331800                    Tel: 0870 3331700

**ENLIGHTENMENT INTERACTIVE**
East End House, 24 Ennerdale
Skelmersdale WN8 6AJ                 Tel: 01695 727555
Website: www.trainingmultimedia.co.uk

**EON PRODUCTIONS Ltd**
Eon House, 138 Piccadilly
London W1J 7NR
Fax: 020-7408 1236                   Tel: 020-7493 7953

**EXTRA DIGIT Ltd**
10 Wyndham Place
London W1H 2PU                       Mobile: 07956 859449
Website: www.extradigit.com
e-mail: edl@extradigit.com

**EYE FILM & TELEVISION**
Epic Studios, 112-114 Magdalen Street
Norwich NR3 1JD
Website: www.eyefilmandtv.co.uk
e-mail: production@eyefilmandtv.co.uk
Fax: 01603 762420                    Tel: 01603 762551

**FARNHAM FILM COMPANY The**
34 Burnt Hill Road, Lower Bourne, Farnham GU10 3LZ
Website: www.farnfilm.com
e-mail: info@farnfilm.com
Fax: 01252 725855                    Tel: 01252 710313

**FEELGOOD FICTION Ltd**
49 Goldhawk Road, London W12 8QP
Website: www.feelgoodfiction.co.uk
e-mail: feelgood@feelgoodfiction.co.uk
Fax: 020-8740 6177                   Tel: 020-8746 2535

**FERRIS ENTERTAINMENT FILMS**
London, Belfast & Cardiff
Number 8, 132 Charing Cross Road
London WC2H 0LA                      Tel: 0845 4724725
Website: www.ferrisentertainment.com
e-mail: info@ferrisentertainment.com

## Television & Film Production
## Studio and Production Offices for Hire
13 Colquhoun Avenue, Hillington Park, Glasgow, G52 4BN
Tel: 0141 443 9301   Fax: 0141 882 5003
**www.effingee.com**

Effingee Productions Ltd

**FESTIVAL FILM & TELEVISION Ltd**
Festival House
Tranquil Passage, London SE3 0BJ
Website: www.festivalfilm.com
e-mail: info@festivalfilm.com
Fax: 020-8297 1155                    Tel: 020-8297 9999

**FILM & GENERAL PRODUCTIONS Ltd**
4 Bradbrook House
Studio Place
London SW1X 8EL                      Tel: 020-7235 4495

**FILMS OF RECORD Ltd**
6 Angler Lane, Kentish Town
London NW5 3DG
Website: www.filmsofrecord.com
Fax: 020-7284 0626                    Tel: 020-7428 3100

**FIREFLY PRODUCTIONS**
Twin Oaks, Hale Purlieu, Fordingbridge SP6 2NN
Website: www.fireflyproductions.info
e-mail: theonlyfirefly@aol.com
Mobile: 07956 675276                 Tel: 01725 514462

**FIRST WRITES THEATRE COMPANY Ltd**
First Writes Radio Drama Company
Lime Kiln Cottage
High Starlings
Banham, Norfolk NR16 2BS
Website: www.first-writes.co.uk
e-mail: ellen@first-writes.co.uk
Fax: 01953 888974                    Tel: 01953 888525

**FLASHBACK TELEVISION Ltd**
58 Farringdon Road, London EC1R 3BP
Website: www.flashbacktelevision.com
e-mail: mailbox@flashbacktv.co.uk
Fax: 020-7253 8765                    Tel: 020-7253 8768

**FLEXSTONE PICTURES Ltd**
5 Cable Street, Formby
Liverpool, Merseyside L37 3LU        Tel: 0870 9192467
Website: www.fpukfilms.com
e-mail: films@fpukfilms.com

**FLYING DUCKS GROUP**
Duck HQ, The Old Mill
The Upper Hattons
Pendeford Hall Lane
Coven WV9 5BD                        Tel: 01902 842888
Website: www.flyingducks.biz
e-mail: enquiries@flyingducks.biz

**FOCUS PRODUCTIONS PUBLICATIONS**
58 Shelley Road
Stratford-upon-Avon
Warwickshire CV37 7JS
Website: www.focusproductions.co.uk
e-mail: maddern@focuspublishers.co.uk
Fax: 01789 294845                    Tel: 01789 298948

**FORSTATER Mark PRODUCTIONS**
11 Keslake Road
London NW6 6DJ            Tel/Fax: 020-8933 5475

**FREMANTLEMEDIA TALKBACKTHAMES**
1 Stephen Street, London W1T 1AL
Fax: 020-7691 6100                   Tel: 020-7691 6000

**FRICKER Ian (FILMS) Ltd**
146 Strand, London WC2R 1JD
e-mail: mail@ianfricker.com
Fax: 020-7836 3078                   Tel: 020-7836 3090

**FULMAR TELEVISION & FILM Ltd**
Pascoe House, 54 Bute Street
Cardiff Bay, Cardiff CF10 5AF
Fax: 029-2045 5111                   Tel: 029-2045 5000

**FUNNY FACE FILMS Ltd**
8A Warwick Road, Hampton Wick
Surrey KT1 4DW                       Mobile: 07506 000256
e-mail: stevendrew40@hotmail.com

**GALA PRODUCTIONS Ltd**
25 Stamford Brook Road
London W6 0XJ
Website: www.galaproductions.co.uk
e-mail: info@galaproductions.co.uk
Fax: 020-8741 2323                   Tel: 020-8741 4200

**GALLEON FILMS Ltd**
Greenwich Playhouse, Station Forecourt
189 Greenwich High Road
London SE10 8JA          Tel/Fax: 020-8310 7276
Website: www.galleonfilms.co.uk
e-mail: alice@galleontheatre.co.uk

**GAMMOND Stephen ASSOCIATES**
24 Telegraph Lane, Claygate
Surrey KT10 0DU                      Tel: 01372 460674

**GAY Noel TELEVISION Ltd**
Shepperton Studios, Studios Road
Shepperton, Middlesex TW17 0QD
e-mail: charles.armitage@virgin.net
Fax: 01932 592172                    Tel: 01932 592569

**GHA GROUP**
1 Great Chapel Street, London W1F 8FA
Website: www.ghagroup.co.uk
e-mail: sales@ghagroup.co.uk
Fax: 020-7437 5880                   Tel: 020-7439 8705

**GLASS PAGE Ltd The**
15 De Montfort Street
Leicester LE1 7GE
Fax: 0116-249 2188                   Tel: 0116-249 2199

**GOLDHAWK ESSENTIAL**
Radio Productions
20 Great Chapel Street, London W1F 8FW
e-mail: enquiries@goldhawk.eu
Fax: 020-7287 3597                   Tel: 020-7439 7113

**GRANT NAYLOR PRODUCTIONS Ltd**
Room 964, David Lean Buildings
Shepperton Studios, Studios Road
Shepperton, Middlesex TW17 0QD
Fax: 01932 592484                    Tel: 01932 592175

**GREAT GUNS Ltd**
43-45 Camden Road, London NW1 9LR
e-mail: reception@greatguns.com
Fax: 020-7692 4422     Tel: 020-7692 4444

**GUERILLA FILMS Ltd**
35 Thornbury Road, Isleworth
Middlesex TW7 4LQ
Website: www.guerilla-films.com
e-mail: david@guerilla-films.com
Fax: 020-8758 9364     Tel: 020-8758 1716

**HAMMERWOOD FILM PRODUCERS**
110 Trafalgar Road, Portslade
Sussex BN41 1GS
Website: www.filmangel.co.uk
e-mail: filmangels@freenetname.co.uk

**HANDS UP PRODUCTIONS Ltd**
7 Cavendish Vale, Sherwood
Nottingham NG5 4DS     Mobile: 07767 828451
Website: www.handsuppuppets.com
e-mail: marcus@handsuppuppets.com

**HARBOUR PICTURES**
21-25 St Annes Court, London W1F 0BJ
Website: www.harbourpictures.com
e-mail: info@harbourpictures.com
Fax: 020-7494 4885     Tel: 020-7287 6289

**HARTSWOOD FILMS**
Twickenham Studios, The Barons
St Margaret's, Twickenham
Middlesex TW1 2AW
Fax: 020-8607 8744     Tel: 020-8607 8736

**HAWK EYE FILMS**
82 Kenley Road, St Margarets
Twickenham TW1 1JU     Tel: 020-8241 7089

**HEAD Sally PRODUCTIONS**
Twickenham Film Studios, The Barons
St Margaret's, Twickenham, Middlesex TW1 2AW
e-mail: admin@shpl.demon.co.uk
Fax: 020-8607 8964     Tel: 020-8607 8730

**HEAVY ENTERTAINMENT Ltd**
111 Wardour Street, London W1F 0UH
Website: www.heavy-entertainment.com
e-mail: info@heavy-entertainment.com
Fax: 020-7494 1100     Tel: 020-7494 1000

**HIT ENTERTAINMENT Ltd**
5th Floor, Maple House
149 Tottenham Court Road
London W1T 7NF
Website: www.hitentertainment.com
e-mail: creative@hitentertainment.com
Fax: 020-7388 9321     Tel: 020-7554 2500

**HOLMES ASSOCIATES & OPEN ROAD FILMS**
The Studio, 37 Redington Road
London NW3 7QY     Tel: 020-7813 4333
e-mail: holmesassociates@blueyonder.co.uk

**HUNGRY MAN Ltd**
1-2 Herbal Hill, London EC1R 5EF
Website: www.hungryman.com
e-mail: ukreception@hungryman.com
Fax: 020-7239 4589     Tel: 020-7239 4550

**HUNKY DORY PRODUCTIONS Ltd**
57 Alan Drive, Barnet
Herts EN5 2PW     Mobile: 07973 655510
Website: www.hunkydory.tv
e-mail: adrian@hunkydory.tv

**HURRICANE FILMS Ltd**
17 Hope Street, Liverpool L1 9BQ
Website: www.hurricanefilms.net
e-mail: sol@hurricanefilms.co.uk
Fax: 0151-707 9149     Tel: 0151-707 9700

**IAMBIC MEDIA Ltd**
89 Whiteladies Road, Clifton, Bristol BS8 2NT
e-mail: admin@iambic.tv
Fax: 0117-923 8343     Tel: 0117-923 7222

**ICE PRODUCTIONS Ltd**
Warwick Corner, 42 Warwick Road
Kenilworth, Warwickshire CV8 1HE     Tel: 01926 864800
Website: www.ice-productions.com
e-mail: web@ice-productions.com

**ICON FILMS Ltd**
1-2 Fitzroy Terrace, Bristol BS6 6TF
Website: www.iconfilms.co.uk
Fax: 0117-973 3890     Tel: 0117-317 1717

**INFORMATION TRANSFER Ltd**
*Training Video Packages*
Burleigh House, 15 Newmarket Road
Cambridge CB5 8EG
Fax: 01223 310200     Tel: 01223 312227

**ISIS PRODUCTIONS Ltd**
387B King Street
London W6 9NJ     Tel: 020-8748 3042
Website: www.isis-productions.com

**JACKSON Brian FILMS Ltd**
39-41 Hanover Steps, St George's Fields
Albion Street, London W2 2YG
Website: www.brianjacksonfilms.com
Fax: 020-7262 5736     Tel: 020-7402 7543

**J. I. PRODUCTIONS**
90 Hainault Avenue, Giffard Park
Milton Keynes, Bucks MK14 5PE     Mobile: 07732 476409
Website: www.jasonimpey.co.uk
e-mail: jason.impey@freeuk.com

**JMS GROUP Ltd The**
Park Farm Studios, Hethersett
Norwich, Norfolk NR9 3DL
Website: www.jms-group.com
e-mail: info@jms-group.com
Fax: 01603 812255     Tel: 01603 811855

**KNOWLES Dave FILMS**
*Also Multimedia Interactive CD-Roms*
34 Ashleigh Close, Hythe SO45 3QP
Website: www.dkfilms.co.uk
e-mail: mail@dkfilms.co.uk
Fax: 023-8084 1600     Tel: 023-8084 2190

**LANDSEER PRODUCTIONS Ltd**
140 Royal College Street
London NW1 0TA     Tel: 020-7485 7333
Website: www.landseerfilms.com
e-mail: ken@landseerproductions.com

**LEFT EYE BLIND**
*Contact: Aurora Fearnley. By e-mail. Commercials. Drama*
*Music Videos. Television*
Studio 81, Kirkstall Road
Leeds LS3 1LH     Mobile: 07816 954492
Website: www.lefteyeblind.net
e-mail: lefteyeguys@gmail.com

**LIME PICTURES**
Campus Manor, Childwall, Abbey Road, Liverpool L16 0JP
Fax: 0151-722 6839     Tel: 0151-722 9122

**LITTLE KING COMMUNICATIONS**
The Studio, 2 Newport Road
Barnes, London SW13 9PE          Tel: 020-8741 7658

**LOOKING GLASS FILMS Ltd**
103 Brittany Point
Ethelred Estate
Kennington, London SE11 6UH     Tel/Fax: 020-7735 1363
e-mail: lookingglassfilm@aol.com

**LOOP COMMUNICATION AGENCY The**
Hanover House
Queen Charlotte Street, Bristol BS1 4EX
e-mail: mail@theloopagency.com
Fax: 0117-311 2041             Tel: 0117-311 2040

**MALLINSON TELEVISION PRODUCTIONS**
*Commercials*
29 Lynedoch Street
Glasgow G3 6EF
e-mail: shoot@mtp.co.uk
Fax: 0141-332 6190            Tel: 0141-332 0589

**MANIC TV & FILM PRODUCTIONS**
77 Brick Lane, Spitalfields
London E1 6QL                Tel: 020-3246 0088
Website: www.manictv.co.uk
e-mail: info@manic.tv

**MANSFIELD Mike TELEVISION Ltd/**
**MANSFIELD PRODUCTIONS Ltd**
The Gatehouse, 4 Ellerton Road
London SW20 0EP              Tel: 020-8947 6884
e-mail: mikemantv@aol.com

**MANS Johnny PRODUCTIONS Ltd**
PO Box 196, Hoddesdon, Herts EN10 7WG
Website: www.johnnymansproductions.co.uk
e-mail: johnnymansagent@aol.com
Fax: 01992 470516            Tel: 01992 470907

**MARTIN William PRODUCTIONS**
The Studio, Tubney Warren Barns
Tubney, Oxfordshire OX13 5QJ
Website: www.wmproductions.co.uk
e-mail: info@wmproductions.co.uk
Fax: 01865 390148            Tel: 01865 390258

**MAVERICK TELEVISION**
Progress Works
Heath Mill Lane, Birmingham B9 4AL
Website: www.mavericktv.co.uk
e-mail: mail@mavericktv.co.uk
Fax: 0121-771 1550           Tel: 0121-771 1812

**MAX MEDIA**
*Contact: Martin Franks. Drama. Comedy. Corporate*
The Lilacs
West End, Woodhurst
Huntingdon
Cambridge PE28 3BH
Website: www.therealmaxmedia.com
e-mail: martin@therealmaxmedia.com
Fax: 01487 825299            Tel: 01487 823608

**MBP TV**
Saucelands Barn, Coolham, Horsham, West Sussex RH13 8QG
Website: www.mbptv.com
e-mail: info@mbptv.com
Fax: 01403 741647            Tel: 01403 741620

**McINTYRE Phil ENTERTAINMENT**
2nd Floor, 35 Soho Square, London W1D 3QX
e-mail: info@mcintyre-ents.com
Fax: 020-7439 2280           Tel: 020-7439 2270

**MENTORN**
77 Fulham Palace Road, London W6 8JA
Fax: 020-7258 6888           Tel: 020-7258 6800

**MET FILM PRODUCTION**
Ealing Studios, Ealing Green, London W5 5EP
Website: www.metfilm.co.uk
e-mail: anetta@metfilm.co.uk
Fax: 020-8280 9111           Tel: 020-8280 9127

**MINAMON FILM**
*Contact: Min Clifford. By e-mail/Telephone*
*Corporate Videos. Documentaries. Drama. Films*
117 Downton Avenue
London SW2 3TX               Tel: 020-8674 3957
Website: www.minamonfilm.co.uk
e-mail: studio@minamonfilm.co.uk

**MINISTRY OF VIDEO**
*Contact: Chris, Andy. By e-mail/Telephone. Casting Videos*
*Children's Entertainment. Commercials. Corporate Videos*
*Live Events. Live Stage Productions. Music Videos*
*Showreels*
1533 High Road, Whetstone
London N20 9PP               Tel: 020-8369 5956
Website: www.ministryofvideo.co.uk
e-mail: info@ministryofvideo.co.uk

**MISTRAL FILMS Ltd**
31 Oval Road, London NW1 7EA
e-mail: info@mistralfilm.co.uk
Fax: 020-7284 0547           Tel: 020-7284 2300

**MOVE A MOUNTAIN PRODUCTIONS**
5 Ashchurch Park Villas
London W12 9SP               Tel: 020-8743 3017
Website: www.moveamountain.com
e-mail: mail@moveamountain.com

**MURPHY Patricia FILMS Ltd**
Lock Keepers Cottage, Lyme Street, London NW1 0SF
e-mail: office@patriciamurphy.co.uk
Fax: 020-7485 0555           Tel: 020-7267 0007

**NEAL STREET PRODUCTIONS Ltd**
1st Floor, 26-28 Neal Street, London WC2H 9QQ
e-mail: post@nealstreetproductions.com
Fax: 020-7240 7099           Tel: 020-7240 8890

**NEW MOON TELEVISION**
63 Poland Street, London W1F 7NY
Website: www.new-moon.co.uk
e-mail: production@new-moon.co.uk
Fax: 020-7479 7011           Tel: 020-7479 7010

**NEW PLANET FILMS Ltd**
PO Box 640, Pinner HA5 9JB          Tel: 020-8426 1090
Website: www.newplanetfilms.com
e-mail: info@newplanetfilms.com

**NEXUS PRODUCTIONS Ltd**
*Animation, Mixed Media, Live Action & Interactive*
*Production for Commercials, Broadcast*
*Pop Promos & Title Sequences*
113-114 Shoreditch High Street
London E1 6JN
Website: www.nexusproductions.com
e-mail: info@nexusproductions.com
Fax: 020-7749 7501          Tel: 020-7749 7500

**NFD PRODUCTIONS Ltd**
*Contact: By Post/e-mail/Telephone. Children's*
*Entertainment. Commercials. Corporate Videos. Drama*
*Films. Television. Short Films. Showreels*
PO Box 76, Leeds LS25 9AG
Website: www.nfdproductions.com
e-mail: info@nfdproductions.com
Mobile: 07966 473455          Tel/Fax: 01977 681949

**OMNI PRODUCTIONS Ltd**
14-16 Wilson Place, Bristol BS2 9HJ          Tel: 0117-954 7170
Website: www.omniproductions.co.uk
e-mail: info@omniproductions.co.uk

**ON COMMUNICATION/ONTV OXFORD & LONDON**
*Work across all Media in Business Communications*
11-12 St James's Square
London SW1Y 4LB          Tel: 020-3170 7235
Website: www.oncommunication.com
e-mail: info@oncommunication.com

5 East St Helen Street
Abingdon, Oxford OX14 5EG
Fax: 01235 530581          Tel: 01235 537400

**ON SCREEN PRODUCTIONS Ltd**
Ashbourne House
33 Bridge Street, Chepstow
Monmouthshire NP16 5GA
Website: www.onscreenproductions.com
e-mail: action@onscreenproductions.co.uk
Fax: 01291 636301          Tel: 01291 636300

**OPEN MIND PRODUCTIONS**
3 Waxhouse Gate
St Albans, Herts AL3 4EW          Tel: 0845 8909192
e-mail: production.manager@openmind.co.uk

**OPEN SHUTTER PRODUCTIONS Ltd**
*Contact: John Bruce. Corporate Videos. Documentaries*
*Drama. Television*
100 Kings Road
Windsor, Berkshire SL4 2AP
e-mail: jonthebruce@talktalk.net
Mobile: 07753 618875          Tel: 01753 841309

**ORIGINAL FILM & VIDEO PRODUCTIONS Ltd**
84 St Dionis Road
London SW6 4TU          Tel: 020-7731 0012
e-mail: original.films@btinternet.com

**OVC MEDIA Ltd**
*Contact: Eliot M. Cohen. By e-mail. Animation.*
*Documentaries. Drama. Feature Films. Films. Television*
88 Berkeley Court
Baker Street, London NW1 5ND
Website: www.ovcmedia.com
e-mail: eliot@ovcmedia.com
Fax: 020-7723 3064          Tel: 020-7402 9111

**PAPER MOON PRODUCTIONS**
Wychwood House
Burchetts Green Lane
Littlewick Green, Maidenhead
Berkshire SL6 3QW          Tel/Fax: 01628 829819
e-mail: insight@paper-moon.co.uk

**PARADINE David PRODUCTIONS Ltd**
The Penthouse, 346 Kensington High Street
London W14 8NS
e-mail: mail@paradine-productions.com
Fax: 020-7602 0411          Tel: 020-7371 3111

**PARK VILLAGE Ltd**
1 Park Village East, London NW1 7PX
e-mail: info@parkvillage.co.uk
Fax: 020-7388 3051          Tel: 020-7387 8077

**PASSION PICTURES Ltd**
*Animation. Documentary. Television*
3rd Floor, 33-34 Rathbone Place, London W1T 1JN
e-mail: info@passion-pictures.com
Fax: 020-7323 9030          Tel: 020-7323 9933

**PATHE PICTURES Ltd**
Kent House, 14-17 Market Place
Great Titchfield Street, London W1W 8AR
Website: www.pathe.co.uk
Fax: 020-7631 3568          Tel: 020-7323 5151

**PENSIVE PENGUIN PRODUCTIONS**
37 Oldstead Grove, Ferncrest
Bolton, Lancs BL3 4XW          Tel: 01204 848333
www.shadowhawkinternational.com/seeingsmokephotos.htm
e-mail: glenmortimer@btinternet.com

**PICTURE PALACE FILMS Ltd**
13 Egbert Street, London NW1 8LJ
Website: www.picturepalace.com
e-mail: info@picturepalace.com
Fax: 020-7586 9048          Tel: 020-7586 8763

**PIER PRODUCTIONS Ltd**
8 St Georges Place, Brighton BN1 4GB
e-mail: info@pierproductionsltd.co.uk
Fax: 01273 693658          Tel: 01273 691401

**PINBALL LONDON**
London N5 2JZ          Mobile: 07941 474721
Website: www.pinballonline.co.uk
e-mail: paula@pinballonline.co.uk

**PODCAST COMPANY The**
101 Wardour Street
London W1F 0UG          Mobile: 07956 468344
Website: www.thepodcastcompany.co.uk
e-mail: info@thepodcastcompany.co.uk

**POSITIVE IMAGE Ltd**
25 Victoria Street, Windsor
Berkshire SL4 1HE
Fax: 01753 830878          Tel: 01753 842248

**POTBOILER PRODUCTIONS Ltd**
9 Greek Street, London W1D 4DQ
e-mail: info@potboiler.co.uk
Fax: 020-7287 5228          Tel: 020-7734 7372

**POZZITIVE TELEVISION Ltd**
Paramount House
162-170 Wardour Street
London W1F 8AB
Website: www.pozzitive.co.uk
e-mail: pozzitive@pozzitive.co.uk
Fax: 020-7437 3130          Tel: 020-7734 3258

**PREACHY PRODUCTIONS**
67A Tavistock Avenue
London E17 6HR     Mobile: 07905 928543
e-mail: info@preachyfilms.com

**PRETTY CLEVER PICTURES**
Hurst Cottage, Old Buddington Lane
Hollist Lane, Eastbourne
Midhurts, West Sussex GU29 0QN
e-mail: pcpics@globalnet.co.uk
Mobile: 07836 616981     Tel: 01730 817899

**PRISM ENTERTAINMENT**
*Television Production & Website Design Company*
The Clockhouse
220 Latimer Road, London W10 6QY
Website: www.prismentertainment.co.uk
e-mail: info@prism-e.com
Fax: 020-8969 1012     Tel: 020-8969 1212

**PRODUCERS The**
8 Berners Mews, London W1T 3AW
Website: www.theproducersfilms.co.uk
e-mail: info@theproducersfilms.co.uk
Fax: 020-7636 4099     Tel: 020-7636 4226

**PRODUCTIONS & PROMOTIONS Ltd**
Apsley Mills Cottage, London Road
Hemel Hempstead, Herts HP3 9QU     Mobile: 07885 811757
Website: www.prodmotions.com
e-mail: reception@prodmotions.com

**PSA Ltd**
52 The Downs, Altrincham WA14 2QJ
e-mail: andy@psafilms.co.uk
Fax: 0161-924 0022     Tel: 0161-924 0011

**PVA MANAGEMENT Ltd**
County House, St Marys Street
Worcester WR1 1HB
e-mail: films@pva.co.uk
Fax: 01905 610709     Tel: 01905 616100

**QUADRILLION**
The Old Barn, Kings Lane
Cookham Dean, Berkshire SL6 9AY     Tel: 01628 487522
Website: www.quadrillion.tv
e-mail: enqs@quadrillion.tv

**READ Rodney**
45 Richmond Road, Twickenham, Middlesex TW1 3AW
Website: www.rodney-read.com
e-mail: rodney_read@blueyonder.co.uk
Fax: 020-8744 9603     Tel: 020-8891 2875

**RECORDED PICTURE COMPANY Ltd**
24 Hanway Street, London W1T 1UH
Fax: 020-7636 2261     Tel: 020-7636 2251

**RED KITE ANIMATION**
89 Giles Street, Edinburgh EH6 6BZ
Website: www.redkite-animation.com
e-mail: info@redkite-animation.com
Fax: 0131-553 6007     Tel: 0131-554 0060

**RED ROSE CHAIN**
1 Fore Hamlet
Ipswich IP3 8AA     Tel: 01473 288886
Website: www.redrosechain.co.uk
e-mail: info@redrosechain.co.uk

**REDWEATHER PRODUCTIONS**
Easton Business Centre
Felix Road, Bristol BS5 0HE
Website: www.redweather.co.uk
e-mail: info@redweather.co.uk
Fax: 0117-941 5851     Tel: 0117-941 5854

**REEL THING Ltd The**
20 The Chase, Coulsdon
Surrey CR5 2EG     Tel: 0844 3576393
Website: www.reelthing.tv
e-mail: info@reelthing.tv

**REPLAY Ltd**
*Contact: Danny Scollard. Animation. Corporate Videos*
*Documentaries. Drama. E-Learning. Live Events*
*Script Writing. Web Design*
Museum House, 25 Museum Street
London WC1A 1JT     Tel: 020-7637 0473
Website: www.replayfilms.co.uk
e-mail: sales@replayfilms.co.uk

**REUTERS Ltd**
The Thompson Reuters Building
South Collonade, Canary Wharf
London E14 5EP     Tel: 020-7250 1122

**REVERE ENTERTAINMENT**
22 Poland Street, London W1F 8QQ
Fax: 020-7292 7391     Tel: 020-7292 8370

**RIVERSIDE TV STUDIOS**
Riverside Studios
Crisp Road, London W6 9RL
Website: www.riversidetv.co.uk
e-mail: info@riversidetv.co.uk
Fax: 020-8237 1121     Tel: 020-8237 1123

**ROOKE Laurence PRODUCTIONS**
14 Aspinall House, 155 New Park Road
London SW2 4EY
Mobile: 07765 652058     Tel: 020-8674 3128

**RSA FILMS**
42-44 Beak Street, London W1F 9RH
Fax: 020-7734 4978     Tel: 020-7437 7426

**RUSSO Denis ASSOCIATES**
Animation
161 Clapham Road, London SW9 0PU
Fax: 020-7582 2725     Tel: 020-7582 9664

**SANDS FILMS**
(Squirrel Films Distribution Ltd)
Grice's Wharf
119 Rotherhithe Street, London SE16 4NF
Website: www.sandsfilms.co.uk
Fax: 020-7231 2119     Tel: 020-7231 2209

**SCALA PRODUCTIONS Ltd**
2nd Floor, 37 Foley Street
London W1W 7TN                     Tel: 020-7637 5720
e-mail: scalaprods@aol.com

**SCIMITAR FILMS Ltd**
219 Kensington High Street
London W8 6BD
e-mail: winner@ftech.co.uk
Fax: 020-7602 9217                 Tel: 020-7734 8385

**SCREEN FIRST Ltd**
The Studios, Funnells Farm
Down Street, Nutley
East Sussex TN22 3LG
e-mail: paul.madden@virgin.net     Tel: 01825 712034

**SEPTEMBER FILMS Ltd**
Glen House, 22 Glenthorne Road
Hammersmith, London W6 0NG
Fax: 020-8741 7214                 Tel: 020-8563 9393

**SEVEN STONES MEDIA Ltd**
The Old Butcher's Shop
St Briavels
Gloucestershire GL15 6TA
e-mail: info@sevenstonesmedia.com
Fax: 01594 530094                  Tel: 01594 530708

**SEVENTH ART PRODUCTIONS**
63 Ship Street, Brighton BN1 1AE
Website: www.seventh-art.com
e-mail: info@seventh-art.com
Fax: 01273 323777                  Tel: 01273 777678

**SHED PRODUCTIONS**
2 Holford Yard, London WC1X 9HD
Website: www.shedproductions.com
e-mail: shed@shedproductions.com
Fax: 020-7239 1011                 Tel: 020-7239 1010

**SHELL FILM & VIDEO UNIT**
Shell Centre
York Road, London SE1 7NA
Fax: 020-7934 7490                 Tel: 020-7934 3318

**SIGHTLINE**
*CD-Rom. Commercials. DVD. Video. Websites*
Dylan House, Town End Street
Godalming, Surrey GU7 1BQ
Website: www.sightline.co.uk
e-mail: action@sightline.co.uk
Fax: 01483 861516                  Tel: 01483 861555

**SILK SOUND**
*Commercials. Corporate Videos. Documentaries*
13 Berwick Street, London W1F 0PW
Website: www.silk.co.uk
e-mail: bookings@silk.co.uk
Fax: 020-7494 1748                 Tel: 020-7434 3461

**SILVER PRODUCTIONS Ltd**
Bridge Farm, Lower Road
Britford, Salisbury, Wiltshire SP5 4DY
Website: www.silver.co.uk
Fax: 01722 336227                  Tel: 01722 336221

**SINDIBAD FILMS Ltd**
Tower House
226 Cromwell Road, London SW5 0SW
Website: www.sindibad.co.uk
e-mail: info@sindibad.co.uk        Tel: 020-7370 9990

**SITCH LIVE**
*2D & 3D Design. Film & Video. Live Design
Exhibitions. Live Events*
G4 Harbour Yard, Chelsea Harbour
London SW10 0XD
Fax: 020-7352 7906                 Tel: 020-7544 7500

**SMITH & WATSON PRODUCTIONS**
The Gothic House
Fore Street
Totnes, Devon TQ9 5EH
Website: www.smithandwatson.com
e-mail: info@smithandwatson.com
Fax: 01803 864219                  Tel: 01803 863033

**SNEEZING TREE FILMS**
1st Floor
37 Great Portland Street
London W1W 8QH
Website: www.sneezingtree.com
e-mail: firstname@sneezingtree.com
Fax: 020-7580 1957                 Tel: 020-7436 8036

**SOLOMON THEATRE COMPANY**
Penny Black, High Street
Damerham, Fordingbridge
Hants SP6 3EU                      Tel/Fax: 01725 518760
Website: www.solomon-theatre.co.uk
e-mail: office@solomon-theatre.co.uk

**SONY PICTURES**
25 Golden Square, London W1F 9LU
Fax: 020-7533 1015                 Tel: 020-7533 1000

**SPACE CITY PRODUCTIONS**
79 Blythe Road, London W14 0HP
Website: www.spacecitystudios.co.uk
e-mail: info@spacecity.co.uk
Fax: 020-7371 4001                 Tel: 020-7371 4000

**SPEAKEASY PRODUCTIONS Ltd**
Wildwood House
Stanley, Perth PH1 4NH
Website: www.speak.co.uk
e-mail: info@speak.co.uk
Fax: 01738 828419                  Tel: 01738 828524

**SPECIFIC FILMS Ltd**
25 Rathbone Street
London W1T 1NQ
e-mail: info@specificfilms.com
Fax: 020-7636 6886                 Tel: 020-7580 7476

**SPIRAL PRODUCTIONS Ltd**
Aberdeen Studios
22 Highbury Grove
London N5 2EA
Fax: 020-7359 6123                 Tel: 020-7354 5492

**STAFFORD Jonathan PRODUCTIONS**
Shepperton Studios
Studios Road
Shepperton, Middlesex TW17 0QD
e-mail: jon@staffordproductions.com
Fax: 01932 592617                  Tel: 01932 562611

**STAMP PRODUCTIONS**
10 Margaret Street
London W1W 8RL                     Tel: 020-3178 2367
Website: www.stamp-productions.com
e-mail: ben@stamp-productions.co.uk

**STANDFAST FILMS**
The Studio, 14 College Road
Bromley, Kent BR1 3NS
Fax: 020-8313 0443     Tel: 020-8466 5580

**STANTON MEDIA**
6 Kendal Close, Aylesbury
Bucks HP21 7HR     Tel/Fax: 01296 489539
Website: www.stantonmedia.com
e-mail: info@stantonmedia.com

**STONE PRODUCTIONS CREATIVE Ltd**
Lakeside Studio, 62 Mill Street
St Osyth, Essex CO16 8EW
Website: www.stone-productions.co.uk
e-mail: kevin@stone-productions.co.uk
Fax: 01255 822160     Tel: 01255 822172

**STUDIO AKA**
*Animation*
30 Berwick Street, London W1F 8RH
Website: www.studioaka.co.uk
Fax: 020-7437 2309     Tel: 020-7434 3581

**TABARD PRODUCTIONS Ltd**
*Contact: John Herbert. By e-mail. Corporate Videos*
*Documentaries*
Adam House, 7-10 Adam Street
London WC2N 6AA
Website: www.tabardproductions.com
e-mail: johnherbert@tabard.co.uk
Fax: 020-7497 0850     Tel: 020-7497 0830

**TABLE TOP PRODUCTIONS**
*Contact: Ben Berry. By e-mail. Drama. Feature Films*
1 The Orchard, Bedford Park
Chiswick, London W4 1JZ
e-mail: berry@tabletopproductions.com
Tel/Fax: 020-8742 0507     Tel: 020-8994 1269

**TAKE 3 PRODUCTIONS Ltd**
72-73 Margaret Street, London W1W 8ST
Website: www.take3.co.uk
e-mail: mail@take3.co.uk
Fax: 020-7637 4678     Tel: 020-7637 2694

**TAKE FIVE PRODUCTIONS**
37 Beak Street, London W1F 9RZ
Website: www.takefivestudio.com
e-mail: info@takefivestudio.com
Fax: 020-7287 3035     Tel: 020-7287 2120

**TALKBACKTHAMES**
20-21 Newman Street, London W1T 1PG
Fax: 020-7861 8001     Tel: 020-7861 8000

**TALKING PICTURES**
Pinewood Studios, Pinewood Road
Iver Heath, Bucks SL0 0NH
Website: www.talkingpictures.co.uk
e-mail: info@talkingpictures.co.uk
Fax: 01865 890504     Tel: 01753 655744

**TANDEM CREATIVE**
*Contact: By e-mail. Corporate Videos. Documentaries*
Charleston House
13 High Street
Hemel Hempstead, Herts HP1 3AA
Website: www.tandemtv.com
e-mail: info@tandemtv.com
Fax: 01442 219250     Tel: 01442 261576

**THIN MAN FILMS**
9 Greek Street, London W1D 4DQ
e-mail: info@thinman.co.uk
Fax: 020-7287 5228     Tel: 020-7734 7372

**TIGER ASPECT PRODUCTIONS**
5 Soho Street
London W1D 3QA
Website: www.tigeraspect.co.uk
e-mail: general@tigeraspect.co.uk
Fax: 020-7434 1798     Tel: 020-7434 6700

**TKO COMMUNICATIONS Ltd**
(A Division of The Kruger Organisation Inc)
PO Box 130, Hove
Sussex BN3 6QU
e-mail: tkoinc@tkogroup.com
Fax: 01273 540969     Tel: 01273 550088

**TOP BANANA**
The Studio, Stourbridge
West Midlands DY9 0HA
Website: www.top-b.com
e-mail: info@top-b.com
Fax: 01562 700930     Tel: 01562 700404

**TOPICAL TELEVISION Ltd**
61 Devonshire Road
Southampton SO15 2GR
Fax: 023-8033 9835     Tel: 023-8071 2233

**TRAFALGAR 1 Ltd**
*Contact: Hasan Shah. By Post/e-mail. Documentaries*
*Feature Films. Film. Music Videos. Television*
153 Burnham Towers
Fellows Road, London NW3 3JN
e-mail: t1ltd@blueyonder.co.uk
Fax: 020-7483 0662     Tel: 020-7722 7789

**TVF**
375 City Road, London EC1V 1NB
Fax: 020-7833 2185     Tel: 020-7837 3000

**TV PRODUCTION PARTNERSHIP Ltd**
4 Fullerton Manor
Fullerton, Hants SP11 7LA     Tel: 01264 861440
Website: www.tvpp.tv
e-mail: dbj@tvpp.tv

**TWOFOUR**
*Corporate Videos. Documentaries. Live Events. Television*
TwoFour Studios
Estover, Plymouth PL6 7RG
Website: www.twofour.co.uk
e-mail: enq@twofour.co.uk
Fax: 01752 727450     Tel: 01752 727400

**TYBURN FILM PRODUCTIONS Ltd**
Cippenham Court
Cippenham Lane
Cippenham, Nr Slough
Berkshire SL1 5AU
Fax: 01753 691785     Tel: 01753 516767

**VECTOR PRODUCTIONS Ltd**
*Videos. Television*
Mill Fields, Higham Ferrers
Northants NN10 8ND
Website: www.vectortv.co.uk
e-mail: production@vectortv.co.uk
Tel: 0845 0535400     Tel: 020-7193 5655

**VERA**
165 Wardour Street, London W1F 8WW
e-mail: phoebe@vera.co.uk
Fax: 020-7292 1481     Tel: 020-7292 1480

**VERA MEDIA**
*Video Production & Training Company*
30-38 Dock Street, Leeds LS10 1JF
e-mail: vera@vera-media.co.uk
Fax: 0113-242 8739     Tel: 0113-242 8646

**VIDEO & FILM PRODUCTION**
Robin Hill, The Ridge
Lower Basildon, Reading, Berks
Website: www.videoandfilm.co.uk
e-mail: david.fisher@videoandfilm.co.uk
Mobile: 07836 544955     Tel: 0118-984 2488

**VIDEO ARTS**
6-7 St Cross Street, London EC1N 8UA
e-mail: info@videoarts.co.uk
Fax: 020-7400 4900     Tel: 020-7400 4800

**VIDEO ENTERPRISES**
*Contact: Maurice Fleisher. Corporate Videos
Documentaries. Live Events. Television*
12 Barbers Wood Road
High Wycombe, Bucks HP12 4EP
Website: www.videoenterprises.co.uk
e-mail: videoenterprises@ntlworld.com
Mobile: 07831 875216     Tel: 01494 534144

**VIDEOTEL PRODUCTIONS**
Corporate Videos
84 Newman Street, London W1T 3EU
Fax: 020-7299 1818     Tel: 020-7299 1800

**VILLAGE PRODUCTIONS**
4 Midas Business Centre
Wantz Road, Dagenham, Essex RM10 8PS
e-mail: village000@btclick.com
Fax: 020-8593 0198     Tel: 020-8984 0322

**VISION CONSULTING**
1 The Old Farmhouse
Mosley Hall Farm, Knutsford
Cheshire WA16 8RB     Tel: 01565 621912
e-mail: nell10_@hotmail.com

**VSI - VOICE & SCRIPT INTERNATIONAL**
132 Cleveland Street, London W1T 6AB    Tel: 020-7692 7700
Website: www.vsi.tv
e-mail: info@vsi.tv

**W3KTS Ltd**
10 Portland Street, York YO31 7EH    Tel: 01904 647822
e-mail: chris@w3kts.com

**W6 STUDIO**
359 Lillie Road, Fulham, London SW6 7PA
Website: www.w6studio.co.uk
Fax: 020-7381 5252     Tel: 020-7385 2272

**WALKING FORWARD Ltd**
Studio 6, Aberdeen Centre
22-24 Highbury Grove
London N5 2EA     Tel/Fax: 020-7359 5249
Website: www.walkingforward.co.uk
e-mail: info@walkingforward.co.uk

**WALKOVERS VIDEO**
Willow Cottage, Church Lane
Kington Langley, Chippenham
Wiltshire SN15 5NR     Tel: 01249 750428
e-mail: walkoversvideo@btinternet.com

**WALSH BROS Ltd**
*Contact: By e-mail. Animation. Documentaries. Drama
Feature Films. Films. Television*
29 Trafalgar Grove, Greenwich
London SE10 9TB     Tel/Fax: 020-8858 6870
Website: www.walshbros.co.uk
e-mail: info@walshbros.co.uk

**WALSH Steve PRODUCTIONS Ltd**
*Contact: Wendy Wolfcarius. Animation. Feature Films
Films. Television*
352 Banbury Road, Oxford OX2 7PP
Website: www.steve-walsh.com
e-mail: info@steve-walsh.com
Fax: 020-7580 6567     Tel: 020-7580 6553

**WARNER BROS PRODUCTIONS Ltd**
Warner Suite, Leavesden Studios
South Way, Leavesden, Herts WD25 7LT
Fax: 01923 685221     Tel: 01923 685222

**WARNER SISTERS PRODUCTIONS Ltd**
Ealing Studios, Ealing Green
London W5 5EP     Tel: 020-8567 6655
e-mail: ws@warnercini.com

**WEST DIGITAL**
*Broadcast Post-Production*
65 Goldhawk Road, London W12 8EG
Fax: 020-8743 2345     Tel: 020-8743 5100

**WHITEHALL FILMS**
10 Lower Common South, London SW15 1BP
e-mail: mwhitehall@msn.com
Fax: 020-8788 2340     Tel: 020-8785 3737

**WINNER Michael Ltd**
219 Kensington High Street, London W8 6BD
e-mail: winner@ftech.co.uk
Fax: 020-7602 9217     Tel: 020-7734 8385

**WORKING TITLE FILMS Ltd**
Oxford House, 76 Oxford Street, London W1D 1BS
Fax: 020-7307 3001     Tel: 020-7307 3000

**WORLD PRODUCTIONS & WORLD FILM SERVICES Ltd**
2nd Floor, 12-14 St Christopher's Place, London W1U 1NH
Website: www.world-productions.com
Fax: 020-3179 1801     Tel: 020-3179 1800

**WORLD WIDE PICTURES**
Unit 30, 10-50 Willow Street, London EC2A 4BH
Website: www.worldwidepictures.tv
e-mail: info@worldwidepictures.tv
Fax: 020-7613 6581     Tel: 020-7613 6580

**WORLD'S END TELEVISION**
16-18 Empress Place, London SW6 1TT
Website: www.worldsendproductions.com
e-mail: info@worldsendproductions.com
Fax: 020-7386 4901     Tel: 020-7386 4900

**WORTHWHILE MOVIE Ltd**
*Providing the services of Bruce Pittman as Film Director*
191 Logan Avenue, Toronto
Ontario, Canada M4M 2NT     Tel: 001 (416) 469-0459
e-mail: bruce.pittman@sympatico.ca

**XINGU FILMS**
12 Cleveland Row, London SW1A 1DH
Fax: 020-7451 0601     Tel: 020-7451 0600

**ZEPHYR FILMS Ltd**
33 Percy Street, London W1T 2DF
e-mail: info@zephyrfilms.co.uk
Fax: 020-7255 3777     Tel: 020-7255 3555

**BRIGHTON FILM SCHOOL**
Contact: Senior Lecturer Franz von Habsbury FBKS (BAFTA)
(Member of the National Association for Higher Education
in the Moving Image (NAHEMI) and the University Film and
Video Association (UFVA). Part-time Day or Evening Film
Directors' Courses includes Screen Writing,
Cinematography etc)
Website: www.brightonfilmschool.org.uk
e-mail: info@brightonfilmschool.org.uk    Tel: 01273 302166

**LEEDS METROPOLITAN UNIVERSITY**
(PG Dip/MA in Film & Moving Image Production, MA
Screenwriting (Fiction), and BA (Hons) in Film & Moving
Image Production and Cert HE/FdA in Film & Television
Production)
Northern Film School
Electric Press, 1 Millennium Square, Leeds LS2 3AD
Website: www.leedsmet.ac.uk
e-mail: filmenquiries@leedsmet.ac.uk
Fax: 0113-812 8080                Tel: 0113-812 0000

**LONDON COLLEGE OF COMMUNICATION**
(Film & Video Course)
Elephant & Castle, London SE1 6SB
Fax: 020-7514 6843                Tel: 020-7514 6569
e-mail: info@lcc.arts.ac.uk
Website: www.lcc.arts.ac.uk

**LONDON FILM ACADEMY**
The Old Church
52A Walham Grove, London SW6 1QR
Website: www.londonfilmacademy.com
e-mail: info@londonfilmacademy.com
Fax: 020-7381 6116                Tel: 020-7386 7711

**LONDON FILM SCHOOL The**
(2-year MA Course in Film Making, 1-year MA in
Screenwriting)
24 Shelton Street, London WC2H 9UB
Website: www.lfs.org.uk
e-mail: info@lfs.org.uk
Fax: 020-7497 3718                Tel: 020-7836 9642

**MIDDLESEX UNIVERSITY**
(School of Arts & Education)
Television Production
Trent Park Campus
Bramley Road
London N14 4YZ                Tel: 020-8411 5000
Website: www.mdx.ac.uk

**NATIONAL FILM AND TELEVISION SCHOOL**
(MA and Diploma Courses in the Key Filmmaking Disciplines
& Short Courses for Freelancers)
Beaconsfield Studios
Station Road
Beaconsfield
Bucks HP9 1LG
Website: www.nfts.co.uk
e-mail: info@nfts.co.uk
Fax: 01494 674042                Tel: 01494 731425

**UNIVERSITY FOR THE CREATIVE ARTS**
(3 & 4 year BA (Hons) Film Production, Digital Film & Screen
Arts, Animation, FdA Music Video Production)
Contact: Claire Barwell (Course Leader, Film)
Falkner Road
Farnham
Surrey GU9 7DS                Tel: 01252 722441
Website: www.ucreative.ac.uk
e-mail: enquiries@ucreative.ac.uk

**UNIVERSITY OF WESTMINSTER SCHOOL OF MEDIA ARTS
& DESIGN**
(Undergraduate courses in Film and Television Production
and Contemporary Media Practice. Postgraduate Courses
in Screenwriting and Producing, Film and Television;
Theory, Culture and Industry)
Admissions & Enquiries:
Watford Road
Northwick Park
Harrow
Middlesex HA1 3TP                Tel: 020-7911 5000
Website: www.wmin.ac.uk/filmschool

# infopage

## What are Film & Television Schools?

The schools listed in this section offer various courses to those who wish to become part of the behind-camera world of the entertainment industry. These courses include filmmaking, producing, screenwriting and animation, to name a few. Students taking these courses usually have to produce a number of short films in order to graduate. The following advice has been divided into two sections: for potential students and for actors.

## Advice For Filmmakers/Writers:

### Why should I take a course?

The schools listed here offer courses which enable a budding filmmaker or script writer to develop their skills with practical training. These courses are designed to prepare you for a career in a competitive industry. They also provide you with an opportunity to begin networking and making contacts with industry professionals.

### How should I use these listings?

Research a number of schools carefully before applying to any courses. Have a look at the websites of the schools listed first to get an idea of the types of courses on offer, what is expected from students, and the individual values of each school. Request a prospectus from the school if they do not have full details online. Word of mouth recommendations are invaluable if you know anyone who has attended or taught at a school. You need to decide what type of course suits you - don't just sign up for the first one you read about. See what is available and give yourself time to think about the various options.

## Advice For Actors:

### Why should I get involved?

Student films can offer new performers the chance to develop skills and experience in front of a camera, learning scripts, working with other actors and working with crew members. Making new contacts and learning how to get on with those you are working with, whether in front of or behind camera, is a vital part of getting along in the acting community.

In addition, you are likely to receive a certain amount of exposure from the film. The student filmmaker may show it to teachers, other students, other actors, and most importantly directors when applying for jobs, and you would normally be given your own copy of the film which you can show to agents or casting directors if requested, or use a clip of it in your showreel (see below).

For more experienced actors, working on a student film can offer the opportunity to hone existing skills and keep involved within the industry. It can also be useful to observe new actors and keep up-to-date with new training ideas and techniques.

### How do I get involved?

It may be helpful to see if the schools' websites have any advice for actors interested in being considered for parts in student films and suggesting how they should make contact. If there is no advice of this kind, it would be worth either phoning or e-mailing to ask if the school or its students would consider actors previously unknown to them. If this is the case, ask who CVs and headshots should be sent to, and whether they would like to see a showreel or voicereel (for animation courses).

If you are asked to play a role in a student film, make sure you are not going to a student's home and that someone knows where you are going and when.

### Should I use a clip of a student film on my showreel?

Casting directors would generally prefer to see some form of showreel than none at all. If you do not have anything else you can show that has been professionally broadcast, or do not have the money to get a showreel made from scratch, then a student film is an acceptable alternative. See the 'Promotional Services' section for more information on showreels.

### Where can I find more information?

Students and actors may want to visit Shooting People's website www.shootingpeople.org for further advice and daily e-mail bulletins of student / short film and TV castings. Filmmakers can upload their films to the site for others to view.

# Film London

Supports over 1,000 film, TV and advertising projects every year. Make us your first point of contact for filming in the capital.

www.filmlondon.org.uk

**3 MILLS STUDIOS**
Three Mill Lane, London E3 3DU
Website: www.3mills.com
e-mail: info@3mills.com
Fax: 08715 944028        Tel: 020-7363 3336

**ARDMORE STUDIOS Ltd**
Herbert Road, Bray. Co. Wicklow, Ireland
Website: www.ardmore.ie
e-mail: film@ardmore.ie
Fax: 00 353 1 2861894        Tel: 00 353 1 2862971

**BBC TELEVISION**
Television Centre, Wood Lane
Shepherds Bush, London W12 7RJ      Tel: 020-8743 8000

**BRAY FILM STUDIOS**
Down Place, Water Oakley, Windsor, Berkshire SL4 5UG
Fax: 01628 623000        Tel: 01628 622111

**BRIGHTON FILM STUDIOS Ltd**
The Brighton Forum, 95 Ditchling Road
Brighton BN1 4ST        Tel: 01273 302166
Website: www.brightonfilmstudios.com
e-mail: franz@brightonfilmstudios.com

**CAPITAL STUDIOS**
Wandsworth Plain, London SW18 1ET
Website: www.capitalstudios.com
e-mail: info@capitalstudios.com
Fax: 020-8877 0234        Mobile: 07974 921018

**EALING STUDIOS**
Ealing Green, London W5 5EP
Website: www.ealingstudios.com
e-mail: info@ealingstudios.com
Fax: 020-8758 8658        Tel: 020-8567 6655

**ELSTREE STUDIOS**
Shenley Road, Borehamwood, Herts WD6 1JG
Website: www.elstreestudios.co.uk
e-mail: info@elstreestudios.co.uk
Fax: 020-8905 1135        Tel: 020-8953 1600

**LONDON STUDIOS The**
London Television Centre, Upper Ground, London SE1 9LT
Website: www.londonstudios.co.uk
e-mail: sales@londonstudios.co.uk
Fax: 020-7157 5757        Tel: 020-7157 5555

**PINEWOOD STUDIOS**
Pinewood Road, Iver Heath
Buckinghamshire SL0 0NH      Tel: 01753 651700
Website: www.pinewoodgroup.com

**REUTERS TELEVISION**
The Reuters Thompson Building
South Colonnade, Canary Wharf
London E14 5EP        Tel: 020-7250 1122

**RIVERSIDE STUDIOS**
Crisp Road, London W6 9RL
Website: www.riversidestudios.co.uk
e-mail: info@riversidestudios.co.uk
Fax: 020-8237 1001        Tel: 020-8237 1000

**SHEPPERTON STUDIOS**
Studios Road, Shepperton, Middlesex TW17 0QD
Website: www.pinewoodgroup.com
Fax: 01932 568989        Tel: 01932 562611

**SQUIRREL & SANDS FILMS/ROTHERHITHE STUDIOS**
119 Rotherhithe Street, London SE16 4NF
Website: www.sandsfilms.co.uk
e-mail: info@sandsfilms.co.uk
Fax: 020-7231 2119        Tel: 020-7231 2209

**TEDDINGTON STUDIOS**
Broom Road, Teddington, Middlesex TW11 9NT
Website: www.pinewoodgroup.com
Fax: 020-8943 4050        Tel: 020-8977 3252

**TWICKENHAM FILM STUDIOS Ltd**
The Barons, St Margaret's, Twickenham, Middlesex TW1 2AW
Website: www.twickenhamstudios.com
e-mail: enquiries@twickenhamstudios.com
Fax: 020-8607 8889        Tel: 020-8607 8888

# ABERDEEN
Milne, Mrs A
5 Sunnyside Walk
Aberdeen AB24 3NZ      Tel: 01224 638951

Woods, Pat
62 Union Grove
Aberdeen AB10 6RX      Tel: 01224 586324

# AYR
Dunn, Sheila
The Dunn-Thing Guest House
13 Park Circus
Ayr KA7 2DJ
Mobile: 07887 928685      Tel: 01292 284531

# BATH
Hutton, Mrs Celia
Bath Holiday Homes
Terranova, Shepherds Walk
Bath BA2 5QT      Tel: 01225 830830
Website: www.bathholidayhomes.co.uk
e-mail: bhh@virgin.net

Tapley, Jane
Camden Lodgings
3 Upper Camden Place, Bath BA1 5HX
e-mail: peter@tapley.ws      Tel: 01225 446561

# BELFAST
McCully, Mrs S
28 Eglantine Avenue
Belfast BT9 6DX
e-mail: shealaghmccully@hotmail.com
Mobile: 07985 947673      Tel: 028-9068 2031

# BIRMINGHAM
Hurst, Mr P
41 King Edward Road
Mosley, Birmingham B13 8HR      Tel: 0121-449 8220
e-mail: phurst1com@aol.com

Mountain, Marlene P
268 Monument Road
Edgbaston
Birmingham B16 8XF      Tel: 0121-454 5900

Wilson, Mrs
17 Yew Tree Road
Edgbaston, Birmingham B15 2LX      Tel: 0121-440 5182

# BLACKPOOL
Lees, Jean
Ascot Flats, 6 Hull Road
Central Blackpool FY1 4QB      Tel: 01253 621059

Somerset Apartments
22 Barton Avenue
Blackpool FY1 6AP      Tel/Fax: 01253 346743
Website: www.blackpool-somerset-apartments.co.uk

Waller, Veronica & Bob
The Brooklyn Hotel
7 Wilton Parade
Blackpool FY1 2HE      Tel: 01253 627003
Website: enquiries@brooklynhotel.co.uk

# BOLTON
Duckworth, Paul
19 Burnham Avenue
Bolton BL1 6BD
Mobile: 07762 545129      Tel: 01204 495732

White, Mrs M
20 Heywood Gardens
Great Lever
Bolton BL3 6RB      Tel: 01204 531589

G

## Good Digs Guide
Compiled By Janice Cramer and David Banks

This is a list of digs recommended by those who have used them.

To keep the list accurate please send recommendations for inclusion to

GOOD DIGS GUIDE
Spotlight
7 Leicester Place
London WC2H 7RJ

If you are a digs owner wishing to be listed, your application must contain a recommendation from a performer who has stayed in your accommodation.

[CONTACTS 2010]

**BOURNEMOUTH**
Sitton, Martin
Flat 2
9 St Winifreds Road
Meyrick Park
Bournemouth BH2 6NX     Tel: 01202 293318

**BRADFORD**
Smith, Theresa
8 Moorhead Terrace
Shipley
Bradford BD18 4LA     Tel: 01274 778568
e-mail: theresaannesmith@hotmail.com

**BRIGHTON**
Benedict, Peter
19 Madeira Place
Brighton BN2 1TN
e-mail: peterdbenedict@hotmail.com
Mobile: 07752 810122     Tel: 020-7703 4104

Chance, Michael
6 Railway Street
Brighton BN1 3PF
e-mail: mchance@lineone.net
Mobile: 07876 223359     Tel: 01273 779585

Cleveland, Carol
13 Belgrave Street
Brighton BN2 9NS
e-mail: info@carolcleveland.com
Mobile: 07973 363939     Tel: 01273 602607

Dyson, Kate
39 Arundel Street
Kemptown BN2 5TH
e-mail: kate.dyson@talktalk.net
Mobile: 07812 949875     Tel: 01273 607490

Stanfield-Miller, Ms
Flat 1
154 Freshfield Road
Brighton BN2 9YD
Website: www.airbnb.com/rooms/6000
e-mail: rowanstanfield@yahoo.com
Tel: 01273 696080     Mobile: 07747 725331

Taudevin, Noreen
19 Temple Street
Brighton
Sussex BN1 3BH     Tel: 01273 530047
e-mail: noreenmt@googlemail.com

**BRISTOL**
Ham, Phil & Jacqui
78 Stackpool Road
Bristol BS3 1NN     Tel: 0117-902 5213

Walsh, Karen
The Courtyard
8 Royal York Crescent
Clifton
Bristol BS8 4JZ     Mobile: 07966 282398

**BURY ST EDMUNDS**
Bird, Mrs S
30 Crown Street
Bury St Edmunds
Suffolk IP33 1QU     Tel: 01284 754492

Harrington-Spier, Sue
39 Well Street
Bury St Edmunds
Suffolk IP33 1EQ     Tel: 01284 768986
e-mail: sue.harringtonspier@googlemail.com

**BUXTON**
Kitchen, Mrs G
Silverlands Holiday Apartments
c/o 156 Brown Edge Road
Buxton
Derbyshire SK17 7AA
e-mail: swiftcaterequip2@aol.com
Tel: 01298 26555     Tel: 01298 79381

**CAMBRIDGE**
Dunn, Anne
The Dovecot
1 St Catherine's Hall
Coton, Cambridge CB23 7EU     Tel: 01954 210291

**CANTERBURY**
Ellen, Nikki
Crockshard Farmhouse
Wingham, Canterbury CT3 1NY     Tel: 01227 720464
Website: www.crockshard.com
e-mail: crockshard_bnb@yahoo.com

**CARDIFF**
Blade, Mrs Anne
25 Romilly Road
Canton, Cardiff CF5 1FH     Tel: 029-2022 5860

Kennedy, Rosie
Duffryn Mawr Cottages
Pendoylan
Vale of Glamorgan     Mobile: 07746 946118
Website: www.duffrynmawrcottages.co.uk
e-mail: rosie.kennedy@ukonline.co.uk

Lewis, Nigel
66 Donald Street
Roath
Cardiff CF24 4TR
e-mail: nigel.lewis66@btinternet.com
Mobile: 07813 069822     Tel: 029-2049 4008

Nelmes, Michael
12 Darran Street
Cathays
Cardiff
South Glamorgan CF24 4JF     Tel: 029-2034 2166

**CHESTERFIELD**
Cook, Linda & Chris
27 Tennyson Avenue
Chesterfield
Derbyshire
e-mail: chris_cook@talk21.com
Mobile: 07929 850561     Tel: 01246 202631

Foston, Mr & Mrs
Anis Louise Guest House
34 Clarence Road
Chesterfield S40 1LN     Tel: 01246 235412
Website: www.anislouiseguesthouse.co.uk
e-mail: anislouise@gmail.com

Popplewell, Mr & Mrs
Alfred House
23 Tennyson Avenue
Chesterfield
Derbyshire S40 4SN     Tel: 01246 201738

**CHICHESTER**
Potter, Iain & Lyn
Hunston Mill Cottages
Selsey Road
Chichester PO20 1AU     Tel: 01243 783375
Website: www.hunstonmill.co.uk
e-mail: hunstonmill@aol.com

# BLACKPOOL

**VERY HIGH STANDARD** - en suite studios & apartments

**Somerset Apartments**

- Wi-Fi • Central Heating • Cooker • Fridge • Microwave & TV - **all new**
- Beds • Linen provided • 'Highly recommended' by members of the profession • 10 minutes walk to the Theatre

**Irene Chadderton, 22 Barton Avenue, Blackpool FY1 6AP**

**Tel/Fax: 01253 346743 www.blackpool-somerset-apartments.co.uk**    visit**Britain** ☆☆☆

**COVENTRY**
Snelson, Paddy & Bob
Banner Hill Farmhouse
Rouncil Lane
Kenilworth CV8 1NN      Tel: 01926 852850

**DARLINGTON**
Bird, Mrs
Gilling Old Mill
Gilling West
Richmond
N Yorks DL10 5JD      Tel: 01748 822771
e-mail: admin@yorkshiredales-cottages.com

Graham, Anne
Holme House
Piercebridge
Darlington DL2 3SY      Tel: 01325 374280
Website: www.holmehouse.com
e-mail: graham.holmehouse@gmail.com

The Proprietor
George Hotel
Piercebridge
Darlington DL2 3SW      Tel: 01325 374576
Website: www.georgeontees.co.uk

**DERBY**
Boddy, Susan
St Wilfrids
Church Lane
Barrow-upon-Trent
Derbyshire DE73 7HB      Tel: 01332 701384

**DUNDEE**
Hill, Mrs J
Ash Villa
216 Arbroath Road
Dundee DD4 7RZ      Tel: 01382 450831
e-mail: ashvilla_guesthouse@talk21.com

**EASTBOURNE**
Allen, Peter
Flat 1
16 Enys Road
Eastbourne BN21 2DN
Mobile: 07712 439289      Tel: 01323 730235

Dullaway, Lisa
No. 3
3 Cavendish Place
Eastbourne
East Sussex BN21 3EJ
Mobile: 07950 707464      Tel: 01323 731258

Guess, Maggie
3 Hardy Drive
Langney Point
Eastbourne
East Sussex BN23 6ED
e-mail: guesswhom@btinternet.com
Mobile: 07710 273288      Tel: 01323 736689

**EDINBURGH**
Glen Miller, Edna
25 Bellevue Road, Edinburgh EH7 4DL      Tel: 0131-556 4131

Stobbart, Joyce
84 Bellevue Road
Edinburgh EH7 4DE
e-mail: joyms@btinternet.com
Mobile: 07740 503951      Day Tel: 0131-222 9889

Tyrrell, Helen
9 Lonsdale Terrace, Edinburgh EH3 9HN
e-mail: helen.tyrrell@vhscotland.org.uk
Tel: 0131-229 7219      Tel: 0131-220 9943 (Office)

**GLASGOW**
Baird, David W
6 Beaton Road
Maxwell Park, Glasgow G41 4LA
e-mail: 6050557@yahoo.com
Tel: 0141-423 1340      Mobile: 07842 195597

Leslie-Carter, Simon
52 Charlotte Street, Glasgow G1 5DW
Website: www.52charlottestreet.co.uk
e-mail: slc@52charlottestreet.co.uk
Fax: 01436 810520      Tel: 0845 2305252

**GRAVESEND**
Greenwood, Mrs S
8 Sutherland Close
Chalk, Gravesend
Kent DA12 4XJ      Tel: 01474 350819
Website: www.chalkbedandbreakfast.co.uk

**INVERNESS**
Blair, Mrs
McDonald House Hotel
1 Ardross Terrace
Inverness IV3 5NQ      Tel: 01463 232878

Kerr-Smith, Jennifer
Ardkeen Tower
5 Culduthel Road
Inverness IV2 4AD      Tel: 01463 233131

**IPSWICH**
Ball, Bunty
56 Henley Road
Ipswich IP1 3SA      Tel: 01473 256653

Bennett, Liz
Gayfers, Playford
Ipswich IP6 9DR      Tel: 01473 623343
e-mail: lizzieb@clara.co.uk

Hyde-Johnson, Anne
64 Benton Street
Hadleigh, Ipswich
Suffolk IP7 5AT      Tel: 01473 823110

Vines, Tina & Toni
43 Upper Dales View Road
Ipswich      Tel: 01473 402006
e-mail: tinavines@talktalk.net

**ISLE OF WIGHT**
Ogston, Sue
Windward House
69 Mill Hill Road
Cowes
Isle of Wight PO31 7EQ          Tel: 01983 280940
e-mail: sueogston1@tiscali.co.uk

**KESWICK**
Bell, Miss A
Flat 4
Skiddaw View
Penrith Road
Keswick CA12 5HF               Mobile: 07740 949250

**LEEDS**
Baker, Mrs M
2 Ridge Mount
(off Cliff Road)
Leeds LS6 2HD                  Tel: 0113-275 8735

Byrne, Ralph
16 Oakwell Crescent
Leeds LS8 4AF
e-mail: ralphjbyrne@googlemail.com
Mobile: 07763 572183           Tel: 0113-249 5303

**LINCOLN**
Carnell, Andrew
Tennyson Court Cottages
3 Tennyson Street
Lincoln LN1 1LZ
Website: www.tennyson-court.co.uk
Tel: 0800 9805408              Tel: 01522 569892

Sharpe, Mavis S
Bight House
17 East Bight
Lincoln LN2 1QH                Tel: 01522 534477

Ye Olde Crowne Inn (Theatre Pub)
Clasketgate
Lincoln LN2 1JS                Tel: 01522 542896

**LIVERPOOL**
de Leng, Ms S
7 Beach Lawn
Waterloo
Liverpool L22 8QA              Tel: 0151-476 1563
e-mail: deleng@blueyonder.co.uk

Double, Ross
5 Percy Street
Liverpool L8 7LT               Tel: 0151-708 8821

Maloney, Anne
16 Sandown Lane
Wavertree
Liverpool L15 8HY
Mobile: 07977 595040           Tel: 0151-734 4839

**LLANDUDNO**
Blanchard, Mr D & Mrs A
Oasis Hotel
4 Neville Crescent
Central Promenade
Llandudno LL30 1AT             Tel: 01492 877822
e-mail: ann@oasis-hotel.co.uk

**LONDON**
Allen, Mrs I
Flat 2, 9 Dorset Square
London NW1 6QB                 Tel: 020-7723 3979

Broughton, Mrs P A
31 Ringstead Road
Catford, London SE6 2BU        Tel: 020-8461 0146

Cardinal, Maggie
17A Gaisford Street
London NW5 2EB                 Tel: 020-7681 7376

Kempton, Victoria
66 Morley Avenue
London N22 6NG
e-mail: vjkempton@onetel.com
Mobile: 07946 344697           Tel: 020-8888 5595

Maya, Ms Y
23 Lena Crescent
London N9 0FB                  Mobile: 07958 461468

Mesure, Nicholas
16 St Alfege Passage
Greenwich, London SE10 9JS     Tel: 020-8853 4337

Montagu, Beverley
13 Hanley Road, London N4 3DU  Tel: 020-7263 3883

Rothner, Dora
23 The Ridgeway
Finchley, London N3 2PG        Tel: 020-8346 0246

Rothner, Stephanie
44 Grove Road
North Finchley
London N12 9DY
Mobile: 07956 406446           Tel: 020-8446 1604

Shaw, Lindy
11 Baronsmede, London W5 4LS   Tel: 020-8567 0877

Walsh, Genevieve
37 Kelvedon House
Guildford Road
Stockwell, London SW8 2DN      Tel: 020-7627 0024

Warren, Mrs Sally
28 Prebend Gardens
Chiswick
London W4 1TW                  Tel: 020-8994 0560

Zahri, L
79 Hazlewood Road, London E17 7AJ    Tel: 020-8281 5050
e-mail: zahrilin@googlemail.com

**MALVERN**
Emuss, Mrs
Priory Holme
18 Avenue Road
Malvern WR14 3AR               Tel: 01684 568455

Martin, Mr N
37 Quest Hills Road
Malvern WR14 1RL
e-mail: nick@questhills.co.uk
Tel: 01684 562442              Mobile: 07979 851529

McLeod, Mr & Mrs
Sidney House, 40 Worcester Road
Malvern WR14 4AA               Tel: 01684 574994
Website: www.sidneyhouse.co.uk
e-mail: info@sidneyhouse.co.uk

## MANCHESTER

Dyson, Mrs Edwina
33 Danesmoor Road
West Didsbury
Manchester M20 3JT     Tel: 0161-434 5410

Heaton, Miriam
58 Tamworth Avenue
Whitefield
Manchester M45 6UA     Tel: 0161-773 4490

Higgins, Mark, Tanzey & Mathew
103 The Arthouse
43 George Street
China Town, Manchester M1 4AB
e-mail: icenlemon30@hotmail.com
Mobile: 07904 520898     Tel: 0161-234 0705

Jones, P M
375 Bury New Road
Whitefield
Manchester M45 7SU     Tel: 0161-766 9243

Prichard, Fiona & John
45 Bamford Road
Didsbury
Manchester M20 2QP
Mobile: 07771 965651     Tel: 0161-434 4877

Twist, Susan
45 Osborne Road
Levenshulme
Manchester M19 2DU     Tel: 0161-225 1591

## MILFORD HAVEN

Henricksen, Bruce & Diana
Belhaven House Hotel Ltd
29 Hamilton Terrace
Milford Haven SA73 3JJ
Website: www.westwaleshotel.com
e-mail: brucehenricksen@mac.com
Fax: 01646 690787     Tel: 01646 695983

## NEWCASTLE UPON TYNE

The Manager
Rosebery Hotel
2 Rosebery Crescent
Jesmond, Newcastle upon Tyne NE2 1ET     Tel: 0191-281 3363
Website: www.roseberyhotel.co.uk

## NEWPORT

Price, Mrs Dinah
Great House
Isca Road
Old Village
Caerleon
Gwent NP18 1QG     Tel: 01633 420216
Website: www.greathousebb.co.uk
e-mail: dinah.price@amserve.net

## NORTHAMPTON

Burns, Maureen
26 Adams Avenue
Northampton NN1 4LQ     Mobile: 07803 266435
e-mail: mburns47@hotmail.com

## NORWICH

Busch, Julia
8 Chester Street
Norwich NR2 2AY
e-mail: juliacbusch@aol.com
Mobile: 07920 133250     Tel: 01603 612833

Youd, Cherry
Whitegates
181 Norwich Road
Wroxham
NR12 8RZ     Tel: 01603 781037

## NOTTINGHAM

Davis, Barbara
3 Tattershall Drive
The Park
Nottingham NG7 1BX     Tel: 0115-947 4179

Offord, Mrs
5 Tattershall Drive
The Park
Nottingham NG7 1BX     Tel: 0115-947 6924

Ripon House Bed & Breakfast
42 Seymour Road
West Bridgford
Nottingham NG2 5EF     Mobile: 07946 208211
Website: www.artywelcome.co.uk
e-mail: jeremy.felix6@googlemail.com

Santos, Mrs S
Eastwood Farm
Hagg Lane
Epperstone
Nottingham NG14 6AX     Tel: 0115-966 3018
e-mail: info@eastwoodfarm.co.uk

Walker, Christine
18A Cavendish Crescent North
The Park
Nottingham NG7 1BA     Tel: 0115-947 2485
e-mail: walker.ce@virgin.net

## OXFORD

Petty, Susan
74 Corn Street
Witney
Oxford OX28 6BS     Tel: 01993 703035

## PETERBOROUGH

Smith, J
Fen-Acre
20 Barber Drove North
Crowland
Peterborough PE6 0BE
Website: www.fen-acreholidaylet.com
e-mail: julie@fen-acreholidaylet.com
Mobile: 07759 661896     Tel: 01733 211847

## PLYMOUTH

Ball, Fleur
3 Hoe Gardens
Plymouth PL1 2JD      Tel: 01752 670967
e-mail: fleur.ball@postgrad.plymouth.ac.uk

Carson, Mr & Mrs
6 Beech Cottages
Parsonage Road
Newton Ferrers
Nr Plymouth PL8 1AX      Tel: 01752 872124
e-mail: beechcottages@aol.com

Humphreys, John & Sandra
Lyttleton Guest House
4 Crescent Avenue
Plymouth PL1 3AN      Tel: 01752 220176

Mead, Teresa
Ashgrove House
218 Citadel Road
The Hoe
Plymouth PL1 3BB      Tel: 01752 664046
e-mail: ashgroveho@aol.com

Spencer, Hugh & Eloise
10 Grand Parade
Plymouth PL1 3DF
Mobile: 07966 412839      Tel: 01752 664066

## POOLE

Saunders, Mrs
1 Harbour Shallows
15 Whitecliff Road
Poole BH14 8DU      Tel: 01202 741637
e-mail: saunders.221@btinternet.com

## READING

Estate Office
Mapledurham House and Watermill
Mapledurham Estate
Reading RG4 7TR      Tel: 0118-972 3350
Website: www.mapledurham.co.uk
e-mail: enquiries@mapledurham.co.uk

## SALISBURY

Brumfitt, Ms S
26 Victoria Road
Salisbury
Wilts SP1 3NG      Tel: 01722 334877

## SHEFFIELD

Craig, J & Rosen, B
59 Nether Edge Road
Sheffield S7 1RW      Tel: 0114-258 1337

Slack, Penny
Rivelin Glen Quarry
Rivelin Valley Road
Sheffield S6 5SE      Tel: 0114-234 0382
Website: www.quarryhouse.org.uk
e-mail: pennyslack@aol.com

## SOUTHSEA & PORTSMOUTH

Tyrell, Wendy
Douglas Cottage
27 Somerset Road
Southsea PO5 2NL      Tel: 023-9282 1453

## STOKE-ON-TRENT

Griffiths, Dorothy
40 Princes Road, Hartshill
Stoke-on-Trent ST4 7JQ
Mobile: 07789 362960      Tel: 01782 416198

Hindmoor, Mrs
Verdon Guest House
44 Charles Street
Hanley, Stoke-on-Trent ST1 3JY      Tel: 01782 264244

Meredith, Mr K
2 Bank End Farm Cottage
Hammond Avenue, Brown Edge
Stoke-on-Trent, Staffs ST6 8QU      Tel: 01782 502160
e-mail: kenmeredith@btinternet.com

## STRATFORD-UPON-AVON

Caterham House
58-59 Rother Street
Stratford-upon-Avon CV37 6LT      Tel: 01789 267309
e-mail: caterhamhousehotel@btconnect.com

## WESTCLIFF

Hussey, Joy
42A Ceylon Road
Westcliff-on-Sea SS0 7HP      Mobile: 07946 413496

## WOLVERHAMPTON

Nixon, Sonia
39 Stubbs Road
Pennfields
Wolverhampton WV3 7DJ      Tel: 01902 339744

Prior, Julia
Treetops
The Hem, Shifnal
Shropshire TF11 9PS      Tel: 01952 460566

Riggs, Peter A
'Bethesda'
56 Chapel Lane, Codsall
Nr Wolverhampton WV8 2EJ
Mobile: 07930 967809      Tel: 01902 844068

## WORTHING

Stewart, Mollie
School House
11 Ambrose Place
Worthing BN11 1PZ      Tel: 01903 206823

Symonds, Mrs Val
23 Shakespeare Road
Worthing BN11 4AR
Mobile: 07951 183252      Tel: 01903 201557

## YORK

Blacklock, Tom
155 Lowther Street, York YO3 7LZ      Tel: 01904 620487

Blower, Iris & Dennis
Dalescroft Guest House
10 Southlands Road
York YO23 1NP      Tel: 01904 626801
Website: www.dalescroft-york.co.uk
e-mail: info@dalescroft-york.co.uk

Harrand, Greg
Hedley House Hotel & Apts
3 Bootham Terrace
York YO30 7DH      Tel: 01904 637404

**ALEXANDER ALLIANCE**
(Alexander Technique, Voice & Audition Coaching)
3 Hazelwood Drive
St Albans, Herts                  Tel: 01727 843633
Website: www.alextech.co.uk
e-mail: bev.keech@ntlworld.com

**ALEXANDER CENTRE The Bloomsbury**
(Alexander Technique)
Bristol House, 80A Southampton Row
London WC1B 4BB                  Tel: 020-7404 5348
Website: www.alexcentre.com
e-mail: enquiries@alexcentre.com

**ALEXANDER TECHNIQUE**
Contact: Jackie Coote MSTAT
27 Britannia Road, London SW6 2HJ      Tel: 020-7731 1061
Website: www.alexandertec.co.uk
e-mail: jackiecoote@alexandertec.co.uk

**ALEXANDER TECHNIQUE**
Contact: Robert Macdonald
13 Ascot Lodge, Greville Place
London NW6 5JD                  Mobile: 07956 852303
Website: www.voice.org.uk

**ALL ABOUT TEETH Ltd**
The Club Room, Miserden
Gloucestershire GL6 7JA
e-mail: nicolas@ceramiccentre.com

**ALTERED IMAGE LIFE COACHING**
Primrose Cottage
6 Lee Place, Ilfracombe EX34 9BQ
Website: www.alteredimage2.co.uk
e-mail: lifecoach@merseymail.com
Fax: 08709 133624              Mobile: 07050 644101

**ARTS CLINIC The**
(Psychological Counselling, Personal & Professional
Development)
14 Devonshire Place, London W1G 6HX
e-mail: mail@artsclinic.co.uk
Fax: 020-7224 6256              Tel: 020-7935 1242

**ASPEY ASSOCIATES**
(Management & Team Training, Executive Coaching,
Human Resources)
90 Long Acre, Covent Garden
London WC2E 9RZ                  Tel: 0845 1701300
Website: www.aspey.com
e-mail: hr@aspey.com

**AURA DENTAL SPA**
5 Queens Terrace
London NW8 6DX                  Tel: 020-7722 0040
Website: www.auradentalspa.com
e-mail: info@auradentalspa.com

**AUTOGENIC THERAPY**
(Stress Management & Relaxation Training)
London                      Tel: 020-8741 2595
e-mail: autogenictherapy@talktalk.net

**BEAUTY BY NATASHA**
7 Spean House, 9 Church Road East
Farnborough GU14 6HQ            Mobile: 07841 511409
Website: www.nwmake-up.co.uk
e-mail: tashwiggins@hotmail.co.uk

**BENWOODFITNESS.COM**
37 Nevil Road, Stoke Newington
London N16 8SW                  Mobile: 07776 222526
Website: www.benwoodfitness.com
e-mail: benwood@benwoodfitness.com

**[ CONTACTS 2010 ]**

# infopage

## How should I use these listings?

You will find a variety of companies in this section which could help you enhance your health and wellbeing physically and mentally. They include personal fitness and lifestyle coaches, counsellors, exercise classes and beauty consultants amongst others. It is worth researching any company or service you are considering using. Many of these listings have websites which you can browse. Even if you feel you have your career and lifestyle under control, you may still find the following advice helpful:

## Your body is part of your business

Your mental and physical health is vital to your career as a performer. Just from a business perspective, your body is part of your promotional package and it needs to be maintained. Try to keep fit and eat healthily to enhance both your outward appearance and your inner confidence. This is particularly important if you are unemployed. You need to ensure that if you are suddenly called for an audition you look suitable for and feel positive about the part you are auditioning for.

## Injury

Keeping fit also helps you to minimise the risk of an injury during a performance. The last thing you want to do is to be prevented from working. An injury is more likely to occur if you are inflexible and unprepared for sudden physical exertion. If you do pick up an injury or an illness you will want to make sure it does not get any worse by getting treatment with a specialist.

## Mental health

Mental health is just as important as bodily health. Just as you would for any physical injury or illness, if you suffer from a psychological problem such as stage fright, an addiction or depression, you should make sure that you address your concerns and deal with the issues involved. You may need to see a counsellor or a life coach for guidance and support.

## Unemployment

If you are unemployed, it can be difficult to retain a positive mindset. The best thing you can do is to keep yourself occupied. You could join a dance or drama class, which would help to maintain your fitness levels as well as developing contacts and keeping involved within the industry. Improve your CV by learning to speak a new language or play a musical instrument. Think about taking on temporary or part-time work outside of acting to earn money until the next job comes along, or you could put yourself forward for acting work in a student film (see 'Film & Television Schools' for more information).

## Where can I find more information?

For more information on health and wellbeing you may wish to contact the British Association for Performing Arts Medicine (BAPAM) www.bapam.org.uk. You may also find their article on the next page helpful. Please refer to the 'Drama Training, Schools & Coaches' and 'Dance Training & Professional Classes' sections if you are interested in taking drama or dance courses or lessons to improve your fitness, keep your auditioning skills sharp between jobs and/or stay occupied and motivated.

Please note that while Spotlight takes every care in screening the companies featured in this section, it cannot be held responsible for services or treatments received.

**Actors who are never out of work are rare creatures. But you can use your resting periods to invest in your physical and mental health. Here are a few suggestions from BAPAM, the charity that provides free health-assessment clinics and reduced-price treatments to artists with performance-related health problems.**

## Look after your health on a budget

If you can't justify the cost of keeping up your gym membership, go for cheaper forms of exercise:

- **Walk** or **cycle** instead of driving or using public transport. If you haven't ridden a bike for years, build your confidence by taking a course.
- **Run** in the open air instead of on a treadmill at a gym. It's much better to be in the fresh air - and it's more sociable.
- **Swimming** is a cheap and effective form of exercise. Think about taking lessons to make your stroke more efficient and avoid putting unnecessary pressure on your joints - especially your neck.
- **Team sports** combine fresh air and being sociable; now could be the time to take up football or netball again. Be careful, though - you wouldn't want a sports injury to come between you and your next job!
- Learn a technique to help with **posture**, such as Alexander Technique, Feldenkrais or Pilates. Techniques that are taught one-to-one can be expensive, but you can often find taster sessions at adult education colleges.
- **Take a refresher** in all those stagecraft skills (breathing; warm-up exercises; stage fighting) you learned at drama school. Enrol on a short course or read some books. When the next job comes up you need to be in peak condition and able to perform safely.

## Think about your diet while you're resting

Everyone knows that eating well has a positive effect on your mental and physical wellbeing - especially important when you need to keep your spirits up.

- Learn about **healthy eating**, and expand your repertoire of recipes. Farmers' markets save money and you'll learn what's in season. Then you can maintain good habits when you're running around or on tour.
- If you ration your **treats**, you make them more special. If a treat becomes a daily habit you won't enjoy real treats so much.
- Now is the time to **phase out junk food**. Why spend money on processed food when you could eat so much better for less? See the BAPAM factsheet *Sensible eating for performers.*
- Don't rely on **alcohol** to keep you going. You develop expectations around alcohol, and that will take its toll on your liver (and your wallet!). Try to make a drink last longer, or alternate alcohol and water over the course of an evening. See the BAPAM factsheet *The drinks are on me!* for more information about drinking responsibly.

## Invest in your mental health too

- Think strategically about your career. Do a **skills audit**, remembering all the skills you've accumulated (numeracy, fundraising, any IT skills). Be creative about how you can put them to use, and fill any skill gaps. Focusing on something developmental can take your mind off your current circumstances.
- Use quiet periods to **organise** your paperwork and electronic filing systems. You will feel empowered when you know everything is in order; it saves time and stress when you do get busy if you already have a workable system in place. Learn to use **spreadsheets** to keep track of your finances. You'll save yourself endless headaches when it's time to file your tax return, and you'll save yourself money on an accountant.
- **Volunteering** is great for stopping you feeling isolated. Try and find an activity that involves **physical exercise** - such as working in a community garden. It might even lead to a job!
- Remember, there's no need to suffer alone if being out of work is beginning to get you down. A few sessions with a **counsellor** can make a big difference. Check out the BAPAM Directory online at www.bapam.org.uk to locate a performer-friendly counsellor in your area.

To find out more about performance-related health issues and BAPAM services, please see the website www.bapam.org.uk

# infopage

**John Byrne is the career advisor and agony uncle for The Stage newspaper, and a columnist for Young Performer magazine. He has over twenty years of experience in the entertainment industry as a performer, writer and artist advocate. The author of several popular books on making a living from performing and creative talents, he has also given workshops and seminars at institutions and events such as The Guildhall, Solent University, Syracuse, Ithaca and Capa colleges, NSDF and The Edinburgh Festival.**

Regular readers of The Stage might be surprised to find their friendly neighbourhood career advisor and agony uncle introducing the 'Health and Wellbeing' section of Contacts. I'd be the first to admit that when I was a little younger and all gung-ho about kick-starting my own entertainment career, I'd have been far more anxious to get stuck into the more 'exciting' sections with all those juicy agent and casting addresses.

However, from personal experience, via the many one-to-one sessions I hold with performers at every level, and especially when speaking to the aforementioned top agents and casting professionals for the Dear John column, I can tell you with all sincerity that keeping yourself fit and healthy is not just something you should be aiming to address "once you get that big break".

Looking after yourself is something you need to build into your weekly routine right now to have any chance of being able to make the most of the breaks which do come along - as well as the even more difficult task of turning those breaks into a sustainable long-term career.

Whether you are an actor, a singer, a comic or any other type of performer, it should be obvious that your voice, your mind and your body are the essential tools of your trade, and as with any other self-employed business person if you don't keep your tools in good condition your chances of doing your best work - which in this business is the only way of getting more work - are severely limited.

While this is true for every business person, there are particular aspects of our profession which can make looking after ourselves particularly hard. For those of us who are working it may be the rigours of touring, working unsociable hours and the sheer physical and mental exertion required to give a great performance night after night which chips away at our wellness. For those of us who are "resting" it may be the uncertainty of whether we will ever work again (and believe me we all have it!), financial insecurity and the very real threat of becoming addicted to daytime television through sheer loneliness and lack of routine. Lack of structure and motivation may not kill a career as fast as drugs, alcohol and other more well-documented showbusiness addictions, but the drip drip effect on self esteem will do so just as effectively in the long run.

It doesn't have to be this way. You may not be able to afford gym membership, but there are lots of forms of physical exercise such as swimming, cycling or simply allowing a little extra journey time and walking more which are cheap and effective. Joining a local team or a group is even better as this also addresses the loneliness factor. Cutting down junk food and learning to cook healthy meals not only improves diet but can have a great benefit to your wallet too.

As for keeping yourself mentally fit, doing something positive with your resting time, whether it is joining a class to polish your performance skills, or organising your paperwork so that when tax time comes around it isn't as traumatic as usual, will do far more to lift your spirits than a diet of trash TV or endless, aimless internet surfing.

If you are already up against the wall healthwise or financial wise there are many organisations such as the BAPAM or Credit Action which can help, often free of charge. One other occupational hazard of working in an industry where we may feel pressured to appear confident and in control at all times is that we may forget the truth that truly confident people aren't afraid to ask for help when it is needed. In the pages that follow you will find many useful organisations and individuals offering support for your health and wellbeing needs in a wide variety of different areas. Do take some time to consider which areas you would most benefit from support in right now, and as with every other service you use in the development of your career, bear in mind that support - whether paid for or unpaid - will only give you the maximum benefit if you have taken the time to work out what results you are aiming for, and are prepared to give the lifestyle changes suggested a proper try to see if they work for you.

Here's to your continued success...and the good health to enjoy it!

John Byrne's weekly Dear John column may be read online at www.thestage.co.uk/connect/dearjohn John's own site www.showbusiness-success.com also offers useful career advice for performers, or alternatively call 0845 396 9972.

**BODY CLINIC The**
(Skincare Specialists)
Harley Street, South Woodford
Gidea Park  Tel: 0800 5424809
Website: www.thebodyclinic.co.uk

**BODYWISE YOGA & NATURAL HEALTH CENTRE**
119 Roman Road
London E2 0QN  Tel: 020-8981 6938
Website: www.bodywisehealth.org
e-mail: info@bodywisehealth.org

**BOXMOOR HOUSE DENTAL PRACTICE**
451 London Road
Hemel Hempstead HP3 9BE
email: d-gardner@btconnect.com
Fax: 01442 244454  Tel: 01442 253253

**BREATHE FITNESS/ANTHONY MAYATT**
22A Station Approach, Hayes
Bromley, Kent BR2 7EH  Mobile: 07840 180094
Website: www.breathefitness.uk.com
e-mail: anthony@breathefitness.uk.com

**BURGESS Chris**
(Counselling and Psychotherapy for Performing Artists)
81 Arne House, Tyers Street
London SE11 5EZ  Tel: 020-7582 8229
e-mail: chrisburgess@netcom.co.uk

**BURT Andrew**
(Counselling)
74 Mill Hill Road
London W3 8JJ  Tel: 020-8992 5992
Website: www.andrewburtcounselling.co.uk
e-mail: burt.counsel@tiscali.co.uk

**COCKBURN Daisy MSTAT**
(Alexander Technique Teacher)
Bloomsbury Alexander Centre
Bristol House, 80A Southampton Row
London WC1B 4BB  Mobile: 07734 725445
e-mail: daisycockburn@btinternet.com

**CONSTRUCTIVE TEACHING CENTRE Ltd**
(Alexander Technique Teacher Training)
18 Lansdowne Road, London W11 3LL  Tel: 020-7727 7222
Website: www.alexandertek.com
e-mail: constructiveteachingcentre@gmail.com

**CORTEEN Paola MSTAT**
(Alexander Technique)
10A Eversley Park Rd, London N21 1JU  Tel: 020-8882 7898
e-mail: pmcorteen@yahoo.co.uk

**COURTENAY Julian**
(NLP Hypnotherapy)
42 Langdon Park Road
London N6 5QG                    Mobile: 07973 139376
e-mail: julian@mentalfitness.uk.com

**CRAIGENTINNY DENTAL CARE**
57 Duddington Crescent
Milton Road, Edinburgh EH15 3AY        Tel: 0131-669 2114
Website: www.craigentinny.co.uk
e-mail: dentist@craigentinny.co.uk

**CROWE Sara**
(Holistic Massage & Reflexology)
23 John Aird Court, London W2 1UY
e-mail: sara@sarabowes.com
Mobile: 07830 375389              Tel: 020-7262 3543

**DAVIES Siobhan STUDIOS**
(Treatment Room)
85 St George's Road, London SE1 6ER
Website: www.siobhandavies.com
e-mail: info@siobhandavies.com
Fax: 020-7091 9669                Tel: 020-7091 9650

**DREAM**
(Massage, Reflexology & Yoga for Events
the Workplace and Home)
117B Gaisford Street
London NW5 2EG                    Mobile: 07973 731026
Website: www.dreamtherapies.co.uk
e-mail: heidi@dreamtherapies.co.uk

**EDGE OF THE WORLD HYPNOTHERAPY & NLP**
Central London, Essex/Suffolk
Website: www.edgehypno.com
e-mail: info@edgehypno.com        Mobile: 07960 755626

**EDWARDS Simon MCA Hyp**
(Hypnotherapy for Professionals in Film, TV & Theatre)
Flat 7, Boatrace Court
Mortlake High Street, London SW14 8HL
Website: www.simonedwards.com
e-mail: simonedwardsltd@googlemail.com
Mobile: 07889 333680              Tel: 01296 651259

**EXPERIENTIAL FOCUSING THERAPY SESSIONS**
Contact: Dr Greg Madison
93-95 Gloucester Place
London W1                        Mobile: 07941 300871
Website: www.gregmadison.net
e-mail: info@gregmadison.net

40 Wilbury Road, Brighton BN1

**EXPLORING U COUNSELLING Ltd**
37 Friars Street, Sudbury
Suffolk CO10 2AG                  Mobile: 07841 979450
Website: www.exploringUcounselling.co.uk
e-mail: euc@exploringUcounselling.co.uk

**FAITH Gordon BA DHC MCHC (UK)**
(Hypnotherapy, Obstacles to Performing, Positive
Affirmation, Focusing)
1 Wavel Mews, Priory Road
West Hampstead
London NW6 3AB                    Tel: 020-7328 0446
Website: www.gordonfaith.co.uk/voice.htm

**FIT 4 THE PART Ltd**
Contact: Jon Trevor (Celebrity Trainer, Health & Fitness
Broadcaster)
One Malthus Path, London SE28 8AJ    Tel: 0845 0066348
Website: www.jontrevor.com
e-mail: info@jontrevor.com

**FITNESS COACH The**
Contact: Jamie Baird
Agua at The Sanderson
50 Berners Street, London W1T 3NG
e-mail: jamie@thefitnesscoach.com
Mobile: 07970 782476             Tel: 020-7300 1414

**HAMMOND John B. Ed (Hons) ICHFST**
(Fitness Consultancy, Sports & Relaxation Massage)
4 Glencree, Billericay
Essex CM11 1EB
Mobile: 07703 185198             Tel/Fax: 01277 632830

**HARLEY STREET VOICE CENTRE The**
The Harley Street ENT Clinic
109 Harley Street
London W1G 6AN
Website: www.harleystreetent.com
e-mail: info@harleystreetent.com
Fax: 020-7935 7701               Tel: 020-7224 2350

**HILLSHYPNOTHERAPY**
30 Tudoe Road, Godmanchester
Huntingdon, Cambs PE29 2DP        Mobile: 07590 466949
e-mail: adamcharleshills@gmail.com

**HYL ENERGISER**
10 Little Newport Street
London WC2H 7JJ                   Mobile: 07768 321092
Website: www.hylenergiser.com
e-mail: info@hylenergiser.com

**HYPNOSIS WORKS**
19 Glengall Road, London SE15 6NJ    Tel: 020-7237 5815
Website: www.hypnosisdoeswork.net
e-mail: sssp@hypnosisdoeswork.net

**HYPNOTHERAPY & PSYCHOTHERAPY**
Contact: Karen Mann DCH DHP (Including Performance
Improvement)
10 Harley Street
London W1G 9PF                    Tel: 020-7794 5843
Website: www.karenmann.co.uk

**INSPIRATIONAL WELLBEING**
(Energy Healer)
12 Mills Close, Taverham
Norwich, Norfolk NR8 6QX          Tel: 01603 867173
Website: www.inspirationalwellbeing.com
e-mail: inspirationalwellbeing@gmail.com

**INSTITUTE OF ADVANCED CLINICAL HYPNOTHERAPY**
(Based North West England)
Manchester BL9 5QA                Mobile: 07726 602772
e-mail: ioach@ymail.com

**JLP FITNESS**
(Personal Training, Group Sessions, Kick/Muay-Thai Boxing
& Boxing)
e-mail: jlpthecoach@jacquileepryce.com  Mobile: 07930 304809

**LIFE COACHING**
Contact: Dr Elspeth Reid (Including Career, Relationship &
Self-Confidence Coaching)
102 Clarence Road
Wimbledon SW19 8QD                Tel: 020-8879 7676
Website: www.elspethreid.com
e-mail: coach@elspethreid.com

**LIFE PRACTICE UK Ltd**
(Specialists in Behavioural Change)
Woodlands, Preston Road
Gosmore, Hitchin, Herts SG4 7QS    Tel/Fax: 01462 451473
Website: www.lifepractice.co.uk
e-mail: info@lifepractice.co.uk

**LUCAS Hazel**
(Qualified Holistic Masseur)
119 Brightwell Avenue
Westcliff-on-Sea, Essex SS0 9EQ    Mobile: 07870 862939
e-mail: onedaylucas@blueyonder.co.uk

**MAGIC KEY PARTNERSHIP The**
Contact: Lyn Burgess (Life Coach)
151A Moffat Road, Thornton Heath
Surrey CR7 8PZ    Tel: 0845 1297401
Website: www.magickey.co.uk
e-mail: lyn@magickey.co.uk

**MATRIX ENERGY FIELD THERAPY**
(Accredited Healer)
Deal Castle House
31 Victoria Road
Deal, Kent CT14 7AS
e-mail: donnie@lovingorganization.org
Mobile: 07762 821828    Tel: 01304 379466

**McCALLION Anna**
(Alexander Technique)
Flat 2, 11 Sinclair Gardens
London W14 0AU    Tel: 020-7602 5599
e-mail: hildegarde007@yahoo.com

**MINDSCI CLINIC**
(Clinical Hypnotism)
34 Willow Bank
Ham, Richmond
Surrey TW10 7QX    Tel/Fax: 020-8948 2439
Website: www.mindsci-clinic.com
e-mail: bt@mindsci-clinic.com

**NOBLE Penny PSYCHOTHERAPY**
8 Shaftesbury Gardens, Victoria Road
North Acton, London NW10 6LJ    Mobile: 07506 579 895
Website: www.pennynoblepsychotherapy.com
e-mail: penny.noble@virgin.net

**NORTON Michael R**
(Implant/Reconstructive Dentistry)
104 Harley Street, London W1G 7JD
Website: www.nortonimplants.com
e-mail: linda@nortonimplants.com
Fax: 020-7486 9119    Tel: 020-7486 9229

**NUTRITIONAL THERAPY FOR PERFORMERS**
Contact: Vanessa May BSc (NTC & BANT Reg)
18 Oaklands Road
Ealing, London W7 2DR    Mobile: 07962 978763
Website: www.wellbeingandnutrition.co.uk
e-mail: vanessamay9@yahoo.co.uk

**OGUNLARU Rasheed**
(Life & Business Coach)
The Coaching Studio, 223A Mayall Road
London SE24 0PS    Tel: 020-7207 1082
Website: www.rasaru.com
e-mail: rasheed@rasaru.com

**PEAK PERFORMANCE TRAINING**
Contact: Tina Reibl (Hypnotherapy, NLP, Success
Strategies)
42 The Broadway
Maidenhead, Berkshire SL6 1LU    Tel: 01628 633509
Website: www.maidenhead-hypnotherapy.co.uk
e-mail: tina.reibl@tesco.net

**POLAND Ken DENTAL STUDIOS**
(Film/Stage Dentistry)
1 Devonshire Place
London W1G 6HH
e-mail: robpoland@btconnect.com
Fax: 020-7486 3952          Tel: 020-7935 6919

**RUOK4SPEX.COM**
PO Box 1027 PE12 0SQ
Website: www.ruok4spex.com
e-mail: info@ruok4spex.com

**SELFSIGHT**
(Counselling & EMDR)
Psycholsynthesis & Education Trust
92-94 Tooley Street
London Bridge, London SE1 2TH
Website: www.selfsight.com
e-mail: rickylock@btinternet.com
Mobile: 07752 681012          Tel: 01322 524707

**SEYRI Kayvan MSc, NSCA-CPT*D, CSCS *D,**
**NASM-PES, CES**
(Performance Enhancement Specialist, Master Personal Trainer)
Unit 3, 69 St Mark's Road
London W10 6JG          Mobile: 07881 554636
Website: www.ultimatefitpro.com
e-mail: info@ultimatefitpro.com

**SHENAS Dr DENTAL STUDIO**
51 Cadogan Gardens
Sloane Square
Chelsea
London SW3 2TH          Tel: 020-7589 2319
Website: www.shenasdental.co.uk
e-mail: info@shenasdental.co.uk

**SHER SYSTEM The**
(Helping Skin with Acne & Rosacea)
30 New Bond Street
London W1S 2RN
Website: www.sher.co.uk
e-mail: skincare@sher.co.uk
Fax: 020-7629 7021          Tel: 020-7499 4022

**SHIATSU HEALTH CENTRE**
Moving Arts Base
134 Liverpool Road
London N1 1LA          Mobile: 07905 504418
Website: www.shiatsuhealth.com
e-mail: japaneseyoga@btinternet.com

**SMILE NW**
Contact: Dr Veronica Morris (Cosmetic & General Dentist)
17 Hallswelle Parade, Finchley Road
Temple Fortune, London NW11 0DL
Website: www.smile-nw.co.uk
e-mail: enquiries@smile-nw.co.uk
Fax: 020-8458 5681          Tel: 020-8458 2333

**SMILE SOLUTIONS**
(Dental Practice)
24 Englands Lane, London NW3 4TG
Website: www.smile-solutions.info
e-mail: enquiries@smile-solutions.info
Fax: 020-7449 1769          Tel: 020-7449 1760

**SMILEMORE DENTAL CARE**
63 St Johns Wood High Street
London NW8 7NL          Tel: 020-7586 1210
Website: www.smilemoredentalcare.com
e-mail: paul.abrahams@smilemoredentalcare.com

**SMILESTUDIO**
First Floor, Wingate House
93-107 Shaftesbury Avenue
London W1D 5DY
Website: www.smile-studio.co.uk          Tel: 020-7439 0888

**STAT (The Society of Teachers of the Alexander Technique)**
1st Floor Linton House
39-51 Highgate Road, London NW5 1RS
Website: www.stat.org.uk
e-mail: enquiries@stat.org.uk
Fax: 020-7482 5435          Tel: 020-7482 5135

**THEATRICAL DENTISTRY**
Contact: Richard D Casson (Cosmetic Dentist)
6 Milford House, 7 Queen Anne Street
London W1G 9HN          Tel/Fax: 020-7580 9696
Website: www.richardcasson.com
e-mail: smile@richardcasson.com

**TOP NOTCH NANNIES**
142 Buckingham Palace Road
London SW1W 9TR
Website: www.topnotchnannies.com
e-mail: jean@topnotchnannies.com
Tel: 020-7881 0893          Tel: 020-7824 8209

**VITAL TOUCH Ltd The**
11 Evering Road, London N16 7PX
Website: www.thevitaltouch.com
e-mail: suzi@thevitaltouch.com          Mobile: 07976 263691

**WALK-IN BACKRUB**
(On-site Massage Company)
14 Neals Yard
London WC2H 9DP          Tel/Fax: 020-7436 9875
Website: www.walkinbackrub.co.uk
e-mail: info@walkinbackrub.co.uk

**WELLBEING**
Contact: Leigh Jones (Personal Training, Yoga, Tai Chi)
22 Galloway Close
Broxbourne, Herts EN10 6BU          Mobile: 07957 333921
e-mail: williamleighjones@hotmail.com

**WOODFORD HOUSE DENTAL PRACTICE**
162 High Road
Woodford Green, Essex IG8 9EF
Website: www.improveyoursmile.co.uk
e-mail: info@improveyoursmile.co.uk
Fax: 020-8252 0835          Tel: 020-8504 2704

## CARL ROSA OPERA
359 Hackney Road
London E2 8PR
Website: www.carlrosaopera.co.uk
e-mail: info@carlrosaopera.co.uk
Fax: 020-7613 0859          Tel: 020-7613 0777

## ENGLISH NATIONAL OPERA
London Coliseum
St Martin's Lane
London WC2N 4ES
Website: www.eno.org
Fax: 020-7845 9277          Tel: 020-7836 0111

## ENGLISH TOURING OPERA
Contact: James Conway
1st Floor
52-54 Rosebery Avenue
London EC1R 4RP
Website: www.englishtouringopera.org.uk
e-mail: admin@englishtouringopera.org.uk
Fax: 020-7713 8686          Tel: 020-7833 2555

## GLYNDEBOURNE FESTIVAL OPERA
Glyndebourne, Lewes
East Sussex BN8 5UU          Tel: 01273 812321
Website: www.glyndebourne.com

## GRANGE PARK OPERA
24-26 Broad Street
Alresford
Hampshire SO24 9AQ          Tel: 01962 737360
Website: www.grangeparkopera.co.uk
e-mail: info@grangeparkopera.co.uk

## GUBBAY Raymond Ltd
Dickens House
15 Tooks Court
London EC4A 1QH
Website: www.raymondgubbay.co.uk
e-mail: info@raymondgubbay.co.uk
Fax: 020-7025 3751          Tel: 020-7025 3750

## KENTISH OPERA
Watermede
Wickhurst Road
Sevenoaks
Weald, Kent TN14 6LX          Tel: 01732 463284
Website: www.kentishopera.fsnet.co.uk
e-mail: sl.sweald@fsmail.net

## MUSIC THEATRE LONDON
Chertsey Chambers
12 Mercer Street
London WC2H 9QD          Mobile: 07831 243942
Website: www.capriolfilms.co.uk
e-mail: musictheatre.london@virgin.net

## OPERA DELLA LUNA
7 Cotmore House
Fringford
Bicester
Oxfordshire OX27 8RQ
Website: www.operadellaluna.org
e-mail: operadellaluna@aol.com
Fax: 01869 323533          Tel: 01869 325131

**[ CONTACTS 2010 ]**

**OPERA NORTH**
Grand Theatre
46 New Briggate, Leeds LS1 6NU
Website: www.operanorth.co.uk
e-mail: info@operanorth.co.uk
Fax: 0113-244 0418
Tel: 0113-243 9999

**OPERAUK**
177 Andrewes House
Barbican
London EC2Y 8BA
Tel: 020-7628 0025
Website: www.operauk.co.uk
e-mail: rboss@aol.com

**PEGASUS OPERA COMPANY Ltd**
The Brix, St Matthew's
Brixton Hill
London SW2 1JF
Tel/Fax: 020-7501 9501
Website: www.pegopera.org
e-mail: admin@pegopera.org

**PIMLICO OPERA**
24 Broad Street
Alresford
Hampshire SO24 9AQ
Tel: 01962 737360
Website: www.grangeparkopera.co.uk
e-mail: pimlico@grangeparkopera.co.uk

**PMB PRESENTATIONS Ltd**
Vicarage House
58-60 Kensington Church Street
London W8 4DB
Website: www.pmbpresentations.co.uk
e-mail: p@triciamurraybett.com
Fax: 020-7368 3338
Tel: 020-7368 3337

**ROYAL OPERA The**
Royal Opera House
Covent Garden,
London WC2E 9DD
Tel: 020-7240 1200
Website: www.roh.org.uk

**SCOTTISH OPERA**
39 Elmbank Crescent
Glasgow G2 4PT
Tel: 0141-248 4567
Website: www.scottishopera.org.uk

**WELSH NATIONAL OPERA**
Wales Millennium Centre
Bute Place
Cardiff CF10 5AL
Website: www.wno.org.uk
e-mail: marketing@wno.org.uk
Fax: 029-2063 5099
Tel: 029-2063 5000

### ACTORS' ADVISORY SERVICE
*Provides Advice to Actors, Agents, Photographers etc*
29 Talbot Road, Twickenham
Middlesex TW2 6SJ                    Tel: 020-8287 2839

### ACTORS' BENEVOLENT FUND
6 Adam Street, London WC2N 6AD
Website: www.actorsbenevolentfund.co.uk
e-mail: office@abf.org.uk
Fax: 020-7836 8978                   Tel: 020-7836 6378

### ACTORS CENTRE (LONDON) The
*Charity. 1700 Classes a year for professional actors. Advice & Information. Introductory Courses*
1A Tower Street
London WC2H 9NP                      Tel: 020-7632 8001
Website: www.actorscentre.co.uk
e-mail: admin@actorscentre.co.uk

### ACTORS CENTRE NORTH
*Contact: Maggie Lackey. Charity. Provides Advice, Support & Information. Workshops in continuing professional development for professionally trained actors*
21-23 Oldham Street
Manchester M1 1JG        Tel/Fax: 0161-819 2513
Website: www.actorscentrenorth.com
e-mail: info@actorscentrenorth.com

### ACTORS' CHARITABLE TRUST
*Provides Advice & Support. Grants for Actors' Children*
58 Bloomsbury Street
London WC1B 3QT
e-mail: robert@tactactors.org
Fax: 020-7637 3368                   Tel: 020-7636 7868

### ACTORS' CHURCH UNION
St Paul's Church, Bedford Street
London WC2E 9ED                      Tel: 020-7240 0344
e-mail: actors-church.union@tiscali.co.uk

### ADVERTISING ASSOCIATION
7th Floor North
Artillery House
11-19 Artillery Row, London SW1P 1RT
Website: www.adassoc.org.uk
e-mail: aa@adassoc.org.uk
Fax: 020-7222 1504                   Tel: 020-7340 1100

### AGENTS' ASSOCIATION (Great Britain)
54 Keyes House, Dolphin Square, London SW1V 3NA
Website: www.agents-uk.com
e-mail: association@agents-uk.com
Fax: 020-7821 0261                   Tel: 020-7834 0515

### ARTS & BUSINESS
Nutmeg House
60 Gainsford Street
Butlers Wharf, London SE1 2NY
Website: www.aandb.org.uk
e-mail: head.office@aandb.org.uk
Fax: 020-7407 7527                   Tel: 020-7378 8143

### ARTS CENTRE GROUP
Menier Chocolate Factory
51 Southwark Street
London SE1 1RU
Website: www.artscentregroup.org.uk
e-mail: info@artscentregroup.org.uk
Tel: 020-7407 1881                   Tel: 0845 4581881

**ARTS COUNCIL ENGLAND**
2 Pear Tree Court, London EC1R 0DS
Website: www.artscouncil.org.uk
e-mail: enquiries@artscouncil.org.uk
Fax: 020-7608 4100                    Tel: 0845 300 6200

**ARTS COUNCIL OF NORTHERN IRELAND**
MacNeice House
77 Malone Road, Belfast BT9 6AQ
Website: www.artscouncil-ni.org
Fax: 028-9066 1715                    Tel: 028-9038 5200

**ARTS COUNCIL OF WALES The**
Bute Place, Cardiff CF10 5AL
Website: www.artswales.org.uk
e-mail: info@artswales.org.uk
Fax: 029-2041 1400                    Tel: 0845 8734900

**ARTSLINE**
*Disability Access Information Service*
c/o 21 Pine Court, Wood Lodge Gardens
Bromley BR1 2WA                    Tel: 020-7388 2227
Website: www.artsline.org.uk
e-mail: admin@artsline.org.uk

**ASSOCIATION OF BRITISH THEATRE TECHNICIANS**
4th Floor, 55 Farringdon Road, London EC1M 3JB
Website: www.abtt.org.uk
e-mail: office@abtt.org.uk
Fax: 020-7242 9303                    Tel: 020-7242 9200

**ASSOCIATION OF LIGHTING DESIGNERS**
PO Box 680, Oxford OX1 9DG        Mobile: 07817 060189
Website: www.ald.org.uk
e-mail: office@ald.org.uk

**ASSOCIATION OF MODEL AGENTS**
11-29 Fashion Street, London E1 6PX
e-mail: amainfo@btinternet.com
Info. Line: 09068 517644              Tel: 020-7422 0699

**BASCA - BRITISH ACADEMY OF SONGWRITERS, COMPOSERS & AUTHORS**
2nd Floor, British Music House
26 Berners Street, London W1T 3LR
Website: www.basca.org.uk
e-mail: info@basca.org.uk
Fax: 020-7636 2212                    Tel: 020-7636 2929

**BFI SOUTH BANK**
Belvedere Road, South Bank
London SE1 8XT                       Tel: 020-7928 3535
Website: www.bfi.org.uk

**BRITISH ACADEMY OF FILM & TELEVISION ARTS**
195 Piccadilly, London W1J 9LN
Website: www.bafta.org
e-mail: membership@bafta.org
Fax: 020-7292 5868                    Tel: 020-7734 0022

**BRITISH ACADEMY OF FILM & TELEVISION ARTS/LOS ANGELES**
8533 Melrose Avenue
West Hollywood, CA 90069
Website: www.baftala.org
e-mail: office@baftala.org
Fax: (310) 854-6002                   Tel: (310) 652-4121

**BRITISH ACADEMY OF STAGE & SCREEN COMBAT**
Suite 280, 10 Great Russell Street
London WC1B 3BQ                   Mobile: 07981 806265
Website: www.bassc.org
e-mail: info@bassc.org

**BRITISH ASSOCIATION FOR PERFORMING ART MEDICINE (BAPAM)**
*Charity*
4th Floor, Totara Park House
34-36 Gray's Inn Road
London WC1X 8HR                    Tel: 020-7404 5888
Website: www.bapam.org.uk
e-mail: clinic@bapam.org.uk

**BRITISH ASSOCIATION OF DRAMATHERAPISTS The**
Waverley, Battledown Approach
Cheltenham, Glos GL52 6RE           Tel: 01242 235515
Website: www.badth.org.uk
e-mail: enquiries@badth.org.uk

**BRITISH BOARD OF FILM CLASSIFICATION**
3 Soho Square, London W1D 3HD
Website: www.bbfc.co.uk
Fax: 020-7287 0141                    Tel: 020-7440 1570

**BRITISH COUNCIL**
*Arts Group*
10 Spring Gardens
London SW1A 2BN                    Tel: 020-7389 3194
Website: www.britishcouncil.org/arts
e-mail: arts@britishcouncil.org

**BRITISH EQUITY COLLECTING SOCIETY**
Hudson House, 8 Tavistock Street
London WC2E 7PP                    Tel: 020-3178 6885
Website: www.equitycollecting.org.uk
e-mail: becs@equity.org.uk

**BRITISH FILM INSTITUTE**
21 Stephen Street, London W1T 1LN
Website: www.bfi.org.uk
Fax: 020-7436 2338                    Tel: 020-7255 1444

**BRITISH LIBRARY SOUND ARCHIVE**
96 Euston Road, London NW1 2DB
Website: www.bl.uk/soundarchive
e-mail: sound-archive@bl.uk
Fax: 020-7412 7441                    Tel: 020-7412 7676

**BRITISH MUSIC HALL SOCIETY**
*Contact: Daphne Masterton (Secretary)*
Meander, 361 Watford Road
Chiswell Green, St Albans
Herts AL2 3DB                        Tel: 01727 768878

**CATHOLIC ASSOCIATION OF PERFOMING ARTS**
*Contact: Ms Molly Steele (Hon Secretary) By Post (SAE)*
1 Maiden Lane
London WC2E 7NB                   Tel: 020-7240 1221
e-mail: secretary@caapa.org.uk

**CELEBRITY BULLETIN The**
8-10 Wiseton Road
London SW17 7EE
e-mail: enquiries@celebrity-bulletin.co.uk
Fax: 020-8672 2282                    Tel: 020-8672 3191

**CHILDREN'S FILM & TELEVISION FOUNDATION Ltd**
e-mail: annahome@cftf.org.uk      Mobile: 07887 573479

**CIDA (CREATIVE INDUSTRIES DEVELOPMENT AGENCY)**
*Professional Development & Business Support for Artists & Creative Businesses*
Media Centre, Huddersfield
West Yorkshire HD1 1RL
Website: www.cida.org
e-mail: info@cida.org
Fax: 01484 483150                     Tel: 01484 483140

**explore** different techniques and new ways of working in over 1700 classes a year, taught by top industry professionals

**extend** your skills and your networks with advanced workshops and groundbreaking labwork led by leading actors and directors

**excel** at your craft with one-to-one tuition and expert advice, all at prices that won't break the bank

The Actors Centre has been the UK's premiere resource for actors for over 30 years.

Discover what becoming a member can do for you and your career at www.actorscentre.co.uk

# the actors centre

## CINEMA & TELEVISION BENEVOLENT FUND (CTBF)
22 Golden Square
London W1F 9AD
Website: www.ctbf.co.uk
e-mail: charity@ctbf.co.uk
Fax: 020-7437 7186          Tel: 020-7437 6567

## CINEMA EXHIBITORS' ASSOCIATION
22 Golden Square, London W1F 9JW
Website: www.cinemauk.org
e-mail: cea@cinemauk.ftech.co.uk
Fax: 020-7734 6147          Tel: 020-7734 9551

## CLUB FOR ACTS & ACTORS
*(Incorporating Concert Artistes Association)*
20 Bedford Street, London WC2E 9HP
Website: www.thecaa.org
e-mail: office@thecaa.org
Office: 020-7836 3172          Members: 020-7836 2884

## COMPANY OF CRANKS
1st Floor, 62 Northfield House
Frensham Street
London SE15 6TN          Mobile: 07963 617981
Website: www.mimeworks.com
e-mail: mimetic16@yahoo.com

## CONCERT ARTISTES ASSOCIATION
(See CLUB FOR ACTS & ACTORS)

## CONFERENCE OF DRAMA SCHOOLS
*Contact: Saul Hyman. Comprises Britain's 22 Leading*
*Drama Schools. Publishes the Guide to Professional*
*Training in Drama & Technical Theatre*
PO Box 34252, London NW5 1XJ
Website: www.drama.ac.uk
e-mail: info@cds.drama.ac.uk

## COUNCIL FOR DANCE EDUCATION & TRAINING (CDET) The
Old Brewer's Yard
17-19 Neal Street, London WC2H 9UY
Website: www.cdet.org.uk
e-mail: info@cdet.org.uk
Fax: 020-7240 2547          Tel: 020-7240 5703

## CPMA
(Co-operative Personal Management Association)
The Secretary, c/o 30 Ambleside
Southfields, London SW19 6JY          Mobile: 07973 173988
Website: www.cpma.coop
e-mail: cpmauk@yahoo.co.uk

## CRITICS' CIRCLE The
c/o Catherine Cooper Events
69 Marylebone Lane
London W1U 2PH          Tel: 020-7224 1410
Website: www.criticscircle.org.uk

## D'OYLY CARTE OPERA COMPANY
First Floor
295 Kennington Road
London SE11 4QE
Website: www.doylycarte.org.uk
e-mail: ian@doylycarte.org.uk
Fax: 020-7820 0240          Tel: 0844 6060007

## DANCE HOUSE
20 St Andrews Street
Glasgow G1 5PD          Tel: 0141-552 2442
Website: www.dancehouse.org
e-mail: info@dancehouse.org

## DANCE UK
*(Including the Healthier Dancer Programme & 'The UK*
*Choreographers' Directory') Professional Body & Charity,*
*providing Advice, Funding, Information & Support*
The Urdang, The Old Finsbury Town Hall
Rosebery Avenue, London EC1R 4QT
Website: www.danceuk.org
e-mail: info@danceuk.org
Fax: 020-7833 2363          Tel: 020-7713 0730

## DENVILLE HALL
*Provides residential & nursing care to actors and other*
*theatrical professions*
62 Ducks Hill Road, Northwood
Middlesex HA6 2SB          Office: 01923 825843
Website: www.denvillehall.org.uk
e-mail: denvillehall@yahoo.com
Fax: 01923 841855          Residents: 01923 820805

## DIRECTORS UK
20-22 Bedford Row, London WC1R 4EB
Website: www.directors.uk.com
e-mail: info@directors.uk.com
Fax: 020-7269 0676          Tel: 020-7269 0677

## DRAMA ASSOCIATION OF WALES
*Specialist Drama Lending Library*
The Old Library, Singleton Road
Splott, Cardiff CF24 2ET          Tel: 029-2045 2200
e-mail: info@dramawales.org.uk

## DRAMATURGS' NETWORK
*Network of Professional Dramaturgs*
Website: www.dramaturgy.co.uk
e-mail: info@dramaturgy.co.uk          Mobile: 07939 270566

## ENGLISH FOLK DANCE & SONG SOCIETY
Cecil Sharp House
2 Regent's Park Road, London NW1 7AY
Website: www.efdss.org
e-mail: info@efdss.org
Fax: 020-7284 0534          Tel: 020-7485 2206

## EQUITY CHARITABLE TRUST
Plouviez House, 19-20 Hatton Place, London EC1N 8RU
e-mail: info@equitycharitabletrust.org.uk
Fax: 020-7242 7995          Tel: 020-7831 1926

## FILM LONDON
Suite 6.10, The Tea Building
56 Shoreditch High Street, London E1 6JJ
Website: www.filmlondon.org.uk
e-mail: info@filmlondon.org.uk
Fax: 020-7613 7677          Tel: 020-7613 7676

## GLASGOW FILM OFFICE
*Free Advice and Liaison Support for all Productions*
City Chambers, Glasgow G2 1DU
e-mail: info@glasgowfilm.com
Fax: 0141-287 0311          Tel: 0141-287 0424

## GRAND ORDER OF WATER RATS
328 Gray's Inn Road, London WC1X 8BZ
Website: www.gowr.net
e-mail: info@gowr.net
Fax: 020-7278 1765          Tel: 020-7278 3248

## GROUP LINE
*Group Bookings for London Theatre*
22-24 Torrington Place, London WC1E 7HJ
Website: www.groupline.com
e-mail: tix@groupline.com
Fax: 020-7436 6287          Tel: 020-7580 6793

# WE CAN HELP ACTORS' CHILDREN

## Are you:

- a professional actor?
- the parent of a child under 21?
- having trouble with finances?

Please get in touch for a confidential chat.

## The Actors' Charitable Trust
## 020 7636 7868
## robert@tactactors.org

TACT can help in many ways: with regular monthly payments, one-off grants, and long-term support and advice.
We help with clothing, child-care, music lessons, school trips, special equipment and adaptations, and in many other ways.

Our website has a link to a list of all the theatrical and entertainment charities which might be able to help you if you do not have children: www.tactactors.org

**TACT**

TACT, 58 Bloomsbury Street, London WC1B 3QT.
Registered charity number 206809.

**GUY Gillian ASSOCIATES**
84A Tachbrook Street
London SW1V 2NB    Tel: 020-7976 5888
e-mail: gillian@gillianguyassoc.com

**HAMMER FILMS PRESERVATION SOCIETY**
*Fan Club*
14 Kingsdale Road
Plumstead, London SE18 2DG    Tel: 020-8854 7383
e-mail: devohammerfilms29@yahoo.co.uk

**HEART OF ENTERTAINMENT The**
PO Box 174, Southgate
Sylvania, NSW 2224
Australia    Tel: 00 614 007 50065
Website: www.theheartofentertainment.com
e-mail: ceo@theheartofentertainment.com

**INDEPENDENT THEATRE COUNCIL (ITC)**
*Professional Body offering Advice, Information, Support
and Political Representation*
12 The Leathermarket
Weston Street, London SE1 3ER
Website: www.itc-arts.org
e-mail: admin@itc-arts.org
Fax: 020-7403 1745    Tel: 020-7403 1727

**IRVING SOCIETY The**
*Contact: Michael Kilgarriff (Hon. Secretary)*
10 Kings Avenue, London W5 2SH    Tel: 020-8566 8301
Website: www.theirvingsociety.org.uk
e-mail: secretary@theirvingsociety.org.uk

**ITC**
(See INDEPENDENT THEATRE COUNCIL)

**ITV Plc**
200 Gray's Inn Road
London WC1X 8HF    Tel: 020-7156 6000
Website: www.itv.com

**LONDON SCHOOL OF CAPOEIRA The**
Units 1 & 2 Leeds Place
Tollington Park, London N4 3RF    Tel: 020-7281 2020
Website: www.londonschoolofcapoeira.co.uk
e-mail: info@londonschoolofcapoeira.co.uk

**LONDON SHAKESPEARE WORKOUT**
PO Box 31855, London SE17 3XP    Tel/Fax: 020-7793 9755
Website: www.londonshakespeare.org.uk
e-mail: londonswo@hotmail.com

**MANDER & MITCHENSON THEATRE COLLECTION**
Jerwood Library of the Performing Arts
King Charles Building
Old Royal Naval College
Greenwich, London SE10 9JF
e-mail: rmangan@tcm.ac.uk
Fax: 020-8305 9426    Tel: 020-8305 4426

**NATIONAL ASSOCIATION OF YOUTH THEATRES (NAYT)**
*Contact: Jo Harker. Charity, providing Advice, Information
& Support. Founded in 1982, the National Association of
Youth Theatres (NAYT) is the flagship/registration
organisation for youth theatre practice in England,
supporting the development of Youth Theatre Activity
through programmes of Training, Advocacy & Participation*
Arts Centre, Vane Terrace
Darlington~
County Durham DL3 7AX
Website: www.nayt.org.uk
e-mail: nayt@btconnect.com
Fax: 01325 363313    Tel: 01325 363330

**NATIONAL CAMPAIGN FOR THE ARTS**
1 Kingly Street
London W1B 5PA
Website: www.artscampaign.org.uk
e-mail: nca@artscampaign.org.uk
Fax: 020-7287 4777    Tel: 020-7287 3777

**NATIONAL COUNCIL FOR DRAMA TRAINING**
249 Tooley Street
London SE1 2JX    Tel: 020-7407 3686
Website: www.ncdt.co.uk
e-mail: info@ncdt.co.uk

**NATIONAL RESOURCE CENTRE FOR DANCE**
University of Surrey
Guildford
Surrey GU2 7XH
Website: www.surrey.ac.uk/nrcd
e-mail: nrcd@surrey.ac.uk
Fax: 01483 689500    Tel: 01483 689316

**NEW PRODUCERS ALLIANCE**
Unit 7.03
The Tea Building
56 Shoreditch High Street
London E1 6JJ
Website: www.npa.org.uk
e-mail: queries@npa.org.uk
Fax: 020-7729 7852    Tel: 020-7613 0440

**NODA (National Operatic & Dramatic Association)**
*Charity, providing Advice, Information & Support. Largest
umbrella body for amateur theatre in the UK offering
advice and assistance on all aspects of amateur theatre
plus workshops, summer school and social events*
Noda House
58-60 Lincoln Road
Peterborough PE1 2RZ
Website: www.noda.org.uk
e-mail: info@noda.org.uk
Fax: 01733 319506    Tel: 01733 865790

**NORTH WEST PLAYWRIGHTS**
18 Express Networks
1 George Leigh Street
Manchester M4 5DL    Tel/Fax: 0161-237 1978
Website: www.newplaysnw.co.uk
e-mail: newplaysnw@hotmail.com

**OFCOM**
Ofcom Media Office
Riverside House
2A Southwark Bridge Road
London SE1 9HA    Tel: 0300 1234000
Website: www.ofcom.org.uk
e-mail: ofcomnews@ofcom.org.uk

**PACT**
*Trade Association for Independent Television, Feature Film
& New Media Production Companies*
3rd Floor Fitzrovia House
153-157 Cleveland Street
London W1T 6QW    Tel: 020-7380 8230
Website: www.pact.co.uk
e-mail: enquiries@pact.co.uk

**PERFORMING RIGHT SOCIETY Ltd**
29-33 Berners Street
London W1T 3AB
Website: www.mcps-prs-alliance.co.uk
Fax: 020-7306 4455    Tel: 020-7580 5544

**RICHARDSON Ralph & Meriel FOUNDATION**
c/o Suite 23
19 Cavendish Square
London W1A 2AW
Website: www.sirralphrichardson.org.uk
e-mail: manager@sirralphrichardson.org.uk
Fax: 020-7664 4489     Tel: 020-7636 1616

**ROYAL TELEVISION SOCIETY**
5th Floor, Kildare House
3 Dorset Rise
London EC4Y 8EN
Website: www.rts.org.uk
e-mail: info@rts.org.uk
Fax: 020-7822 2811     Tel: 020-7822 2810

**ROYAL THEATRICAL FUND**
11 Garrick Street
London WC2E 9AR
e-mail: admin@trtf.com
Fax: 020-7379 8273     Tel: 020-7836 3322

**SAMPAD SOUTH ASIAN ARTS**
*Promotes the appreciation & practice of South Asian Arts*
c/o Mac, Cannon Hill Park
Birmingham B12 9QH     Tel: 0121-452 8899
Website: www.sampad.org.uk
e-mail: info@sampad.org.uk

**SCOTTISH SCREEN**
249 West George Street
Glasgow G2 4QE
Website: www.scottishscreen.com
e-mail: info@scottishscreen.com
Fax: 0141-302 1711     Tel: 0141-302 1700

**SCRIPT**
*West Midlands Playwrights, Scriptwriters. Provides Training & Support*
Unit 107 The Greenhouse
The Custard Factory, Gibb Street
Birmingham B9 4AA     Tel: 0121-224 7415
Website: www.scriptonline.net

**SOCIETY OF AUTHORS**
*Trade Union for Professional Writers. Providing Advice, Funding, Information & Support*
84 Drayton Gardens
London SW10 9SB     Tel: 020-7373 6642
Website: www.societyofauthors.org
e-mail: info@societyofauthors.org

**SOCIETY OF BRITISH THEATRE DESIGNERS**
*Professional Body. Charity. Providing Advice and Information*
RBC, Burnt Oak Lane
Sidcup, Kent DA15 9DF     Tel: 020-8308 2664
Website: www.theatredesign.org.uk
e-mail: admin@theatredesign.org.uk

**SOCIETY OF LONDON THEATRE (SOLT)**
32 Rose Street, London WC2E 9ET
e-mail: enquiries@solttma.co.uk
Fax: 020-7557 6799     Tel: 020-7557 6700

**SOCIETY OF TEACHERS OF SPEECH & DRAMA The**
Registered Office:
73 Berry Hill Road, Mansfield
Nottinghamshire NG18 4RU     Tel: 01623 627636
Website: www.stsd.org.uk
e-mail: ann.k.jones@btinternet.com

**SOCIETY OF THEATRE CONSULTANTS**
27 Old Gloucester Street
London WC1N 3AX                    Tel: 020-7419 8767
Website: www.theatreconsultants.org.uk

**STAGE CRICKET CLUB**
39-41 Hanover Steps
St George's Fields
Albion Street, London W2 2YG
Website: www.stagecc.co.uk
e-mail: brianjfilm@aol.com
Fax: 020-7262 5736                 Tel: 020-7402 7543

**STAGE GOLFING SOCIETY**
Sudbrook Park
Sudbrook Lane
Richmond, Surrey TW10 7AS          Tel: 020-8940 8861
e-mail: sgs@richmondgolfclub.co.uk

**STAGE MANAGEMENT ASSOCIATION**
Providing Advice, Information & Support. Supports,
represents & promotes stage management and all its
practitioners. Provides help finding work, training and
networking opportunities and advice
55 Farringdon Road
London EC1M 3JB
Website: www.stagemanagementassociation.co.uk
e-mail: admin@stagemanagementassociation.co.uk
Fax: 020-7242 9303                 Tel: 020-7242 9250

**STAGE ONE (Operating Name of The Theatre
Investment Fund Ltd)**
32 Rose Street
London WC2E 9ET
Website: www.stageone.uk.com
e-mail: enquiries@stageone.uk.com
Fax: 020-7557 6799                 Tel: 020-7557 6737

**THEATRE WRITING PARTNERSHIP**
Nottingham Playhouse
Wellington Circus
Nottingham NG1 5AF
e-mail: info@theatrewritingpartnership.org.uk
Fax: 0115-947 5759                 Tel: 0115-947 4361

**THEATREMAD**
(Theatre: Make A Difference)
c/o The Make a Difference Trust
1st Floor
54 Greek Street
Soho, London W1D 3DS               Tel: 020-7734 5683
Website: www.theatremad.org.uk
e-mail: office@theatremad.org.uk

**THEATRES TRUST The**
*Contact: Kate Carmichael (Resources Officer).*
*(National Advisory Public Body for Theatres, Protecting
Theatres for Everyone) Charity. Social Membership.
Provides Advice, Support & Information*
22 Charing Cross Road
London WC2H 0QL
Website: www.theatrestrust.org.uk
e-mail: info@theatrestrust.org.uk
Fax: 020-7836 3302                 Tel: 020-7836 8591

**THEATRICAL GUILD The**
*Charity for Backstage & Front of House Staff*
PO Box 22712
London N22 5WQ                     Tel: 020-8889 7570
Website: www.ttg.org.uk
e-mail: admin@ttg.org.uk

**THEATRICAL MANAGEMENT ASSOCIATION**
(See TMA)

**TMA**
(Theatrical Management Association)
32 Rose Street
London WC2E 9ET
Website: www.tmauk.org
e-mail: enquiries@solttma.co.uk
Fax: 020-7557 6799                 Tel: 020-7557 6700

**TYA - UK CENTRE OF ASSITEJ**
*Contact: Paul Harman. International Association of Theatre
for Children and Young People*
16 Victoria Embankment
Darlington DL1 5JR                 Tel: 01325 483259
Website: www.tya-uk.org
e-mail: paul.harman@ntlworld.com

**UK CHOREOGRAPHERS' DIRECTORY The**
(See DANCE UK)

**UK FILM COUNCIL**
10 Little Portland Street
London W1W 7JG
Website: www.ukfilmcouncil.org.uk
e-mail: info@ukfilmcouncil.org.uk
Fax: 020-7861 7862                 Tel: 020-7861 7861

**UK THEATRE CLUBS**
54 Swallow Drive
London NW10 8TG                    Tel/Fax: 020-8459 3972
e-mail: uktheatreclubs@aol.com

**UNITED KINGDOM COPYRIGHT BUREAU**
110 Trafalgar Road
Portslade
East Sussex BN41 1GS               Tel: 01273 277333
Website: www.copyrightbureau.co.uk
e-mail: info@copyrightbureau.co.uk

**VARIETY & LIGHT ENTERTAINMENT COUNCIL**
54 Keyes House, Dolphin Square
London SW1V 3NA
Fax: 020-7821 0261                 Tel: 020-7798 5622

**VARIETY CLUB CHILDREN'S CHARITY**
Variety Club House
93 Bayham Street
London NW1 0AG
Website: www.varietyclub.org.uk
e-mail: info@varietyclub.org.uk
Fax: 020-7428 8111                 Tel: 020-7428 8100

**WOMEN IN FILM AND TELEVISION**
*Contact: Rebecca Brand. WFTV is the premier membership
organisation for women working in the Film, Television and
Digital Media industries in the UK. Provides Advice,
Information, Social Membership & Support*
Unit 2, Wedgewood Mews
12-13 Greek Street
London W1D 4BB
Website: www.wftv.org.uk
e-mail: info@wftv.org.uk
Fax: 020-7287 1500                 Tel: 020-7287 1400

**YOUTH MUSIC THEATRE: UK**
40 Parkgate Road
Battersea
London SW11 4JH                    Tel: 0844 4154858
Website: www.youthmusictheatreuk.org
e-mail: mail@ymtuk.org

**ABBEY Vincent**
Website: www.vincentabbey.co.uk
Tel: 0161-860 6794

**ACTORHEADSHOTS.CO.UK**
Website: www.actorheadshots.co.uk
e-mail: info@actorheadshots.co.uk
Mobile: 07740 507970

**ALLEN Stuart**
Website: www.stuartallenphotos.com
Mobile: 07776 258829

**AM LONDON**
Website: www.am-london.com
Mobile: 07974 188105
Tel: 020-7193 1868

**ANKER Matt**
Website: www.mattanker.com
Mobile: 07835 241835

**ANNAND Simon**
Website: www.simonannand.com
Mobile: 07884 446776
Tel: 020-7241 6725

**ARNETT PHOTOGRAPHY**
Website: www.artnett-photography.com
e-mail: anetphotography@aim.com
Mobile: 07951 991530

**BACON Ric**
Website: www.ricbacon.co.uk
Mobile: 07970 970799

**BAKER Chris**
Website: www.chrisbakerphotographer.com
e-mail: chrisbaker@photos2000.demon.co.uk
Tel: 020-8441 3851

**BAKER Sophie**
Tel: 020-8340 3850

**BARRASS Paul**
Website: www.paulbarrass.co.uk
e-mail: paul@paulbarrass.co.uk
Mobile: 07973 265931

**BARTLETT Pete**
Website: www.petebartlettheadshots.co.uk
e-mail: info@petebartlett.com
Mobile: 07971 653994

**BEVAN David J.**
Website: www.djbevanphotography.co.uk
e-mail: djbevan83@gmail.com
Mobile: 07811 368889

Photographers

Each photographer listed in this section has taken
an advertisement in this edition.
See Index to Advertisers pages to view each
advertisement.

Promotional Services
(CVs, Showreels, Websites etc)
Properties & Trades
Publications

[CONTACTS 2010]

**BIRNIE Paige**
Website: www.paigebirniephotos.com
e-mail: paige@paigebirnie.com
Mobile: 07531 721546

**BISHOP Brandon**
Website: www.brandonbishopphotography.com
Mobile: 07931 383830
Tel: 020-7275 7468

**BRITTON Anthony**
Website: www.anthonybritton.co.uk
e-mail: anthony-britton@btconnect.com
Tel: 01784 488343

**BROUSSELY Marc**
Website: www.10x8headshots.com
e-mail: info@10x8headshots.com
Mobile: 07738 920225

**BURNETT Sheila**
Website: www.sheilaburnett-photography.com
Tel: 020-7289 3058

**CABLE Paul**
Website: www.paulcable.com
e-mail: info@paulcable.com
Mobile: 07958 932764

**CANNON Luke**
Website: www.lukecannonphotography.com
Mobile: 07803 908858

**CARPENTER Ben**
Website: www.bencarpenterphotography.com
Mobile: 07505 442829

**CARDWELL Simon**
Website: www.headshotsbysimon.com
e-mail: simoncardwell@googlemail.com
Mobile: 07949 660043

**CARTER Charlie**
Website: www.charliecarter.com
Tel: 020-8222 8742

**CLARK John**
Website: www.johnclarkphotography.com
e-mail: info@johnclarkphotography.com
Mobile: 07702 627237
Tel: 020-8854 4069

**CROLLA Anna Isola**
Website: www.annaisolacrolla.co.uk
Mobile: 07980 551468

**CW PHOTOS**
Website: www.cwphotos.co.uk
Tel: 023-8073 2550

**DANCE SCENE PHOTOGRAPHIC**
Website: www.dancepics4u.co.uk
Tel: 01737 552874

**DAVISON PICTURES**
Website: www.davisonpictures.co.uk
e-mail: maggie@davisonpictures.co.uk
Mobile: 07917 758754
Tel: 020-8579 7006

**DAWKES Nicholas**
Website: www.nicholasdawkesphotography.co.uk
Mobile: 07787 111997

**DNC PHOTOGRAPHY**
Website: www.dnc-photography.co.uk
e-mail: info@dnc-photography.co.uk
Tel: 01908 234138

**GIBB Adrian**
Website: www.adriangibb.co.uk
e-mail: adriangibb@googlemail.com
Tel: 020-7639 6215

**GREGAN Nick**
Website: www.nickgregan.com
e-mail: info@nickgregan.com
Mobile: 07774 421878
Tel: 020-8533 3003

**GROGAN Claire**
Website: www.clairegrogan.co.uk
e-mail: claire@clairegrogan.co.uk
Mobile: 07932 635381
Tel: 020-7272 1845

**HAINES Rob**
Mobile: 07775 758164
Tel: 020-8538 9990

**HARWOOD-STAMPER Dan**
Website: www.danharwoodstamper.co.uk
Mobile: 07779 165777
Tel: 01442 242410

**HEARN Anthony**
Website: www.aphearn-photography.com
e-mail: hearn698@btinternet.com
Mobile: 07809 502763

## How do I find a photographer?

Having a good quality, up-to-date promotional headshot is crucial for every performer. Make sure you choose your photographer very carefully: do some research and try to look at different examples. Photographers' adverts run throughout this book, featuring many sample shots, although to get a real feel for their work you should also try to see their portfolio or website since this will give a more accurate impression of the quality of their photography.

If you live in or around London, please feel free to visit the Spotlight offices and look through current editions of our directories to find a style you like. We also have nearly sixty photographers' portfolios available for you to browse, many of them from photographers listed over the next few pages. Our offices are open Monday - Friday, 10.00am - 5.30pm at 7 Leicester Place, London WC2H 7RJ (nearest tube is Leicester Square).

## What should I expect from the photo shoot?

When it comes to your photo shoot, bear in mind that a casting director, agent or production company will want to see a photo of the 'real' you. Keep your appearance as neutral as possible so that they can imagine you in many different roles, rather than type-casting yourself from the outset and limiting your opportunities.

Your eyes are your most important feature, so make sure they are visible: face the camera straight-on and try not to smile too much because it makes them harder to see. Wear something simple and avoid jewellery, hats, scarves, glasses or props, since these will all add character. Do not wear clothes that detract from your face such as polo necks, big collars, busy patterns or logos. Always keep your hands out of the shot.

Also consider the background: some photographers like to do outdoor shots. A contrast between background and hair colour works well, whereas dark backgrounds work less well with dark hair, and the same goes for light hair on light backgrounds.

## Which photograph should I choose?

When you get your contact sheet back from the photographer, make sure you choose a photo that looks like you - not how you would like to look. If you are unsure, ask friends or your agent for an honest opinion. Remember, you will be asked to attend meetings and auditions on the basis of your photograph, so if you turn up looking completely different you will be wasting everyone's time.

## Due to copyright legislation, you must always credit the photographer when using the photo.

## How should I submit my photo to Spotlight and to casting professionals?

All photographs submitted to Spotlight must be of the highest possible quality, otherwise casting professionals will not see you in the best possible light. If you are sending your photo by hard copy, we would expect a 10 x 8 sized print, which is the industry standard. It is not necessary to provide an original print: a high quality, clear focused repro is fine. If you are sending a digital image by e-mail or disk, we have certain technical specifications which can be found on our website (see below). We would recommend that you follow similar guidelines when sending your headshot directly to casting professionals.

## What are Spotlight portfolio photographs?

Every Spotlight performer can also add extra photographs onto their web page, in addition to their principal photograph. These are called portfolio photos, and they give you the opportunity to show yourself in a range of different shots and / or roles. Members can upload up to 15 digital photos to their online CV free of charge by logging on from www.spotlight.com with their update PIN.

Please visit www.spotlight.com/artists/appear/multimedia/photos for further information

**HUGHES Jamie**
Website: www.jamiehughesphotography.com/headshots
e-mail: jhpixx@gmail.com
Mobile: 07850 122977

**HULL Anna**
Website: www.annahullphotography.com
Tel: 020-7498 5023

**JAMES Katherine**
Website: www.katherine-james.com
e-mail: info@katherine-james.com
Mobile: 07734 680543

**JAMES Nick**
Website: www.nickjamesphotography.co.uk
Mobile: 07961 122030

**JAMIE Matt**
Website: www.mattjamie.co.uk/portraits
Mobile: 07976 890643

**JEFFERSON Paris**
Website: www.parisjefferson.com
Mobile: 07876 586601

**JOHNSON Beaj**
Website: www.beajpix.com
e-mail: info@beajpix.com
Mobile: 07973 382859

**JONES Denis**
Website: www.djpix.co.uk
Mobile: 07836 241158

**KEATES James**
Website: www.jk-photography.net
Mobile: 07816 825578

**KENNEDY Eamon**
Website: www.eamon-kennedy.co.uk
e-mail: epkfoto@gmail.com
Mobile: 07949 581069

**KOVAL STUDIO PHOTOGRAPHY**
Website: www.piotrkowalik.co.uk
Mobile: 07946 323631

**LADENBURG Jack**
Website: www.jackladenburg.co.uk
e-mail: info@jackladenburg.co.uk
Mobile: 07932 053743

**LATIMER Carole**
Website: www.carolelatimer.com
e-mail: carole.latimer@freenet.co.uk
Tel: 020-7727 9371

**LAWTON Steve**
Website: www.stevelawton.com
Mobile: 07973 307487

**LE MAY Pete**
Website: www.petelemay.co.uk
Mobile: 07703 649246

**LEE Daniel R.**
Website: www.danielrlee.co.uk
e-mail: dan@danielrlee.co.uk
Mobile: 07985 586412

**LOOKER James**
Website: www.jameslookerphotography.com
Mobile: 07973 566537

**M.A.D. PHOTOGRAPHY**
Website: www.mad-photography.co.uk
Mobile: 07949 581909
Tel: 020-8363 4182

**MERCHANT Natasha**
Website: www.natashamerchant.com
Mobile: 07932 618111
Tel: 020-8653 5399

**MOUNT Gemma**
Website: www.gemmamountphotography.com
e-mail: gemma@gemmamountphotography.com
Mobile: 07976 824923

**MULHOLLAND Ruth**
Website: www.ruthmulholland.com
Mobile: 07939 516987

**NAMDAR Fatimah**
Website: www.fatimahnamdar.com
e-mail: fnamdar@mac.com
Mobile: 07973 287535
Tel: 020-8341 1332

**POLLARD Michael**
Website: www.michaelpollard.co.uk
e-mail: info@michaelpollard.co.uk
Tel: 0161-456 7470

**POWER Eliza**
Website: www.elizapower.co.uk
e-mail: eliza.ckpower@gmail.com
Mobile: 07590 370261

**PRICE David**
Website: www.davidpricephotography.co.uk
e-mail: info@davidpricephotography.co.uk
Mobile: 07950 542494

**PROCTOR Carl**
Website: www.carlproctorphotography.com
e-mail: carlphotos@btconnect.com
Mobile: 07956 283340

**RAFIQUE Harry**
Website: www.hr-photographer.co.uk
Mobile: 07986 679498

**RICHMOND Eric**
Website: www.ericrichmond.net
Tel: 020-8880 6909

**ROUND ISLAND**
Website: www.roundisland.net
e-mail: photos@roundisland.net

**SAVAGE Robin**
Website: www.robinsavage.co.uk
e-mail: contact@robinsavage.co.uk
Mobile: 07901 927597

**SAYER Howard**
Website: www.howardsayer.com
e-mail: howard@howardsayer.com
Mobile: 07860 559891

**SCOTT Karen**
Website: www.karenscottphotography.com
e-mail: info@karenscottphotography.com
Mobile: 07958 975950

**SHAKESPEARE LANE Catherine**
Website: www.csl-art.co.uk
Tel: 020-7226 7694

**SIMPKIN Peter**
Website: www.petersimpkin.co.uk
e-mail: petersimpkin@aol.com
Mobile: 07973 224084
Tel: 020-8364 2634

**SUMMERS Caroline**
Website: www.gallery.me.com/carolinesummers
Mobile: 07799 301234
Tel: 020-7223 7669

**THORNE Philip**
Website: www.philipthorne.co.uk/filmandportraits
Mobile: 07931 350329
Tel: 01582 873165

**TURNER Mike**
Website: www.miketurner-photography.co.uk
Mobile: 07751 442792
Tel: 01942 519702

**ULLATHORNE Steve**
Website www.steveullathorne.com
e-mail: steve@steveullathorne.com
Mobile: 07961 380969

**VALENTINE Vanessa**
Website: www.vanessavalentinephotography.com
Mobile: 07904 059541

**VARLEY Luke**
Website: www.lukevarley.com
Mobile: 07711 183631

**VERASTEGUI Ana**
Website: www.anaverastegui.com
e-mail: ana_verastegui@hotmail.com
Mobile: 07818 067557

**WALK TALL**
e-mail: info@walk-tall.org.uk
Tel: 0845 2708130

**WEBSTER Caroline**
Website: www.carolinewebster.co.uk
Mobile: 07867 653019
Tel: 020-8883 4961

**WILL C**
Website: www.london-photographer.com
e-mail: billy_snapper@hotmail.com
Mobile: 07712 669953
Tel: 020-8438 0303

**WILKINSON Howard**
Website: www.howardwilkinsonphotography.co.uk
Mobile: 07947 345305
Tel: 01706 645203

**WILSON Jamie**
Website: www.jamiewilsonphotography.com
e-mail: jamie@jamiewilsonphotography.com
Mobile: 07790 023532

**WINDHAM Marco**
Website: www.flickr.com/photos/marcowindham
Mobile: 07768 330027
Tel: 020-7737 5954

**WORKMAN Robert**
Website: www.robertworkman.demon.co.uk
Tel: 020-7385 5442

**A1 VOX Ltd**
(Spoken Word Audio, ISDN Links, Demo CDs & Audio Clips)
20 Old Compton Street
London W1D 4TW                          Tel: 020-7434 4404
Website: www.a1vox.com
e-mail: info@a1vox.com

**ABBEY ROAD STUDIOS**
3 Abbey Road, St John's Wood
London NW8 9AY
Website: www.abbeyroad.com
e-mail: bookings@abbeyroad.com
Fax: 020-7266 7250                       Tel: 020-7266 7000

**ACTOR SHOWREELS**
(Showreel Service)
97B Central Hill
London SE19 1BY
Website: www.actorshowreels.co.uk
e-mail: post@actorshowreels.co.uk
Mobile: 07939 241377          Mobile: 07835 637965

**ACTORS CENTRE**
(Showreels for Actors & Presenters)
1A Tower Street
London WC2H 9NP                          Tel: 020-7632 8013
Website: www.actorscentre.co.uk
e-mail: admin@actorscentre.co.uk

**ACTORS ILLUMINATED.COM**
Contact: Kosha Engler
(Websites for People in The Performing Arts)
131 Glengall Road
London NW6 7HG                 Mobile: 07769 626074
Website: www.actorsilluminated.com
e-mail: mail@actorsilluminated.com

**ACTORS INTERACTIVE**
(Web Design)
10 Frobisher Street
London SE10 9XB                          Tel: 020-8465 5457
Website: www.actorsinteractive.com
e-mail: office@actorsinteractive.com

**ACTOR'S ONE-STOP SHOP The**
(Showreels, Websites, Photography
CVs for Performing Artists)
First Floor
Above The Gate Pub
Station Road
London N22 7SS                           Tel: 020-8888 7006
Website: www.actorsonestopshop.com
e-mail: info@actorsonestopshop.com

**ACTORSSHOWREELS.COM**
241 Crystal Palace Road
London SE22 9JQ                  Mobile: 07915 662767
e-mail: info@actorsshowreels.com

**ACTUALLYACTORS.COM**
(Websites)
3 Milestone Road
London SE19 2LL                          Tel: 020-8325 1946
Website: www.actuallyactors.com
e-mail: mail@actuallyactors.co.uk

**AIR-EDEL RECORDING STUDIOS Ltd**
18 Rodmarton Street
London W1U 8BJ
e-mail: bethan.barron@air-edel.co.uk
Fax: 020-7224 0344                       Tel: 020-7486 6466

**ANGEL RECORDING STUDIOS Ltd**
311 Upper Street, London N1 2TU
e-mail: bookings@angelstudio.co.uk
Fax: 020-7226 9624                       Tel: 020-7354 2525

**ANT FARM STUDIOS VOICE-OVERS**
Southend Farm
Southend Lane
Waltham Abbey EN9 3SE                    Tel: 01992 714664
Website: www.antfarmstudios.co.uk
e-mail: antfarmstudio@yahoo.co.uk

**APPLE VIDEO FACILITIES**
The Studio, 821 Chorley Old Road
Lancashire BL1 5SL
Website: www.applevideo.co.uk
e-mail: info@applevideo.co.uk
Fax: 01204 495020                        Tel: 01204 847974

**ASCENT MEDIA Ltd**
Film House, 142 Wardour Street
London W1F 8DD
Website: www.ascentmedia.co.uk
Fax: 020-7878 7870                       Tel: 020-7878 0000

**BEWILDERING PICTURES**
Contact: Graeme Kennedy
(Showreel Service & Duplication, West London)
Website: www.bewildering.co.uk
e-mail: gk@bewildering.co.uk       Mobile: 07974 916258

**BLUE JOY STUDIO**
(Voice Tapes, Musical Demos)
12 Rutford Road, London SW16 2DH
Website: www.sound2picture.com
e-mail: guyholden@post.com         Mobile: 07961 100006

**CHANNEL 2020 Ltd**
The Clerkenwell Workshops (G15)
27-31 Clerkenwell Close
London EC1R 0AT                          Tel: 0844 8402020
Website: www.channel2020.co.uk
e-mail: info@channel2020.co.uk

2020 House, 26-28 Talbot Lane
Leicester LE1 4LR
Fax: 0116-222 1113                       Tel: 0844 8402020

# YOUR OWN PERSONALISED WEBPAGE!

*Send out your link and Casting Directors can view it in just one click.*

## MANONKAHLE

**Contact & Links**

Agentur Hobrig
Nantesstraße 70
13127 Berlin

Agent's Website

E-Mail

Spotlight

Powered by:
Take Five Studio

▶ ■ 00:00 |             01:03

Manon Kahle is an American actress and has been working in Berlin since late 2003.
Since learning the lanugage, she's had the opportunity to work on various German films and
TV-series as well as films in English.
For more information, please link to her agent's site.

**TAKE FIVE** webpages provide:

- online showreel streaming

- a world-wide audience

- a place to display your headshot

- links to email & other websites

To see an example webpage please visit:
www.takefivestudio.com/showreels

Your exclusive webpage will allow fast and easy viewing of your showreel.

Simply submit your showreel to us and we'll do the rest.

For more information on prices and options, call **020 7287 2120** or email info@takefivestudio.com.

TAKE FIVE STUDIO
37 BEAK ST
LONDON W1F 9RZ
TEL: +44 (0) 20 7287 2120
FAX: +44 (0) 20 7287 3035

[AUDITIONS]    [CASTING STUDIOS]    [SHOWREEL EDITING]

# infopage

## What are promotional services?

This section contains listings for companies who provide practical services to help performers promote themselves. You might need to improve or create your CV; record a showreel or voicereel; design your own website; duplicate CDs; or print photographic repros, CVs or Z-cards: all essential ways to create a good impression with those that count in the industry.

## Why do I need to promote myself?

Performers need to invest in marketing and promotion as much as any other self-employed businessperson. Even if you have trained at a leading drama school, have a well-known agent, or have just finished work on a popular TV series, you should never sit back and wait for your phone to ring or for the next job opportunity just to knock on your door. In such a competitive industry, successful performers are usually the ones who market themselves pro-actively and treat their careers as a 'business'.

Having up-to-date and well-produced promotional material makes a performer look professional and serious about their career: and hence a desirable person for a director or agent to work with.

## Why is my CV important?

Poor presentation, punctuation and grammar create a bad first impression and you risk your CV being dismissed before it is even read. Make sure that you continually update your CV - you don't want it to look as if you haven't been working recently when you have, and you don't want to miss out on an audition because you haven't included skills you have put time and effort into achieving. Your CV should be kept to a maximum of one page and printed on good-quality paper.

## Why is my covering letter important?

Always include a covering letter to introduce your CV and persuade casting professionals that it is worth reading. Remember that they receive hundreds each week. Keep your communication concise and be professional at all times. We also recommend that your letter has some kind of focus: perhaps you can tell them about your next showcase, or where they can see you currently appearing on stage. Ideally this should be addressed to an individual, not "Dear Sir or Madam".

## Why is my headshot important?

Your CV should feature, or be accompanied by, a recent headshot which is an accurate current likeness. See the 'Photographers' section for more information about promotional photography. You may need to print copies of your headshot through a repro company, some of whom are listed over the following pages.

## Why do I need a voicereel?

If you are interested in voice-over and/or radio work, you will need a professional-sounding voicereel to show agents, casting directors and potential employers what your voice is capable of. For commercial and corporate voice-over work this should be no more than two minutes long with a number of short clips demonstrating your range, but showcase the strengths of your natural voice as much as possible. It should contain a mixture of commercials and narrations.

A radio voicereel should be around eight minutes long, with four clips no longer than two minutes each, and read in your natural voice. To achieve a good balance of material, one clip should be 'classical', one 'contemporary', one 'comic' and one a poem. This is designed to give an overview of your suitability to various areas of radio work.

Record your voicereel in a professional studio to ensure a high-quality result, otherwise you are unlikely to be considered in this competitive industry. For further information please see the 'Agents - Voice-over' and 'Radio' sections.

## Why do I need a showreel?

Some casting directors nowadays will only consider a performer for an audition if they have first seen them demonstrating their skills in a showreel. A CV and headshot give some indication of their potential, but can only provide a basic summary.

## What should I do if I don't currently have anything on film?

Showreels are expensive to produce if you don't currently have any broadcasted material to use, but it is advisable to get one professionally recorded and edited if at all possible. Showreels help you to promote yourself, but a casting director may be put off by a poor quality one. You might want to consider a *Spotlight Intro* as a temporary alternative to a full showreel (see below). It may also be worth considering working on a student film. Students are usually willing to let you keep a copy of their film and casting professionals would consider this an acceptable alternative. See 'Film & Television Schools' for further advice and listings.

## How long should my showreel be?

We would recommend no more than three or four minutes. Casting professionals receive thousands of CVs and showreels and do not have time to watch every actor for ten minutes each. This is why we suggest you do not send your showreel out with your CV, but instead mention in your covering letter that one is available.

## What should I use in my showreel?

Rather than one long excerpt, it is more beneficial to demonstrate your versatility with a number of different clips. Focus on your strongest characters to enable the casting director to picture you in the roles you play best.

The first 30 seconds are the most important in your showreel, and can be the only part a busy casting director or agent has time to look at. You may wish to start with a brief montage summarising the clips that are to follow, or with a headshot of yourself so that they know who to watch out for.

The focus should be on you, not on the other actors, so close-up shots ought to be included. You should be speaking most if not all of the time. A visual contrast is good, whether this means filming in a different location or setting, or changing your outfit. You should avoid well-known scripts in order to prevent drawing comparisons between yourself and previous successful interpretations.

## What is a *Spotlight Intro?*

If you are a Spotlight member, a *Spotlight Intro* is your opportunity to give casting professionals a quick introduction to you, your character and your voice with a one or two minute video as part of your Spotlight CV. Think of it as a video version of a covering letter you might enclose with a paper CV. It could also be used as a temporary alternative to a showreel, although ideally you should include both.
Please visit www.spotlight.com/spotlightintro for further information.

## How should I use these listings?

If you are looking for a company to help you with any of these promotional items, browse through this section carefully and get quotes from a number of places to compare. If you are a Spotlight member, some companies offer a discount on their services. Always ask to see samples of a company's work, and ask friends in the industry for their own recommendations.

# infopage

**Ben Warren established Round Island in 2002. They produce showreels, voicereels and headshots along with marketing and web solutions for actors and other creatives.**

The way you are marketed is really important. Material that is not up to scratch draws attention for all the wrong reasons, but get it right and you're putting yourself in the best position from which to approach the business. Know what your strengths are and then package them in a way that is attractive to the industry. Take a step back, forget you're an artist for a moment and concentrate on the product you are selling.

A well produced **showreel** offers a three-dimensional insight into you and your work. It needs to be well presented, professionally edited and the right length. It is not an archive of your work; it offers a taster, an introduction. It should leave nothing but a good impression, leave the viewer wanting more, and be as individual as you are. There is no set formula, so look for a company who can take you through the process step by step, will work with you on what to include, can suggest how best to exploit your scenes and who won't clutter the reel with photos and contact information before the reel has even got going. You should be involved at every stage. We encourage clients to be present at the edit. Use a company that archives your work and with whom you can develop a relationship so that as your career and needs change, so too can your showreel.

When producing a **voicereel**, so often people make the mistake of trying to showcase too much. Of course if you are highly skilled with character voices and accents then don't ignore these, but don't forget that your natural voice is totally unique so it should feature heavily on your reel. The market is forever developing - there are many avenues of work available to the voice artist today that were unthinkable ten years ago. Your voicereel is the gateway to that work. Talk to voicereel companies and get a feel for the service and the people you will be working with. Listen to samples and make sure the service can be tailored to your needs. Look for a company that won't rush you, has an environment where you will feel comfortable and relaxed and offers the right kind of directional support. Finally, you don't want your reel to sound like anyone else's so steer clear of people who offer folders of scripts and who don't produce their own bespoke sound effects and jingles.

When sending out your **promotional material**, quality is key - using the best products doesn't have to cost the earth. Use a good quality paper and keep letters short, personal and to the point. Don't let previous rejections bleed onto the page - the tiniest hint of bitterness or desperation is a huge turn-off. Make sure your CV is always up-to-date, easy on the eye and that the most important information is quickly accessible. If you have many credits, select the most relevant. If you are just starting out, a sparse CV is no bad thing. Don't find things to fill it - you are unknown, undiscovered. Casting directors love discovering new talent, so use that - you won't be a newcomer forever.

You want a **headshot** that looks like you with an edge about it that will get you through the door. It is a combination of the photographer's skill with the camera and your relationship with it. The more comfortable you are the better your photos will be. Resist printing your own repros - you can tell the difference a mile off and although there may be some great home printers available they do not touch professional printers. When sending out disk media make sure you use a **CD/DVD duplication** company who burn onto the most compatible and highest grade disks. There should be no reduction in quality from your original and the company should be able to offer you a bespoke design and print service too - the last thing you want is your reel to look like everyone else's. Steer clear of labels and ask how they print the disks - some printing methods can leave disks unprotected, meaning they might smudge or smear easily. So make sure artwork is sealed and finished well - a glossy surface also looks great.

Whatever marketing materials you need there are top quality options out there for everyone's budget.

Please visit www.roundisland.net for further information.

**CHASE Stephan PRODUCTIONS Ltd**
(Director for Voice Overs and Showreels)
The Studio
22 York Avenue
London SW14 7LG     Tel: 020-8878 9112
Website: www.stephanchase.com
e-mail: stephan@stephanchase.com

**CLAW FILMS**
Website: www.clawfilms.com
e-mail: info@clawfilms.com     Tel: 020-7193 2197

**CLICKS**
Media Studios, Grove Road
Rochester, Kent ME2 4BX
e-mail: info@clicksstudios.co.uk
Fax: 01634 726000     Tel: 01634 723838

**CONCEPT**
PO Box 192
Liverpool L69 1JA     Tel: 0151-737 1794
Website: www.soundconcept.co.uk
e-mail: info@soundconcept.co.uk

**COURTWOOD PHOTOGRAPHIC Ltd**
(Photographic Reproduction)
Profile Prints
Freepost T055
Penzance
Cornwall TR20 8DU
Website: www.courtwood.co.uk
e-mail: people@courtwood.co.uk
Fax: 01736 741255     Tel: 01736 741222

**CROWE Ben**
(Voice Clip Recording)
23 John Aird Court
London W2 1UY
e-mail: bencrowe@hotmail.co.uk
Mobile: 07952 784911     Tel/Fax: 020-7262 3543

**CRYING OUT LOUD PRODUCTIONS**
(Voice-over Specialists, Demo CDs, Voice Training, Radio-Ad
Production. Studio based in Soho, London)
25 Eastlake Road
London SE5 9QJ
Website: www.cryingoutloud.co.uk
e-mail: simon@cryingoutloud.co.uk
Mobile: 07809 549887     Tel: 020-3262 3076

**CRYSTAL MEDIA**
28 Castle Street
Edinburgh EH2 3HT
Website: www.crystal-media.co.uk
e-mail: hello@crystal-media.co.uk
Fax: 0131-240 0989     Tel: 0131-240 0988

**CTS/LANSDOWNE RECORDING STUDIOS Ltd**
PO Box 47189
London W6 6DA
Website: www.cts-lansdowne.co.uk
e-mail: info@cts-lansdowne.co.uk
Fax: 056-0115 5009     Tel: 020-8846 9444

**CUT GLASS PRODUCTIONS**
(Voice-over Showreels/Voice-over Production)
Studio 187
181-187 Queens Crescent
Camden
London NW5 4DS     Tel: 020-7267 2339
Website: www.cutglassproductions.com
e-mail: info@cutglassproductions.com

**DARK SIDE**
(Photographic Repro Service)
4 Helmet Row
London EC1V 3QJ
Website: www.darksidephoto.co.uk
e-mail: info@darksidephoto.co.uk
Fax: 020-7250 1771     Tel: 020-7250 1200

WWW.HARVEYHOUSEFILMS.CO.UK
# SHOWREELS
IT'S ABOUT THE PERSONAL TOUCH WITH THE PROFESSIONAL LOOK

CHRIS@HARVEYHOUSEFILMS.CO.UK
TEL: +44(0)7968 830536          BASED IN WEST LONDON

**DE LANE LEA SOUND**
(Post-Production, Re-Recording Studios)
75 Dean Street, London W1D 3PU
Website: www.delanelea.com
e-mail: solutions@delanelea.com
Fax: 020-7432 3838          Tel: 020-7432 3800

**DENBRY REPROS Ltd**
(Photographic Reproduction)
57 High Street
Hemel Hempstead
Herts HP1 3AF          Tel: 01442 242411
Website: www.denbryrepros.com
e-mail: info@denbryrepros.com

**DESIGN CREATIVES & OCTOPUS REACH**
Contact: Anthony Rosato (Artistic Promotions &
Graphic/Web Design & Hosting)
Suite B, 5 South Bank Terrace
Surbiton
Surrey KT6 6DG
Website: www.octopusreach.com
e-mail: octopusreach1@aol.com
Mobile: 07787 995604          Tel: 020-8390 8535

**DV2BROADCAST**
3 Carolina Way, Salford M50 2ZY
Website: www.dv2broadcast.co.uk
e-mail: info@dv2broadcast.co.uk          Tel: 0161-736 5300

**DYNAMIC ISLE STUDIO**
58 Selhurst New Road, South Norwood
London SE25 5PU          Mobile: 07956 951090
Website: www.olympicrecordsuk.com
e-mail: olympicrecords@tiscali.co.uk

**ELMS STUDIOS**
Contact: Phil Lawrence (Intel Power Mac, Live Studio,
Composing/Scoring for Film & Television)
10 Empress Avenue
London E12 5ES          Tel: 020-8518 8629
Website: www.elmsstudios.com
e-mail: info@elmsstudios.com

**ESSENTIAL MUSIC**
20 Great Chapel Street, London W1F 8FW
e-mail: info@essentialmusic.co.uk
Fax: 020-7287 3597          Tel: 020-7439 7113

**EXECUTIVE AUDIO VISUAL**
(Showreels for Actors & Presenters, DVD Duplication
Service)
80 York Street
London W1H 1QW          Tel/Fax: 020-7723 4488

**FIREFLY PRODUCTIONS**
Twin Oaks, Hale Purlieu
Fordingbridge SP6 2NN          Mobile: 07956 675276
Website: www.fireflyproductions.info
e-mail: theonlyfirefly@aol.com

**FLOURISH NEW BIZ Ltd**
13 Temple Close
London E11 1JN          Tel: 020-8539 5400
Website: www.flourishnewbiz.co.uk
e-mail: simone@flourishnewbiz.co.uk

**FLUTTERLASH.COM**
19 Nelson Street, Tyledsley
Lancs M29 8NJ          Mobile: 07815 128125
Website: www.flutterlash.com
e-mail: lynette@flutterlash.com

**FREEDALE PRESS Ltd**
(Printing)
36 Hedley Street, Maidstone
Kent ME14 5AD
e-mail: michael@freedale.co.uk
Fax: 01622 200131          Tel: 01622 200123

**GENESIS UK.COM Ltd**
18 Pendre Enterprise Park
Tywyn, Gwynedd LL36 9LW
Website: www.genesis-uk.com
e-mail: info@genesis-uk.com
Fax: 01654 712461          Tel: 01654 710137

**GYROSCOPE STUDIOS**
Contact: Frank Sanderson
Hökmossevägen 34
SE12638 Hägersten
Sweden          Tel: 00 46 86 45 92 23
Website: www.gyroscope-studios.com
e-mail: frank@gyroscope-studios.com

**HARVEY HOUSE FILMS**
(Showreels)
71 Shouthfield Road
London W4 1BB          Mobile: 07719 555419
Website: www.harveyhousefilms.co.uk
e-mail: chris@harveyhousefilms.co.uk

**HEAVY ENTERTAINMENT Ltd**
111 Wardour Street
London W1F 0UH
Website: www.heavy-entertainment.com
e-mail: info@heavy-entertainment.com
Fax: 020-7494 1100          Tel: 020-7494 1000

**HOTQS**
(Showreels)
2nd Floor, 18 Kingsland Road
London E2 8DA          Mobile: 07903 017819
Website: www.houseofthequietstorm.com
e-mail: pat@houseofthequietstorm.com

**HOTREELS**
(Voice and Showreels)
Website: www.hotreels.co.uk
e-mail: info@hotreels.co.uk
Mobile: 07793 394951          Tel: 020-7952 4362

**HOUSE OF WEB**
(Web Design)
16 Duncombe House
Windlesham Grove
London SW19 6AJ
Website: www.houseofweb.co.uk
e-mail: marte@houseofweb.co.uk
Mobile: 07962 471118          Tel: 0800 4488675

**IMAGE PHOTOGRAPHIC**
(Photographic Reproduction)
54 Shepherds Bush Road
London W6 7PH
Website: www.imagephotographic.com
e-mail: sales@imagephotographic.com
Fax: 020-7602 6219          Tel: 020-7602 1190

**JMS GROUP Ltd The**
Park Farm Studios
Norwich Road
Hethersett, Norfolk NR9 3DL
Website: www.jms-group.com
e-mail: info@jms-group.com
Fax: 01603 812255          Tel: 01603 811855

**KONK STUDIOS**
84-86 Tottenham Lane
London N8 7EE
e-mail: linda@konkstudios.com
Fax: 020-8348 3952          Tel: 020-8340 7873

**LONDON FILM COMPANY Ltd**
Suite B
5 South Bank Terrace
Surbiton
Surrey KT6 6DG
Website: www.doncapo.com
e-mail: doncapoandco@aol.com
Mobile: 07787 995604          Tel: 020-8390 8535

**LONDON SHOWREELS**
PO Box 55278
London N22 9FZ          Tel: 020-8144 6750
Website: www.londonshowreels.co.uk
e-mail: sales@londonshowreels.co.uk

**LUMEN STUDIO**
103 Islingword Road
Brighton
East Sussex BN2 9SG          Tel/Fax: 01273 690149
Website: www.lumenstudio.co.uk
e-mail: info@lumenstudio.co.uk

**MEDIAWEBS**
(Graphic & Web Design)
20 Parker Road
Millbank Place
Colchester CO4 5BE          Mobile: 07887 480241
Website: www.mediawebs.co.uk
e-mail: jon@mediawebs.co.uk

**MERGE MEDIA**
Cambridge Chambers
200-202 High Street
Bromley
Kent BR1 1PN          Mobile: 07933 272297
Website: www.mergemedia.co.uk
e-mail: mergemedia@graphic-designer.com

**MINAMON FILM**
(Specialist in Showreels)
117 Downton Avenue
London SW2 3TX          Tel: 020-8674 3957
Website: www.minamonfilm.co.uk
e-mail: studio@minamonfilm.co.uk

**MOTIVATION SOUND STUDIOS**
35A Broadhurst Gardens
London NW6 3QT
Website: www.motivationsound.co.uk
e-mail: info@motivationsound.co.uk
Fax: 020-7624 4879          Tel: 020-7328 8305

**MUSIC IN MOTION Ltd**
4 Ravenshaw Street
London NW6 1NN          Mobile: 07813 070961
Website: www.neilmyers.com
e-mail: neil@neilmyers.com

**MYCLIPS**
Flat 1, 2 Blackdown Close
East Finchley
London N2 8JF          Tel: 020-8371 9526
Website: www.myclipsdvd.com
e-mail: info@myclipsdvd.com

**PERFORMERS ONLINE Ltd**
(Design, Web & Print)
18B High Street
London N8 7PB          Tel: 020-8347 0221
Website: www.performersonline.co.uk
e-mail: info@performersonline.co.uk

**PROFESSIONAL SHOWREELS OF MANCHESTER**
10 Old Hall Court
Old Hall Lane
Manchester M45 7JW
e-mail: showreels@btinternet.com
Mobile: 07777 641773                    Tel: 0161-272 1029

**PROFILE PRINTS**
(Photographic Reproduction)
Unit 2, Plot 1A
Rospeath Industrial Estate
Crowlas TR20 8DU
Website: www.courtwood.co.uk
e-mail: sales@courtwood.co.uk
Fax: 01736 741255                       Tel: 01736 741222

**RED FACILITIES**
61 Timberbush
Leith
Edinburgh EH6 6QH
Website: www.redfacilities.com
e-mail: doit@redfacilities.com
Fax: 0131-555 0088                       Tel: 0131-555 2288

**REEL McCOY The**
(Showreel Editing Service)
4 Kirkdale
Sydenham SE26 4NE                       Mobile: 07708 626477
Website: www.reelmccoy.notlong.com
e-mail: reelmccoyservice@aol.com

**REMOTE LIVE RECORDINGS**
244A Kingston Road
Leatherhead
Surrey KT22 7QA                          Mobile: 07968 100557
Website: www.remoteliverecordings.co.uk
e-mail: info@remoteliverecordings.co.uk

**REPLAY Ltd**
(Showreels & Performance Recording)
Museum House
25 Museum Street, London WC1A 1JT
Website: www.replayfilms.co.uk
e-mail: sales@replayfilms.co.uk          Tel: 020-7637 0473

**RETRO REELS**
Queens Park
London NW6
Website: www.retroreels.co.uk
e-mail: mail@retroreels.co.uk           Mobile: 07896 299932

**ROUND ISLAND SHOWREELS & VOICEREELS**
Contact: Ben Warren, Guy Michaels
Website: www.roundisland.net
e-mail: mail@roundisland.net            Mobile: 07701 093183

**SARM WEST STUDIOS Ltd**
8-10 Basing Street
London W11 1ET
Website: www.sarmstudios.com
e-mail: clare@spz.com
Fax: 020-7221 9247                       Tel: 020-7229 1229

**SCARLET INTERNET**
Suite 4, 15 Market Square
Bishop's Stortford
Herts CM23 3UT
Website: www.scarletinternet.com
e-mail: info@scarletinternet.com
Fax: 0870 2241418                        Tel: 0870 7771820

**SHOWREEL The**
(Voice-Over Workshops & Demo Production)
Knightsbridge House
229 Acton Lane
Chiswick, London W4 5DD
Website: www.theshowreel.com
e-mail: info@theshowreel.com
Fax: 020-8995 2144                       Tel: 020-7043 8660

**SHOWREELS 1**
45-46 Poland Street
London W1F 7NA
Website: www.ukscreen.com/company/showreels1
e-mail: showreels1@aol.com
Fax: 020-7437 2830                      Mobile: 07932 021232

**SHOWREELZ**
28 Eastbury Grove
Chiswick
London W4 2JZ                           Mobile: 07885 253477
Website: www.showreelz.com
e-mail: brad@showreelz.com

**SILVER-TONGUED PRODUCTIONS**
(Specialising in the recording and production of
Voicereels)
Greater London                          Tel: 020-8309 0659
Website: www.silver-tongued.co.uk
e-mail: contactus@silver-tongued.co.uk

**SMALL SCREEN SHOWREELS**
The Production Office
17 Knole Road
Crayford, London                        Tel: 020-8816 8896
Website: www.smallscreenshowreels.co.uk
e-mail: info@smallscreenshowreels.co.uk

**SO-MEDIA.CO.UK**
7 Knight House
22 Scott Avenue
Putney, London SW15 3PB                 Tel: 020-8789 7495
Website: www.so-media.co.uk
e-mail: info@so-media.co.uk

**SOHO SHOWREELS**
101 Wardour Street
London W1F 0UG
Website: www.sohoshowreels.co.uk
e-mail: info@sohoshowreels.co.uk

**SONICPOND STUDIO**
(Specialising in Voicereels. Showreels & Websites)
70 Mildmay Grove South
Islington
London N1 4PJ                           Tel: 020-7690 8561
Website: www.sonicpond.co.uk
e-mail: info@sonicpond.co.uk

**SOUND**
4 St Paul's Road, Clifton
Bristol BS8 1LT                         Tel: 0117-973 4595
Website: www.soundat4.com
e-mail: kenwheeler@mac.com

**SOUND COMPANY Ltd**
23 Gosfield Street
London W1W 6HG
Website: www.sound.co.uk
e-mail: bookings@sound.co.uk
Fax: 020-7580 6454                       Tel: 020-7580 5880

**SHOWREELS**
Professional Lighting Cameramen & Editors
Fully Equipped Studio
Auditions/Showreels Online
Duplication • Free Consultation

37 Beak Street, London W1F 9RZ
Tel +44(0)20 7287 2120 • Fax: +44(0) 20 7287 3035
info@takefivestudio.com • www.takefivestudio.com

**SOUND HOUSE POST PRODUCTION Ltd The**
10th Floor, Astley House
Quay Street
Manchester M3 4AE
Website: www.thesoundhouse.tv
e-mail: mail@thesoundhouse.tv
Fax: 0161-832 7266                    Tel: 0161-832 7299

**SOUND MARKETING**
Strattons House
Strattons Walk, Melksham, Wiltshire SN12 6JL
Website: www.soundm.com
e-mail: nicki@soundm.com
Fax: 01225 701601                     Tel: 01225 701600

**STAGES CAPTURE THE MOMENT**
(Showreels)
31 Evensyde
Croxley Green
Watford, Herts WD18 8WN               Tel: 020-7193 8519
www.stagescapturethemoment.com/videopages/showreels.php
e-mail: info@stagescapturethemoment.com

**STAMP PRODUCTIONS**
10 Margaret Street
London W1W 8RL                        Tel: 020-3178 2367
e-mail: ben@stamp-productions.co.uk

**STEDEFORD WEBSITE DESIGN**
Actors Online Resumés. Creative PR & Website Design
Website: www.stedeford.com           Mobile: 07793 741604
e-mail: stedefordwebsitedesign@gmail.com

**STUDIO17**
Unit 11, 407-409 Hornsey Road
London N19 4DX                        Tel: 020-7431 1883
Website: www.studio17productions.com
e-mail: info@studio17productions.com

**SUPPORT ACT SERVICES**
Contact: Ian McCracken (CD Duplication & Web Design)
243A Lynmouth Avenue
Morden
Surrey SM4 4RX                        Tel: 0845 0940796
Website: www.supportact.co.uk
e-mail: info@supportact.co.uk

**SYNCREDIBLE A**
26-28 Hammersmith Grove
London W6 7BA
Website: www.syncredible.com
e-mail: contact@syncredible.com       Tel: 020-7117 6776

**TAKE FIVE CASTING STUDIO**
(Showreels)
37 Beak Street, London W1F 9RZ
Website: www.takefivestudio.com
e-mail: info@takefivestudio.com
Fax: 020-7287 3035                    Tel: 020-7287 2120

**TM DESIGN Ltd**
(Web Design, Model Cards, Actors CVs)
Suites 14-15, Marlborough Business Centre
96 George Lane
South Woodford, London E18 1AD       Tel: 020-8530 4382
Website: www.tmphotography.co.uk
e-mail: info@tmphotography.co.uk

**TOP TV ACADEMY**
(Showreels)
309 Kentish Town Road, London NW5 2TJ
Website: www.toptvacademy.co.uk
e-mail: liz@toptvacademy.co.uk
Fax: 020-7485 7536                    Mobile: 07971 284958

**TOUCHWOOD AUDIO PRODUCTIONS**
6 Hyde Park Terrace
Leeds, West Yorkshire LS6 1BJ
Website: www.touchwoodaudio.com
e-mail: bruce@touchwoodaudio.com      Tel: 0113-278 7180

**TV PRESENTER TRAINING - ASPIRE**
3 Mills Studios, Three Mill Lane
London E3 3DU                         Tel: 0800 030 5471
Website: www.aspirepresenting.com
e-mail: info@aspirepresenting.com

**TWITCH FILMS**
(Showreels)
22 Grove End Gardens
18 Abbey Road, London NW8 9LL        Tel: 020-7266 0946
Website: www.twitchfilms.co.uk
e-mail: post@twitchfilms.co.uk

**UNIVERSAL SOUND (JUST PLAY) Ltd**
Old Farm Lane, London Road East
Amersham, Buckinghamshire HP7 9DH
Website: www.universalsound.co.uk
e-mail: foley@universalsound.co.uk
Fax: 01494 723500        Tel: 01494 723400

**VISUALEYES IMAGING SERVICES**
(Photographic Reproduction)
95 Mortimer Street, London W1W 7ST
Website: www.visphoto.co.uk
e-mail: imaging@visphoto.co.uk
Fax: 020-7323 7438        Tel: 020-7323 7430

**VOICE MASTER**
(Specialised Training in the PSR Method - The World's only
Technique for Voice-Overs & Autocue)
88 Erskine Hill, London NW11 6HR        Tel: 020-8455 2211
Website: www.voicemaster.co.uk
e-mail: stevehudson@voicemaster.co.uk

**VOICE TAPE SERVICES INTERNATIONAL**
(Professional Management Voice-Over Direction & CDs)
80 Netherlands Road
New Barnet, Herts EN5 1BS
Website: www.vtsint.co.uk
e-mail: info@vtsint.co.uk
Fax: 020-8441 4828        Tel: 020-8440 4848

**VSI - VOICE & SCRIPT INTERNATIONAL**
(Foreign Language Specialists - Translation, Subtitling
Casting, Dubbing, Recording Studios, Editing)
132 Cleveland Street, London W1T 6AB
Website: www.vsi.tv
e-mail: info@vsi.tv
Fax: 020-7692 7711        Tel: 020-7692 7700

**WARWICK HALL OF SOUND**
Warwick Hall, Off Banastre Avenue
Heath, Cardiff CF14 3NR        Tel/Fax: 029-2069 4455
Website: www.warwickhall.co.uk
e-mail: jennchampion@btconnect.com

**WARWICK SOUND**
(Sound Transfer/Optical & Magnetic)
Warwick Sound
111A Wardour Street, London W1F 0UJ
Website: www.warwicksound.com
e-mail: studio@warwicksound.com
Fax: 020-7439 0372        Tel: 020-7437 5532

**WORLDWIDE PICTURES Ltd**
Unit 30, 10-50 Willow Street
London EC2A 4BH
Website: www.worldwidepictures.tv
e-mail: anthead@worldwidepictures.tv
Fax: 020-7613 6581        Tel: 020-7613 6580

**WOW FACTOR The**
Unit 39, Cornmill Shopping Centre
Darlington, Durham DL3 6EN
Website: www.wowfactorautographs.co.uk
e-mail: wowfactor@hotmail.co.uk
Fax: 01325 253468        Tel: 01325 241680

**07000 BIG TOP**
(Big Top, Seating, Circus)
The Arts Exchange, Congleton, Cheshire CW12 1JG
Website: www.arts-exchange.com
e-mail: info@arts-exchange.com
Fax: 01260 270777     Tel: 01260 276627

**10 OUT OF 10 PRODUCTIONS Ltd**
(Lighting, Sound, AV Hire, Sales & Installation)
5 Orchard Business Centre
Kangley Bridge Road, London SE26 5AQ
Website: www.10outof10.co.uk
e-mail: sales@10outof10.co.uk
Fax: 020-8778 9217     Tel: 0845 1235664

**147RESEARCH**
Chaucers, Oare, Hermitage
Thatcham RG18 9SD     Tel: 01635 200147
Website: www.147research.com
e-mail: jenniferdalton@147research.com

**3D CREATIONS**
(Production Design, Scenery Contractors, Prop Makers &
Scenic Artists)
9A Bells Road, Gorleston-on-Sea
Great Yarmouth, Norfolk NR31 6BB
Website: www.3dcreations.co.uk
e-mail: info@3dcreations.co.uk
Fax: 01493 443124     Tel: 01493 652055

**ACROBAT PRODUCTIONS**
(Artistes & Advisors)
12 Oaklands Court, Hempstead Road
Watford WD17 4LF     Tel: 01923 224938
Website: www.acrobatproductions.com
e-mail: info@acrobatproductions.com

**ACTION CARS Ltd**
Steven Royffe
Room 586, East Side Complex
Pinewood Studios, Pinewood Road
Iver Heath, Bucks SL0 0NH
Website: www.actioncars.co.uk
e-mail: info@actioncars.co.uk
Fax: 01753 652027     Tel: 01753 785690

**ADAMS ENGRAVING**
Unit G1A, The Mayford Centre
Mayford Green, Woking GU22 0PP
Website: www.adamsengraving.co.uk
e-mail: adamsengraving@pncl.co.uk
Fax: 01483 751787     Tel: 01483 725792

**AIRBOURNE SYSTEMS INTERNATIONAL**
(All Skydiving Requirements Arranged. Parachute Hire -
Period & Modern)
8 Burns Crescent
Chelmsford, Essex CM2 0TS     Tel: 01245 268772

**ALCHEMICAL LABORATORIES ETC**
(Medieval Science & Technology Recreated for
Museums & Films)
2 Stapleford Lane, Coddington
Newark, Nottinghamshire NG24 2QZ     Tel: 01636 707836
Website: www.jackgreene.co.uk

**ALL SCENE ALL PROPS**
(Props, Masks, Painting & Scenery Makers)
Units 2 & 3, Spelmonden Farm, Goudhurst, Kent TN17 1HE
Website: www.allscene.net
e-mail: info@allscene.net
Fax: 01580 211131     Tel: 01580 211121

**ALL STARS**
Fieldgate, Station Road
Northiam, Rye TN31 6QT     Tel: 01797 252528
Website: www.allstarsamericanlimo.co.uk
e-mail: twtg@aol.com

**AMERICAN DREAMS**
(Vehicle Supply)
47 Wilsons Lane, Mark's Tey
Essex CO6 1HP     Tel: 0800 8488032
Website: www.americandreams.co.uk
e-mail: tphj47@aol.com

**ANELLO & DAVIDE**
(Handmade Shoes)
15 St Albans Grove
London W8 5BP     Tel: 020-7938 2255
Website: www.handmadeshoes.co.uk

**ANNUAL CLOWNS DIRECTORY The**
(Salvo The Clown)
13 Second Avenue
Kingsleigh Park
Thundersley, Essex SS7 3QD     Tel: 01268 745791
Website: www.annualclownsdirectory.com
e-mail: salvo@annualclownsdirectory.com

**AQUARIUS**
(Film & TV Stills Library)
PO Box 5, Hastings TN34 1HR     Tel: 01424 721196
Website: www.aquariuscollection.com
e-mail: aquarius.lib@clara.net

**AQUATECH**
(Camera Boats)
2 Cobbies Rock, Epney
Gloucestershire GL2 7LN
Website: www.aquatech-uk.com
e-mail: office@aquatech-uk.com
Fax: 01452 741958     Tel: 01452 740559

**ARCHERY CENTRE The**
PO Box 39, Battle
East Sussex TN33 0ZT     Tel: 01424 777183
Website: www.archerycentre.co.uk

**ARMS & ARCHERY**
(Armour, Weaponry, Chainmail, X-bows, Longbows, Tents)
Thrift Lane, Off London Road
Ware, Herts SG12 9QS     Tel: 01920 460335
e-mail: armsandarchery@btconnect.com

**ART\***
(Art Consultant, Supplier of Paintings & Sculpture)
Website: www.artstar.clara.net
e-mail: h_artstar@hotmail.com     Mobile: 07967 294985

**ART DIRECTORS & TRIP PHOTO LIBRARY**
(Digital Scans, Colour Slides - All Subjects)
57 Burdon Lane
Cheam, Surrey SM2 7BY
Website: www.artdirectors.co.uk
e-mail: images@artdirectors.co.uk
Fax: 020-8395 7230     Tel: 020-8642 3593

**A. S. DESIGNS**
(Theatrical Designer, Sets, Costumes, Heads, Masks,
Puppets etc)
Website: www.astheatricaldesign.co.uk
e-mail: maryannscadding@btinternet.com   Tel: 01279 722416

**ASH Riky**
(Equity Registered Stunt Performer/Co-ordinator)
Website: www.fallingforyou.tv
e-mail: stuntmanriky@fallingforyou.tv
Mobile: 07850 471227                    Tel: 01476 407383

**AUTOMOTIVE ACTION**
(Suppliers of Replica Humvees/H1 Hummers, Prototypes
and Constructor of Specialist Vehicles)
Website: www.carstunts.co.uk
e-mail: carstunts@hotmail.co.uk        Mobile: 07974 919589

**AWESOME**
(Bespoke Custom Upholstery Specialists)
The Stables, Grange Farm, Green End
Great Stukeley, Huntingdon, Cambridgeshire PE28 4AE
Website: www.awesome.eu.com
e-mail: glenn@awesome.eu.com
Fax: 01480 464879                       Tel: 01480 457007

**BAPTY 2000 Ltd**
(Weapons, Dressing, Props etc)
1A Witley Gardens, Norwood Green, Middlesex UB2 4ES
e-mail: info@bapty.demon.co.uk
Fax: 020-8571 5700                      Tel: 020-8574 7700

**BARNES CATERERS Ltd**
9 Ripley Drive, Normanton, Wakefield
West Yorkshire WF6 1QT
Fax: 01924 223730                       Tel: 01924 892332

**BARTON Joe**
(Puppeteer, Model & Prop Maker)
7 Brands Hill Avenue, High Wycombe
Buckinghamshire                         Tel: 01494 439056

**BEAT ABOUT THE BUSH Ltd**
(Musical Instrument Hire)
Unit 23, Enterprise Way, Triangle Business Centre
Salter Street (Off Hythe Road), London NW10 6UG
Website: www.beataboutthebush.com
e-mail: info@beataboutthebush.com
Fax: 020-8969 2281                      Tel: 020-8960 2087

**BEAVEROCK PRODUCTIONS Ltd**
(Location & Transport services)
39 Orangefield Drive, Prestwick, Ayrshire KA9 1HF
e-mail: dayoot@aol.com
Mobile: 07979 818915                    Tel: 01292 479577

**BIANCHI AVIATION FILM SERVICES**
(Historic & Other Aircraft)
Wycombe Air Park, Booker Marlow
Buckinghamshire SL7 3DP
Website: www.bianchiaviation.com
e-mail: info@bianchiaviation.com
Fax: 01494 461236                       Tel: 01494 449810

**BIG BREAK CARDS**
(Theatrical greetings cards featuring Hamlet the Pig, made
by actors for actors)
PO Box 45
Chipping Campden GL55 6WH             Tel: 01386 438952
Website: www.bigbreakcards.co.uk
e-mail: info@bigbreakcards.co.uk

**BLUE MILL Ltd**
(Dyers & Finishers)
84 Halstead Street, Leicester LE5 3RD
Website: www.bluemill.co.uk
e-mail: info@bluemill.co.uk
Fax: 0116-253 7633                      Tel: 0116-248 8130

**BLUEBELL RAILWAY Plc**
(Steam Locomotives, Pullman Coaches, Period Stations,
Much Film Experience)
Sheffield Park Station, East Sussex TN22 3QL
Website: www.bluebell-railway.co.uk
e-mail: info@bluebell-railway.co.uk
Fax: 01825 720804                       Tel: 01825 720800

**BOLD BLUE DESIGN Ltd**
(Design, Web & Print)
18B High Street, London N8 7PB
Website: www.boldblue.co.uk
e-mail: info@boldblue.co.uk
Mobile: 07985 245971                    Tel: 020-8347 0221

**BOLDGATE COMMERCIAL SERVICES Ltd**
The Crossbow Centre, 40 Liverpool Road
Slough, Berkshire SL1 4QZ
Website: www.boldgate.co.uk
e-mail: info@boldgate.co.uk
Fax: 01753 610587                       Tel: 01753 610525

**BOSCO LIGHTING**
(Design/Technical Consultancy)
47 Woodbourne Avenue
London SW16 1UX                         Tel: 020-8769 3470
e-mail: boscolx@lineone.net

**BOUNCY CASTLES BY P. A. LEISURE**
(Specialists in Amusements & Fairground Equipment)
Delph House, Park Bridge Road
Towneley Park, Burnley, Lancs BB10 4SD
Website: www.paleisure.com
e-mail: paleisure@btconnect.com
Mobile: 07968 399053                    Tel: 01282 453939

**BRIGHTON TUKTUKS**
16 Downland Road, Woodingdean
Brighton, East Sussex BN2 6DJ          Tel: 01273 233953
Website: www.brightontuktuk.com
e-mail: brightontuktuks@aol.com

**BRISTOL (UK) Ltd**
(Scenic Paint & StageFloor Duo Suppliers, VFX Solutions)
Unit 3, Sutherland Court
Tolpits Lane, Watford WD18 9SP
Website: www.bristolpaint.com
e-mail: tech.sales@bristolpaint.com
Fax: 01923 779666                       Tel: 01923 779333

**BRODIE & MIDDLETON Ltd**
(Theatrical Suppliers, Paints, Powders, Glitter etc)
68 Drury Lane, London WC2B 5SP
Website: www.brodies.net
e-mail: info@brodies.net
Fax: 020-7497 0554                      Tel: 020-7836 3289

**BRUNEL'S THEATRICAL SERVICES**
(Removal Services)
20A Walnut Lane
Kingswood, Bristol BS15  5JG           Tel: 0117-907 7855
Website: www.brunelsremovalservices.co.uk
e-mail: enquiries@brunelsremovalservices.co.uk

**CAMDEN ATTIC**
(Period Prop Hire & Making)
Location House, 5 Dove Lane, Bristol BS2 9HP
Website: www.camdenattic.co.uk
e-mail: genie@camdenattic.co.uk
Fax: 0117-955 2480                      Tel: 0117-941 1969

**CANDLE MAKERS SUPPLIES**
The Wax & Dyecraft Centre
28 Blythe Road, London W14 0HA
Website: www.candlemakers.co.uk
e-mail: candles@candlemakers.co.uk
Fax: 020-7602 2796                      Tel: 020-7602 4031

**CARLINE & CREW TRANSPORTATION**
(Celebrity Services)
12A Bridge Industrial Estate
Balcombe Road, West Sussex RH6 9HU
Website: www.carlineprivatehire.co.uk
e-mail: carlinehire@btconnect.com
Fax: 01293 430432                Tel: 01293 400505

**CHASE 55**
(Prop Hire Specialist Victorian - Present Day)
55 Chase Road, London NW10 6LU
Website: www.chase55.com
e-mail: trez.evans@chase55.com
Fax: 020-8965 8107                Tel: 0871 2310900

**CHRISANNE Ltd**
(Specialist Fabrics & Accessories for Theatre & Dance)
110-112 Morden Road
Mitcham, Surrey CR4 4XB
Website: www.chrisanne.com
e-mail: sales@chrisanne.com
Fax: 020-8640 2106                Tel: 020-8640 5921

**CIRCUS MANIACS**
(Circus Equipment, Rigging & Training)
Office 8A, The Kingswood Foundation
Britannia Road
Kingswood, Bristol BS15 8DB
Website: www.circusmaniacs.com
e-mail: info@circusmaniacs.com
Mobile: 07977 247287            Tel/Fax: 0117-947 7042

**CIRCUS PROMOTIONS**
(Entertainers)
36 St Lukes Road
Tunbridge Wells, Kent TN4 9JH        Tel: 01892 537964
Website: www.heyprestoentertainment.co.uk

**CLASSIC CAR AGENCY The**
(Film, Promotional, Advertising, Publicity)
PO Box 427, Dorking, Surrey RH5 6WP
Website: www.theclassiccaragency.com
e-mail: theclassiccaragency@btopenworld.com
Mobile: 07788 977655             Tel: 01306 731052

**CLASSIC CAR HIRE**
(Over 30 Classic and Vintage Vehicles in our
private collection)
Unit 2 Hampton Court Estate
Summer Road
Thames Ditton KT7 0RG
Website: www.classic-hire.com
e-mail: info@classic-hire.co.uk
Fax: 020-8939 3987               Tel: 020-8398 8304

**CLASSIC COLLECTION The**
(Bespoke Wedding Cars)
43 Dunstan Close
Chester Le Street DH2 3HX        Tel: 0191-388 2387
Website: www.the-classic-collection.co.uk
e-mail: info@the-classic-collection.co.uk

**CLASSIC OMNIBUS**
(Vintage Open-Top Buses & Coaches)
44 Welson Road
Folkestone, Kent CT20 2NP
Website: www.opentopbus.co.uk
Fax: 01303 241245                Tel: 01303 248999

**COBO MEDIA Ltd**
(Performing Arts, Entertainment & Leisure Marketing)
43A Garthorne Road, London SE23 1EP
Website: www.cobomedia.com
e-mail: admin@cobomedia.com
Fax: 020-8291 4969               Tel: 020-8291 7079

**COMPTON Mike & Rosi**
(Props, Models & Costumes)
11 Woodstock Road, Croydon, Surrey CR0 1JS
e-mail: mikeandrosicompton@btopenworld.com
Fax: 020-8681 3126            Tel: 020-8680 4364

**CONCEPT ENGINEERING Ltd**
(Smoke, Fog, Snow etc)
7 Woodlands Business Park, Woodlands Park Avenue
Maidenhead, Berkshire SL6 3UA
Website: www.concept-smoke.co.uk
e-mail: info@conceptsmoke.com
Fax: 01628 826261            Tel: 01628 825555

**COOK Sheila TEXTILES**
(Textiles, Costumes & Accessories for Hire/Sale)
26 Addison Place, London W11 4RJ       Tel: 020-7603 3003
Website: www.sheilacook.co.uk
e-mail: sheilacook@sheilacook.co.uk

**COSTUMES & SHOWS UNLIMITED**
(Ice Rink Rental, Costume Rental & Design, Show
Production)
PO Box 57, Poulton-le-Fylde
Lancs FY6 8GN            Tel: 01253 827092
Website: www.ice-shows-and-costumes-unlimited.co.uk
e-mail: iceshowpro@aol.com

**CREATIVE WORKS**
(Floral Design)
Unit 1, The Stable Block, Brewer Street
Bletchingley, Surrey RH1 4QP            Tel: 01883 742999
Website: www.ckworks.net
e-mail: info@ckworks.net

**CRESTA BLINDS Ltd**
(Supplier of Vertical Blinds)
Crown Works, Tetnall Street, Dudley DY2 8SA
Website: www.crestablindsltd.co.uk
e-mail: info@crestablindsltd.co.uk
Fax: 01384 457675            Tel: 01384 255523

**CROCKSHARD FARMHOUSE**
Contact: Nicola Ellen (Bed & Breakfast)
Wingham, Canterbury, Kent CT3 1NY       Tel: 01227 720464
Website: www.crockshard.com
e-mail: crockshard_bnb@yahoo.com

**CROFTS Andrew**
(Book Writing Services)
Westlands Grange, West Grinstead
Horsham, West Sussex RH13 8LZ        Tel/Fax: 01403 864518
Website: www.andrewcrofts.com

**CUE ACTION POOL PROMOTIONS**
(Advice for UK & US Pool, Snooker, Trick Shots)
PO Box 3941, Colchester, Essex CO2 8HN
Website: www.stevedaking.com
e-mail: sales@cueaction.com
Fax: 01206 729480            Tel: 07000 868689

**CUPCAKE EMPORIUM**
27 Craven Terrace, London W2 3EL       Tel: 020-7402 8673
Website: www.cupcakeemporium.co.uk
e-mail: info@cupcakeemporium.co.uk

**CURTAIN TRACKS & DRAPES**
28 The Street, Brettenham, Ipswich, Suffolk IP7 7QP
Website: www.suffolkscenery.info
e-mail: piehatch@aol.com
Fax: 01449 737620            Tel: 01449 736679

**DAVEY Brian**
(See NOSTALGIA AMUSEMENTS)

**DESIGN PROJECTS**
Perrysfield Farm, Broadham Green
Old Oxted, Surrey RH8 9PG
Website: www.designprojects.co.uk
Fax: 01883 723707            Tel: 01883 730262

**DEVEREUX DEVELOPMENTS Ltd**
(Removals, Haulage, Trucking)
Daimler Drive, Cowpen Industrial Estate
Billingham, Cleveland TS23 4JD
e-mail: mikebell@britdev.com
Fax: 01642 566664            Tel: 01642 560854

**DORANS PROPMAKERS/SET BUILDERS**
53 Derby Road, Ashbourne
Derbyshire DE6 1BH            Tel/Fax: 01335 300064
Website: www.doransprops.com
e-mail: info@doransprops.com

**DURRENT Peter**
(Audition & Rehearsal Pianist, Cocktail Pianist
Composer, Vocalist)
Blacksmiths Cottage, Bures Road, Little Cornard, Sudbury
Suffolk CO10 0NR            Tel: 01787 373483

**EAT TO THE BEAT**
(Production & Location Caterers)
Studio 4-5, Garnett Close, Watford, Herts WD24 7GN
Website: www.globalinfusiongroup.com
e-mail: enquiries@eattothebeat.com
Fax: 01923 211704            Tel: 01923 211702

**ELECTRO SIGNS Ltd**
97 Vallentin Road, London E17 3JJ
e-mail: info@electrosigns.co.uk
Fax: 020-8520 8127            Tel: 020-8521 8066

**ELMS LESTERS PAINTING ROOMS**
(Scenic Painting)
1-3-5 Flitcroft Street, London WC2H 8DH
e-mail: office@elmslesters.co.uk
Fax: 020-7379 0789            Tel: 020-7836 6747

**ES GROUP Ltd**
(Project Management, Staging, Temporary Structure
Trucking)
Bell Lane, North Woolwich Road, London E16 2AB
Website: www.esgroup-uk.com
e-mail: info@esgroup-uk.com
Fax: 020-7055 7201            Tel: 020-7055 7200

**ESCORT GUNLEATHER**
(Custom Leathercraft)
602 High Road, Benfleet, Essex SS7 5RW
Website: www.escortgunleather.com
e-mail: info@escortgunleather.com
Fax: 01268 566775            Tel: 0870 7515957

**EVANS Peter STUDIOS Ltd**
(Scenic Embellishment, Vacuum Forming)
12-14 Tavistock Street, Dunstable, Bedfordshire LU6 1NE
e-mail: sales@peterevansstudios.co.uk
Fax: 01582 481329            Tel: 01582 725730

**EXL CARS / LAIT Nick**
29 The Gluyas, Falmouth
Cornwall TR11 4SE            Tel: 01326 210306
Website: www.exlcars.com
e-mail: exlcars@aol.com

**FACADE**
(Musical Production Services)
43A Garthorne Road, London SE23 1EP
e-mail: facade@cobomedia.com
Fax: 020-8291 4969            Tel: 020-8291 7079

**FAIRGROUNDS TRADITIONAL**
Halstead, Fovant, Salisbury, Wiltshire SP3 5NL
Website: www.pozzy.co.uk
e-mail: sv@pozzy.co.uk
Mobile: 07710 287251            Tel: 01722 714786

**FELLOWES Mark TRANSPORT SERVICES**
(Transport/Storage)
59 Sherbrooke Road, London SW6 7QL
Website: www.fellowesproductions.com
Mobile: 07850 332818            Tel: 020-7386 7005

**FILM MEDICAL SERVICES**
Units 5 & 7, Commercial Way, Park Royal, London NW10 7XF
Website: www.filmmedical.co.uk
e-mail: filmmed@aol.com
Fax: 020-8961 7427     Tel: 020-8961 3222

**FINAL CREATION**
Unit 19, The Left Studio
Hill Lane Industrial Estate, Markfield
Leicestershire LE67 9PN
Website: www.finalcreation.co.uk
e-mail: gemma@finalcreation.co.uk
Fax: 01530 249400     Tel: 01530 249100

**FIREBRAND**
(Flambeaux Hire & Sales)
Leac Na Ban, Tayvallich
By Lochgilphead, Argyll PA31 8PF     Tel/Fax: 01546 870310
e-mail: firebrand.props@btinternet.com

**FLAME RETARDING Ltd**
Grove Farm, Grove Farm Road
Tolleshunt Major, Maldon, Essex CM4 8LR
Website: www.flameretarding.co.uk
e-mail: email@flameretarding.co.uk
Fax: 07092 036931     Tel: 01621 818477

**FLAMENCO PRODUCTIONS**
(Entertainers)
Sevilla 4 Cormorant Rise, Lower Wick
Worcester WR2 4BA     Tel: 01905 424083

**FLINT HIRE & SUPPLY Ltd**
Queen's Row, London SE17 2PX
Website: www.flints.co.uk
e-mail: sales@flints.co.uk
Fax: 020-7708 4189     Tel: 020-7703 9786

**FLYING BY FOY**
(Flying Effects for Theatre, TV, Corporate Events etc)
Unit 4, Borehamwood Enterprise Centre
Theobald Street, Borehamwood, Herts WD6 4RQ
Website: www.flyingbyfoy.co.uk
e-mail: mail@flyingbyfoy.co.uk
Fax: 020-8236 0235     Tel: 020-8236 0234

**FRANKIE'S YANKEES**
(Classic 1950s American Cars, Memorabilia, New
Superstretch Limos & Action Vehicles)
283 Old Birmingham Road, Bromsgrove B60 1HQ
e-mail: wow@frankiesyankees.com
Mobile: 07970 062142     Tel: 0121-445 5522

**FREEDALE PRESS Ltd**
(Printing)
36 Hedley Street, Maidstone, Kent ME14 5AD
e-mail: michael@freedale.co.uk
Fax: 01622 200131     Tel: 01622 200123

**FROST John NEWSPAPERS**
(Historical Newspaper Service)
22B Rosemary Avenue, Enfield
Middlesex EN2 0SS     Tel: 020-8366 1392
Website: www.johnfrostnewspapers.com
e-mail: andrew@johnfrostnewspapers.com

**GARRATT Jonathan FRSA**
(Suppliers of Traditional & Unusual Garden Pots &
Installations. Glazed Tableware)
Hare Lane Farmhouse
Cranborne, Dorset BH21 5QT     Tel: 01725 517700
Website: www.jonathangarratt.com
e-mail: jonathan.garratt@talk21.com

**GAV NICOLA THEATRICAL FOOTWEAR**
West Wick, Marshes, Burnham-on-Crouch, Essex CM0 8NE
Website: www.theatricalshoes.com
e-mail: gavnicola@yahoo.com
Mobile: 07961 974278     Tel/Fax: 01621 785623

**GET STUFFED**
(Taxidermy)
105 Essex Road, London N1 2SL
Website: www.thegetstuffed.co.uk
e-mail: taxidermy@thegetstuffed.co.uk
Fax: 020-7359 8253     Tel: 020-7226 1364

**GHOSTWRITER/AUTHOR**
Contact: John Parker
Dove Cottage, The Street
Ickham CT3 1QP     Tel: 01227 721071
e-mail: parkerwrite@aol.com

**GORGEOUS GOURMETS Ltd**
(Caterers & Equipment Hire)
Gresham Way, Wimbledon SW19 8ED
Website: www.gorgeousgourmets.co.uk
e-mail: hire@gorgeousgourmets.co.uk
Fax: 020-8946 1639     Tel: 020-8944 7771

**GOULD Gillian ANTIQUES**
(Scientific & Marine Antiques & Collectables)
38 Denman Drive South
London NW11 6RH
Website: www.gilliangouldantiques.co.uk
e-mail: gillgould@dealwith.com
Mobile: 07831 150060     Tel: 020-8458 7675

**GRADAV HIRE & SALES Ltd**
(Lighting & Sound Hire/Sales)
Units C6 & C9 Hastingwood Trading Estate
Harbet Road, Edmonton, London N18 3HU
e-mail: office@gradav.co.uk
Fax: 020-8803 5060     Tel: 020-8803 7400

**GRAY Robin COMMENTARIES**
(Saddles, Bridles, Racing Colours & Hunting Attire)
Comptons, Isington
Alton, Hampshire GU34 4PL
e-mail: gray@isington.fsnet.co.uk
Mobile: 07831 828424     Tel: 01420 23347

**GREENPROPS**
(Prop Suppliers, Artificial Trees, Plants, Flowers
Fruit, Grass etc)
West Bovey Farm, Waterrow
Somerset TA4 2BA
Website: www.greenprops.org
e-mail: trevor@greenprops.org     Tel: 01398 361531

**GREENSOURCE SOLUTIONS Ltd**
(Providers of Mobile Phone Props)
14 Kingsland Trading Estate
St Phillips Road, Bristol BS2 0JZ
Website: www.greensource.co.uk
e-mail: props@greensource.co.uk
Fax: 0117-304 2391     Tel: 0845 3100200

**HAMPTON COURT HOUSE**
Hampton Court Road, East Molesey KT8 9BS
Website: www.hamptoncourthouse.co.uk
Fax: 020-8977 5357          Tel: 020-8943 0889

**HANDS UP PUPPETS**
7 Cavendish Vale, Nottingham
Nottinghamshire NG5 4DS          Mobile: 07909 824630
Website: www.handsuppuppets.com
e-mail: marcus@handsuppuppets.com

**HARLEQUIN (BRITISH HARLEQUIN Plc)**
(Floors for Stage, Opera, Dance, Concert, Shows & Events)
Festival House, Chapman Way
Tunbridge Wells, Kent TN2 3EF
Website: www.harlequinfloors.com
e-mail: enquiries@harlequinfloors.com
Fax: 01892 514222          Tel: 01892 514888

**HAWES Joanne**
(Children's Administrator for Theatre, Film & TV)
21 Westfield Road, Maidenhead, Berkshire SL6 5AU
e-mail: jo.hawes@virgin.net
Mobile: 07824 337222          Tel: 01628 773048

**HERON & DRIVER**
(Scenic Furniture & Prop Makers)
Unit 7, Dockley Road Industrial Estate
Rotherhithe, London SE16 3SF
Website: www.herondriver.co.uk
e-mail: mail@herondriver.co.uk
Fax: 020-7394 8680          Tel: 020-7394 8688

**HI-FLI (Flying Effects)**
2 Boland Drive, Manchester M14 6DS   Tel/Fax: 0161-224 6082
e-mail: mikefrost@hi-fli.co.uk

**HISTORICAL INTERPRETER & ROLE PLAYING**
Contact: Donald Clarke
80 Warden Avenue, Rayners Lane
Harrow, Middlesex HA2 9LW
Website: www.historicalinterpretations.co.uk
e-mail: info@historicalinterpretations.co.uk
Mobile: 07811 606285          Tel: 020-8866 2997

**HISTORY IN THE MAKING Ltd**
(Weapon & Costume Hire)
4A Aysgarth Road, Waterlooville
Hampshire PO7 7UG          Tel: 023-9225 3175
Website: www.history-making.com
e-mail: enquiries@history-making.com

**HOME JAMES CHAUFFEUR SERVICE**
Moor Lane, Witton, Birmingham B6 7HH   Tel: 0121-323 4717
Website: www.homejamescars.com
e-mail: julie.homejames@virgin.net

**HOMESITE ESTATE AGENTS**
16 Lambton Place, London W11 2SH
Website: www.homesite.co.uk
e-mail: info@homesite.co.uk
Fax: 020-7243 5794          Tel: 020-7243 3535

**HOTCHPOTCHPROPS**
21 Silvan Drive, Braunton
Devon EX33 2EQ          Mobile: 07734 685254
Website: www.hotchpotchprops.com
e-mail: jo@hotchpotchprops.com

**HOWARD Rex DRAPES**
Unit F, Western Trading Estate, London NW10 7LU
e-mail: rex.howard@hawthorns.uk.com
Fax: 020-8955 6901          Tel: 020-8740 5881

**IMPACT**
(Private & Contract Hire of Coaches)
1 Leighton Road, Ealing, London W13 9EL
Website: www.impactgroup.co.uk
e-mail: sales@impactgroup.co.uk
Fax: 020-8840 4880          Tel: 020-8579 9922

**IMPACT PERCUSSION**
(Percussion Instruments for Sale)
Unit 7 Goose Green Trading Estate
47 East Dulwich Road, London SE22 9BN
e-mail: sales@impactpercussion.com
Fax: 020-8299 6704          Tel: 020-8299 6700

**IMPACT PRINT DISPLAY**
(Leaflet & Poster Distribution & Display)
Tuscany Wharf
4B Orsman Road, London N1 5QJ
Website: www.impactprintdisplay.com
e-mail: contactus@impactprintdisplay.com
Fax: 020-7729 5994          Tel: 020-7729 5978

**IMPACT SCHOOL OF MOTORING**
(Expert Driving Instructors on All Vehicles)
248A Columbia Road, Bournemouth BH10 4DS
e-mail: andyd@mail2world.com
Mobile: 07775 713780          Tel: 01202 666001

**JAPAN PROMOTIONS**
(Japanese Costumes & Props)
200 Russell Court, 3 Woburn Place
London WC1H 0ND          Tel/Fax: 020-7278 4099
Website: www.japan-promotions.co.uk
e-mail: info@japan-promotions.co.uk

**JASON'S**
(Up-market Cruising Canal Wideboat, Daily Scheduled Trips
to Camden Lock) (3 Boats Available)
Opposite 60 Blomfield Road
Little Venice, London W9 2PD          Tel: 020-7286 3428
Website: www.jasons.co.uk
e-mail: boats@jasons.co.uk

**JULIETTE DESIGNS**
(Diamante Jewellery Manufacturer, Necklaces, Crowns etc)
90 Yerbury Road, London N19 4RS
Website: www.stagejewellery.com
e-mail: juliettedesigns@hotmail.com
Fax: 020-7281 7326          Tel: 020-7263 7878

**KEIGHLEY & WORTH VALLEY LIGHT RAILWAY Ltd**
(Engines, Stations, Carriages, Props & Crew)
The Railway Station, Haworth, Keighley
West Yorkshire BD22 8NJ
Website: www.kwvr.co.uk
e-mail: admin@kwvr.co.uk
Fax: 01535 647317          Tel: 01535 645214

**KENSINGTON EYE CENTRE Ltd**
(Special Eye Effects)
37 Kensington Church Street
London W8 4LL          Tel/Fax: 020-7937 8282

**KEW BRIDGE STEAM MUSEUM**
Green Dragon Lane, Brentford
Middlesex TW8 0EN
Website: www.kbsm.org
e-mail: jo@kbsm.org
Fax: 020-8569 9978          Tel: 020-8568 4757

**KIRBY'S AFX Ltd**
8 Greenford Avenue, Hanwell, London W7 3QP
Website: www.kirbysflying.co.uk
e-mail: mail@afxuk.com
Mobile: 07958 285608          Tel/Fax: 020-8723 8552

**KNEBWORTH HOUSE, GARDENS & PARK**
(Knebworth)
Herts SG3 6PY          Tel: 01438 812661
Website: www.knebworthhouse.com
e-mail: info@knebworthhouse.com

**LAREDO Alex**
(Expert with Ropes, Bullwhips, Shooting, Riding)
29 Lincoln Road, Dorking, Surrey RH4 1TE
Mobile: 07906 271766          Tel: 01306 889423

**LAREDO WILD WEST TOWN**
(Wild West Entertainment)
1 Bower Walk, Staplehurst
Tonbridge, Kent TN12 0LU
Website: www.laredo.org.uk
e-mail: enquiries@laredo.org.uk
Mobile: 07947 652771          Tel: 01580 891790

**LEES-NEWSOME Ltd**
(Manufacturers of Flame Retardant Fabrics)
Ashley Works, Unit 2
Rule Business Park, Grimshaw Lane}
Middleton, Manchester M24 2AE
Website: www.leesnewsome.co.uk
e-mail: info@leesnewsome.co.uk
Fax: 0845 0708006          Tel: 0845 0708005

**LEIGHTON HALL**
(Historic House)
Carnforth, Lancashire LA5 9ST
Website: www.leightonhall.co.uk
e-mail: info@leightonhall.co.uk
Fax: 01524 720357          Tel: 01524 734474

**LEVRANT Stephen - HERITAGE ARCHITECTURE Ltd**
(Architects & Historic Building Consultants)
62 British Grove, Chiswick, London W4 2NL
e-mail: info@heritagearchitecture.co.uk
Fax: 020-8748 4992          Tel: 020-8748 5501

**LIMELIGHT ENTERTAINMENT**
(Theatre Merchandise)
Unit 13, The io Centre
The Royal Arsenal
Seymour Street, London SE18 6SS          Tel: 020-8858 6141
e-mail: enquiries@mcmlimelight.co.uk

**LONDON BUSINESS EQUIPMENT**
(Authorised Canon Dealer)
527-529 High Road, Leytonstone, London E11 4PB
Website: www.londonbusinessequipment.com
e-mail: sales@londonbusinessequipment.com
Fax: 020-8556 4865          Tel: 020-8558 0024

**LONDON QUALITY DRY CLEANERS Ltd**
(Dry Cleaners, Launderers & Dyers, Stage Curtains &
Costumes)
222 Baker Street
London NW1 5RT          Tel: 020-7935 7316

**LONO DRINKS COMPANY The**
The Hawthorns, Driffield, Cirencester
Gloucestershire GL7 5PY
Website: www.lono.co.uk
e-mail: info@lono.co.uk
Fax: 01285 850455          Tel: 01285 850682

**LOS KAOS**
(Street Theatre, Circus, Puppetry & Animatronics)
Quay House, Quayside, Brockweir
Gloucestershire NP16 7NQ          Tel/Fax: 01291 680074
Website: www.loskaos.co.uk
e-mail: kaos@loskaos.co.uk

**LUCKINGS**
(Transporters/Storage/Stage Hands)
63 Kew Green, Richmond, Surrey TW9 3AH
Website: www.luckings.co.uk
e-mail: info@luckings.co.uk
Fax: 020-8332 3000          Tel: 020-8332 2000

**LUCKINGS SCREEN SERVICES**
(Artists' Trailers/Splits/2-3 Ways)
63 Kew Green, Richmond, Surrey TW9 3AH
Website: www.luckings.co.uk
e-mail: info@luckings.co.uk
Fax: 020-8332 3000          Tel: 020-8332 2000

**LYON EQUIPMENT**
(Petzl & Beal Rope Access Equipment (PPE) for Industrial &
Theatrical Work)
Rise Hill Mill, Dent, Sedbergh, Cumbria LA10 5QL
Website: www.lyon.co.uk
e-mail: info@lyon.co.uk
Fax: 01539 625454          Tel: 01539 625493

**M A C**
(Sound Hire)
1-2 Attenburys Park, Park Road
Altrincham, Cheshire WA14 5QE
Website: www.macsound.co.uk
e-mail: hire@macsound.co.uk
Fax: 0161-962 9423          Tel: 0161-969 8311

**MACKIE Sally LOCATIONS**
(Location Finding & Management)
Cownham Farm, Broadwell
Moreton-in-Marsh
Gloucestershire GL56 0TT          Tel: 01451 830294
Website: www.sallymackie-locations.com
e-mail: sally@mackie.biz

**MADDERMARKET THEATRE**
Contact: Rhett Davies (Resident Stage Manager)
St John's Alley, Norwich NR2 1DR
Website: www.maddermarket.co.uk
e-mail: mmtheatre@btconnect.com
Fax: 01603 661357          Tel: 01603 626560

**MAGICAL MART**
(Magic, Ventriloquists' Dolls, Punch & Judy, Hire & Advising.
Callers by Appointment)
42 Christchurch Road, Sidcup
Kent DA15 7HQ          Tel/Fax: 020-8300 3579
Website: www.johnstylesentertainer.co.uk

**MAINSTREAM LEISURE GROUP**
(Riverboat/Canal Boat Hire)
5 The Mews, 6 Putney Common, London SW15 1HL
Website: www.mainstreamleisure.co.uk
Fax: 020-8788 0073          Tel: 020-8788 2669

**MARCUS HALL PROPS**
Unit 2B/C Vanguard Court
Rear of 36-38 Peckham Road
London SE5 8QT          Mobile: 07802 873127
Website: www.marcushallprops.com
e-mail: info@marcushallprops.com

**MARKSON PIANOS**
8 Chester Court, Albany Street, London NW1 4BU
Website: www.marksonpianos.com
e-mail: info@marksonpianos.com
Fax: 020-7224 0957          Tel: 020-7935 8682

**MATT-LX**
(Lighting & Technical Production)
Gunnery House, 9 Gunnery Terrace, London SE18 6SW
Website: www.mattlx.com
e-mail: intray@mattlx.com
Fax: 020-8301 8149                     Tel: 020-8301 8692

**McNEILL Brian**
(Vintage Truck & Coaches)
Hawk Mount, Kebcote, Todmorden
Lancashire OL14 8SB                    Tel: 01706 812291
Website: www.rollingpast.com
e-mail: autotrans@uk2.net

**MIDNIGHT ELECTRONICS**
(Sound Hire)
Off Quay Building, Foundry Lane
Newcastle upon Tyne NE6 1LH
Website: www.midnightelectronics.co.uk
e-mail: info@midnightelectronics.co.uk
Fax: 0191-224 0080                     Tel: 0191-224 0088

**MILITARY, MODELS & MINATURES**
(Model Figures)
38A Horsell Road, London N5 1XP
e-mail: minaturesmodels@aol.com
Fax: 020-7700 4624                     Tel: 020-7700 7036

**MODDED MOTORS AGENCY**
(Suppliers of Modified Cars)
38 Williamson Way, Rickmansworth
Hertfordshire WD3 8GL               Mobile: 07989 128131
Website: www.moddedmotorsagency.com
e-mail: daniellechristie@hotmail.com

**MODEL BOX**
(Computer Aided Design & Design Services)
2 Saddlers Way, Okehampton
Devon EX20 1TL                         Tel: 01837 54026
Website: www.modelbox.co.uk
e-mail: info@modelbox.co.uk

**MOORFIELDS PHOTOGRAPHIC Ltd**
2 Old Hall Street
Liverpool L3 9RQ                       Tel: 0151-236 1611
Website: www.moorfieldsphoto.com
e-mail: info@moorfieldsphoto.com

**MORTON G & L**
(Horses/Farming)
Hashome Carr, Holme-on-Spalding Moor
Yorkshire YO43 4BD                     Tel: 01430 860393

**MOTORHOUSE HIRE Ltd**
Contact: Michael Geary (Action Vehicles)
Oatleys Hall, Turweston, Northants NN13 5JX
e-mail: michael@motorhouseltd.co.uk
Fax: 01280 704944                      Tel: 020-7495 1618

**MPG BIDDLES Ltd**
Unit 24, Rollesby Road, Hardwick Industrial Estate
King's Lynn, Norfolk PE30 4LS
Website: www.biddles.co.uk
e-mail: enquiries@mpg-biddles.co.uk
Fax: 01553 766820                      Tel: 01553 764728

**MPG BOOKS Ltd**
(Quality Book Manufacturers)
Victoria Square, Bodmin
Cornwall PL31 1EB                      Tel: 01208 73266
Website: www.mpg-books.com
e-mail: print@mpg-books.co.uk

**M V DIXIE QUEEN**
(Thames Luxury Charters)
5 The Mews
6 Putney Common, London SW15 1HL
Website: www.thamesluxurycharters.co.uk
e-mail: sales@thamesluxurycharters.co.uk
Fax: 020-8788 0072                     Tel: 020-8780 1562

**NATIONAL MOTOR MUSEUM**
John Montagu Building, Beaulieu
Brockenhurst
Hampshire SO42 7ZN
Website: www.beaulieu.co.uk
e-mail: info@beaulieu.co.uk
Fax: 01590 612624                      Tel: 01590 612345

**NEWMAN HIRE COMPANY**
(Lighting Hire)
16 The Vale, Acton
London W3 7SB                          Tel: 020-8743 0741
e-mail: info@newmanhire.co.uk

**NINE-NINE CARS Ltd**
Hyde Meadow Farm, Hyde Lane
Hemel Hempstead HP3 8SA          Tel: 01923 266373
e-mail: david@nineninecars.com

**NORTHERN LIGHT**
Assembly Street, Leith, Edinburgh EH6 7RG
Website: www.northernlight.co.uk
e-mail: enquiries@northernlight.co.uk
Fax: 0131-622 9101          Tel: 0131-622 9100

**NOSTALGIA AMUSEMENTS**
Contact: Brian Davey
22 Greenwood Close, Thames Ditton, Surrey KT7 0BG
Mobile: 07973 506869          Tel: 020-8398 2141

**NOTTINGHAM JOUSTING ASSOCIATION SCHOOL OF
NATIONAL EQUITATION Ltd**
(Jousting & Medieval Tournaments, Horses & Riders for
Films & TV)
Bunny Hill Top, Costock, Loughborough
Leicestershire LE12 6XE
Website: www.bunnyhill.co.uk
e-mail: info@bunnyhill.co.uk
Fax: 01509 856067          Tel: 01509 852366

**OCEAN LEISURE**
(Scuba Diving, Watersports Retail)
11-14 Northumberland Avenue, London WC2N 5AQ
Website: www.oceanleisure.co.uk
e-mail: info@oceanleisure.co.uk
Fax: 020-7930 3032          Tel: 020-7930 5050

**OFFSTAGE**
(Theatre & Film Book)
BlackGull Bookshop, 121 High Road
London N2 8AG          Tel: 020-8444 4717
e-mail: offstagebookshop@aol.com

**PAPERFLOW Plc**
(Stationery & Office Equipment)
Units 5 & 6
Meridian Trading Estate
20 Bugsbys Way, Charlton, London SE7 7SJ
e-mail: info@paperflowgroup.com
Fax: 020-8331 2001          Tel: 020-8331 2000

**PATCHETTS EQUESTRIAN CENTRE**
(Location)
Hillfield Lane, Aldenham
Watford, Herts WD25 8PE
Website: www.patchetts.co.uk
e-mail: info@patchetts.co.uk
Fax: 01923 859289          Tel: 01923 852255

**PATERSON Helen**
(Typing Services)
40 Whitelands House
London SW3 4QY          Tel: 020-7730 6428
e-mail: pater@waitrose.com

**PERIOD PETROL PUMP COLLECTION**
c/o Diss Ironworks, 7 St Nicholas Street
Diss, Norfolk IP22 4LB          Tel: 01379 643978
Website: www.periodpetrolpump.co.uk

**PHOSPHENE**
(Lighting & Sound. Design, Sales, Hire)
Milton Road South, Stowmarket
Suffolk IP14 1EZ          Tel: 01449 770011
Website: www.phosphene.co.uk
e-mail: phosphene@btconnect.com

**PIANO PEOPLE The**
(Piano Hire & Transport)
74 Playford Road, London N4 3PH          Tel: 0845 6076713
Website: www.pianopeople.co.uk
e-mail: info@pianopeople.co.uk

**PICKFORDS REMOVALS Ltd**
Laxcon Close, London NW10 0TG          Tel: 020-3188 2100
Website: www.pickfords.com
e-mail: enquiries@pickfords.com

**PICTURES PROPS CO Ltd**
(TV, Film & Stage Hire)
12-16 Brunel Road, London W3 7XR
e-mail: picturesprops@tiscali.co.uk
Fax: 020-8740 5846          Tel: 020-8749 2433

**PINK POINTES DANCEWEAR**
1A Suttons Lane
Hornchurch, Essex RM12 6RD          Tel/Fax: 01708 438584
e-mail: pink.pointes@btconnect.com

**PLUNGE PRODUCTIONS**
(Props, Graphic Design, Creative Services)
Unit 10, 18A Arthur Street
Hove BN3 5FD          Tel/Fax: 01273 557550
Website: www.plungeproductions.com
e-mail: info@plungeproductions.com

**PLUS FILM Ltd**
(All Periods Vehicle Hire)
1 Mill House Cottages
Winchester Road
Bishop's Waltham SO32 1AH          Tel/Fax: 01489 895559
e-mail: stephen@plusfilms7.freeserve.co.uk

**POLAND Anna: SCULPTOR AND MODELMAKER**
(Sculpture, Models, Puppets, Masks etc)
Salterns, Old Bursledon, Southampton
Hampshire SO31 8DH          Tel: 023-8040 5166
e-mail: polandanna@hotmail.com

**POLLEX PROPS / FIREBRAND**
(Prop Makers)
Leac Na Ban, Tayvallich
Lochgilphead, Argyll PA31 8PF          Tel/Fax: 01546 870310
e-mail: firebrand.props@btinternet.com

**PRAETORIAN ASSOCIATES/PROCUREMENT SERVICES -
SA**
(Personal Safety & Anti-Stalking Consultancy & Services for
Film/TV industry within South Africa)
Tintagel, 1 St Clairs Road
St Osyth, Essex CO16 8QG
Website: www.praetorianasc.com
e-mail: martin.beale@praetorianasc.com
Mobile: 07973 505981          Tel: 020-7096 1827

**PREMIER CHAUFFEUR SERVICES**
164 Haydock Street
Newton-le-Willows, Merseyside WA12 9DH
e-mail: mike.vizard@hotmail.co.uk
Mobile: 07890 661050          Tel: 01925 299112

**PROBLOOD**
11 Mount Pleasant
Framlingham, Suffolk IP13 9HQ          Tel/Fax: 01728 723865

**PROFESSOR PATTEN'S PUNCH & JUDY**
(Hire & Performances/Advice on Traditional Show)
14 The Crest, Goffs Oak
Hertfordshire EN7 5NP          Tel: 01707 873262
Website: www.dennispatten.co.uk

**PROP FARM Ltd**
Contact: Pat Ward
Grange Farm, Elmton
Nr Creswell, North Derbyshire S80 4LX
e-mail: pat/les@propfarm.co.uk
Fax: 01909 721465          Tel: 01909 723100

**PROPS GALORE**
(Period Textiles/Jewellery)
15 Brunel Road, London W3 7XR
e-mail: propsgalore@farley.co.uk
Fax: 020-8354 1866          Tel: 020-8746 1222

**PROPS STUDIOS Ltd**
Unit 3, Old Kiln Works
Ditchling Common Industrial Estate
Hassocks BN6 8SG
Website: www.propsstudios.co.uk
e-mail: info@propsstudios.co.uk
Fax: 0870 7700961          Tel: 0870 7700960

**PUNCH & JUDY PUPPETS & BOOTHS**
(Hire & Advisory Service, Callers by Appointment)
42 Christchurch Road
Sidcup, Kent DA15 7HQ          Tel/Fax: 020-8300 3579
Website: www.johnstylesentertainer.co.uk

**Q2Q GROUP**
(Technical Resources)
187 Drury Lane
Covent Garden, London WC2B 5QD
Website: www.q2qgroup.com
e-mail: solutions@q2qgroup.com
Fax: 0870 9506727          Tel: 0870 9505727

**RAINBOW PRODUCTIONS Ltd**
(Creation & Appearances of Costume Characters/Stage Shows)
Unit 3, Greenlea Park
Prince George's Rd, London SW19 2JD
Website: www.rainbowproductions.co.uk
e-mail: info@rainbowproductions.co.uk
Fax: 020-8254 5306          Tel: 020-8254 5300

**RENT-A-CLOWN**
Contact: Mattie Faint
37 Sekeforde Street, Clerkenwell
London EC1R 0HA          Tel/Fax: 020-7608 0312

**REPLAY Ltd**
(Showreels & TV Facilities Hire)
Museum House, 25 Museum Street
London WC1A 1JT          Tel: 020-7637 0473
Website: www.replayfilms.co.uk
e-mail: sales@replayfilms.co.uk

**ROBERTS Chris INTERIORS**
(Specialist Painters & Decorators to The Film Industry)
117 Colebrook Lane
Loughton IG10 2HP          Mobile: 07956 512074

**ROOTSTEIN Adel Ltd**
(Mannequin Manufacturer)
9 Beaumont Avenue, London W14 9LP
Website: www.rootstein.com
Fax: 020-7381 3263          Tel: 020-7381 1447

**ROYAL HORTICULTURAL HALLS & CONFERENCE CENTRE**
(Film Location: Art Deco & Edwardian Buildings)
80 Vincent Square
London SW1P 2PE
Website: www.horticultural-halls.co.uk
e-mail: horthalls@rhs.org.uk
Fax: 020-7834 2072          Tel: 0845 3704606

**RUDKIN DESIGN**
(Design Consultants, Brochures, Advertising
Corporate etc)
10 Cottesbrooke Park
Heartlands Business Park
Daventry, Northamptonshire NN11 8YL
Website: www.rudkindesign.com
e-mail: arudkin@rudkindesign.co.uk
Fax: 01327 311715          Tel: 01327 301770

**RUMBLE Jane**
(Props to Order, No Hire)
121 Elmstead Avenue, Wembley
Middlesex HA9 8NT          Tel: 020-8904 6462

**SABAH STYLIST**
(Wardrobe, Sets, Props)
2841 N. Ocean Blvd, Apt 501
Fort Lauderdale, Florida 33308 USA
e-mail: sabah561@aol.com
Mobile: (954) 383-2179          Tel/Fax: (954) 566-6219

**SALVO THE CLOWN**
13 Second Avenue
Kingsleigh Park
Thundersley, Essex SS7 3QD          Tel: 01268 745791
Website: www.annualclownsdirectory.com
e-mail: salvo@annualclownsdirectory.com

**SAPEX SCRIPTS**
The Maxwell Building
Elstree Film Studios, Shenley Road
Borehamwood, Herts WD6 1JG
Website: www.sapex.co.uk
e-mail: scripts@sapex.co.uk
Fax: 020-8324 2771          Tel: 020-8236 1600

**SCHULTZ & WIREMU FABRIC EFFECTS Ltd**
(Dyeing/Printing/Distressing)
Unit B202 Faircharm Studios
8-12 Creekside, London SE8 3DX          Tel/Fax: 020-8469 0151
Website: www.schultz-wiremufabricfx.co.uk
e-mail: swfabricfx@hotmail.com

**SCRIPTRIGHT**
(S.C. Hill - Script/Manuscript Typing Services/Script
Reading Services)
6 Valetta Road, London W3 7TN          Tel: 020-8740 7303
e-mail: samc.hill@virgin.net

**SCRIPTS BY ARGYLE**
(Play, Film & Book. Word Processing, Copying & Binding)
St John's Buildings
43 Clerkenwell Road
London EC1M 5RS
Website: www.scriptsbyargyle.co.uk
e-mail: argyle.associates@virgin.net
Fax: 0871 4336130          Mobile: 07905 293319

**SFD**
Ground Floor, Sunningdale
The Belfry, Colonial Way
Watford, Herts WD24 4WH
Website: www.sfd.co.uk
e-mail: sales@sfd.co.uk
Fax: 01923 232326          Tel: 01923 232425

**SHAOLIN WAY**
(Martial Arts Supplies, Lion Dance & Kung Fu Instruction)
10 Little Newport Street
London WC2H 7JJ                      Tel: 020-7734 6391
Website: www.shaolinway.com
e-mail: shaolinway@btconnect.com

21 Baron Street, Angel, London N1 9EX    Tel: 020-7833 8388
**SHIRLEY LEAF & PETAL COMPANY**
(Flower Makers Museum)
58A High Street, Old Town, Hastings
East Sussex TN34 3EN                 Tel/Fax: 01424 427793
**SIDE EFFECTS**
(Props, Models & FX)
92 Fentiman Road, London SW8 1LA
e-mail: sfx@lineone.net
Fax: 020-7207 0062                   Tel: 020-7587 1116
**SNOW BUSINESS**
(Snow/Winter Effects on Any Scale)
The Snow Mill, Bridge Road
Ebley, Stroud
Gloucestershire GL5 4TR              Tel/Fax: 01453 840077
Website: www.snowbusiness.com
e-mail: snow@snowbusiness.com

**SOFT PROPS**
(Costume & Modelmakers)
92 Fentiman Road, London SW8 1LA
e-mail: jackie@softprops.co.uk
Fax: 020-7207 0062                   Tel: 020-7587 1116
**SPUR CREATIVE WORKSHOP**
Unit 1A, North Yard, Pennybridge Lane
Mayfield, East Sussex TN20 6QB
Website: www.spurcreative.co.uk
e-mail: info@spurcreative.co.uk
Mobile: 07970 805871                 Tel: 01435 873755
**STEELDECK RENTALS/SALES Ltd**
(Stage Equipment Hire & Modular Staging)
Unit 58, T Marchant Trading Estate
42-72 Verney Road, London SE16 3DH
Website: www.steeldeck.co.uk
e-mail: rentals@steeldeck.co.uk
Fax: 020-7232 1780                   Tel: 020-7833 2031
**STEVENSON Scott**
(Prop Maker)
60 Ripley Road, Sawmills, Belper
Derbyshire DE56 2JQ                  Mobile: 07739 378579
Website: www.bodymechprops.co.uk
e-mail: scott@bodymechprops.co.uk
**STOKE BRUERNE BOAT COMPANY Ltd**
(Passenger & Commercial Boats)
Wharf Cottage, Stoke Bruerne
Northants NN12 7SE                   Tel: 01604 862107
Website: www.stokebrueneboats.co.uk

**SUFFOLK SCENERY**
(Curtain Tracks & Drapes Only)
Pie Hatch Farm, Brettenham Road
Buxall, Stowmarket, Suffolk IP14 3DZ
Website: www.suffolkscenery.info
e-mail: piehatch@aol.com
Fax: 01449 737620                    Tel: 01449 736679
**SUPERSCRIPTS**
51 Buckingham Gardens
West Moseley, Surrey KT8 1TJ
e-mail: super_scripts@sky.com
Mobile: 07793 160138                 Tel: 020-8979 8048

**SUPERSCRIPTS**
(Audio Typing, Rushes, Post-Prod Scripts)
56 New Road, Hanworth
Middlesex TW13 6TQ
e-mail: jackie@superscripts.fsnet.co.uk
Mobile: 07971 671011                 Tel: 020-8898 7933
**TALK TO THE HAND PUPPETS**
(Custom Puppets for Film, Television & Theatre)
Studio 277, Wimbledon Art Studios
Riverside Yard, Riverside Road
Earlsfield, London SW17 0BB
Website: www.talktothehandpuppets.com
e-mail: info@talktothehandpuppets.com
Mobile: 07813 682293                 Mobile: 07855 421454
**TAYLOR Charlotte**
(Stylist/Props Buyer)
18 Eleanor Grove
Barnes, London SW13 0JN
e-mail: charlottetaylor1@blueyonder.co.uk
Mobile: 07836 708904                 Tel/Fax: 020-8876 9085
**THAMES LUXURY CHARTERS Ltd**
5 The Mews, 6 Putney Common, London SW15 1HL
Website: www.thamesluxurycharters.co.uk
e-mail: sales@thamesluxurycharters.co.uk
Fax: 020-8788 0072                   Tel: 020-8780 1562
**THEATRESEARCH**
(Theatre Consultants)
Dacre Hall, Dacre, North Yorkshire HG3 4ET
Website: www.theatresearch.co.uk
e-mail: info@theatresearch.co.uk
Fax: 01423 781957                    Tel: 01423 780497
**THEATRICAL SHOEMAKERS Ltd**
(Footwear)
Unit 7A, Thames Road Industrial Estate
Thames Road, Silvertown, London E16 2EZ
Website: www.shoemaking.co.uk
e-mail: ts@shoemaking.co.uk
Fax: 020-7476 5220                   Tel: 020-7474 0500
**THEME TRADERS Ltd**
(Props)
The Stadium, Oaklands Road, London NW2 6DL
Website: www.themetraders.com
e-mail: mailroom@themetraders.com
Fax: 020-8450 7322                   Tel: 020-8452 8518
**TOP SHOW**
(Props & Scenery, Conference Specialists)
North Lane, Huntington
Yorks YO32 9SU                       Tel/Fax: 01904 750022
**TOTAL LOGISTICS MANAGEMENT**
Unit 1, 42 Hanworth Road
Sunbury, Middlesex TW16 5LN
Website: www.tlmltd.co.uk
e-mail: sales@tlmltd.co.uk
Fax: 01932 733009                    Tel: 01932 733000
**TRACK THAT**
(Tracking Vehicle/Camera Car Supplier)
Wandsworth, London SW18              Mobile: 07941 234254
Website: www.trackthat.co.uk
e-mail: info@trackthat.co.uk
**TRANSCRIPTS**
(I/Vs, Scripts, Conferences, Videos from CD, DVD,
Downloads & Tapes)
#2, 6 Cornwall Gardens, London SW7 4AL
e-mail: lucy@transcripts.demon.co.uk
Mobile: 07973 200197                 Tel: 020-7584 9758

**TRAPEZE & AERIAL COACH/CHOREOGRAPHER**
Contact: Jacqueline Welbourne
c/o Circus Maniacs Agency, Office 8A
The Kingswood Foundation, Britannia Road
Kingswood, Bristol BS15 8DB
Website: www.circusmaniacs.com
e-mail: jackie@circusmaniacs.com
Mobile: 07977 247287        Tel/Fax: 0117-947 7042

**TRISTAR WORLDWIDE CHAUFFEUR SERVICES**
Unit 1-2, Horton Road
West Drayton UB7 8BQ        Tel: 01895 432000
Website: www.tristarworldwide.com
e-mail: reservations@tristarworldwide.com

**TRYFONOS Mary MASKS**
(Mask, Headdress & Puppet Specialist)
59 Shaftesbury Road, London N19 4QW
e-mail: marytryfonos@aol.com
Mobile: 07764 587433        Tel: 020-7561 9880

**TURN ON LIGHTING**
(Antique Lighting c1850-1950)
11 Camden Passage, London N1 8EA   Tel/Fax: 020-7359 7616

**UK SAME DAY DELIVERY SERVICE**
Contact: Philip Collings
18 Billingshurst Road
Broadbridge Heath, West Sussex RH12 3LW
Fax: 01403 266059        Mobile: 07785 717179

**UPBEAT EVENT DESIGN**
(Corporate Hospitality Caterers)
Studio 4-5, Garnett Close
Watford, Herts WD24 7GN
Website: www.upbeateventdesign.com
e-mail: enquiries@upbeateventdesign.com
Fax: 01923 211704        Tel: 01923 211703

**UPSTAGE**
(Live Communications Agency)
Studio A, 7 Maidstone Buildings Mews
72-76 Borough High Street, London SE1 1GD
Website: www.upstagelivecom.co.uk
e-mail: post@upstagelivecom.co.uk
Fax: 020-7403 6511        Tel: 020-7403 6510

**VENTRILOQUIST DOLLS HOME**
(Hire & Helpful Hints, Callers by Appointment)
42 Christchurch Road
Sidcup, Kent DA15 7HQ        Tel/Fax: 020-8300 3579
Website: www.johnstylesentertainer.co.uk

**VENTRILOQUIST DUMMY HIRE**
Contact: Dennis Patten (Hire & Advice)
14 The Crest, Goffs Oak
Herts EN7 5NP        Tel: 01707 873262
Website: www.dennispatten.co.uk

**VINMAG ARCHIVE Ltd**
84-90 Digby Road, London E9 6HX
Website: www.vinmagarchive.com
e-mail: piclib@vinmagarchive.com
Fax: 020-8525 9209        Tel: 020-8533 7588

**VINTAGE CARRIAGES TRUST**
(Owners of the Museum of Rail Travel at Ingrow Railway
Centre)
Keighley, West Yorkshire BD22 8NJ
Website: www.vintagecarriagestrust.org
e-mail: admin@vintagecarriagestrust.org
Fax: 01535 610796        Tel: 01535 680425

**VOCALEYES**
(Providers of Audio Description for Theatrical
Performance)
1st Floor
54 Commercial Street
London E1 6LT
Website: www.vocaleyes.co.uk
e-mail: enquiries@vocaleyes.co.uk
Fax: 020-7247 5622        Tel: 020-7375 1043

**WALKING YOUR DOG**
(Dog Walking Service for South East London)
92 Wricklemarsh Road
London SE3 8DS
Website: www.walkingyourdog.net
e-mail: info@walkingyourdog.net
Mobile: 07867 502333        Tel/Fax: 020-8319 1806

**WEB AND PRINT**
Suite 14, Space House
Space Business Park
Abbey Road
Park Royal, London NW10 7SU        Tel: 020-8838 3555
Website: www.webandprint.co.uk
e-mail: info@webandprint.co.uk

**WEBBER Peter HIRE/RITZ STUDIOS**
(Music Equipment Hire, Rehearsal Studios)
110-112 Disraeli Road
London SW15 2DX
e-mail: ben@peterwebberhire.com
Fax: 020-8877 1036        Tel: 020-8870 1335

**WESTED LEATHERS COMPANY**
(Suede & Leather Suppliers/Manufacturers)
Little Wested House
Wested Lane
Swanley, Kent BR8 8EF
e-mail: wested@wested.com
Fax: 01322 667039        Tel: 01322 660654

**WESTWARD Lynn BLINDS**
(Window Blind Specialist)
458 Chiswick High Road
London W4 5TT
Website: www.lynnwestward.com
e-mail: info@lynnwestward.com
Fax: 020-8742 8444        Tel: 020-8742 8333

**WILLIAMS Frank**
(Bottles, Jars, Footwarmers, Flagons, Spitoons, Poisons,
Milk, Beers & Inks 1870-1940)
33 Enstone Road, Ickenham
Uxbridge, Middlesex        Tel: 01895 672495
e-mail: wllmsfrn4@aol.com

**WILTSHIRE A. F. LLP**
(Agricultural Vehicle Engineers, Repairs, etc)
The Agricultural Centre
Alfold Road, Dunsfold
Surrey GU8 4NP
e-mail: team@afwiltshire.co.uk
Fax: 01483 200491        Tel: 01483 200516

**WORBEY Darryl STUDIOS**
(Specialist Puppet Design)
Ground Floor
33 York Grove
London SE15 2NY
e-mail: info@darrylworbeystudios.com
Fax: 020-7635 6397        Tel: 020-7639 8090

**A & C BLACK**
(Publicity Dept)
36 Soho Square, London W1D 3QY
e-mail: publicity@acblack.com
Fax: 020-7758 0222          Tel: 020-7758 0200

**ACADEMY PLAYERS DIRECTORY**
(See PLAYERS DIRECTORY)

**A C I D PUBLICATIONS**
The Basement, Minus One House
Lyttelton Road, London E10 5NQ     Tel/Fax: 07050 205206
e-mail: acidnews@aol.com

**ACTING: A DRAMA STUDIO SOURCE BOOK**
(Peter Owen Publishers)
73 Kenway Road, London SW5 0RE     Tel: 020-7373 5628
Website: www.peterowen.com
e-mail: admin@peterowen.com

**ACTIONS: THE ACTORS' THESAURUS**
(By Marina Caldarone & Maggie Lloyd-Williams)
Nick Hern Books
The Glasshouse
49A Goldhawk Road, London W12 8QP
Website: www.nickhernbooks.co.uk
e-mail: info@nickhernbooks.demon.co.uk
Fax: 020-8735 0250          Tel: 020-8749 4953

**ACTORS' YEARBOOK 2010**
(A & C Black Publishers)
36 Soho Square, London W1D 3QY
Website: www.acblack.com
e-mail: methuendrama@acblack.com
Fax: 020-7758 0222          Tel: 020-7758 0200

**AMATEUR STAGE MAGAZINE & COMMUNITY ARTS DIRECTORY**
(Next Phase Media Ltd)
Suite 404, Albany House
324-326 Regent Street
London W1B 3HH          Tel: 0870 2332040
Website: www.asmagazine.co.uk
e-mail: editor@asmagazine.co.uk

**ANNUAIRE DU CINEMA BELLEFAYE**
(French Actors' Directory, Production, Technicians & All
Technical Industries & Suppliers)
30 rue Saint Marc, 75002 Paris
Website: www.bellefaye.com
e-mail: contact@bellefaye.com
Fax: 00 331 42 33 39 00     Tel: 00 331 42 33 52 52

**ARTISTES & AGENTS**
(Richmond House Publishing Co Ltd)
70-76 Bell Street, Marylebone, London NW1 6SP
Website: www.rhpco.co.uk
e-mail: sales@rhpco.co.uk
Fax: 020-7224 9688          Tel: 020-7224 9666

**AUDITIONS: A PRACTICAL GUIDE**
Website: www.auditionsapracticalguide.com

**AUDITIONS UNDRESSED**
(By Dan Bowling)
c/o Global Artists, 23 Haymarket
London SW1Y 4DG          Tel: 020-7839 4888
e-mail: nikiwinterson@globalartists.co.uk

**AURORA METRO PRESS (1989)**
(Biography, Drama, Fiction, Humour, Reference &
International Literature in English Translation)
67 Grove Avenue
Twickenham TW2 4HX
Website: www.aurorametro.com
e-mail: info@aurorametro.com
Fax: 020-8898 0735          Tel: 020-3261 0000

**BIG BREAK CARDS Ltd**
(Theatrical greetings cards featuring Hamlet the pig, made
by actors for actors)
PO Box 45
Chipping Campden GL55 6WH     Tel: 01386 438952
Website: www.bigbreakcards.co.uk
e-mail: info@bigbreakcards.co.uk

**BIRTH OF THEATRE The - STAGE BY STAGE**
(Drama/Theatre Studies/History/Reference)
(Peter Owen Publishers), 73 Kenway Road, London SW5 0RE
Website: www.peterowen.com
e-mail: admin@peterowen.com
Fax: 020-7373 6760          Tel: 020-7373 5628

**BRITISH PERFORMING ARTS YEARBOOK**
(Rhinegold Publishing), 241 Shaftesbury Avenue
London WC2H 8TF          Tel: 020-7333 1720
Website: www.rhinegold.co.uk
e-mail: bpay@rhinegold.co.uk

**BRITISH THEATRE DIRECTORY**
(Richmond House Publishing Co Ltd)
70-76 Bell Street, Marylebone, London NW1 6SP
Website: www.rhpco.co.uk
e-mail: sales@rhpco.co.uk
Fax: 020-7224 9688          Tel: 020-7224 9666

**BROADCAST**
Greater London House
Hampstead Road, London NW1 7EJ
Website: www.broadcastnow.co.uk
Fax: 020-7728 5555          Tel: 020-7728 5542

**CASTCALL**
(Casting Information Services) (Incorporating Castfax)
106 Wilsden Avenue, Luton LU1 5HR
Website: www.castcall.co.uk
e-mail: admin@castcall.co.uk
Fax: 01582 480736          Tel: 01582 456213

**CASTWEB**
7 St Luke's Avenue
London SW4 7LG          Tel: 020-7720 9002
Website: www.castweb.co.uk
e-mail: info@castweb.co.uk

**CELEBRITY BULLETIN The**
10 Wiseton Road, London SW17 7EE
e-mail: enquiries@celebrity-bulletin.co.uk
Fax: 020-8672 2282          Tel: 020-8672 3191

**CHAPPELL OF BOND STREET**
(Sheet Music, Musical Instruments, Pianos, Synthesizers,
Keyboards)
152-160 Wardour Street, London W1F 8YA
Website: www.chappellofbondstreet.co.uk
Fax: 020-7432 4410          Tel: 020-7432 4400

**CONFERENCE & INCENTIVE TRAVEL MAGAZINE**
174 Hammersmith Road, London W6 7JP
Website: www.citmagazine.com
e-mail: cit@haymarket.com
Fax: 020-8267 4192          Tel: 020-8267 4307

**CREATIVE HANDBOOK**
(Centaur Media Plc)
50 Poland Street
London W1F 7AX          Tel: 020-7970 6455
Website: www.creativehandbook.co.uk

**DANCE EXPRESSION**
(A. E. Morgan Publications Ltd)
8A High Street, Epsom
Surrey KT19 8AD          Tel: 01372 741411
Website: www.danceexpression.co.uk
e-mail: sue@aemorgan.co.uk

**DANCERS SPOTLIGHT**
7 Leicester Place, London WC2H 7RJ
Website: www.spotlight.com
e-mail: questions@spotlight.com
Fax: 020-7437 5881                          Tel: 020-7437 7631

**DIRECTING DRAMA**
(Peter Owen Publishers)
73 Kenway Road, London SW5 0RE       Tel: 020-7373 5628
Website: www.peterowen.com
e-mail: admin@peterowen.com

**DRAMA STUDENT MAGAZINE The**
(MarcoMatt Media LLP)
Top Floor 3, 66 Wansey Street, London SE17 1JP
Website: www.thedramastudent.co.uk
e-mail: editor@thedramastudent.co.uk
Fax: 07092 846523                          Tel: 020-7701 4536

**EQUITY MAGAZINE**
Guild House, Upper St Martin's Lane, London WC2H 9EG
Website: www.equity.org.uk
e-mail: mmcgrath@equity.org.uk
Fax: 020-7379 6074                          Tel: 020-7670 0211

**FILMLOG**
(Subscriptions)
Marketing Department, 6-14 Underwood Street
London N1 7JQ                              Tel: 020-7549 2578
Website: www.pcrnewsletter.com

**FORESIGHT-NEWS**
(The Profile Group (UK) Ltd)
The Johnson Building, 77 Hatton Garden, London EC1N 8JS
Website: www.profilegroup.co.uk
e-mail: uknews@foresightnews.co.uk
Fax: 020-7900 3684                          Tel: 020-7190 7777

**HERN Nick BOOKS**
(Plays, Theatrebooks, Screenplays & Performing Rights)
The Glasshouse, 49A Goldhawk Road, London W12 8QP
Website: www.nickhernbooks.co.uk
e-mail: info@nickhernbooks.demon.co.uk
Fax: 020-8735 0250                          Tel: 020-8749 4953

**HOLLYWOOD REPORTER The**
5th Floor, Endeavour House
189 Shaftesbury Avenue, London WC2H 8TJ
Website: www.thr.com
e-mail: london_one@eu.hollywoodreporter.com
Fax: 020-7420 6014                          Tel: 020-7420 6000

**KAY'S UK & EUROPEAN PRODUCTION MANUALS**
Pinewood Studios, Pinewood Road
Iver Heath, Bucks SL0 0NH
Website: www.kays.co.uk
e-mail: info@kays.co.uk
Fax: 020-8960 6700                          Tel: 020-8960 6900

**KEMP'S FILM, TV & VIDEO**
(Reed Business Information)
East Grinstead House, East Grinstead, West Sussex RH19 1XA
Website: www.kftv.com
e-mail: kemps@reedinfo.co.uk
Fax: 01342 336113                          Tel: 01342 335779

**KNOWLEDGE The**
Paulton House, 8 Shepherdess Walk, London N1 7LB
Website: www.theknowledgeonline.com
e-mail: knowledge@wilmington.co.uk
Fax: 020-7549 8668                          Tel: 020-7549 8666

**LIMELIGHT The**
(Limelight Publications, Contacts & Casting Directory)
PO Box 760, Randpark Ridge, 2156, Gauteng, South Africa
Website: www.limelight.co.za
e-mail: info@limelight.co.za
Fax: 00 27 86 545 7231                     Tel: 00 27 11 793 7231

**MAKING OF THE PROFESSIONAL ACTOR The**
(Peter Owen Publishers)
73 Kenway Road, London SW5 0RE       Tel: 020-7373 5628
Website: www.peterowen.com
e-mail: admin@peterowen.com

**METHUEN DRAMA**
(A & C Black)
36 Soho Square, London W1D 3QY
e-mail: methuendrama@acblack.com
Fax: 020-7758 0222                          Tel: 020-7758 0200

**MOVIE MEMORIES MAGAZINE**
(Devoted to Films & Stars of the 40s, 50s & 60s)
10 Russet Close, Scunthorpe, N. Lincs DN15 8YJ
e-mail: crob.mvm@ntlworld.com

**MUSIC WEEK DIRECTORY/MUSIC WEEK**
(UBM)
8th Floor, Ludgate House
245 Blackfriars Road
London SE1 9UY                             Tel: 020-7921 8320
Website: www.musicweek.com
e-mail: enquiries@musicweek.com

**MUSICAL STAGES**
(Musical Theatre Magazine)
PO Box 8365, London W14 0GL          Tel/Fax: 020-7603 2227
Website: www.musicalstages.co.uk
e-mail: editor@musicalstages.co.uk

**OFFICIAL LONDON SEATING PLAN GUIDE The**
(Richmond House Publishing Co Ltd)
70-76 Bell Street
Marylebone, London NW1 6SP
Website: www.rhpco.co.uk
e-mail: sales@rhpco.co.uk
Fax: 020-7224 9668                          Tel: 020-7224 9666

**PA ENTERTAINMENT**
292 Vauxhall Bridge Road
Victoria, London SW1V 1AE
Website: www.pressassociation.com
e-mail: events@pressassociation.com
Fax: 0870 1203201                          Tel: 0870 1203200

**PANTOMIME BOOK The**
(Peter Owen Publishers)
73 Kenway Road, London SW5 0RE       Tel: 020-7373 5628
Website: www.peterowen.com
e-mail: admin@peterowen.com

**PCR**
(See PRODUCTION & CASTING REPORT)

**PLAYERS DIRECTORY**
2210 W. Olive Avenue, Suite 320
Burbank, California 91506               Tel: (310) 247-3058
Website: www.playersdirectory.com
e-mail: info@playersdirectory.com

**PLAYS INTERNATIONAL**
33A Lurline Gardens
London SW11 4DD                            Tel: 020-7720 1950
Website: www.playsinternational.org.uk

**PRESENTERS CLUB The**
Presenter Promotions
123 Corporation Road, Gillingham
Kent ME7 1RG                               Tel/Fax: 01634 851077
Website: www.presenterpromotions.com
e-mail: info@presenterpromotions.com

**PRESENTERS SPOTLIGHT**
7 Leicester Place, London WC2H 7RJ
Website: www.spotlight.com
e-mail: questions@spotlight.com
Fax: 020-7437 5881                          Tel: 020-7437 7631

**PRESENTING FOR TV & VIDEO**
(By Joanne Zorian-Lynn, published by A & C Black)
A & C Black Customer Services, c/o Robert Smith Literacy
Agency, 12 Bridge Wharf
156 Caledonian Road, London N1 9UU    Tel: 01256 302692
e-mail: mdl@macmillan.co.uk

**PRODUCTION & CASTING REPORT**
(Editorial)
PO Box 11, London N1 7JZ
Website: www.pcrnewsletter.com
e-mail: info@pcrnewsletter.com
Fax: 020-7566 8284    Tel: 020-7566 8282

**PRODUCTION & CASTING REPORT**
(Subscriptions)
Marketing Department, 6-14 Underwood Street
London N1 7JQ    Tel: 020-7549 2578
Website: www.pcrnewsletter.com

**RADIO TIMES**
201 Wood Lane, London W12 7TQ
Website: www.radiotimes.com
e-mail: radio.times@bbc.co.uk
Fax: 020-8433 3923    Tel: 020-8433 3999

**RICHMOND HOUSE PUBLISHING COMPANY Ltd**
70-76 Bell Street, Marylebone, London NW1 6SP
Website: www.rhpco.co.uk
e-mail: sales@rhpco.co.uk
Fax: 020-7224 9688    Tel: 020-7224 9666

**ROGUES & VAGABONDS**
(On-line Theatre Magazine)
13 Elm Road, London SW14 7JL    Mobile: 07773 770781
Website: www.roguesandvagabonds.co.uk
e-mail: contact@roguesandvagabonds.co.uk

**ROUTLEDGE PUBLISHING**
2 Park Square, Milton Park, Abington, Oxon OX14 4RN
Website: www.routledge.com
e-mail: info@tandf.co.uk
Fax: 020-7017 6336    Tel: 020-7017 6000

**SBS Ltd**
Suite 204, 254 Belsize Road, London NW6 4BT
e-mail: office@sbscasting.co.uk
Fax: 020-7372 1992    Tel: 020-7372 6337

**SCREEN INTERNATIONAL**
Greater London House, Hampstead Road, London NW1 7EJ
Website: www.screendaily.com
e-mail: mai.le@emap.com
Fax: 020-7728 5555    Tel: 020-7728 5605

**SHOWBIZ FRIENDS**
(Community Website for Showbiz People)
Website: www.showbizfriends.com

**SHOWCALL**
47 Bermondsey Street, London SE1 3XT
Website: www.showcall.co.uk
e-mail: marcus@thestage.co.uk
Fax: 020-7378 0480    Tel: 020-7403 1818

**SHOWCAST**
PO Box 2001, Leumeah, NSW 2560 Australia
Website: www.showcast.com.au
e-mail: danelle@showcast.com.au
Fax: 02 4647 4167    Tel: 02 4647 4166

**SHOWDIGS.CO.UK**
Website: www.showdigs.co.uk
e-mail: info@showdigs.co.uk    Mobile: 07984 422353

**SIGHT & SOUND**
(British Film Institute)
21 Stephen Street, London W1T 1LN
Website: www.bfi.org.uk/sightandsound
e-mail: s&s@bfi.org.uk
Fax: 020-7436 2327    Tel: 020-7255 1444

**SO YOU WANT TO BE AN ACTOR?**
(By Timothy West & Prunella Scales)
Nick Hern Books
The Glasshouse
49A Goldhawk Road, London W12 8QP
Website: www.nickhernbooks.co.uk
e-mail: info@nickhernbooks.demon.co.uk
Fax: 020-8735 0250    Tel: 020-8749 4953

**SO YOU WANT TO BE A THEATRE DIRECTOR?**
(By Stephen Unwin)
Nick Hern Books, The Glasshouse
49A Goldhawk Road
London W12 8QP
Website: www.nickhernbooks.co.uk
e-mail: info@nickhernbooks.demon.co.uk
Fax: 020-8735 0250    Tel: 020-8749 4953

**SPEECH FOR THE SPEAKER**
(Peter Owen Publishers)
73 Kenway Road, London SW5 0RE    Tel: 020-7373 5628
Website: www.peterowen.com
e-mail: admin@peterowen.com

**SPOTLIGHT**
7 Leicester Place
London WC2H 7RJ
Website: www.spotlight.com
e-mail: questions@spotlight.com
Fax: 020-7437 5881    Tel: 020-7437 7631

**STAGE NEWSPAPER Ltd The**
47 Bermondsey Street
London SE1 3XT
Website: www.thestage.co.uk
e-mail: editor@thestage.co.uk
Fax: 020-7939 8478    Tel: 020-7403 1818

**TELEVISUAL MEDIA UK Ltd**
48 Charlotte Street, London W1T 2NS
Website: www.televisual.com
Fax: 020-3008 5784    Tel: 020-3008 5750

**THEATRE LIST The**
Society of London Theatre
32 Rose Street, London WC2E 9ET    Tel: 020-7557 6700
e-mail: gemma@solttma.co.uk

**THEATRE RECORD**
131 Sherringham Avenue
London N17 9RU    Tel/Fax: 01243 539437
Website: www.theatrerecord.com
e-mail: editor@theatrerecord.com

**TIME OUT GROUP Ltd**
Universal House
251 Tottenham Court Road
London W1T 7AB
Website: www.timeout.com
Fax: 020-7813 6001    Tel: 020-7813 3000

**TV TIMES**
IPC Media
Blue Fin Building
110 Southwark Street, London SE1 0SU
Fax: 020-3148 8115    Tel: 020-3148 5615

**VARIETY NEWSPAPER**
Procter House
Procter Street, London WC1V 6EU
Website: www.variety.com
Fax: 020-7911 1922    Tel: 020-7911 1701

**WHITE BOOK The**
Bank House
23 Warwick Road, Coventry CV1 2EW
Website: www.whitebook.co.uk
e-mail: admin@whitebook.co.uk
Fax: 024-7657 1172    Tel: 024-7657 1171

**ARTHUR Leone PR**
The Ground Floor, 3 Charlotte Mews, London W1T 4DZ
Website: www.arthurleone.com
e-mail: info@arthurleone.com
Fax: 020-7637 2984                    Tel: 020-7637 2994

**AVALON PUBLIC RELATIONS**
(Marketing/Arts)
4A Exmoor Street, London W10 6BD
Website: www.avalonuk.com
e-mail: markj@avalonuk.com
Fax: 020-7598 7223                    Tel: 020-7598 8000

**BARLOW Tony ASSOCIATES**
(Press & Marketing for Music, Dance & Theatre)
13 Burns Court, Park Hill Road, Wallington SM6 0SF
e-mail: artspublicity@hotmail.com
Mobile: 07711 929170                  Tel: 020-8773 1919

**BOLTON Erica & QUINN Jane Ltd**
6 Addison Avenue, London W11 4QR
Website: www.boltonquinn.com
e-mail: name@boltonquinn.com
Fax: 020-7221 8100                    Tel: 020-7221 5000

**BORKOWSKI**
65 Clerkenwell Road, London EC1R 5BL
Website: www.borkowski.co.uk
e-mail: suresh@borkowski.co.uk
Fax: 020-7404 5000                    Tel: 020-7404 3000

**CENTRESTAGE PUBLIC RELATIONS**
1 Barricane, St Johns, Woking GU21 7RB
Website: www.centrestage.com
e-mail: mail@centrestagepr.com
Fax: 0870 2882398              Mobile: 07838 995736

**CHESTON Judith PUBLICITY**
30 Telegraph Street
Shipston-on-Stour, Warwickshire CV36 4DA
e-mail: jacheston@tiscali.co.uk
Fax: 01608 663772                     Tel: 01608 661198

**CLARKE Duncan PR**
24 Severus Street, York
North Yorkshire YO24 4NL              Tel: 01904 345247
Website: www.duncanclarkepr.wordpress.com
e-mail: duncanrpclarke@hotmail.com

**CLOUT COMMUNICATIONS Ltd**
79 Wardour Street, London W1D 6QD     Tel: 020-7851 8625
Website: www.cloutcom.co.uk
e-mail: info@cloutcom.co.uk

**DAVEY Christine ASSOCIATES**
29 Victoria Road, Eton Wick, Windsor, Berkshire SL4 6LY
Fax: 01753 851123                     Tel: 01753 852619

**DDA PUBLIC RELATIONS Ltd**
192-198 Vauxhall Bridge Road, London SW1V 1DX
Website: www.ddapr.com
e-mail: info@ddapr.com
Fax: 020-7932 4950                    Tel: 020-7932 9800

**ELSON Howard PROMOTIONS**
(Marketing & Management)
16 Penn Avenue, Chesham, Buckinghamshire HP5 2HS
e-mail: helson1029@aol.com
Fax: 01494 784760                     Tel: 01494 785873

**EMPICA Ltd**
1 Lyons Court, Long Ashton Business Park
Yanley Lane, Bristol BS41 9LB
Website: www.empica.com
e-mail: info@empica.com
Fax: 01275 393933                     Tel: 01275 394400

**GADABOUTS Ltd**
(Theatre Marketing & Promotions)
54 Friary Road, London N12 9PB
Website: www.gadabouts.co.uk
e-mail: info@gadabouts.co.uk
Fax: 0870 7059140                     Tel: 020-8445 5450

**GAYNOR Avril ASSOCIATES**
126 Brudenell Road
London SW17 8DE                 Mobile: 07958 623013
e-mail: gaynorama@aol.com

**GOODMAN Deborah PUBLICITY (DGPR)**
25 Glenmere Avenue, London NW7 2LT
Website: www.dgpr.co.uk
e-mail: publicity@dgpr.co.uk
Fax: 020-8959 7875                    Tel: 020-8959 9980

**HYMAN Sue ASSOCIATES Ltd**
St Martin's House, 59 St Martin's Lane, London WC2N 4JS
Website: www.suehyman.com
e-mail: sue.hyman@btinternet.com
Fax: 020-7379 4944                    Tel: 020-7379 8420

**IMPACT AGENCY The**
3 Bloomsbury Place, London WC1A 2QL
e-mail: mail@impactagency.co.uk
Fax: 020-7580 7200                    Tel: 020-7580 1770

**KEAN LANYON Ltd**
Contact: Sharon Kean
Rose Cottage, The Aberdeen Centre
22 Highbury Grove, London N5 2EA
Website: www.keanlanyon.com
e-mail: sharon@keanlanyon.com
Fax: 020-7359 0199                    Tel: 020-7354 3574

**KELLER Don ARTS MARKETING**
65 Glenwood Road, Harringay
London N15 3JS                        Tel: 020-8800 4882
e-mail: info@dakam.org.uk

**LAKE-SMITH GRIFFIN ASSOCIATES**
Walter House, 418 Strand, London WC2R 0PT
e-mail: info@lakesmithgriffin.co.uk
Fax: 020-7836 1040                    Tel: 020-7836 1020

**LEEP MARKETING & PR**
(Marketing, Press and Publicity)
5 Nassau House
122 Shaftesbury Avenue, London W1D 5ER
e-mail: philip@leep.biz
Fax: 020-7439 8833                    Tel: 020-7439 9777

**MATTHEWS Liz PR**
83 Charlotte Street, London W1T 4PR   Tel: 020-7436 4433
Website: www.lizmatthewspr.com
e-mail: liz@lizmatthewspr.com

**MAYER Anne PR**
82 Mortimer Road, London N1 4LH
e-mail: annemayer@btopenworld.com
Mobile: 07764 192842                  Tel: 020-7254 7391

**McAULEY ARTS MARKETING Ltd**
118 Broxholm Road
London SE27 0BT                       Tel: 020-8676 4773
Website: www.mcauleyartsmarketing.co.uk
e-mail: sam@mcauleyartsmarketing.co.uk

**MITCHELL Jackie**
(JM Communications)
4 Sims Cottages, The Green, Claygate, Surrey KT10 0JH
Website: www.jackiem.com
e-mail: pr@jackiem.com
Fax: 01372 471073                     Tel: 01372 465041

**MOBIUS**
8A Great Newport Street
London WC2H 7JA     Tel: 020-7836 3864
Website: www.mobiusindustries.com
e-mail: info@mobiusindustries.com

**MORGAN Jane ASSOCIATES (JMA)**
(Marketing & Media)
8 Heathville Road, London N19 3AJ
e-mail: jma@janemorganassociates.com
Fax: 020-7263 9877     Tel: 020-7263 9867

**NELSON BOSTOCK COMMUNICATIONS**
Compass House
22 Redan Place, London W2 4SA
Website: www.nelsonbostock.com
e-mail: info@nelsonbostock.com
Fax: 020-7727 2025     Tel: 020-7229 4400

**PARKER James ASSOCIATES**
67 Richmond Park Road
London SW14 8JY     Tel/Fax: 020-8876 1918
e-mail: jimparkerjpa@hotmail.com

**PR OFFICE The**
720 Highgate Studios
53-79 Highgate Road
London NW5 1TL
Website: www.theproffice.com
e-mail: kphillips@theproffice.com
Fax: 020-7485 0345     Tel: 020-7284 6969

**PR PEOPLE The**
1 St James Drive, Sale
Cheshire M33 7QX     Tel: 0161-976 2729
Website: www.pr-people.uk.com
e-mail: graham@pr-people.uk.com

**PREMIER PR**
91 Berwick Street, London W1F 0NE
Website: www.premierpr.com
Fax: 020-7734 2024     Tel: 020-7292 8330

**PUBLIC EYE COMMUNICATIONS Ltd**
Suite 313, Plaza
535 Kings Road, London SW10 0SZ
e-mail: ciara@publiceye.co.uk
Fax: 020-7351 1010     Tel: 020-7351 1555

**RAW-PHOTOS.COM**
5 Clos y Berllan, Newbridge-on-Wye
Llandrindod Wells LD1 6LZ
Website: www.raw-photos.com
e-mail: studio@raw-photos.com     Tel: 01597 860124

**RICHMOND TOWERS COMMUNICATIONS Ltd**
26 Fitzroy Square, London W1T 6BT
Fax: 020-7388 7761     Tel: 020-7388 7421

**RKM COMMUNICATIONS Ltd**
(London & Los Angeles)
5th Floor, 4 New Burlington Street
London W1S 2JG
Website: www.rkmcom.com
e-mail: info@rkmcom.com
Fax: 020-7287 1704     Tel: 020-3130 7090

**S & X MEDIA**
Contact: Roulla Xenides
The Gatehouse
2B Victoria Works, Vittoria Street
Birmingham B1 3PE
Website: www.sx-media.com
e-mail: roulla@sx-media.com
Fax: 0121-694 6494     Tel: 0121-604 6366

**SAVIDENT Paul**
(Marketing & Press Management)
The Office, 27 St Dunstan's Road, London W7 2EY
Website: www.savident.com
e-mail: info@savident.com
Fax: 0870 0516418     Tel: 020-8567 2089

**SHIPPEN Martin MARKETING & MEDIA**
88 Purves Road, London NW10 5TB
e-mail: m.shippen@virgin.net
Mobile: 07956 879165     Tel: 020-8968 1943

**SILVEY Denise MANAGEMENT**
St Martin's Theatre
West Street, London WC2N 9NH
e-mail: ds@denisesilvey.com
Mobile: 07711 245848     Tel: 020-7240 3659

**SNELL Helen Ltd**
4th Floor
80-81 St Martin's Lane, London WC2N 4AA
e-mail: info@helensnell.com
Fax: 020-7240 2947     Tel: 020-7240 5537

**SOCIETY OF LONDON THEATRE**
32 Rose Street
London WC2E 9ET     Tel: 020-7557 6743
e-mail: susannah@solttma.co.uk

**STOTT Barbara**
20 Sunbury Lane, London SW11 3NP
e-mail: b-stott@talktalk.net     Tel: 020-7350 1159

**TARGET LIVE Ltd**
(Marketing, Press, Media & Design)
Fitzroy House
11 Chenies Street, London WC1E 7EY
Website: www.target-live.co.uk
e-mail: admin@target-live.co.uk
Fax: 020-7907 1751     Tel: 020-7907 1777

**TAYLOR HERRING PUBLIC RELATIONS**
11 Westway Centre
69 St Marks Road, London W10 6JG
Website: www.taylorherring.com
e-mail: james.herring@taylorherring.com
Fax: 020-8206 5155     Tel: 020-8206 5151

**THOMPSON Peter ASSOCIATES**
Flat One, 12 Bourchier Street
London W1V 5HN
Fax: 020-7439 1202     Tel: 020-7439 1210

**TRE-VETT Eddie**
Brink House, Avon Castle
Ringwood, Hampshire BH24 2BL     Tel: 01425 475544

**WILLIAMS Tei PRESS & ARTS MARKETING**
Post Office Cottage, Clifton, Oxon OX15 0PD
e-mail: artsmarketing@btconnect.com
Mobile: 07957 664116     Tel: 01869 337940

**WILSON Stella PUBLICITY & PERSONAL MANAGEMENT**
293 Faversham Road, Seasalter
Whitstable, Kent CT5 4BN     Mobile: 07860 174301
e-mail: stella@stellawilson.com

**WINGHAM Maureen PRESS & PUBLIC RELATIONS**
PO Box 125, Stowmarket
Suffolk IP14 1PB     Tel: 01449 771200
e-mail: maureen.wingham@mwmedia.uk.com

**WORKS PR The**
11 Marshalsea Road, London SE1 1EN     Tel: 020-7940 4686
Website: www.theworkspr.com
e-mail: nick@theworkspr.com

Radio
*BBC Radio*
*BBC Local Radio Stations*
*Independent Local Radio*
**Rehearsal Rooms & Casting Suites**
**Role Play Companies/Theatre Skills**
**in Business**

BBC RADIO, Broadcasting House
London W1A 1AA
Tel: 020-7580 4468 (Main Switchboard)

## • DRAMA

BBC Radio Drama
Bush House
The Aldwych, London WC2B 4PH
Tel: 020-7580 4468 (Main Switchboard)

### Production

| | |
|---|---|
| Head | Alison Hindell |
| Production Executive | Rebecca Wilmshurst |
| Administrator Radio Drama Company | Cynthia Fagan |

### Executive Producers

| | |
|---|---|
| World Service | Marion Nancarrow |
| London | Sally Avens |
| | David Hunter |
| | Jeremy Mortimer |
| | Di Speirs |
| Manchester | Sue Roberts |
| Birmingham | Vanessa Whitburn |

### Producers – London

| | |
|---|---|
| Marc Beeby | Pam Marshall |
| Steven Canny | Duncan Minshull |
| Jessica Dromgoole | Tracey Neale |
| Claire Grove | Jonquil Panting |
| Emma Harding | Mary Peate |
| Gemma Jenkins | Toby Swift |
| Peter Kavanagh | Justin Willett |

### Producers – Manchester

| | |
|---|---|
| Gary Brown | Nadia Molinari |
| Pauline Harris | |

### Producers – Birmingham

| | |
|---|---|
| Nasreen Ahmed (Silver Street) | Kate Oates (Archers) |
| Naylah Ahmed (Silver Street) | James Peries (Silver Street) |
| Julie Beckett (Archers) | Rosemary Watts (Archers) |
| Kim Greengrass (Silver Street) | Peter Wild |

### Development Producers

| | |
|---|---|
| Charlotte Riches (Manchester) | Faith Collingwood |
| Fiona Kelcher (Birmingham) | Abigail Le Fleming |

### Writersroom

| | |
|---|---|
| Director | Kate Rowland |

## Why should I work in radio?

To make a smooth transition from stage or camera to radio acting, everything that would otherwise be conveyed through body language and facial expressions must all be focused into the tone and pitch of the actor's voice.

If you have only ever considered visual acting work before, pursuing radio work would certainly enable you to expand your horizons and add additional skills to your CV. It is an opportunity to work in a different way and meet new requirements. Rehearsal and recording time is reduced in radio, which may allow you to pursue visual and radio acting alongside each other. Time constraints can be a pressure, and you have to get used to working without props (just sound effects), but this 'back to basics' existence is appealing to a lot of actors.

## How can I become a radio presenter?

Presenting work in any medium comes under a different category as this is not classed as acting. It is a skill in its own right. Please refer to the 'Agents - Presenters' section for more information.

## Do I need a voicereel?

This has to be your first and most important step into getting work as a radio actor. Your CV is not enough to get you a job without a professional-sounding voicereel. Voice-over work in commercial and corporate sectors requires a different type of reel. Please see the 'Promotional Services' section for more detailed voicereel advice.

## Do I need an agent?

It is not strictly necessary to have an agent for radio work. The BBC is by far the main producer of radio drama and welcomes applications directly from actors, but some independent radio stations prefer using agents to put actors forward. It might be worth doing some research on your local radio stations and finding out their preferred method of contact and making a decision from there. If you are looking for a new agent and are interested in radio work as well as straight acting work, find out whether they deal with this area of the industry before signing up. If you only want to pursue radio and/or voice-over work, or are looking for a specialist agent in addition to your main agent, please see the 'Agents - Voice-over' section for further advice and listings.

## How do I find work in radio?

You can send your CV and voicereel directly out to producers of radio drama, but make sure you target your search. Listen to radio plays and make a note of any producers whose work you particularly liked. This may also help you to identify what types of dramas you feel your voice would be most suited to. Once you have done your research and made a shortlist, send your voicereel with a personalised letter. Mention the plays you liked and explain that you feel he or she will be able to use your voice in productions like these. This method is likely to be much more effective than sending out a generic covering letter en masse, and will make you stand out. You don't need to send a headshot with your CV, but you could incorporate your photo in the body of your CV. It would be a good idea to have your name and contact details professionally printed onto the CD in case it becomes separated from your CV - see 'Promotional Services' for listings of companies that can do this for you.

## BROADCAST

### Radio Drama - BBC Scotland

| | |
|---|---|
| Head | Patrick Rayner |
| Editor, Radio Drama | Bruce Young |
| Management Assistant | Sue Meek |

### Producers

| | |
|---|---|
| Gaynor Macfarlane | David Jackson Young |
| Lu Kemp | |

### Radio Drama - BBC Wales

Kate McAll

### Radio Drama - BBC Northern Ireland

All enquiries to Anne Simpson

### • RADIO COMEDY/RADIO PRODUCTION

| | |
|---|---|
| Head, Radio Comedy | Jane Berthoud |
| Executive Producers | Katie Tyrrell |
| | Alison Vernon-Smith |

### Producers

| | |
|---|---|
| Colin Anderson | Victoria Lloyd |
| Tilusha Ghelani | Ed Morrish |
| Claire Jones | Pamela Norris |
| | Ben Walker |

| | |
|---|---|
| **Production Executive** | Sophie Butler |
| **Production Manager** | Mel Almond |

### • NEWS AND CURRENT AFFAIRS

BBC News (Television & Radio)
Television Centre
Wood Lane, London W12 7RJ
Tel: 020-8743 8000 (Main Switchboard)

| | |
|---|---|
| Director, News | Helen Boaden |
| Deputy Director, BBC News & Head of Multimedia Programmes | Stephen Mitchell |
| Head of Mulitmedia News Room | Mary Hockaday |
| Head of Newsgathering | Fran Unsworth |
| Controller of BBC News Channel (incl. One o'clock News) | Kevin Bakhurst |
| Controller of Operations & Technology | Peter Coles |
| Head of Political Programmes, Analysis & Research | Sue Inglish |

| | |
|---|---|
| Executive Editor & Commissioning Editor for Current Affairs | Clive Edwards |
| Executive Editor, Radio Current Affairs | Nicola Meyrick |
| Head of Editorial Development, Multimedia | Peter Clifton |
| Director of MC & QA, BBC Journalism | Chris Gottlieb |
| Editor, Six & Ten o'clock News and Deputy Head of Multimedia Newsroom | Craig Oliver |
| Editor, Newsnight | Peter Rippon |
| Editor, Breakfast | Alison Ford |
| Editor, Panorama | Sandy Smith |

### Radio Programmes

| | |
|---|---|
| Editor, Today | Ceri Thomas |
| Editor, PM/Broadcasting House The World This Weekend/The World at One | Joanna Carr |

### • RADIO SPORT

| | |
|---|---|
| Head of Sport | Gordon Turnbull |
| Commissioning Editor | Jonathan Wall |

### • CONTROLLERS

| | |
|---|---|
| **Director of Audio & Music** | Tim Davie |

**RADIO 1**

| | |
|---|---|
| Controller | Andy Parfitt |

**RADIO 2**

| | |
|---|---|
| Controller | Bob Shennan |

**RADIO 3**

| | |
|---|---|
| Controller | Roger Wright |

**RADIO 4**

| | |
|---|---|
| Controller | Mark Damazer |

**RADIO 5 LIVE**

| | |
|---|---|
| Controller | Adrian Van Klaveren |

### • BBC NEW WRITING

**BBC Writersroom**
**Grafton House**
**379-381 Euston Road**
**London NW1 3AU**　　**Tel: 020-7765 2703**
e-mail: writersroom@bbc.co.uk
Website: www.bbc.co.uk/writersroom

| | |
|---|---|
| Creative Director | Kate Rowland |
| Development Manager | Paul Ashton |

**BBC BEDFORDSHIRE, HERTFORDSHIRE &**
**BUCKINGHAMSHIRE THREE COUNTIES RADIO**
1 Hastings Street, Luton LU1 5XL
Website: www.bbc.co.uk/threecounties
e-mail: 3cr@bbc.co.uk
Fax: 01582 401467                      Tel: 01582 637400
Managing Editor: Mark Norman

**BBC RADIO BRISTOL**
PO Box 194, Bristol BS99 7QT
Website: www.bbc.co.uk/bristol
e-mail: radio.bristol@bbc.co.uk
Fax: 0117-923 8323                     Tel: 0117-974 1111
Managing Editor: Tim Pemberton
News Editor: Charlotte Callen

**BBC RADIO CAMBRIDGESHIRE**
Broadcasting House
104 Hills Road, Cambridge CB2 1LQ    Tel: 01223 259696
Website: www.bbc.co.uk/cambridgeshire
e-mail: cambs@bbc.co.uk
Managing Editor: Jason Horton
Assistant Editor: Will Chambers

**BBC RADIO CORNWALL**
Phoenix Wharf, Truro, Cornwall TR1 1UA
Website: www.bbc.co.uk/cornwall
Fax: 01872 240679                     Tel: 01872 275421
Managing Editor: Pauline Causey

**BBC COVENTRY & WARWICKSHIRE**
Priory Place, Coventry CV1 5SQ
Website: www.bbc.co.uk/coventry
e-mail: coventry.warwickshire@bbc.co.uk
Fax: 024-7655 2000                    Tel: 024-7655 1000
Senior Broadcast Journalist: Sue Curtis

**BBC RADIO CUMBRIA**
Annetwell Street, Carlisle, Cumbria CA3 8BB
Website: www.bbc.co.uk/radiocumbria
e-mail: radio.cumbria@bbc.co.uk
Fax: 01228 511195                     Tel: 01228 592444
Managing Editor: Nigel Dyson

**BBC RADIO DERBY**
PO Box 104.5, Derby DE1 3HL          Tel: 01332 361111
Website: www.bbc.co.uk/derby
Managing Editor: Simon Cornes

**BBC RADIO DEVON**
PO Box 1034, Plymouth PL3 5BD
Website: www.bbc.co.uk/devon
e-mail: radio.devon@bbc.co.uk
Fax: 01752 234595                     Tel: 01752 260323
Managing Editor: Mark Grinnell

**BBC ESSEX**
PO Box 765, Chelmsford, Essex CM2 9AB
Website: www.bbc.co.uk/essex
e-mail: essex@bbc.co.uk
Fax: 01245 492983                     Tel: 01245 616000
Managing Editor: Gerald Main

**BBC RADIO GLOUCESTERSHIRE**
London Road, Gloucester GL1 1SW      Tel: 01452 308585
Website: www.bbc.co.uk/gloucestershire
e-mail: radio.gloucestershire@bbc.co.uk
Managing Editor: Mark Hurrell

**BBC GUERNSEY**
Broadcasting House, Bulwer Avenue
St Sampsons, Channel Islands GY2 4LA
Website: www.bbc.co.uk/guernsey
e-mail: bbcguernsey@bbc.co.uk
Fax: 01481 200361                     Tel: 01481 200600
Managing Editor: Robert Wallace
Assistant Editor: Kay Langlois
Senior Broadcast Journalists: Simon Alexander, David Earl

**BBC HEREFORD & WORCESTER**
Hylton Road, Worcester WR2 5WW       Tel: 01905 748485
Website: www.bbc.co.uk/herefordandworcester
Managing Editor: James Coghill

**BBC RADIO HUMBERSIDE**
Queens Court, Queens Gardens, Hull HU1 3RH
Website: www.bbc.co.uk/humberside
e-mail: radio.humberside@bbc.co.uk
Fax: 01482 226409                     Tel: 01482 323232
Editor: Simon Pattern

**BBC RADIO JERSEY**
18 & 21 Parade Road, St Helier, Jersey JE2 3PL
Website: www.bbc.co.uk/jersey
e-mail: radiojersey@bbc.co.uk
Fax: 01534 732569                     Tel: 01534 870000
Editor: Denzil Dudley
Assistant Editor: Matthew Price

**BBC RADIO KENT**
The Great Hall, Mount Pleasant Road
Tunbridge Wells, Kent TN1 1QQ        Tel: 01892 670000
Website: www.bbc.co.uk/kent
e-mail: radio.kent@bbc.co.uk
Managing Editor: Paul Leaper

**BBC RADIO LANCASHIRE**
20-26 Darwen Street, Blackburn
Lancashire BB2 2EA                    Tel: 01254 262411
Website: www.bbc.co.uk/lancashire
e-mail: radio.lancashire@bbc.co.uk
Editor: John Clayton

**BBC RADIO LEEDS**
BBC Broadcasting Centre
2 St Peter's Square, Leeds LS9 8AH
Website: www.bbc.co.uk/leeds
Fax: 0113-224 7316                    Tel: 0113-244 2131
Managing Editor: Phil Squire

**BBC RADIO LEICESTER**
9 St Nicholas Place, Leicester LE1 5LB
Website: www.bbc.co.uk/leicester
e-mail: leicester@bbc.co.uk
Fax: 0116-251 1463                    Tel: 0116-251 6688
Managing Editor: Kate Squire

**BBC RADIO LINCOLNSHIRE**
Newport, Lincoln LN1 3XY
Website: www.bbc.co.uk/lincolnshire
Fax: 01522 511058                     Tel: 01522 511411
Managing Editor: Charlie Partridge

**BBC LONDON 94.9 FM**
35C Marylebone High Street
London W1U 4AA                        Tel: 020-7224 2424
Website: www.bbc.co.uk/london
Managing Editor: David Robey

**BBC RADIO MANCHESTER**
PO Box 951, Oxford Road
Manchester M60 1SD                    Tel: 0161-200 2000
Website: www.bbc.co.uk/manchester
Managing Editor: John Ryan

**BBC RADIO MERSEYSIDE**
PO Box 95.8, Liverpool L69 1ZJ       Tel: 0151-708 5500
Website: www.bbc.co.uk/liverpool
e-mail: radio.merseyside@bbc.co.uk
Managing Editor: Mick Ord

**BBC RADIO NEWCASTLE**
Broadcasting Centre
Barrack Road, Newcastle upon Tyne NE99 1RN
Website: www.bbc.co.uk/tyne
e-mail: radionewcastle.news@bbc.co.uk
Fax: 0191-232 5082                    Tel: 0191-232 4141
Editor: Andrew Robson

**BBC RADIO NORFOLK**
The Forum, Millennium Plain
Norwich NR2 1BH
Website: www.bbc.co.uk/norfolk
e-mail: radionorfolk@bbc.co.uk
Fax: 01603 284488                    Tel: 01603 617411
Managing Editor: David Clayton

**BBC NORTHAMPTON**
Broadcasting House
Abington Street
Northampton NN1 2BH
Website: www.bbc.co.uk/northamptonshire
e-mail: northampton@bbc.co.uk
Fax: 01604 230709                    Tel: 01604 239100
Manager: Laura Moss

**BBC RADIO NOTTINGHAM**
London Road
Nottingham NG2 4UU
Website: www.bbc.co.uk/nottingham
Fax: 0115-902 1984                   Tel: 0115-955 0500
Editor: Sophie Stewart
Editor News Gathering: Emma Agnew

**BBC RADIO SHEFFIELD**
54 Shoreham Street
Sheffield S1 4RS
Website: www.bbc.co.uk/southyorkshire
e-mail: radio.sheffield@bbc.co.uk
Fax: 0114-267 5454                   Tel: 0114-273 1177
Managing Editor: Gary Keown

**BBC RADIO SHROPSHIRE**
2-4 Boscobel Drive
Shrewsbury
Shropshire SY1 3TT
Website: www.bbc.co.uk/shropshire
e-mail: radio.shropshire@bbc.co.uk
Fax: 01743 271702                    Tel: 01743 248484
Editor: Tim Beech
Senior Broadcast Journalist News: Tracey Higgins

**BBC RADIO SOLENT**
Broadcasting House
Havelock Road
Southampton SO14 7PW
Website: www.bbc.co.uk/hampshire
e-mail: radio.solent@bbc.co.uk
Fax: 023-8033 9648                   Tel: 023-8063 1311
Managing Editor: Chris Carnegy

**BBC RADIO STOKE**
Cheapside, Hanley
Stoke-on-Trent, Staffordshire ST1 1JJ
Website: www.bbc.co.uk/stoke
e-mail: radio.stoke@bbc.co.uk
Fax: 01782 289115                    Tel: 01782 208080
Managing Editor: Sue Owen

**BBC RADIO SUFFOLK**
Broadcasting House
St Matthews Street, Ipswich IP1 3EP
Website: www.bbc.co.uk/radiosuffolk
e-mail: radiosuffolk@bbc.co.uk
Fax: 01473 210887                    Tel: 01473 250000
Editor: Peter Cook

**BBC SOUTHERN COUNTIES RADIO**
Broadcasting Centre, Guildford, Surrey GU2 7AP
Website: www.bbc.co.uk/southerncounties
e-mail: southern.counties.radio@bbc.co.uk
Fax: 01483 304952                    Tel: 01483 306306
Managing Editor: Nicci Holliday
Assistant Editor: Sara David

**BBC RADIO SWINDON & BBC RADIO WILTSHIRE**
Broadcasting House, 56-58 Prospect Place
Swindon SN1 3RW                      Tel: 01793 513626
Website: www.bbc.co.uk/wiltshire
e-mail: bbcwiltshire@bbc.co.uk
Manager: Rose Aston

**BBC TEES**
PO Box 95 FM
Broadcasting House
Newport Road, Middlesbrough TS1 5DG
Website: www.bbc.co.uk/tees
Fax: 01642 211356                    Tel: 01642 225211
Managing Editor: Matthew Barraclough

**BBC WEST MIDLANDS**
The Mailbox, Birmingham B1 1RF       Tel: 0121-567 6767
Website: www.bbc.co.uk/westmidlands
e-mail: bbcwm@bbc.co.uk
Editor Local Services: Keith Beech

**BBC RADIO YORK**
20 Bootham Row
York YO30 7BR
Website: www.bbc.co.uk/northyorkshire
e-mail: radio.york@bbc.co.uk
Fax: 01904 540339                    Tel: 01904 641351
Managing Editor: Sarah Drummond

**ABERDEEN**
Northsound Radio
Abbotswell Road, West Tullos, Aberdeen AB12 3AJ
Website: www.northsound.com
Fax: 01224 400003     Tel: 01224 337000

**AYR**
West Sound Radio
(Incorporating West Sound 1035 AM & 96.7 West FM)
Radio House, 54A Holmston Road
Ayr KA7 3BE     Tel: 01292 283662
Website: www.westsound.co.uk
e-mail: carolyn.mcallister@westsound.co.uk

**BELFAST**
City Beat 96.7 FM & 102.5 FM
2nd Floor, Arena Building
85 Ormeau Road, Belfast BT7 1SH
Website: www.citybeat.co.uk
e-mail: newsdesk@citybeat.co.uk
Fax: 028-9089 0100     Tel: 028-9023 4967

**BELFAST**
Cool FM
Kiltonga Industrial Estate, Newtownards
Belfast BT23 4ES     Tel: 028-9181 7181
Website: www.coolfm.co.uk
e-mail: info@coolfm.co.uk

**BELFAST**
Downtown Radio
Kiltonga Industrial Estate
Newtownards, Co Down BT23 4ES     Tel: 028-9181 5555
Website: www.downtown.co.uk
e-mail: info@downtown.co.uk

**BERKSHIRE & NORTH HAMPSHIRE**
Heart
PO Box 2020, Reading
Berkshire RG31 7FG     Tel: 0118-945 4400
Website: www.heart.co.uk
e-mail: news1029@heart.co.uk

**BIRMINGHAM**
96.4 BRMB & Gold
Nine Brindley Place, 4 Oozells Square
Birmingham B1 2DJ     Tel: 0121-566 5200
Website: www.brmb.co.uk

**BORDERS The**
Radio Borders Ltd
Tweedside Park, Galashiels TD1 3TD
Website: www.radioborders.com
e-mail: info@radioborders.com
Fax: 0845 3457080     Tel: 01896 759444

**BRADFORD**
Sunrise Radio
55 Leeds Road, Bradford BD1 5AF
Website: www.sunriseradio.fm
Fax: 01274 728534     Tel: 01274 735043

**BRADFORD, HUDDERSFIELD, HALIFAX, KEIGHLEY & DEWSBURY**
Pulse 2
Forster Square, Bradford BD1 5NE     Tel: 01274 203040
Website: www.pulse2.net
e-mail: general@pulse.co.uk

**BRIGHTON, EASTBOURNE & HASTINGS**
Southern FM
Radio House, Franklin Road
PO Box 2000, Brighton BN41 2SS
Website: www.southernfm.co.uk
Fax: 01273 316909     Tel: 01273 430111

**BRISTOL**
Heart
1 Passage Street, PO Box 2000, Bristol BS99 7SN
Website: www.heartbristol.co.uk
Fax: 0117-984 3202     Tel: 0117-984 3200

**CAMBRIDGE & NEWMARKET**
Heart
Enterprise House, The Vision Park
Chivers Way, Histon
Cambridge CB24 9ZR     Tel: 01223 235255
Website: www.heart.co.uk
e-mail: cambridge.news@heart.co.uk

**CARDIFF & NEWPORT**
Red Dragon FM & Gold
Atlantic Wharf, Cardiff Bay
Cardiff CF10 4DJ     Tel: 029-2066 2066
Website: www.reddragonfm.co.uk

**CHESTER, NORTH WALES & WIRRAL**
Heart
The Studios, Mold Road
Wrexham LL11 4AF     Tel: 01978 752202
Website: www.marchersound.co.uk
e-mail: news@marchersound.co.uk
Programme Controller: Steve Simms

**COVENTRY**
Mercia
Hertford Place, Coventry CV1 3TT
Website: www.mercia.co.uk
Fax: 024-7686 8209     Tel: 024-7686 8200

**DERBY**
Ram FM
35-36 Irongate, Derby DE1 3GA     Tel: 01332 324000
Website: www.ramfm.co.uk

**DUMFRIES**
South West Sound FM
Unit 40, The Loreburn Centre
High Street, Dumfries DG1 2BD
Website: www.southwestsound.co.uk
Fax: 01387 265629     Tel: 01387 250999

**DUNDEE & PERTH**
Tay FM & Radio Tay AM
PO Box 123, 6 North Isla Street
Dundee DD3 7JQ     Tel: 01382 200800
Website: www.radiotay.co.uk
e-mail: tayfm@radiotay.co.uk

**EDINBURGH**
Radio Forth Ltd
Forth House, Forth Street
Edinburgh EH1 3LE     Tel: 0131-556 9255
Website: www.radioforth.com
e-mail: info@radioforth.com

**EXETER & TORBAY**
Heart
Hawthorn House, Exeter Business Park, Exeter EX1 3QS
Website: www.heart.co.uk
Fax: 01392 354249     Tel: 01392 444444

**FALKIRK**
Central FM
201-203 High Street, Falkirk FK1 1DU
Website: www.centralfm.co.uk
Fax: 01324 611168     Tel: 01324 611164

**GLASGOW**
Radio Clyde 1 & Clyde 2
3 South Avenue, Clydebank Business Park, Glasgow G81 2RX
Website: www.clyde1.com / www.clyde2.com
Fax: 0141-565 2265     Tel: 0141-565 2200

**GLOUCESTER & CHELTENHAM**
Heart
Bridge Studios, Eastgate Centre, Gloucester GL1 1SS
Website: www.heart.co.uk
Fax: 01452 572409                    Tel: 01452 572400

**GREAT YARMOUTH & NORWICH**
Heart
St Georges Plain
47-49 Colegate, Norwich NR3 1DB
Website: www.heart.co.uk
Fax: 01603 671189                    Tel: 01603 630621

**GUILDFORD**
96.4 Eagle Radio
Eagle Radio Ltd, Dolphin House
3 North Street, Guildford, Surrey GU1 4AA
Website: www.964eagle.co.uk
e-mail: onair@964eagle.co.uk
Fax: 01483 454443                    Tel: 01483 300964

**HEREFORD & WORCESTER**
Wyvern FM
1st Floor, Kirkham House
John Comyn Drive
Worcester WR3 7NS                    Tel: 01905 612212
Website: www.wyvernfm.co.uk

**INVERNESS**
Moray Firth Radio
PO Box 271, Scorguie Place, Inverness IV3 8UJ
Website: www.mfr.co.uk
e-mail: mfr@mfr.co.uk
Fax: 01463 227714                    Tel: 01463 224433

**IPSWICH**
Heart 97.1 & 96.4 FM
Radio House, Alpha Business Park
Whitehouse Road, Ipswich IP1 5LT
Website: www.heart.co.uk
Fax: 01473 467549                    Tel: 01473 461000

**ISLE OF WIGHT**
Isle of Wight Radio
Dodnor Park, Newport, Isle of Wight PO30 5XE
Website: www.iwradio.co.uk
e-mail: admin@iwradio.co.uk
Fax: 01983 822109                    Tel: 01983 822557

**KENT**
Heart 103.1/102.8 & Gold Kent
Radio House, John Wilson Business Park
Whitstable, Kent CT5 3QX              Tel: 01227 772004
Website: www.heart.co.uk
e-mail: neil.webster@thisisglobal.com

**LEEDS**
96.3 Radio Aire & Magic 828
51 Burley Road, Leeds LS3 1LR
Website: www.radioaire.com
Fax: 0113-283 5501                    Tel: 0113-283 5500

**LEICESTER**
Leicester Sound
6 Dominus Way, Meridian Way Business Park
Leicester LE19 1RP
Website: www.leicestersound.co.uk
Fax: 0116-256 1309                    Tel: 0116-256 1300

**LIVERPOOL**
Radio City
St Johns Beacon, 1 Houghton Street
Liverpool L1 1RL                      Tel: 0151-472 6800
Website: www.radiocity.co.uk

**LONDON**
102.2 Smooth Radio
26-27 Castlereagh Street
London W1H 5DL                        Tel: 020-7706 4100
Website: www.smoothradio.com
e-mail: info@smoothradio.com

**LONDON**
Absolute Radio
1 Golden Square, London W1F 9DJ
Website: www.absoluteradio.co.uk
Fax: 020-7434 1197                    Tel: 020-7434 1215

**LONDON**
Choice FM
(Global)
30 Leicester Square, London WC2H 7LA
Website: www.thisisglobal.com
Fax: 020-7766 6100                    Tel: 020-7766 6810

**LONDON**
Classic FM
(Global)
30 Leicester Square, London WC2H 7LA
Website: www.thisisglobal.com
Fax: 020-7344 2700                    Tel: 020-7343 9000

**LONDON**
Gold
(Global)
30 Leicester Square, London WC2H 7LA
Website: www.thisisglobal.com
Fax: 020-7766 6100                    Tel: 020-7766 6810

**LONDON**
Independent Radio News
(Sky News Radio)
Mappin House, 4 Winsley Street
London W1W 8HF                        Tel: 020-7182 8591
Website: www.irn.co.uk
e-mail: radio@bskyb.com

**LONDON**
London Greek Radio
437 High Road, Finchley
London N12 0AP                        Tel: 020-8349 6950
Website: www.lgr.co.uk

**LONDON**
Magic 105.4 FM
Mappin House, 4 Winsley Street
London W1W 8HF                        Tel: 020-7182 8233
Website: www.magic.co.uk

**LUTON & BEDFORD**
Heart
Broadcast Centre, Chiltern Road
Dunstable LU6 1HQ
Website: www.heart.co.uk
Fax: 01582 676209                     Tel: 01582 676200

**MANCHESTER**
Key 103 FM & Magic 1152
Piccadilly Radio Ltd, Castle Quay
Castle Field, Manchester M15 4PR
Website: www.key103.co.uk
Fax: 0161-288 5151                    Tel: 0161-288 5000

**MILTON KEYNES**
Heart
14 Vincent Avenue
Milton Keynes Broadcast Centre
Crownhill, Milton Keynes MK8 0AB      Tel: 01908 269111
Website: www.heart.co.uk

**NORTHAMPTON**
Heart & Gold
19-21 St Edmunds Road
Northampton NN1 5DT                     Tel: 01604 795600
Website: www.heart.co.uk

**NORTHAMPTONSHIRE**
Connect FM 97.2 & 107.4 FM
2nd Floor
5 Church Street
Peterborough PE1 1XB
Website: www.connectfm.com
Fax: 01733 898107                       Tel: 0844 8001769

**NOTTINGHAM**
96 Trent FM
Chapel Quarter, Maid Marion Way
Nottingham NG1 6JR
Website: www.trentfm.co.uk
Fax: 0115-873 1509                      Tel: 0115-873 1500

**OXFORD & BANBURY**
Heart
Brush House, Pony Road
Oxford OX4 2XR                          Tel: 01865 871000
Website: www.heart.co.uk

**PETERBOROUGH**
Heart
PO Box 225, Queensgate Centre
Peterborough PE1 1XJ                    Tel: 01733 460460
Website: www.heart.co.uk

**PLYMOUTH**
Heart & Gold
Earl's Acre, Alma Road
Plymouth PL3 4HX                        Tel: 01752 275600
Website: www.heart.co.uk

**PORTSMOUTH & SOUTHAMPTON**
Galaxy South Coast, Heart & Gold
(Global Radio)
Radio House
Whittle Avenue
Segensworth West, Fareham
Hampshire PO15 5SX                      Tel: 01489 587600
Website: www.thisisglobal.com

**SOMERSET**
Heart
Haygrove House
Shoreditch Road
Taunton TA3 7BT                         Tel: 01823 338448
Website: www.heart.co.uk

**SOUTH MANCHESTER**
Imagine FM (104.9)
Waterloo Place
Watson Square
Stockport, Cheshire SK1 3AZ            Tel: 0161-609 1400
Website: www.imaginefm.net
e-mail: info@imaginefm.net

**STOKE-ON-TRENT & STAFFORD**
Signal Radio
Stoke Road
Stoke-on-Trent
Staffordshire ST4 2SR                  Tel: 01782 441300
Website: www.signalone.co.uk
e-mail: info@signalradio.com

**SWANSEA**
96.4 FM The Wave
Victoria Road, Gowerton
Swansea SA4 3AB                        Tel: 01792 511964
Website: www.thewave.co.uk

**TEESSIDE**
TFM Radio & Magic 1170
Yale Crescent, Teesdale
Thornaby
Stockton on Tees TS17 6AA             Tel: 01642 888222
Website: www.tfmradio.com

**TYNE & WEAR, NORTHUMBERLAND & DURHAM**
Metro Radio & Magic 1152
55 Degrees North
Pilgrim Street
Newcastle upon Tyne NE1 6BF           Tel: 0191-230 6100
Website: www.metroradio.co.uk

**WOLVERHAMPTON & BLACK COUNTRY/
SHREWSBURY & TELFORD**
West Midlands Beacon Radio
267 Tettenhall Road
Wolverhampton WV6 0DE                 Tel: 01902 461200
Website: www.beaconradio.co.uk

**YORKSHIRE**
Hallam FM & Magic AM
Radio House, 900 Herries Road
Hillsborough, Sheffield S6 1RH        Tel: 0114-209 1000
Website: www.hallamfm.co.uk

**YORKSHIRE & LINCOLNSHIRE**
96.9 Viking FM & Magic 1161 AM
Commercial Road
Hull HU1 2SG                          Tel: 01482 325141
Website: www.vikingfm.co.uk

# JERWOOD **SPACE**

### Excellent Central London Rehearsal Facilities for Theatre, Dance, Film & TV

- Magnificent Rooftop Studio (16.3m x 15.6m)
- 6 x Spaces (2 x 50 sq.m/2 x 108 sq.m/2 x 155 sq.m)
- 2 x Business Meeting Rooms with City views
- Production Offices + phones/wireless/photocopying
- Sprung floors/Lighting rig/Pianos/Mirrors/Audio

- Air-conditioned/Showers/Café 171/Gallery/Green Room
- Open 9am-9pm weekdays & 10am-6pm weekends
- Car parking (by arrangement)/Security card access
- Fully accessible convenient Bankside location nr. Southwark tube (Jubilee Line)/Borough/London Bridge/Waterloo

**Call** 020 7654 0171/fax 0172  **E-mail** space@jerwoodspace.co.uk  **Visit** www.jerwoodspace.co.uk for rates & details

**JERWOOD SPACE   171 UNION STREET   LONDON SE1 0LN   excellent facilities for the work of art**

## 3 MILLS STUDIOS
Three Mill Lane, London E3 3DU
Website: www.3mills.com
e-mail: info@3mills.com
Fax: 0871 5944028                    Tel: 020-7363 3336

## ACTORS CENTRE (LONDON) The
(Auditioning, Casting, Rehearsals, Room Hire)
1A Tower Street, London WC2H 9NP    Tel: 020-7632 8012
Website: www.actorscentre.co.uk
e-mail: operations@actorscentre.co.uk

## ACTORS STUDIO REHEARSAL & CASTING SPACE
Pinewood Studios, Pinewood Road
Iver Heath, Bucks SL0 0NH            Tel: 01753 650951
Website: www.actorsstudio.co.uk
e-mail: info@actorsstudio.co.uk

Unit 10, 21 Wren Street
London WC1 0HX                       Tel: 01753 650951

## ACTOR'S TEMPLE The
13-14 Warren Street, London W1T 5LG
Website: www.actorstemple.com
e-mail: info@actorstemple.com
Mobile: 07771 734670                 Tel: 020-3004 4537

## ADI PERFORMING ARTS CENTRE
218 Lambeth Road
London SE1 7JY                       Tel: 020-7928 6160
e-mail: playltd@btconnect.com

## AIRCRAFT CIRCUS
Unit 7A, Mellish House, Harrington Way
London SE18 5NR                      Tel: 020-8317 8401
Website: www.aircraftcircus.com
e-mail: nick@aircraftcircus.com

## BLOOMSBURY THEATRE

### REHEARSAL STUDIO

Attractive and modern, 11m x 8m (36ft x 26ft 4in)
Sprung dance floor, mirrored wall, piano,
kitchenette, adjustable lighting.
Shop and café on site.

Easily accessible central location

Available Mon through Sat, daytime and evening

Contact the Administration Officer
on **020 7679 2777**

15 Gordon Street, London WC1H 0AH
www.thebloomsbury.com

## ALBANY The
Contact: Miles Eady
Douglas Way, Deptford, London SE8 4AG
Website: www.thealbany.org.uk
e-mail: miles.eady@thealbany.org.uk
Fax: 020-8469 2253                   Tel: 020-8692 0231

## ALFORD HOUSE
Aveline Street
London SE11 5DQ                      Tel: 020-7735 1519
Website: www.alfordhouse.org.uk
e-mail: tim@alfordhouse.org.uk

## ALL TALENT, THE SONIA SCOTT AGENCY
Unit 325, 95 Morrison Street, Glasgow G5 8BE
Website: www.alltalentuk.co.uk
e-mail: enquiries@alltalentuk.co.uk
Mobile: 07971 337074                 Tel: 0141-418 1074

## ALRA (Academy of Live and Recorded Arts)
The Royal Victoria Patriotic Building
John Archer Way, London SW18 3SX
Website: www.alra.co.uk
e-mail: info@alra.co.uk
Fax: 020-8875 0789                   Tel: 020-8870 6475

## AMADEUS CENTRE The
50 Shirland Road, London W9 2JA
Website: www.amadeuscentre.co.uk
e-mail: info@amadeuscentre.co.uk
Fax: 020-7266 1225                   Tel: 020-7286 1686

## AMERICAN CHURCH IN LONDON The
Whitefield Memorial Church
79A Tottenham Court Road, London W1T 4TD
Website: www.latchcourt.com
e-mail: latchcourt@amchurch.co.uk
Fax: 020-7580 5013                   Tel: 020-7580 2791

## ARCH 468 THEATRE STUDIO
Arch 468, 209A Coldharbour Lane
London SW9 8RU                       Mobile: 07973 302908
Website: www.arch468.com

## ARTSADMIN
Toynbee Studios, 28 Commercial Street
London E1 6AB
Website: www.artsadmin.co.uk
e-mail: admin@artsadmin.co.uk
Fax: 020-7247 5103                   Tel: 020-7247 5102

## AVIV DANCE STUDIOS
Wren House, 1st Floor
19-23 Exchange Road
Watford WD18 6JD                     Tel/Fax: 01923 250000
Website: www.avivdance.com
e-mail: nikkiavron@btconnect.com

## How should I prepare for an audition?

When you are called to a casting you should make sure you are fully prepared with accurate information about the audition time, venue and format. Research the casting director too: look on his or her website and pay attention to media news. What productions have they worked on previously? What do they seem to look for and expect from the actors they cast?

For most auditions you will be given a script to learn, but you could be provided with a brief in advance and asked to find something suitable yourself. It would be advisable to have about five or six pieces ready to choose from that demonstrate your range before you are even called to a casting. You should select two relevant but contrasting pieces of about two to three minutes each for your audition, with the others as backups. If you can, read the whole play in addition to your speech.

It is generally best not to use 'popular' or very well-known pieces and instead to use original modern speeches, as this prevents the likelihood of the casting director comparing you, perhaps unfavourably, with anyone else. Having said this, however, you should still rehearse at least one Shakespeare piece. To find suitable speeches you should read widely for inspiration, or you could search online. If you are still struggling, think about who your favourite playwrights are and find out if they have written anything that is not too well-known.

## What should I expect when I arrive at the audition?

Arrive early for your audition, but be prepared to wait! Time slots are allocated but auditions can overrun for various reasons. Be presentable and think about how your character might choose to dress, but overall you will feel more comfortable and confident if you don't differ too much from what you would normally wear. Don't come in costume unless specifically asked.

When you enter the audition room, you may have just the casting director in the room, or you could be confronted with a panel including the director and/or producer, and an editor and cameraman if you are being filmed. Don't let this disconcert you. Nerves are to be expected, but try to be positive and enjoy yourself. Remember, the casting director doesn't want to spend several days auditioning - they want you to get the job!

Take a few moments to work out where you should stand and where everything is. Don't ask too many questions as this can be irritating but you could ask whether to address your monologue to the casting director / camera, or whether to speak into the 'middle distance'. Make sure that your face, and in particular your eyes, can be seen as much as possible.

Once you have performed your monologue, pause and wait for the casting director to speak to you. Don't ask if they want to see a second speech. If they want another one, and if there's time, they will ask you. You may be asked your opinion on the speech so be prepared with possible answers. Never criticise previous productions you have worked on. At the end of the casting, remember to take your script away unless you are asked to leave it, otherwise it can look as if you're not interested.

Auditions are never a waste of time, even if you don't get the part. You may have performed well but you might not have been quite right for that particular role. Every audition is great practice and experience, and the casting director may very well keep you in mind for future productions.

## Should I attend a casting in a house or flat?

Professional auditions are rarely held anywhere other than an official casting studio or venue. Be very wary if you are asked to go elsewhere. Trust your instincts. If something doesn't seem right to you, it probably isn't. Always take someone with you if you are in any doubt.

**BAC**
(Battersea Arts Centre)
Lavender Hill, London SW11 5TN
Website: www.bac.org.uk
e-mail: venues@bac.org.uk
Fax: 020-7978 5207                Tel: 020-7326 8211

**BELSIZE MUSIC ROOMS**
(Casting, Auditioning, Filming)
67 Belsize Lane, Hampstead, London NW3 5AX
Website: www.belsize-music-rooms.co.uk
e-mail: info@belsize-music-rooms.co.uk
Fax: 020-7916 0222                Tel: 020-7916 0111

**BIG CITY STUDIOS**
Montgomery House
159-161 Balls Pond Road
Islington, London N1 4BG
Website: www.pineappleagency.com
Fax: 020-7241 3006                Tel: 020-7241 6655

**BLACK BOX MERSEYSIDE Ltd**
The Black Box
21 Hutchinson Walk, Liverpool L6 1JW
Website: www.blackboxmerseyside.co.uk
e-mail: admin@blackboxmerseyside.co.uk
Fax: 0151-260 3001                Tel: 0151-260 3000

**BLOOMSBURY THEATRE The**
15 Gordon Street, London WC1H 0AH     Tel: 020-7679 2777
Website: www.thebloomsbury.com
e-mail: blooms.theatre@ucl.ac.uk

**BRIXTON COMMUNITY SPACE**
(Formerly Brixton St Vincent's Community Centre)
Talma Road, London SW2 1AS        Tel: 020-7326 4417
Website: www.bsvcc.org
e-mail: carofunnell@bsvcc.org

Located in
**West Hampstead, London NW6**
a suite of five, light, spacious rooms
available for hire 7 days per week
by the hour (8am - 10pm)

**Perfect for rehearsals, auditions
and castings!**

**www.theroomsabove.org.uk
Tel: 0845 686 0802**

**The affordable creative spaces
and consulting places venue.**

**CARAVANSERAI PRODUCTIONS & ACTING STUDIO**
Unit 30, Grand Union Centre
West Row, London W10 5AS          Tel: 020-8968 3769
Website: www.caravanseraiproductions.com
e-mail: info@caravanseraiproductions.com

**CARDINBROOK Ltd**
32 Barkston Gardens
London SW5 0EN                    Tel: 020-7373 1665
Website: www.ycbc.co.uk/roomhire.htm
e-mail: info@ycbc.co.uk

**CAST IN SPACE**
Lupus House, 2nd Floor
11-13 Macklin Street, Covent Garden
London WC2B 5NH                   Tel: 020-7404 9637
Website: www.castinspace.com
e-mail: castinspace@btconnect.com

**CASTING AT SWEET**
Sweet Entertainments Ltd
42 Theobalds Road, London WC1X 8NW
e-mail: info@sweet-uk.net
Fax: 07092 863782                 Tel: 020-7404 6411

**CASTING STUDIOS INTERNATIONAL Ltd**
Ramillies House
1-2 Ramillies Street, London W1F 7LN
Website: www.castingstudios.com
e-mail: info@castingstudios.com
Fax: 020-7437 2080                Tel: 020-7437 2070

**CASTING SUITE The**
8-10 Lower James Street
(Off Golden Square), London W1F 9EL
Website: www.thecastingsuite.com
e-mail: info@thecastingsuite.com
Fax: 020-7494 0803                Tel: 020-7534 5757

**CECIL SHARP HOUSE**
2 Regent's Park Road, London NW1 7AY
Website: www.efdss.org
e-mail: hire@efdss.org
Fax: 020-7284 0534                Tel: 020-7485 2206

**CENTRAL LONDON GOLF CENTRE**
Burntwood Lane, London SW17 0AT
Website: www.clgc.co.uk
Fax: 020-8874 7447                Tel: 020-8871 2468

**CENTRAL STUDIOS**
470 Bromley Road, Bromley, Kent BR1 4PN
Website: www.dandbperformingarts.co.uk
e-mail: bonnie@dandbmanagement.com
Fax: 020-8697 8100                Tel: 020-8698 8880

**CHATS PALACE ARTS CENTRE**
42-44 Brooksby's Walk
Hackney, London E9 6DF            Tel: 020-8533 0227
Website: www.chatspalace.com
e-mail: info@chatspalace.com

**CHELSEA THEATRE**
Contact: Francis Alexander
World's End Place, King's Road, London SW10 0DR
Website: www.chelseatheatre.org.uk
e-mail: admin@chelseatheatre.org.uk
Fax: 020-7352 2024                Tel: 020-7349 7811

**CIRCUS MANIACS SCHOOL OF CIRCUS ARTS**
(Circus Skills Rehearsal & Casting Facilities)
Office 8A, The Kingswood Foundation
Britannia Road, Kingswood, Bristol BS15 8DB
Website: www.circusmaniacs.com
e-mail: info@circusmaniacs.com
Mobile: 07977 247287             Tel/Fax: 0117-947 7042

**CLAPHAM COMMUNITY PROJECT**
St Anne's Hall, 31-33 Bromells Road
London SW4 0BN　　　　　Tel/Fax: 020-7720 8731
Website: www.rehearseatccp.co.uk
e-mail: admin@claphamcommunityproject.org.uk

**CLEAN BREAK**
2 Patshull Road, London NW5 2LB
Website: www.cleanbreak.org.uk
e-mail: general@cleanbreak.org.uk
Fax: 020-7482 8611　　　　　Tel: 020-7482 8600

**CLUB FOR ACTS & ACTORS**
(Incorporating Concert Artistes Association)
20 Bedford Street
London WC2E 9HP　　　　　Tel: 020-7836 3172
Website: www.thecaa.org
e-mail: office@thecaa.org

**COLOMBO CENTRE The**
(Rehearsal & Audition Space)
34-68 Colombo Street
London SE1 8DP　　　　　Tel: 020-7261 1658
Website: www.colombo-centre.org
e-mail: colombodm@jubileehallclubs.co.uk

**COPTIC STREET STUDIO Ltd**
9 Coptic Street
London WC1A 1NH　　　　　Tel: 020-7636 2030
e-mail: studio@copticstreet.com

**CRAGRATS Ltd**
The Mill, Dunford Road
Holmfirth, Huddersfield HD9 2AR
Website: www.cragrats.com
e-mail: chrislunn@cragrats.com
Fax: 01484 686212　　　　　Tel: 01484 686451

**CUSTARD FACTORY The**
Gibb Street, Digbeth, Birmingham B9 4AA
Website: www.custardfactory.co.uk
e-mail: info@custardfactory.co.uk
Fax: 0121-604 8888　　　　　Tel: 0121-224 7777

**DANCE ATTIC STUDIOS**
368 North End Road
London SW6　　　　　Tel: 020-7610 2055
e-mail: danceattic@hotmail.com

**DANCE COMPANY STUDIOS**
76 High Street
Beckenham BR3 1ED　　　　　Tel: 020-8402 2424
Website: www.dancecompanystudios.co.uk
e-mail: hire@dancecompanystudios.co.uk

**DANCEWORKS**
16 Balderton Street, London W1K 6TN
Website: www.danceworks.net
Fax: 020-7629 2909　　　　　Tel: 020-7318 4100

**DAVIES Siobhan STUDIOS**
85 St George's Road, London SE1 6ER
Website: www.siobhandavies.com
e-mail: info@siobhandavies.com
Fax: 020-7091 9669　　　　　Tel: 020-7091 9650

**DRILL HALL The**
16 Chenies Street, London WC1E 7EX
Website: www.drillhall.co.uk
e-mail: box.office@drillhall.co.uk
Fax: 020-7307 5062　　　　　Tel: 020-7307 5060

**EALING STUDIOS**
Ealing Green, London W5 5EP
Website: www.ealingstudios.com
e-mail: bookings@ealingstudios.com
Fax: 020-8758 8658　　　　　Tel: 020-8567 6655

## The Questors Theatre
### Rehearsal Rooms

For Hire **Daytimes** Monday - Friday

- Emmet Room 11m X 9m
  (Sprung Floor)
- Shaw Room 12m X 8.5m
- Redgrave Room 11m X 8.5m
- Piano available upon request

### Additional Facilities:

On-Site Car Park, Café
Break-Out Spaces, Toilets

Quiet and attractive location opposite park with shopping centre nearby. 5 Minutes from Ealing Broadway Tube and B.R. Station. 20 Minutes from Heathrow.

**The Questors Theatre**
12 Mattock Lane
London W5 5BQ
T: 020 8567 0011
www.questors.org.uk

**THE QUESTORS THEATRE**

**ELMS LESTERS PAINTING ROOMS**
1-3-5 Flitcroft Street, London WC2H 8DH
Website: www.elmslesters.co.uk
e-mail: info@elmslesters.co.uk
Fax: 020-7379 0789                    Tel: 020-7836 6747

**ENGLISH FOLK DANCE & SONG SOCIETY**
Cecil Sharp House
2 Regent's Park Road, London NW1 7AY
Website: www.efdss.org
e-mail: hire@efdss.org
Fax: 020-7284 0534                    Tel: 020-7485 2206

**ENGLISH NATIONAL OPERA**
Lilian Baylis House
165 Broadhurst Gardens, London NW6 3AX
Website: www.eno.org
e-mail: receptionlbh@eno.org
Fax: 020-7625 3398                    Tel: 020-7624 7711

**ENGLISH TOURING THEATRE**
25 Short Street, Waterloo, London SE1 8LJ
Website: www.ett.org.uk
e-mail: admin@ett.org.uk
Fax: 020-7633 0188                    Tel: 020-7450 1990

**EPMC TALENT CASTING STUDIO**
Unit 67, Ability Plaza, Arbutus Street, London E8 4DT
Website: www.epmctalent.com
e-mail: info@epmctalent.com
Fax: 0871 5593947                    Tel: 0844 8243888

**ETCETERA THEATRE**
265 Camden High Street, London NW1 7BU
Website: www.etceteratheatre.com
e-mail: etc@etceteratheatre.com
Fax: 020-7482 0378                    Tel: 020-7482 4857

**EUROKIDS & EKA CASTING STUDIOS**
The Warehouse Studios, Glaziers Lane
Culcheth, Warrington, Cheshire WA3 4AQ
Website: www.eka-agency.com
e-mail: castings@eka-agency.com
Fax: 01925 767563                    Tel: 01925 761088

**EXCHANGE The**
Old Market Hill
Sturminster Newton DT10 1FH           Tel: 01258 475137
Website: www.stur-exchange.co.uk
e-mail: info@stur-exchange.co.uk

**EXPRESSIONS STUDIOS**
Linton House, 39-51 Highgate Road, London NW5 1RT
Website: www.expressionsstudios.com
e-mail: info@expressionsstudios.com
Fax: 020-7813 1582                    Tel: 020-7813 1580

**FACTORY FITNESS & DANCE CENTRE The**
407 Hornsey Road, London N19 4DX      Tel: 020-7272 1122
e-mail: info@tangolondon.com

**FSU LONDON STUDY CENTRE**
99 Great Russell Street, London WC1B 3LH
Fax: 020-7813 3270                    Tel: 020-7813 3223

**FUNK PHYSICS Ltd**
Bernie Grant Enterprise Building
Town Hall Approach Road
London N15 4RX                        Tel: 020-8885 0500
Website: www.funkphysics.com
e-mail: info@funkphysics.com

**HAMPSTEAD THEATRE**
Eton Avenue, Swiss Cottage, London NW3 3EU
Website: www.hampsteadtheatre.com
e-mail: info@hampsteadtheatre.com
Fax: 020-7449 4201                    Tel: 020-7449 4200

# CENTRAL LONDON REHEARSAL ROOMS

**four large rooms with pianos**

**photos and dimensions:**
**www.drillhall.co.uk**

facilities: **reception** | **production office** | **catering** | **free wi-fi access**
also for hire: two **theatres** | four **meeting rooms**
just off **Tottenham Court Road** | two minutes' walk: ⊖ **Goodge Street**

16 Chenies Street
London WC1E 7EX

**www.drillhall.co.uk**
**020 7307 5060**

the **drillhall**

---

**HANGAR ARTS TRUST**
Unit 7A, Mellish House, Harrington Way
London SE18 5NR    Tel: 020-8317 8401
Website: www.hangaruk.com
e-mail: alex@aircraftcircus.com

**HOLY INNOCENTS CHURCH**
Paddenswick Road, London W6 0UB
Website: www.hisj.co.uk
e-mail: administrator@hisj.co.uk
Fax: 020-8563 8735    Tel: 020-8748 2286

**HOLY TRINITY W6**
Holy Trinity Parish Centre
41 Brook Green, London W6 7BL    Tel: 020-7603 3832
Website: www.holytrinityw6.org
e-mail: brookgreen@rcdow.org.uk

**HOMES FOR ISLINGTON**
Highbury House, 5 Highbury Crescent
London N5 1RN    Tel: 020-7527 8632
Website: www.homesforislington.org.uk
e-mail: service.development@homesforislington.org.uk

**HOPE STREET Ltd**
13A Hope Street, Liverpool L1 9BQ
Website: www.hope-street.org
e-mail: arts@hope-street.org
Fax: 0151-709 3242    Tel: 0151-708 8007

**HOXTON HALL THEATRE & YOUTH ARTS CENTRE**
130 Hoxton Street, London N1 6SH
Website: www.hoxtonhall.co.uk
e-mail: carolyn@hoxtonhall.co.uk
Fax: 020-7729 3815    Tel: 020-7684 0060

**HUB The @ TOOTING & MITCHAM**
Imperial Fields, Bishops Ford Road
Morden, Surrey SM4 6BF
Website: www.thehubattmufc.co.uk
e-mail: reception@thehubattmufc.co.uk
Fax: 020-8685 6190    Tel: 020-8685 6193

**IMT SPACE Ltd**
Unit 2, 210 Cambridge Heath Road
London E2 9NQ    Tel: 020-8980 5475
Website: www.imagemusictext.com
e-mail: mail@imagemusictext.com

**INC SPACE**
9-13 Grape Street, Covent Garden, London WC2H 8ED
Website: www.inc-space.com
e-mail: studiohire@inc-space.com

**ISLINGTON ARTS FACTORY**
2 Parkhurst Road, London N7 0SF
Website: www.islingtonartsfactory.org.uk
e-mail: iaf@islingtonartsfactory.fsnet.co.uk
Fax: 020-7700 7229    Tel: 020-7607 0561

---

*NEWLY REFURBISHED REHEARSAL ROOMS IN WEST LONDON*
**Holy Trinity Parish Centre**, **41 Brook Green, Hammersmith W6 7BL**

has recently undergone a complete refurbishment and has two rehearsal rooms for hire. Parking for 3 cars and pay and display available on the street. Private office available / fitting room. Wifi, lift and disabled access.

**T: 020 7603 3832   brookgreen@rcdow.org.uk   www.holytrinityw6.org**

**Tube:** Hammersmith Broadway (Piccadilly, District and Hammersmith and City lines) and Barons Court, both 12 min walk. **Buses:** 9, 10, 27 and 391 to Brook Green.
**GROUND FLOOR** Lower Hall - 14 x 9m (10.75m into bay)   **MEETING ROOM** 4 x 5.5m   **FIRST FLOOR** Upper Hall - 14 x 5.5m

**JACKSONS LANE**
(Various Spaces incl Rehearsal Rooms & Theatre Hire)
269A Archway Road
London N6 5AA
Website: www.jacksonslane.org.uk
e-mail: reception@jacksonslane.org.uk
Tel: 020-8340 5226                    Tel: 020-8340 8902

**JERWOOD SPACE**
171 Union Street, London SE1 0LN
Website: www.jerwoodspace.co.uk
e-mail: space@jerwoodspace.co.uk
Fax: 020-7654 0172                    Tel: 020-7654 0171

**LIVE THEATRE**
27 Broad Chare, Quayside
Newcastle upon Tyne NE1 3DQ          Tel: 0191-261 2694
Website: www.live.org.uk
e-mail: info@live.org.uk

**LONDON BUBBLE THEATRE COMPANY Ltd**
5 Elephant Lane, London SE16 4JD
Website: www.londonbubble.org.uk
e-mail: admin@londonbubble.org.uk
Fax: 020-7231 2366                    Tel: 020-7237 4434

**LONDON SCHOOL OF CAPOEIRA**
Units 1 & 2 Leeds Place
Tollington Park, London N4 3RF       Tel: 020-7281 2020
Website: www.londonschoolofcapoeira.co.uk
e-mail: info@londonschoolofcapoeira.co.uk

**LONDON STUDIO CENTRE**
42-50 York Way, London N1 9AB
e-mail: info@london-studio-centre.co.uk
Fax: 020-7837 3248                    Tel: 020-7837 7741

**LONDON WELSH TRUST Ltd**
157-163 Gray's Inn Road, London WC1X 8UE
Website: www.londonwelsh.org
Fax: 020-7837 6268                    Tel: 020-7837 3722

**LYRIC HAMMERSMITH**
King Street, London W6 0QL
Website: www.lyric.co.uk
e-mail: enquiries@lyric.co.uk
Fax: 020-8741 5965                    Tel: 0871 2211722

**MACKINTOSH Cameron REHEARSAL STUDIO**
The Tricycle, 269 Kilburn High Road, London NW6 7JR
Website: www.tricycle.co.uk
e-mail: admin@tricycle.co.uk
Fax: 020-7328 0795                    Tel: 020-7372 6611

**MADDERMARKET THEATRE**
St John's Alley, Norwich, Norfolk NR2 1DR
Website: www.maddermarket.co.uk
e-mail: mmtheatre@btconnect.com
Fax: 01603 661357                     Tel: 01603 626560

**MARIA ASSUMPTA CENTRE**
Heythrop College
23 Kensington Square
London W8 5HN                        Tel: 020-7795 6600
Website: www.heythrop.ac.uk
e-mail: conferences@heythrop.ac.uk

**MENIER CHOCOLATE FACTORY**
53 Southwark Street, London SE1 1RU
Website: www.menierchocolatefactory.com
e-mail: office@menierchocolatefactory.com
Fax: 020-7378 1713                    Tel: 020-7378 1712

**MOBERLY SPORTS & EDUCATION CENTRE**
Kilburn Lane, Kensal Rise, London W10 4AE
Fax: 020-7641 5878                    Tel: 020-7641 4807

**MOVING EAST STUDIO**
(Harlequin Sprung Floor, Quadrophonic Sound System)
St Matthias Church Hall
Wordsworth Road
London N16 8DD                       Tel: 020-7503 3101
Website: www.movingeast.co.uk
e-mail: admin@movingeast.co.uk

**MUSIC ROOM AT COLE KITCHENN The**
212 Strand, London WC2R 1AP          Tel: 020-7427 5680
e-mail: info@colekitchenn.com

**NATIONAL YOUTH THEATRE OF GREAT BRITAIN**
443-445 Holloway Road, London N7 6LW
Website: www.nyt.org.uk
e-mail: info@nyt.org.uk
Fax: 020-7281 8246                    Tel: 020-7281 3863

**NEALS YARD MEETING ROOMS**
14 Neals Yard, Covent Garden
London WC2H 9DP
Tel/Fax: 020-7436 9875
Website: www.meetingrooms.org.uk
e-mail: info@walkinbackrub.co.uk

**NETTLEFOLD The**
West Norwood Library Centre
1 Norwood High Street
London SE27 9JX
Tel: 020-7926 8070
e-mail: thenettlefold@lambeth.gov.uk

**NEW DIORAMA THEATRE The**
(80 Seat Blackbox Theatre)
Regents Place
London NW1
Tel: 020-7916 5467
Website: www.diorama-arts.org.uk
e-mail: admin@diorama-arts.org.uk

**NEW PLAYERS THEATRE**
The Arches, Off Villiers Street, London WC2N 6NG
Website: www.newplayerstheatre.com
e-mail: info@newplayerstheatre.com
Fax: 0845 6382102
Tel: 020-7930 5868

**NITRO**
6 Brewery Road, London N7 9NH
Website: www.nitro.co.uk
e-mail: info@nitro.co.uk
Fax: 020-7609 1221
Tel: 020-7609 1331

**NLPAC PERFORMING ARTS**
(Production & Casting Office Facilities)
76 St James Lane, Muswell Hill, London N10 3DF
Website: www.nlpac.co.uk
e-mail: nlpac@aol.com
Fax: 020-8444 4040
Tel: 020-8444 4544

**OBSERVATORY STUDIOS The**
45-46 Poland Street, London W1F 7NA
e-mail: info@theobservatorystudios.com
Fax: 020-7437 2830                    Tel: 020-7437 2823

**OCTOBER GALLERY**
24 Old Gloucester Street, London WC1N 3AL
Website: www.octobergallery.co.uk
e-mail: rentals@octobergallery.co.uk
Fax: 020-7405 1851                    Tel: 020-7831 1618

**OLD VIC THEATRE The**
The Cut, London SE1 8NB              Tel: 020-7928 2651
Website: www.oldvictheatre.com
e-mail: hires@oldvictheatre.com

**ONLY CONNECT UK**
32 Cubitt Street
London WC1X 0LR                      Tel: 0845 3707990
Website: www.onlyconnecttheatre.com
e-mail: info@onlyconnectuk.org

**OPEN DOOR COMMUNITY CENTRE**
Beaumont Road
Wimbledon SW19 6TF                   Tel/Fax: 020-8871 8174
Website: www.wandsworth.gov.uk
e-mail: opendoor@wandsworth.gov.uk

**OUT OF JOINT**
7 Thane Works, Thane Villas, London N7 7NU
Website: www.outofjoint.co.uk
e-mail: ojo@outofjoint.co.uk
Fax: 020-7609 0203                    Tel: 020-7609 0207

**OVAL HOUSE**
52-54 Kennington Oval
London SE11 5SW                      Tel: 020-7582 0080
Website: www.ovalhouse.com
e-mail: info@ovalhouse.com

**PAINES PLOUGH REHEARSAL & AUDITION SPACE**
4th Floor, 43 Aldwych, London WC2B 4DN
Website: www.painesplough.com
e-mail: office@painesplough.com
Fax: 020-7240 4534                    Tel: 020-7240 4533

**PEOPLE SHOW**
(3 Rehearsal Rooms, Set Building Workshop, Casting Suites,
Sound & Lighting Equipment for Hire)
People Show Studios
Pollard Row, London E2 6NB
Website: www.peopleshow.co.uk
e-mail: people@peopleshow.co.uk
Fax: 020-7739 0203                    Tel: 020-7729 1841

**PHA CASTING SUITE**
Tanzaro House, Ardwick Green North
Manchester M12 6FZ
Website: www.pha-agency.co.uk
e-mail: info@pha-agency.co.uk
Fax: 0161-273 4567                    Tel: 0161-273 4444

**PINEAPPLE DANCE STUDIOS**
7 Langley Street, Covent Garden, London WC2H 9JA
Website: www.pineapple.uk.com
e-mail: studios@pineapple.uk.com
Fax: 020-7836 0803                    Tel: 020-7836 4004

**PLACE The**
Robin Howard Dance Theatre
17 Duke's Road, London WC1H 9PY
Website: www.theplace.org.uk
e-mail: info@theplace.org.uk
Fax: 020-7121 1142                    Tel: 020-7121 1100

**PLAYGROUND STUDIO The**
Unit 8, Latimer Road
London W10 6RQ                       Tel/Fax: 020-8960 0110
Website: www.the-playground.co.uk
e-mail: info@the-playground.co.uk

**POOR SCHOOL The**
242 Pentonville Road
London N1 9JY                        Tel: 020-7837 6030
Website: www.thepoorschool.com
e-mail: acting@thepoorschool.com

**PRECINCT THEATRE The**
Units 2/3 The Precinct, Packington Square, London N1 7UP
Website: www.breakalegman.com
e-mail: studiohire@breakalegman.com
Fax: 020-7359 3660                    Tel: 020-7359 3594

**PUPPET CENTRE TRUST**
BAC Lavender Hill, London SW11 5TN
Website: www.puppetcentre.org.uk
e-mail: space@puppetcentre.org.uk    Tel: 020-7228 5335

**QUESTORS THEATRE EALING The**
12 Mattock Lane, London W5 5BQ
Website: www.questors.org.uk
e-mail: alice@questors.org.uk
Fax: 020-8567 2275                    Tel: 020-8567 0011

**QUICKSILVER THEATRE**
The Glasshouse, 4 Enfield Road, London N1 5AZ
Website: www.quicksilvertheatre.org
e-mail: talktous@quicksilvertheatre.org
Fax: 020-7254 3119                    Tel: 020-7241 2942

# Rehearsal space for hire

very close to Clapham Common tube (1min)

## Main Hall
- New Harlequin sprung floor and new lighting
- 12.21 x 18.17m approx
- piano
- toilets
- kitchen area
- adjoining Green Room with water machine

## Lower Hall
- 9.15 x 7.92 approx
- additional Audition/Production Meeting room 8 x 4.5m approx also available
- both with water machines

**clapham community project**
St Anne's Hall, 31-33 Bromells Road, London SW4 0BN
Tel/Fax: **0207 720 8731** www.rehearseatccp.co.uk

Clapham Community Project is a registered charity, number 299072

---

**RAG FACTORY The**
16-18 Heneage Street, London E1 5LJ
Website: www.ragfactory.org.uk
e-mail: hello@ragfactory.org.uk
Fax: 020-7092 9099    Tel: 020-7650 8749

**RAMBERT DANCE COMPANY**
94 Chiswick High Road, London W4 1SH
Website: www.rambert.org.uk
e-mail: rdc@rambert.org.uk
Fax: 020-8747 8323    Tel: 020-8630 0600

**REALLY USEFUL GROUP THEATRES**
Contact: Michael Townsend
22 Tower Street, London WC2H 9TW
Website: www.reallyuseful.com
e-mail: mike.townsend@reallyuseful.co.uk
Fax: 020-7240 1292    Tel: 020-7240 0880

**RED ONION DANCE STUDIO**
6-28 Hilton Grove Business Centre
Hatherley Mews
London E17 4QP
Website: www.redonion.uk.com
e-mail: info@redonion.uk.com    Tel/Fax: 020-8520 3975

**RIDGEWAY STUDIOS**
Fairley House, Andrews Lane
Cheshunt, Herts EN7 6LB
e-mail: info@ridgewaystudios.co.uk
Fax: 01992 633844    Tel: 01992 633775

**RITZ STUDIOS**
110-112 Disraeli Road, London SW15 2DX
Website: www.ritzstudios.com
e-mail: lee@ritzstudios.com
Fax: 020-8877 1036    Tel: 020-8870 1335

**The Playground Studio**
2,500sq.ft beautiful rehearsal space
London W10

**Sprung Floor**
**Mirrored Wall**
**Natural Day Light**

www.the-playground.co.uk
info@the-playground.co.uk
T: 020 8960 0110

**RIVERSIDE STUDIOS**
Crisp Road, Hammersmith, London W6 9RL
Website: www.riversidestudios.co.uk
e-mail: online@riversidestudios.co.uk
Fax: 020-8237 1001          Tel: 020-8237 1000

**ROOFTOP STUDIO THEATRE**
Rooftop Studio, Somerfield Arcade
Stone, Staffordshire ST15 8AU
Website: www.rooftopstudio.co.uk
Fax: 01785 818176          Tel: 01785 761233

**ROOMS ABOVE The**
Westheath Yard, (Opposite The Emmanuel School)
174 Mill Lane, West Hampstead, London NW6 1TB
Website: www.theroomsabove.org.uk
e-mail: info@theroomsabove.org.uk
Fax: 020-8201 9464          Tel: 0845 6860802

**ROSE STUDIO**
Rose Theatre, Kingston
24-26 High Street
Kingston upon Thames
Surrey KT1 1HL
Website: www.rosetheatrekingston.org
e-mail: hiresandevents@rosetheatrekingston.org
Fax: 020-8546 8783          Tel: 020-8546 6983

**ROTHERHITHE STUDIOS**
119 Rotherhithe Street
London SE16 4NF
Website: www.sandsfilms.co.uk
e-mail: ostockman@sandsfilms.co.uk
Fax: 020-7231 2119          Tel: 020-7231 2209

**ROYAL ACADEMY OF DANCE**
36 Battersea Square, London SW11 3RA
Website: www.rad.org.uk
e-mail: info@rad.org.uk
Fax: 020-7924 3129          Tel: 020-7326 8000

**ROYAL ACADEMY OF DRAMATIC ART**
62-64 Gower Street, London WC1E 6ED
e-mail: bookings@rada.ac.uk          Tel: 020-7908 4754

**ROYAL SHAKESPEARE COMPANY**
35 Clapham High Street
London SW4 7TW
Website: www.rsc.org.uk
e-mail: london@rsc.org.uk
Fax: 020-7845 0505          Tel: 020-7845 0500

**RTM STUDIOS**
Central Chambers
93 Hope Street, Glasgow G2 6LD
Website: www.rtmstudios.co.uk
Fax: 0141-221 8622          Tel: 0141-221 2258

**RUDEYE STUDIOS**
The Basement, 73 St John Street
Farringdon, London EC1M 4NJ
Website: www.rudeye.com
e-mail: info@rudeye.com          Tel: 020-7014 3023

**SADLER'S WELLS THEATRE**
Rosebery Avenue, London EC1R 4TN
Website: www.sadlerswells.com
e-mail: events@sadlerswells.com
Fax: 020-7863 8061          Tel: 020-7863 8065

**SMA CENTRE**
Vicarage Gate
Kensington, London W8 4HN
Website: www.smacentre.com
e-mail: manager@smacentre.com
Fax: 020-7368 6505          Tel: 020-7937 8885

**SOHO GYMS**
Camden Town Gym
193 Camden High Street
London NW1 7JY
Website: www.sohogyms.com
Fax: 020-7267 0500     Tel: 020-7482 4524

Clapham Common Gym
95-97 Clapham High Street
London SW4 7TB
Fax: 020-7720 6510     Tel: 020-7720 0321

Covent Garden Gym
12 Macklin Street
London WC2B 5NF
Fax: 020-7242 0899     Tel: 020-7242 1290

Earl's Court Gym
254 Earl's Court Road
London SW5 9AD
Fax: 020-7244 6893     Tel: 020-7370 1402

**SOHO THEATRE**
21 Dean Street
London W1D 3NE
Website: www.sohotheatre.com
e-mail: hires@sohotheatre.com
Fax: 020-7287 5061     Tel: 020-7478 0117

**SPACE @ CLARENCE MEWS**
40 Clarence Mews, London E5 8HL
e-mail: frith.salem@virgin.net     Tel: 020-8986 5260

**SPACE ARTS CENTRE The**
269 Westferry Road, London E14 3RS
Website: www.space.org.uk
e-mail: info@space.org.uk     Tel: 020-7515 7799

**SPACE CITY STUDIOS**
79 Blythe Road, London W14 0HP
Website: www.spacecitystudios.co.uk
e-mail: info@spacecity.co.uk
Fax: 020-7371 4001     Tel: 020-7371 4000

**S.P.A.C.E. The**
(Studio for Performing Arts & Creative Enterprise)
34 Argyle Arcade Chambers, Buchanan Street
Glasgow G2 8BD     Tel: 0141-222 2942
Website: www.glasgowactingacademy.com
e-mail: info@glasgowactingacademy.com

**SPOTLIGHT**
(Casting Studios & Room Hire)
7 Leicester Place, London WC2H 7RJ
Website: www.spotlight.com/rooms
e-mail: rooms@spotlight.com
Fax: 020-7437 5881     Tel: 020-7437 7631

**ST GEORGE'S CHURCH BLOOMSBURY**
Vestry Hall
6 Little Russell Street
London WC1A 2HR                     Tel: 020-7242 1979
Website: www.stgeorgesbloomsbury.org.uk
e-mail: hiring@stgeorgesbloomsbury.org.uk

**ST JAMES'S CHURCH PICCADILLY**
197 Piccadilly, London W1J 9LL
Website: www.st-james-piccadilly.org
e-mail: roomhire@st-james-piccadilly.org
Fax: 020-7734 7449                   Tel: 020-7734 4511

**ST JOHN'S CHURCH**
Waterloo Road, Southbank
London SE1 8TY                       Tel: 020-7633 9819
Website: www.stjohnswaterloo.co.uk

**ST MARTINS-IN-THE-FIELDS**
6 St Martins Place
London WC2N 4JJ
Website: www.smitf.org
e-mail: jennifer.lang@smitf.org      Tel: 020-7766 1130

**ST MARY NEWINGTON CHURCH HALL**
The Parish Office
57 Kennington Park Road
London SE11 4JQ                      Tel: 020-7735 1894

**ST MARY'S CHURCH HALL PADDINGTON**
c/o Bill Kenwright Ltd
1 Venice Walk, London W2 1RR
e-mail: julia.redican@kenwright.com
Fax: 020-7446 6222                   Tel: 020-7446 6200

**STUDIO 326**
Royal Exchange
St Ann's Square, Manchester M2 7BR
Website: www.emmastafford.tv
e-mail: info@emmastafford.tv
Fax: 0161-833 4264                   Tel: 0161-833 4263

**STUDIO The**
4 Great Queen Street
London WC2B 5DG
Website: www.studiocoventgarden.com
e-mail: will@studiocoventgarden.com  Tel: 020-7831 7899

**SUMMERS Mark CASTING STUDIOS**
1 Beaumont Avenue
West Kensington
London W14 9LP
Website: www.marksummers.com
e-mail: info@marksummers.com         Tel: 020-7229 8413

**SUMMIT STUDIOS**
2-4 Spring Bridge Mews
Spring Bridge Road
Ealing, London W5 2AB
Website: www.summitstudios.co.uk
e-mail: info@summitstudios.co.uk
Fax: 020-8840 2446                   Tel: 020-8840 2200

**TAKE FIVE CASTING STUDIO**
(Casting Suite)
37 Beak Street, London W1F 9RZ
Website: www.takefivestudio.com
e-mail: info@takefivestudio.com
Fax: 020-7287 3035                   Tel: 020-7287 2120

**TREADWELL'S**
34 Tavistock Street
Covent Garden, London WC2E 7PB
Website: www.castingspacecoventgarden.co.uk
e-mail: info@treadwells-london.com   Tel: 020-7240 8906

**TRESTLE ARTS BASE**
(Home of Trestle Theatre Company)
Russet Drive, St Albans, Herts AL4 0JQ
Website: www.trestle.org.uk
e-mail: admin@trestle.org.uk
Fax: 01727 855558                    Tel: 01727 850950

**TRICYCLE The**
269 Kilburn High Road, London NW6 7JR
Website: www.tricycle.co.uk
e-mail: trish@tricycle.co.uk
Fax: 020-7328 0795                   Tel: 020-7372 6611

**TT DANCE STUDIOS**
Parkwood Health & Fitness Centre
Darkes Lane, Potters Bar, Herts EN6 2AU
Mobile: 07930 400647                 Mobile: 07904 771980

**TWICKENHAM SEA CADETS**
Fairways, Off Broom Road, Teddington
Middlesex TW11 9PL                   Tel: 020-8977 7575

**UNICORN THEATRE**
147 Tooley Street
London SE1 2HZ                       Tel: 020-7645 0500
Website: www.unicorntheatre.com
e-mail: stagedoor@unicorntheatre.com

**UNION CHAPEL PROJECT**
Compton Avenue, London N1 2XD
Website: www.unionchapel.org.uk
e-mail: spacehire@unionchapel.org.uk
Fax: 020-7354 8343                   Tel: 020-7226 3750

## HANGAR ARTS TRUST

- Rehearsal and Studio Space
- Large blue screen for CGI Effects
- Fully Riggable for flying and Effects
- Sprung Dance Floors • Cafe and Child Care Facilities
- Parking Nr Greenwich and The O2 Centre

**Studio 1 - 10m High, 15m x 18m**
**Studio 2 - 10m High, 10m x 10m**

Contact: Alex Frith 020 8317 8401

**www.hangaruk.com  a.frith@hangarartstrust.org**

Hangar Arts Trust, Unit 7A, Mellish House
Harrington Way, London SE18 5NR

### 32 Cubitt Street

32 Cubitt Street, London WC1X 0LR between Kings Cross and Holborn, is a former Baptist church with seating for 220 in the main hall and balcony. The hall measures 13m X 11.5m (42' X 37'). It has an upright piano, a Bose audio system and sound desk, an adaptable Steeldeck stage, wooden floors and wall mirrors. Downstairs at Cubitt Street is a full catering kitchen.

Cubitt Street is available for rehearsals, auditions, recitals, film shoots and private parties.

**For bookings, prices or more information please call 0845 370 7990 or email info@onlyconnectuk.org**

**URDANG ACADEMY The**
Finsbury Town Hall, Rosebery Avenue, London EC1R 4RP
Website: www.theurdangacademy.com
e-mail: info@theurdangacademy.com
Fax: 020-7278 6727                    Tel: 020-7713 7710

**WALKING FORWARD Ltd**
Studio 6, The Aberdeen Centre
22-24 Highbury Grove
London N5 2EA                    Tel/Fax: 020-7359 5249
Website: www.walkingforward.co.uk
e-mail: info@walkingforward.co.uk

**WATERMANS**
40 High Street, Brentford TW8 0DS
Website: www.watermans.org.uk
e-mail: info@watermans.org.uk
Fax: 020-8232 1030                    Tel: 020-8232 1020

**Y TOURING THEATRE COMPANY**
One KX, 120 Cromer Street
London WC1H 8BS                    Tel: 020-7520 3090
Website: www.ytouring.org.uk
e-mail: info@ytouring.org.uk

**YOUNG ACTORS THEATRE**
70-72 Barnsbury Road
London N1 0ES
Website: www.yati.org.uk
e-mail: info@yati.org.uk
Fax: 020-7833 9467                    Tel: 020-7278 2101

**YOUNG Sylvia THEATRE SCHOOL**
Rossmore Road
Marylebone, London NW1 6NJ
e-mail: info@sylviayoungtheatreschool.co.uk
Fax: 020-7723 1040                    Tel: 020-7402 0673

**ACTIVATION**
Riverside House
Feltham Avenue
Hampton Court
Surrey KT8 9BJ
Website: www.activation.co.uk
e-mail: info@activation.co.uk
Fax: 020-8783 9345                    Tel: 020-8783 9494

**ACT UP**
Unit 88, 99-109 Lavender Hill
London SW11 5QL
Website: www.act-up.co.uk
e-mail: info@act-up.co.uk
Fax: 020-7924 6606                    Tel: 020-7924 7701

**APROPOS PRODUCTIONS Ltd**
2nd Floor
91A Rivington Street
London EC2A 3AY
Website: www.aproposltd.com
e-mail: info@aproposltd.com
Fax: 020-7739 3852                    Tel: 020-7739 2857

**BARKING PRODUCTIONS/INSTANT WIT**
(Drama Based Training, Barking Productions. Comedy
Improvisation Show/Corporate Entertainment, Instant Wit)
Regus, 1 Friary
Temple Quay
Bristol BS1 6EA                    Tel/Fax: 0117-908 5384
Website: www.barkingproductions.co.uk
e-mail: info@barkingproductions.co.uk

**BROWNE Michael ASSOCIATES Ltd**
The Cloisters
168C Station Road
Lower Stondon
Bedfordshire SG16 6JQ            Tel/Fax: 01462 812483
Website: www.mba-roleplay.co.uk
e-mail: enquiries@mba-roleplay.co.uk

**BUZZWORD FILMS**
(Role Play, Film Training Dramas)
Website: www.buzzwordfilms.co.uk
e-mail: mike.charles@buzzwordfilms.co.uk
Mobile: 07974 355885                    Tel: 01363 772752

**CRAGRATS Ltd**
Cragrats Mill
Dunford Road
Holmfirth
Huddersfield HD9 2AR
Website: www.cragrats.com
e-mail: info@cragrats.com
Fax: 01484 686212                    Tel: 01484 686451

**DRAMANON**
Langtons House
Templewood Lane
Farnham Common
Slough SL2 3HD
Website: www.dramanon.co.uk
e-mail: info@dramanon.co.uk
Fax: 01753 647783                    Tel: 01753 647795

**GLOBAL7**
PO Box 56232
London N4 4XP
Website: www.global7casting.com
e-mail: global7castings@gmail.com
Mobile: 07956 956652     Tel/Fax: 020-7281 7679

**IMPACT UNIVERSAL**
Hopebank House
Woodhead Road
Honley, Huddersfield HD9 6PF
Website: www.impactuniversal.com
e-mail: jill.beckwith@impactuniversal.com
Fax: 01484 660088     Tel: 01484 668881

**INTERACT**
138 Southwark Bridge Road
London SE1 0DG
Website: www.interact.eu.com
e-mail: info@interact.eu.com
Fax: 020-7793 7755     Tel: 020-7793 7744

**LADA PRODUCTIONS**
Sparkhouse Studios
Ropewalk, Lincoln, Lincs LN6 7DQ
Website: www.lada.org.uk
e-mail: info@lada.org.uk
Fax: 01522 837201     Tel: 01522 837242

**NV MANAGEMENT Ltd**
Central Office
4 Carters Leaze, Great Wolford
Warwickshire CV36 5NS
Website: www.nvmanagement.co.uk
e-mail: hello@nvmanagement.co.uk

**PERFORMANCE BUSINESS The**
78 Oatlands Drive
Weybridge, Surrey KT13 9HT     Tel: 01932 888885
Website: www.theperformance.biz
e-mail: lucy@theperformance.biz

**ROLEPLAY UK**
2 St Mary's Hill, Stamford PE9 2DW
Website: www.roleplayuk.com
Fax: 01780 764436     Tel: 01780 761960

**STEPS DRAMA LEARNING DEVELOPMENT**
Unit 4.1.1
The Leathermarket
Weston Street
London SE1 3ER
Website: www.stepsdrama.com
e-mail: mail@stepsdrama.com
Fax: 020-7403 0909     Tel: 020-7403 9000

**THEATRE & Ltd**
Church Hall, St James Road
Marsh, Huddersfield HD1 4QA
Website: www.theatreand.com
e-mail: cmitchell@theatreand.com
Fax: 01484 532962     Tel: 01484 532967

**UNUSUAL CONNECTIONS**
20 Rupert Street, London W1D 6DF     Tel: 0845 0094583
Website: www.unusualconnections.co.uk
e-mail: info@unusualconnections.co.uk

**WEST END WORKSHOPS**
(Audition Coaching/Arts Workshops)
Website: www.westendworkshops.co.uk
e-mail: info@westendworkshops.co.uk   Mobile: 07989 422808

## 3D SET COMPANY
(Sets, Exhibition Stands, Scenery Design & Construction)
Unit 8 Temperance Street
Manchester M12 6HR
Website: www.3dsetco.com
e-mail: twalsh@3dsetco.com
Fax: 0161-273 6786                    Tel: 0161-273 8831

## ALBEMARLE SCENIC STUDIOS
(Suppliers of Scenery & Costumes Construction/Hire)
Admin: PO Box 240
Rotherfield TN6 9BN                   Tel: 0845 6447021
Website: www.albemarleproductions.com
e-mail: albemarle.productions@virgin.net

## ALL SCENE ALL PROPS
(Scenery, Props, Painting Contractors)
Units 2 & 3, Spelmonden Farm
Goudhurst, Kent TN17 1HE
Website: www.allscene.net
e-mail: info@allscene.net
Fax: 01580 211131                     Tel: 01580 211121

## BRISTOL (UK) Ltd
(Scenic Paint)
Unit 3, Southerland Court
Tolpits Lane, Watford WD18 9SP
Website: www.bristolpaint.com
e-mail: tech.sales@bristolpaint.com
Fax: 01923 779666                     Tel: 01923 779333

## CAP PRODUCTION SOLUTIONS
116 Wigmore Road, Carshalton
Surrey SM5 1RQ                        Mobile: 07973 432576
e-mail: leigh@leighporter.com

## CCT LIGHTING UK Ltd
(Lighting, Dimmers, Sound & Stage Machinery)
Unit 3, Ellesmere Business Park
Haydn Road, Sherwood
Nottingham NG5 1DX
Website: www.cctlighting.com
e-mail: office@cctlighting.co.uk
Fax: 0115-985 7091                    Tel: 0115-985 8919

## COD STEAKS
(Set Construction, Design, Model Making, Exhibitions,
Costume)
2 Cole Road, Bristol BS2 0UG          Tel: 0117-980 3910
Website: www.codsteaks.com
e-mail: mail@codsteaks.com

## CREW CO
(Stage & Technical Crew for London & Midlands)
55 Main Street, Long Compton
Warwickshire CV36 5JS
Website: www.crewco.net
e-mail: contactus@crewco.net
Fax: 0845 4589411                     Tel: 0845 4589400

## DAP STUDIO
94 Kenley Road
Merton Park, London SW19 3DS          Tel/Fax: 01892 730897
Website: www.dapstudio.co.uk
e-mail: james@dapstudio.co.uk

## DISPLAY MAINTENANCE Ltd
Unit 1, Calder Trading Estate
Lower Quarry Road, Bradley
Huddersfield HD5 0RR                  Tel: 0870 8508500
Website: www.dmnsolutions.co.uk
e-mail: enquiries@dmnsolutions.co.uk

S

**Set Construction, Lighting,
Sound & Scenery**

[ CONTACTS 2010 ]

**DOBSON SOUND PRODUCTION Ltd**
(Sound Hire, Design & Installation)
66 Windsor Avenue
Merton, London SW19 2RR
e-mail: enquiries@dobsonsound.co.uk
Fax: 020-8543 3636                    Tel: 020-8545 0202

**DOVETAIL SPECIALIST SCENERY**
(Scenery, Prop & Furniture Builders)
42-50 York Way, London N1 9AB     Tel/Fax: 020-7278 7379
e-mail: dovetail.ss@btopenworld.com

**FUTURIST SOUND & LIGHT Ltd**
Unit 15, Carlton Trading Estate
Pickering Street, Leeds LS12 2QG
Website: www.futurist.co.uk
e-mail: info@futurist.co.uk
Fax: 0113-279 0066                    Tel: 0113-279 0033

**GILL Perry**
(Set Construction, Installation & Production Management)
e-mail: perry_gill100@hotmail.com     Mobile: 07815 048164

**HALL STAGE Ltd**
Unit 4, Cosgrove Way, Luton, Beds LU1 1XL
Website: www.hallstage.com
e-mail: sales@hallstage.com
Fax: 0845 3454256                    Tel: 0845 3454255

**HARLEQUIN (British Harlequin Plc)**
Festival House, Chapman Way
Tunbridge Wells, Kent TN2 3EF
Website: www.harlequinfloors.com
e-mail: sales@harlequinfloors.com
Fax: 01892 514222                    Tel: 01892 514888

**HENSHALL John**
(Director of Lighting & Photography)
68 High Street
Stanford in the Vale
Oxfordshire SN7 8NL                    Tel: 01367 710191
e-mail: john@epi-centre.com

**HERON & DRIVER**
(Scenic Furniture & Structural Prop Makers)
Unit 7, Dockley Road Industrial Estate
Rotherhithe, London SE16 3SF
Website: www.herondriver.co.uk
e-mail: mail@herondriver.co.uk
Fax: 020-7394 8680                    Tel: 020-7394 8688

**LIGHT WORKS Ltd**
2A Greenwood Road, London E8 1AB
Fax: 020-7254 0306                    Tel: 020-7249 3627

**LIVERPOOL SCENIC WORKSHOP Ltd**
Baltic Road, Bootle, Liverpool L20 1AW
Website: www.liverpoolscenicworkshop.co.uk
e-mail: info@liverpoolscenicworkshop.co.uk
Fax: 0151-933 6699                    Tel: 0151-933 6677

**MALTBURY STAGING**
(Portable Staging Sales & Consultancy)
Unit 9, Level 5 (South)
New England House
New England Street
Brighton BN1 4GH
Website: www.maltbury.com
e-mail: info@maltbury.com
Fax: 0845 1308882                    Tel: 0845 1308881

**MASSEY Bob ASSOCIATES**
(Electrical & Mechanical Stage Consultants)
9 Worrall Avenue, Arnold
Nottinghamshire NG5 7GN            Tel/Fax: 0115-967 3969
e-mail: bm.associates@virgin.net

**MATT-LX**
(Lighting & Technical Production)
Gunnery House
9 Gunnery Terrace
London SE18 6SW
Website: www.mattlx.com
e-mail: intray@mattlx.com
Fax: 020-8301 8149                    Tel: 020-8301 8692

**MODELBOX**
(Computer Aided Design & Design Services)
2 Saddlers Way
Okehampton
Devon EX20 1TL                    Tel: 01837 54026
Website: www.modelboxplans.com
e-mail: info@modelbox.co.uk

**MODERNEON LONDON Ltd**
(Lighting & Signs)
Cromwell House
27 Brabourne Rise
Park Langley
Beckenham, Kent BR3 6SQ
Website: www.moderneon.co.uk
e-mail: info@moderneon.co.uk
Fax: 020-8658 2770                    Tel: 020-8650 9690

**MOUNSEY Matthew**
(Scenic Artist)
16 White Cliff House
Vermont Road, London SW18 2LH     Mobile: 07941 355450
e-mail: matthewmounsey@hotmail.com

**NEED Paul J**
(Lighting Designer)
c/o 10 out of 10 Productions, 5 Orchard Business Centre
Kangley Bridge Road
London SE26 5AQ
Website: www.pauljneed.co.uk
e-mail: paul@10outof10.co.uk
Fax: 020-8778 9217                    Tel: 020-8659 2558

**NORTHERN LIGHT**
(Lighting, Sound, Communications & Stage Equipment)
Assembly Street
Leith, Edinburgh EH6 7RG
Website: www.northernlight.co.uk
e-mail: info@northernlight.co.uk
Fax: 0131-622 9101                    Tel: 0131-622 9100

**ORBITAL**
(Sound Hire & Design)
57 Acre Lane
Brixton, London SW2 5TN
Website: www.orbitalsound.co.uk
e-mail: hire@orbitalsound.co.uk
Fax: 020-7501 6869     Tel: 020-7501 6868

**PANALUX**
12 Waxlow Road
London NW10 7NU
Website: www.panalux.biz
e-mail: info@panalux.biz
Fax: 020-8233 7001     Tel: 020-8233 7000

**PMB THEATRE & EXHIBITION SERVICES Ltd**
The Barn, Kingston Wood Manor
Arrington
Royston, Herts SG8 0AP
Website: www.pmbltd.co.uk
e-mail: pmb.com@virgin.net
Fax: 01954 718032     Tel: 01954 718227

**PROPS2ORDER Ltd**
Thorncliff, Hacking Lane
South Elmsall
Pontefract
West Yorkshire WF9 2SU     Mobile: 07799 863179
Website: www.props2order.co.uk
e-mail: laurensimmonds@btinternet.com

**RE VAMP EVENTS & ENTERTAINMENT**
(Cabaret, Decor, Event Management & Entertainment)
Ealing House, 33 Hanger Lane
London W5 3HJ     Tel: 020-8997 3355
e-mail: revampevents@aol.com

**REVOLVING STAGE COMPANY Ltd The**
Unit F5
Little Heath Industrial Estate
Old Church Road
Coventry
Warwickshire CV6 7ND
Website: www.therevolvingstagecompany.co.uk
e-mail: enquiries@therevolvingstagecompany.co.uk
Fax: 024-7668 9355     Tel: 024-7668 7055

**RK RESOURCE**
2 Wyvern Way
Henwood
Ashford, Kent TN24 8DW
e-mail: rkresource2007@aol.co.uk
Fax: 01233 750133     Tel: 01233 750180

**RWS ELECTRICAL & AUDIO CONTRACTORS Ltd**
(All Aspects of Electrical Services including Installation,
Design & Consultancy)
1 Spinners Close
Biddenden, Kent TN27 8AY     Tel: 01580 291764
Website: www.rwselectrical.com
e-mail: dick@rwselectrical.com

**S + H TECHNICAL SUPPORT Ltd**
(Starcloths, Drapes)
Starcloth Way
Mullacott Industrial Estate
Ilfracombe
Devon EX34 8PL
Website: www.starcloth.co.uk
e-mail: shtsg@aol.com
Fax: 01271 865423     Tel: 01271 866832

**S2 EVENTS**
(Production - Lighting, Set Construction & Scenery)
3-5 Valentine Place
London SE1 8QH
Website: www.s2events.co.uk
e-mail: info@s2events.co.uk
Fax: 020-7928 6082          Tel: 020-7928 5474

**SCENA PROJECTS Ltd**
(Set Construction)
240 Camberwell Road
London SE5 0DP
Website: www.scenapro.com
e-mail: info@scenapro.com
Fax: 020-7703 7012          Tel: 020-7703 4444

**SCOTT FLEARY PRODUCTIONS Ltd**
Unit 1-4 Block A
Vale Industrial Park
170 Rowan Road
London SW16 5BN
e-mail: info@scottflearyltd.com
Fax: 0870 4448322          Tel: 0870 4441787

**SETS IN THE CITY**
Location House, 5 Dove Lane
Bristol BS2 9HP
Website: www.setsinthecity.co.uk
e-mail: info@setsinthecity.co.uk
Fax: .0117-955 2480          Tel: 0117-955 5538

**SHOWSTORM Ltd**
24 The Poplars
Littlehampton BN17 6GZ
Website: www.showstorm.tv
e-mail: mark@showstorm.tv
Fax: 0871 8575062          Tel: 020-8123 3453

**SMITH Paul Don**
(Graffiti Mural Artist, Graphics, Scenery)
11A Cadogan Road
Surbiton, Surrey KT6 4DQ          Mobile: 07949 710306
e-mail: firedon_1@hotmail.com

**STAGE MANAGEMENT COMPANY**
36 Oak Avenue
Bingley
West Yorkshire BD16 1ES          Mobile: 07731 429544
Website: www.stagemanagementcompany.co.uk
e-mail: peter@stagemanagementcompany.co.uk

**STAGE SYSTEMS**
(Designers & Suppliers of Modular Staging, Tiering &
Auditorium Seating)
Stage House
Prince William Road
Loughborough LE11 5GU
Website: www.stagesystems.co.uk
e-mail: info@stagesystems.co.uk
Fax: 01509 233146          Tel: 01509 611021

**STAGECRAFT Ltd**
(Hire & Sales of Lighting, Sound, Audio Visual & Staging for
Conference & Live Events)
Ashfield Trading Estate
Salisbury, Wiltshire SP2 7HL
Website: www.stagecraft.co.uk
e-mail: hire@stagecraft.co.uk
Fax: 01722 412562          Tel: 01722 326055

**STAGEWORKS WORLDWIDE PRODUCTIONS**
(Scenery, Props, Lighting & Sound)
525 Ocean Boulevard
Blackpool, FY4 1EZ
Website: www.stageworkswwp.com
e-mail: info@stageworkswwp.com
Fax: 01253 342702          Tel: 01253 342426

**STEWART Helen**
(Theatre Designer)
Unit 111A, Belgravia Workshops
Marlborough Road N19 4NF          Mobile: 07887 682186
Website: www.helenstewart.co.uk
e-mail: design@helenstewart.co.uk

**STORM LIGHTING Ltd**
Warwick House
Monument Way West
Woking, Surrey GU21 5EN
Website: www.stormlighting.co.uk
e-mail: hire@stormlighting.co.uk
Fax: 01483 757710          Tel: 01483 757211

**STRAND LIGHTING EUROPE Ltd**
(Lighting Equipment for Stage, Studio, Film & TV)
Unit 2 Royce Road
Fleming Way
Crawley
West Sussex RH10 9JY
Website: www.strandlighting.com
Fax: 01293 554019          Tel: 01293 554010

**SVIDSMYNDIR SCENIC STUDIOS**
Steinhella 17B
221 Hafnarfjordur
Iceland
Website: www.svidsmyndir.is
e-mail: smynd@svidsmyndir.is
Fax: 00 35 45 88 93 95          Tel: 00 35 45 88 93 93

**TMS INTERNATIONAL Ltd**
(Terry Murphy Scenery) (Set Construction & Painting)
306 St James's Road
London SE1 5JX
Website: www.terrymurphy.co.uk
e-mail: production@tmsi.co.uk
Fax: 020-7232 2347          Tel: 020-7394 9519

**TOP SHOW**
(Props, Scenery, Conference Specialists)
North Lane, Huntington
York YO32 9SU          Tel: 01904 750022

**WEST John**
(Artwork & Design)
103 Abbotswood Close
Winyates Green
Redditch
Worcestershire B98 0QF
Website: www.johnwestartist.co.uk
e-mail: johnwest@blueyonder.co.uk
Mobile: 07753 637451          Tel/Fax: 01527 516771

**WHITE LIGHT Ltd**
20 Merton Industrial Park
Jubilee Way
Wimbledon, London SW19 3WL
Website: www.whitelight.ltd.uk
e-mail: info@whitelight.ltd.uk
Fax: 020-8254 4801          Tel: 020-8254 4800

BBC Television
Wood Lane, London W12 7RJ
Tel: 020-8743 8000

## • TALENT & RIGHTS NEGOTIATION GROUP

Room 3400
201 Wood Lane
White City
London W12 7TS

| | |
|---|---|
| Head of Talent Rights & Negotiation | Simon Hayward-Tapp |
| Head of Copyright Contracting | Rob Kirkham |
| Head of Performance Contracting | Annie Thomas |
| Literary Copyright Manager | Neil Hunt |

### LITERARY COPYRIGHT
**Room 395 Drama Building**
**BBC Television Centre, London W12 7RJ**

| | |
|---|---|
| Manager | Neil Hunt |

**Senior Executives**

| | |
|---|---|
| Sue Dickson | Julieann May |
| Julie Gallagher | Sally Millwood |
| David Knight | Hilary Sagar |

### MUSIC COPYRIGHT
**Room 201 EBX Building**
**BBC Television Centre, London W12 7RJ**

| | |
|---|---|
| News & Current Affairs Rights Manager | Tessa Beckett |

### LONDON FACTUAL
**Room 3205**
**White City**
**201 Wood Lane**
**London W12 7TS**

| | |
|---|---|
| Rights Manager | Chris Dabbs |

**Executives**

| | |
|---|---|
| Alice Brandon | Matthew Hickling |
| Selena Harvey | Stuart Krelle |
| | Shelagh Morrison |

### LONDON FICTION
**Rooms 341-344/350-253**
**Drama Building**
**BBC Television Centre**
**London W12 7RJ**

| | |
|---|---|
| Rights Negotiation Manager (London & Birmingham) | Nicola Hill |

**Executives (TV)**

| | |
|---|---|
| Mike Bickerdike | Jemma McGee |
| Lorraine Clark | Annie Pollard |
| Teresa Cordall | Thalia Reynolds |
| | Colette Robertson |

| | |
|---|---|
| Classical Music Rights Manager | Simon Brown |

**Executives (Radio)**

| | |
|---|---|
| Stephanie Beynon | Sally Dean |

Where appropriate, Rep periods are indicated,
e.g. (4 Weekly) and matinee times e.g. Th 2.30 for
Thursday 2.30pm.
**SD** Stage Door
**BO** Box Office
**TIE** Theatre in Education (For further details of
TIE/YPT
See Theatre - Children's, Young People's & TIE

# [ CONTACTS 2010 ]

## BRISTOL

| | |
|---|---|
| Rights Manager | Chris Dabbs |

**Executives**

| | |
|---|---|
| Jane Armstrong | Sophie Clark |

## BIRMINGHAM

**Executives**

| | |
|---|---|
| Rachel Amos | Andrea Coles |
| | Jill Ridley |

## MANCHESTER

**Executives**

| | |
|---|---|
| Colleen Burrows | Sarah McHugh |
| | Collette Tanner |

## • DRAMA

Room 265, Drama Room
Wood Lane, London W12 7RJ    Tel: 020-8743 8000

| | |
|---|---|
| Controller, Drama Production & New Talent | John Yorke |
| Director, Drama Production | Nicolas Brown |
| Controller, Series & Serials | Kate Harwood |
| Executive Producer, EastEnders | Diederick Santer |
| Creative Director | Manda Levin |
| Head of Production | Susy Liddell |
| Head of Development | Emma Broughton |

**Executive Producers, Drama Production**

| | |
|---|---|
| Ruth Caleb | Sue Hogg |
| Belinda Campbell | Jessica Pope |
| Phillippa Giles | Hilary Salmon |
| Kate Harwood | Diederick Santer |
| | Will Trotter |

**Producers, Drama Production**

| | |
|---|---|
| Sarah Brown | George Ormond |
| Ben Evans | Sally Stokes |
| Mike Hobson | Annie Tricklebank |
| Kate Lewis | Pier Wilkie |
| Peter Lloyd | Colin Wratten |

## • COMMISSIONING

| | |
|---|---|
| Controller, BBC Knowledge | George Entwistle |
| Commissioning Editors, Drama | Sarah Brandist |
| | Polly Hill |
| Commissioning Editor, Independent Drama | Lucy Richer |
| Controller, Drama Production Studios | John Yorke |

| | |
|---|---|
| Controller, BBC Four | Richard Klein |
| Head of In-house Commissioning | Emma Swain |
| Controller, Series & Serials | Kate Harwood |
| Controller, Drama Commissioning | Ben Stephenson |

## • NEWS AND CURRENT AFFAIRS

**BBC News (Television & Radio)**
Television Centre, Wood Lane, London W12 7RJ
Tel: 020-8743 8000 (Main Switchboard)

| | |
|---|---|
| Director, News | Helen Boaden |
| Deputy Director, News & Head of Multimedia Programmes, News | Stephen Mitchell |
| Head of Newsgathering | Fran Unsworth |
| Head of Newsroom | Mary Hockaday |
| Head of Political Programmes, Research & Analysis | Sue Inglish |
| Head of Communications, BBC Journalism | John Shield |
| Controller of Production, News | Jenny Baxter |
| Controller, English Regions | David Holdsworth |

**London Factual Executive Producers**
**Tel main switchboard: 020-8743 8000**
**All based in the Media Centre at White City Media Village.**

| | |
|---|---|
| Arts | Basil Comely |
| Documentaries & Features | Tina Fletcher |
| | Gary Hunter |
| | Dinah Lord |
| | Nick Mirsky |
| | Clare Sillery |
| Consumer | Lisa Ausden |
| Science | John Lynch |
| Horizon Editor | Andrew Cohen |
| Science | Tina Fletcher |
| | Anne Laking |
| | Michael Mosley |
| The Money Programme | Dominic Crossley-Holland |
| The Culture Show | Eddie Morgan |
| Series Editor, Imagine | Janet Lee |

## • CHILDREN

| | |
|---|---|
| Controller | Richard Deverell |
| Controller, CBBC | Anne Gilchrist |
| Controller, CBeebies | Michael Carrington |

| | | | |
|---|---|---|---|
| Head of News, Factual Entertainment (inc on-air talent management) | Joe Godwin | | |
| Head of Drama | Steven Andrew | | |
| Head of Children's Programmes, Scotland | Simon Parsons | | |
| Head of Interactive & On-Demand | Marc Goodchild | | |

## • MUSIC

| | |
|---|---|
| Head of Television, Classical Music & Performance | Peter Maniura |
| Managing Editor, Classical Music, Television | Caroline Speed |
| Editor Music Programmes, Television, Classical Music & Performance | Oliver Macfarlane |
| Programme Development Manager | Tory Jones |

**Executive Producers**

| | |
|---|---|
| Sue Judd | Celina Parker |

**Producers/Directors**

| | |
|---|---|
| Jonathan Haswell | Andy King-Dabbs |
| Francesca Kemp | Helen Mansfield |

**Production Executive**      Ian Taitt

## • SPORT

| | |
|---|---|
| Director of Sport | Barbara Slater |
| Head of Major Events | Dave Gordon |
| Head of TV Sport | Philip Bernie |
| Head of Radio Sport | Gordon Turnbull |
| Head of Interactive & Formula 1 | Ben Gallop |
| Head of Sports News | James Porter |
| Acting Head of Production | Marney Shears |
| Head of HR Development | Pam Sikora |

## • NEW WRITING

BBC Writersroom
Grafton House, 379-381 Euston Road
London NW1 3AU      Tel: 020-7765 2703
e-mail: writersroom@bbc.co.uk
Website: www.bbc.co.uk/writersroom

| | |
|---|---|
| Creative Director | Kate Rowland |
| Development Manager | Paul Ashton |

## • BBC BRISTOL

Broadcasting House
Whiteladies Road
Bristol BS8 2LR                              Tel: 0117-973 2211

### NETWORK TELEVISION FEATURES AND DOCUMENTARIES

Head of Bristol Factual                            Ben Gale

### Executive Producers

| | |
|---|---|
| Pete Lawrence | Michael Poole |
| Julian Mercer | Simon Shaw |

### Series Producers

| | |
|---|---|
| Lynn Barlow | Alastair Laurence |
| Kate Broome | Kimberley Littlemore |
| Michele Burgess | Peter Smith |
| Chris Hutchins | Ben Southwell |

### Producers/Directors

| | |
|---|---|
| Robert Bayley | David Olusoga |
| Louise Hibbins | Tuppence Stone |
| Colin Napthine | |

### NETWORK RADIO

| | |
|---|---|
| Unit Manager, Radio 4 | Kate Chaney |
| Editor, Radio 4 | Clare McGinn |

### Producers

| | |
|---|---|
| John Byrne | Chris Ledgard |
| Sara Davies | Mark Smalley |
| Tim Dee | Mary Ward Lowery |
| Jolyon Jenkins | Miles Warde |

### NATURAL HISTORY UNIT

Head of Natural History Unit                   Neil Nightingale

### Executive Producers

| | |
|---|---|
| Wendy Darke | Julian Hector |
| Sara Ford | Brian Leith |
| Alastair Fothergill | Tim Martin |
| Mike Gunton | Fiona Pitcher |
| | Tim Scoones |

## • BBC WEST

Whiteladies Road
Bristol BS8 2LR                              Tel: 0117-973 2211

Head of Regional & Local Programmes,
including BBC West, Radio Bristol
BBC Somerset, BBC Gloucestershire
BBC Wiltshire                                 Lucio Mesquita
Editor, Output                            Stephanie Marshall
News Gathering                                 Neil Bennett

## • BBC SOUTH WEST

Seymour Road
Mannamead
Plymouth PL3 5BD                             Tel: 01752 229201

| | |
|---|---|
| Head of BBC South West | Jane McCloskey |
| Editor TV Current Affairs | Simon Willis |
| Output Editor | Simon Read |

## • BBC SOUTH

Havelock Road
Southampton SO14 7PU                         Tel: 023-8022 6201

| | |
|---|---|
| Head of Regional & Local Programmes | Mike Hapgood |
| TV News Editor | Lee Desty |
| Executive Editor, BBC Oxford | Steve Taschini |
| Managing Editor, BBC Solent | Chris Carnegy |
| Managing Editor, Berkshire | Marianne Bell |

## • BBC LONDON

35C Marylebone High Street
London W1M 4AA                               Tel: 020-7224 2424

BBC London News:
TV: *The Politics Show*
Radio: *BBC London Radio 94.9FM*
Online: *BBC London online*

| | |
|---|---|
| Head of BBC London | Michael MacFarlane |
| News/Output Editor | Antony Dore |
| Editor, Inside Out | Dippy Chaudhary |
| Managing Editor, BBC Radio London 94.9FM | David Robey |
| Political Editor | Tim Donovan |
| Editor, BBC London Online | Claire Timms |

## • BBC SOUTH EAST

The Great Hall Arcade
Mount Pleasant Road
Tunbridge Wells
Kent TN1 1QQ                                 Tel: 01892 670000

| | |
|---|---|
| Head of Regional & Local Programmes BBC South East | Michael Rawsthorne |
| Managing Editor BBC Radio Kent | Paul Leaper |
| Managing Editor BBC Southern Counties | Nicki Holliday |
| Editor BBC South East Today | Quentin Smith |
| Editor Inside Out | Linda Bell |
| Editor Politics Show | Dan Fineman |

## • BBC NORTH WEST

New Broadcasting House
Oxford Road
Manchester M60 1SJ          Tel: 0161-200 2020
Website: www.bbc.co.uk/manchester

### Entertainment & Features
Editor, Entertainment & Features          Helen Bullough

### Religion & Ethics
Head of Religion & Ethics &
Commissioning Editor for Religion TV          Aaqil Ahmed
Executive Editor &
    Head of Religion Radio          Christine Morgan

### Network News & Current Affairs
Executive Producer, Network News
& Current Affairs          Sinead Rocks

### Regional & Local Programmes
Head of Regional & Local
    Programmes, North West          Aziz Rashid
Head of Regional & Local Programmes,
    North East & Cumbria          Phil Roberts

## • BBC BIRMINGHAM

BBC Birmingham
The Mailbox
Birmingham B1 1RF
Fax: 0121-567 6875          Tel: 0121-567 6767

### English Regions
Controller, English Regions          David Holdsworth
Head of New Services, English Regions          Laura Ellis
Chief Operating Officer, English Regions          Ian Hughes
Senior Officer, Press & PR          Becky Jones-Owen
Secretary, BBC Trust          Louise Hall
Head of Regional & Local
    Programmes, West Midlands          Cath Hearne

### Factual & Learning
### BBC Birmingham
Head of Studios          Nick Patten
Managing Editor, BBC Vision,
    Birmingham & Manchester          Jane Booth

### Network Radio
Executive Editor          Andrew Thorman
Head of Compliance, Radio 2 & 6 Music          Joe Graham
Head of Programmes 2 & 6          Lewis Carnie

### Drama
BBC Brimingham TV Drama Village
Archibald House
1059 Bristol Road, Selly Oak
Birmingham B29 6LT          Tel: 0121-567 7350
Executive Producer          Will Trotter

## • BBC SCOTLAND

40 Pacific Quay
Glasgow G51 1DA          Tel: 0141-422 6000
Website: www.bbc.co.uk/scotland

### Scottish Executive Board
Director, Scotland          Ken MacQuarrie
Head of Programmes & Services          Donalda MacKinnon
Head of Public Policy          Ian Small
Chief Operating Officer          Bruce Malcolm
Head of Talent Division          Donald-Iain Brown
Head of HR & Development          Wendy Aslett
Head of Marketing, Communications
    & Audiences          Mairead Ferguson

### Genre Heads
Commissioning Editor,
    Television & Head of Sport          Ewan Angus
Head of News & Current Affairs          Atholl Duncan
Head of Radio          Jeff Zycinski
Head of Gaelic Digital Service          Margaret Mary Murray
Managing Editor, Gaelic          Marion MacKinnon
Head Factual          Andrea Miller
Head of Drama, Television          Anne Mensah
Head of Drama, Radio          Patrick Rayner
Head of Children's          Simon Parsons
Executive Editor, Learning          Nick Simons
Executive Editor, Cross Media          Matthew Lee
Director, BBC Scottish Symphony Orchestra          Gavin Reid

BBC Scotland provides television and radio programmes for Scotland and the UK networks as well as online and interactive content. Based in the new digital headquarters in Glasgow since 2007, there are also centres throughout Scotland which includes City Halls, the home of the BBC Scottish Symphony Orchestra.

### Aberdeen
Broadcasting House, Beechgrove Terrace
Aberdeen AB15 5ZT          Tel: 01224 625233

## BBC Scotland Cont'd

**Dumbarton**
Strathleven Bottling Plant, Dumbarton
Dumbartonshire G82 2AP          Tel: 01389 736666

**Dumfries**
Elmbank, Lover's Walk
Dumfries DG1 1NZ          Tel: 01387 268008

**Dundee**
Nethergate Centre, 4th Floor, 66 Nethergate
Dundee DD1 4ER          Tel: 01382 202481

**Edinburgh**
The Tun, 4 Jackson's Entry, 111 Holyrood Road
Edinburgh EH8 8PJ          Tel: 0131-557 5888

**Glasgow**
Glasgow City Halls (BBC Scottish Symphony Orchestra)
87 Albion Street, Glasgow G1 1NQ          Tel: 0141-552 0909

**Inverness**
7 Culduthel Road, Inverness IV2 4AD          Tel: 01463 720720

**Orkney**
Castle Street, Kirkwall
Orkney KW15 1DF          Tel: 01856 873939

**Portree**
Clydesdale Bank Buildings, Somerled Square, Portree
Isle of Skye IV51 9BT          Tel: 01478 612005

**Selkirk**
Unit 1, Ettrick Riverside
Dunsdale Road, Selkirk TD7 5EB          Tel: 01750 724567

**Shetland**
Pitt Lane, Lerwick
Shetland ZE1 0DW          Tel: 01595 694747

**Stornoway**
Radio nan Gaidheal, Rosebank, 52 Church Street
Stornoway, Isle of Lewis HS1 2LS          Tel: 01851 705000

## • BBC WALES

**Broadcasting House**
**Llandaff**
**Cardiff CF5 2YQ**          **Tel: 029-2032 2000**

Director                          Menna Richards
Head of Programmes (Welsh)                Keith Jones
Head of Programmes (English)              Clare Hudson
Head of Strategy & Communications    Rhodri Talfan Davies
Head of News & Current Affairs        Mark O'Callaghan

Head of HR & Development                      Jude Gray
Chief Operating Officer                  Gareth Powell
Head of Drama                            Piers Wenger
Head of Broadcast Development            Cathryn Allen
Head of Sport                          Geoff Williams
Head of North Wales                  Marian Wyn Jones
Head of Factual & Music                Adrian Davies
Head of Education & Learning        Eleri Wyn-Williams
Editor Radio Wales                        Sali Collins
Editor Radio Cymru                      Sian Gwynedd
Editor New Media                        Iain Tweedale

## • BBC NORTHERN IRELAND

**Belfast**
**BBC Broadcasting House**
**Ormeau Avenue**
**Belfast BT2 8HQ**          **Tel: 028-9033 8000**
**Website: www.bbc.co.uk/ni**

Director, BBC Northern Ireland        Peter Johnston
Head of Programmes                          Ailsa Orr
Head of News & Current Affairs        Andrew Coleman
Chief Operating Officer                  Mark Taylor
Head of Public Policy, Corporate
  & Community Affairs                      Mark Adair
Head of Drama                          Patrick Spence
Head of Marketing, Communications
  & Audiences                            Kathy Martin
Head of HR & Development              Lawrence Jackson
Head of TV Current Affairs              Jeremy Adams
Head of Entertainment & Events            Mike Edgar
Head of Factual                        Paul McGuigan
Head of Radio                            Susan Lovell
Editor of Sport                          Shane Glynn
Head of Multi-platform Commissioning    Fergus Keeling
Managing Editor, Learning, Language
  & Social Action                        Jane Cassidy
Editor of Radio Royle                  Paul McCauley

**BBC Radio Ulster**
BBC Broadcasting House
Ormeau Avenue
Belfast BT2 8HQ          Tel: 028-9033 8000

**BBC Radio Foyle**
8 Northland Road
Londonderry BT48 7JD          Tel: 028-7126 2244

## itv Anglia

**ITV ANGLIA**
**Head Office**
Anglia House, Norwich NR1 3JG
Fax: 0844 5563931          Tel: 0844 8816900
*East of England: Weekday & Weekend*

**Regional News Centres**
**Cambridge**
Link House
Station Road, Great Shelford
Cambridge CB22 5LT          News: 0844 8816985

**Northampton**
Portfolio Innovation Centre
University of Northampton
St George's Avenue
Northampton NN2 6JD          Tel: 0844 8816974

**Ipswich**
Hubbard House
Civic Drive, Ipswich IP1 2QA          Tel: 0844 8816999

## itv Channel Television

**CHANNEL TELEVISION Ltd**
**Registered Office**
The Television Centre
La Pouquelaye, St Helier
Jersey JE1 3ZD, Channel Islands
Fax: 01534 816817          Tel: 01534 816816
Website: www.channelonline.tv
*Channel Islands: Weekday and Weekend*

Managing Director (Broadcast)          Karen Rankine
Head of News and Content          Allan Watts
Managing Director (Commercial)          Mike Elsey
Director of Resource & Transmission          Kevin Banner
News Editor          Alex Blakeley

**Producers**
Alex Blakeley          Melissa Goguelin

**CHANNEL FOUR TELEVISION CORPORATION**
**London Office**
124 Horseferry Road
London SW1P 2TX
Textphone: 020-7396 8691          Tel: 020-7396 4444

**Members of the Board**
Chairman          Luke Johnson
Deputy Chairman          Lord David Puttnam
Chief Executive          Andy Duncan
Director of Television          Kevin Lygo
Group Finance Director          Anne Bulford
Sales Director          Andy Barnes
New Business Director          Rod Henwood

**Non-Executive Directors**
Sue Ashtiany          Tony Hall
Karren Brady          Stephen Hill
Martha Lane Fox          Andy Mollett

**Heads of Department**
Head of Features          Walter Iuzzolino
Head of E4 & Big Brother          Angela Jain
Head of Factual Entertainment          Andrew Mackenzie
Head of Specialist Factual          Ralph Lee
Controller of Broadcasting          Rosemary Newell
Head of Scheduling & T4          Julie Oldroyd
Heads of More 4          Peter Dale
          Hamish Mykura
Head of News & Current Affairs          Dorothy Byrne
Head of Entertainment          Andrew Newman
Head of Drama & FilmFour          Tessa Ross
Head of Documentaries          Hamish Mykura
Head of Education
   & Managing Editor Commissioning          Janey Walker
Director of Nations & Regions          Stuart Cosgrove
Director of Corporate Relations          Nick Toon
Controller of Research & Insight          Claire Grimmond
Director of Human Resources          Diane Herbert
Head of Facilities Management          Julie Kortens
Head of Media Planning          Greg Smith
Controller of Press & Publicity          Matt Baker
Network Creative Director          Brett Foraker
Head of Marketing          Rufus Radcliffe
Head of Sponsorship          David Charlesworth
Head of Airtime Management          Merlin Inkley
Head of Agency Sales          Matt Shreeve
Head of Strategic Sales          Mike Parker
Head of Channel 4          Julian Bellamy

## five

### CHANNEL FIVE BROADCASTING
22 Long Acre
London WC2E 9LY
Fax: 020-7550 5554                    Tel: 020-7550 5555
Website: www.five.tv

| | |
|---|---|
| Managing Director | Mark White |
| Controller | Richard Woolfe |
| Director of Strategy | Charles Constable |
| Director of Finance | David Hockley |
| Director of Legal | Paul Chinnery |
| Head of Scheduling | Richard Brent |
| Senior Programme Controller, | |
|   News & Current Affairs | Chris Shaw |
| Head of Factual Entertainment | |
|   & Multi Channel Commissioner | Steve Gowans |
| Controller of Sport | Robert Charles |
| Controller of Children's | Nick Wilson |

### GMTV
London Television Centre
Upper Ground, London SE1 9TT
Fax: 020-7827 7001                    Tel: 020-7827 7000
Website: www.gm.tv

| | |
|---|---|
| Chairman | Clive Jones |
| Acting Chief Operating Officer | Clive Crouch |
| Director of Programmes | Peter McHugh |
| Sales & Marketing Director | Simon Poole |
| Finance Director | Andy Whitaker |
| Editor | Martin Frizell |
| Deputy Editor | Malcolm Douglas |
| Deputy Editor (Presentation) | Emma Gormley |
| Operations Director | Di Holmes |
| Avid Project Manager | Henry Clark |
| Head of Futures | Annemarie Leahy |
| Deputy Head of Futures | Caroline Sigley |
| Head of Entertainment | Corine Bishop |
| Deputy Head of Entertainment | Amy Vosburgh |
| Head of Press | Nikki Johnceline |

## ITN

### INDEPENDENT TELEVISION NEWS
200 Gray's Inn Rd
London WC1X 8XZ                    Tel: 020-7833 3000

| | |
|---|---|
| Chief Executive | John Hardie |
| Editor-in-Chief, ITV News | David Mannion |
| Editor, ITV News | Deborah Turness |
| Editor, Channel 4 News | Jim Gray |

### ITV Plc Registered Office
200 Gray's Inn Road, London WC1V 8HF
Fax: 020-7849 9344                    Tel: 020-7156 6000
Website: www.itv.com

### Executive Board:

| | |
|---|---|
| Executive Chairman, ITV Plc | Michael Grade |
| Chief Operating Officer, ITV Plc | John Cresswell |
| Director of Television Channels | |
|   & Online, ITV | Peter Fincham |
| Director of ITV Studios | John Whiston |
| Director of Strategy & Development | Carolyn Fairburn |
| Director of Group Corporate Affairs | Mark Gallagher |
| Group Finance Director, ITV Plc | Ian Griffiths |
| Managing Director, | |
|   Global Content, ITV Plc | Lee Bartlett |
| Acting Group HR Director | Andy Doyle |
| Group Legal Director | |
|   & Company Secretary | Andrew Garard |
| Managing Director, ITV Brand | |
|   & Commercial, ITV Plc | Rupert Howell |

### Casting Directors at ITV Studios

#### Manchester
Gennie Radcliffe, Coronation Street
June West, Casting Director
Rick Laxton, Casting Assistant (to Gennie Radcliffe)
Katy Belshaw, Casting Assistant (to June West)

#### Leeds
Faye Styring, Emmerdale
Louise Bennett, Casting Assistant

*If you would like one of the casting teams to cover your performance in a stage production, please e-mail casting@itv.com including your name, the theatre and the dates*

 Meridian

### ITV MERIDIAN
### ITV Meridian is part of ITV BROADCASTING Ltd
Forum One
Solent Business Park
Whiteley, Hants PO15 7PA
Fax: 0844 881207                    Tel: 0844 8812000

### Meridian Board

| | |
|---|---|
| Director of Regional Sales | David Croft |
| Regional Director, ITV Meridian | |
|   & ITV London | Mark Southgate |

### Executives

| | |
|---|---|
| Head of Personnel | Elaine Austin |
| Finance Manager | Natasha Coxhead |
| Head of News | Robin Britton |

Wales     West

**ITV WALES & ITV WEST**
Television Centre
Culverhouse Cross
Cardiff CF5 6XJ                     Tel: 0844 8810100

Television Centre
Bath Road
Bristol BS4 3HG                     Tel: 0844 8812345

*Wales/West of England: All week*

Director, ITV West                  Mark Southgate

# S4/C

**S4C - THE WELSH FOURTH CHANNEL AUTHORITY**

Parc Tŷ Glas
Llanishen, Cardiff CF14 5DU
Fax: 029-2075 4444                  Tel: 029-2074 7444
e-mail: s4c@s4c.co.uk

**The Welsh Fourth Channel Authority**
Chair                               John Walter Jones OBE

**Board Members**
Bill Davies                         Sir Roger Jones OBE
Elra Davies                         Dr Chris Llewelyn
Cenwyn Edwards                      Winston Roddick CB QC
Dyfrig Jones                        Rheon Tomos

**Senior Staff**
Chief Executive                             Iona Jones
Director of Commissioning                   Rhian Gibson
Director of Communications           Garffild Lloyd Lewis
Director of Finance & Human Resources    Kathryn Morris
Director of Broadcast & Distribution      Arshad Rasul
Director of Business Affairs    Delyth Wynne Griffiths
Director of Commercial & Corporate Policy   Elin Morris

# stv productions

**STV CENTRAL**
Pacific Quay, Glasgow G51 1PQ
Tel: 0141-300 3000                Website: www.stv.tv

**STV NORTH**
Television Centre, Craigshaw Business Park
West Tullos, Aberdeen AB12 3QH
Tel: 01224 848848                 Website: www.stv.tv

Managing Director                   Bobby Hain
Head of News & Current Affairs      Gordon MacMillan

**STV PRODUCTIONS**
**Glasgow Office**
Pacific Quay
Glasgow G51 1PQ
Fax: 0141-300 3030                  Tel: 0141-300 3000
Chief Executive                     Rob Woodward
Deputy Director of Content          Elizabeth Partyka
Head of Drama                       Eric Coulter

**London Office**
1st Floor
3 Waterhouse Square
138-142 Holborn
London EC1N 2NY                     Tel: 020-7882 1010

 Tyne Tees     Border

**ITV TYNE TEES & ITV BORDER**
Television House
The Watermark
Gateshead NE11 9SZ                  Tel: 0844 8815000

**Teesside News Gathering**
20 Manor Way
Belasis Hall Technology Park
Billingham
Cleveland TS23 4HN
e-mail: tttvnews@itv.com            Tel: 0844 8815000

*North East and North Yorkshire:*
*Weekday and Weekend*

Executive Chair ITV                 Michael Grade
Head of News                        Catherine Houlihan
Managing Director, SignPost         Malcolm Wright

**UTV Plc**
Ormeau Road
Belfast BT7 1EB
Fax: 028-9024 6695                  Tel: 028-9032 8122

*Northern Ireland: Weekday and Weekend*

Chairman                       J B McGuckian BSc (Econ)
Group Chief Executive               J McCann BSc, FCA
Group Financial Director            Jim Downey
Managing Director, Television       Michael Wilson
Head of Communications              Orla McKibbin
Head of News & Current Affairs      Rob Morrison
Sales Director                      Paul Hutchinson

 **Yorkshire**

**ITV YORKSHIRE**
The Television Centre, Leeds LS3 1JS
Fax: 0113-244 5107                    Tel: 0113-222 7000

**London Office**
London Television Centre
Upperground, London SE1 9LT           Tel: 020-7620 1620

**Hull Office**
23 Brook Street
The Prospect Centre
Hull HU2 8PN                          Tel: 01482 324488

**Sheffield Office**
Charter Square, Sheffield S1 3EJ      Tel: 0114-272 7772

**Lincoln Office**
88 Bailgate, Lincoln LN1 3AR          Tel: 01522 530738

**Grimsby Office**
Margaret Street, Immingham
North East Lincs DN40 1LE             Tel: 01469 515151

**York Office**
8 Coppergate, York YO1 1NR            Tel: 01904 610066

**Executives**
Head of News                          Will Venters
Controller of Comedy Drama
  & Drama Features                    David Reynolds
Controller of Drama, Leeds            Keith Richardson
Director of ITV Productions           John Whiston

# sky

**SKY Satellite Television**
**BRITISH SKY BROADCASTING LIMITED (BSkyB)**
6 Centaurs Business Park
Grant Way, Isleworth, Middlesex TW7 5QD
Fax: 0870 240 3060                    Tel: 0870 240 3000

Chief Executive                       Jeremy Darroch
Chief Financial Officer               Andrew Griffith
Managing Director, Sky Networks       Sophie Turner-Laing
Director for People                   Deborah Baker
Group Commercial and Strategy Director   Mike Darcey
Group Director of Corporate Affairs   Graham McWilliam
Managing Director, Customer Group     Brian Sullivan
Group Director for IT & Strategy      Jeff Hughes
General Counsel                       James Conyers
Managing Director, Sky Media          Nick Milligan
Head of Regulatory Affairs            Vicky Sandy
Managing Director, Sky Sports         Barney Francis
Group Director of Engineering
  & Platform Technology               Alun Webber

**10TH PLANET PRODUCTIONS**
75 Woodland Gardens
London N10 3UD Tel/Fax: 020-8442 2659
Website: www.10thplanetproductions.com
e-mail: admin@10thplanetproductions.com

**30 BIRD PRODUCTIONS**
17 Emery Street
Cambridge CB1 2AX Mobile: 07970 960995
Website: www.30birdproductions.org
e-mail: info@30birdproductions.org

**A STAGE KINDLY**
7 Northiam, Cromer Street
London WC1H 8LB Mobile: 07947 074887
Website: www.astagekindly.com
e-mail: astagekindly@aol.com

**ACORN ENTERTAINMENTS Ltd**
PO Box 64, Cirencester, Glos GL7 5YD
Website: www.acornents.co.uk
e-mail: info@acornents.co.uk
Fax: 01285 642291 Tel: 01285 644622

**ACT PRODUCTIONS Ltd**
20-22 Stukeley Street, London WC2B 5LR
Website: www.actproductions.co.uk
e-mail: info@actproductions.co.uk
Fax: 020-7242 3548 Tel: 020-7438 9520

**ACTOR'S TEMPLE The**
13-14 Warren Street, London W1T 5LG
Website: www.actorstemple.com
e-mail: info@actorstemple.com
Mobile: 07771 734670 Tel: 020-3004 4537

**AJTC THEATRE COMPANY**
28 Rydes Hill Crescent
Guildford, Surrey GU2 9UH Tel/Fax: 01483 232795
Website: www.ajtctheatre.co.uk

**ALGERNON Ltd**
24 Cleveleys Road, London E5 9JN
Website: www.algernonproductions.com
e-mail: info@algernonproductions.com
Fax: 0870 1388516 Tel: 07092 805026

**AMBASSADOR THEATRE GROUP**
39-41 Charing Cross Road, London WC2H 0AR
Website: www.ambassadortickets.com
e-mail: atglondon@theambassadors.com
Fax: 020-7534 6109 Tel: 020-7534 6100

**ANTIC DISPOSITION**
4A Oval Road, London NW1 7EB Tel: 020-7284 0760
Website: www.anticdisposition.co.uk
e-mail: info@anticdisposition.co.uk

**AOD - ACTORS OF DIONYSUS**
14 Cuthbert Road
Brighton BN2 0EN Tel/Fax: 01273 692604
Website: www.actorsofdionysus.com
e-mail: info@actorsofdionysus.com

**ARDEN ENTERTAINMENT**
2nd Floor, 23 Tavistock Street, London WC2E 7NX
Website: www.arden-entertainment.co.uk
e-mail: info@arden-entertainment.co.uk
Fax: 020-7420 7748 Tel: 020-7420 7730

**ARTS MANAGEMENT (Redroofs Associates)**
Contact: By Post
Novello Theatre, High Street, Sunninghill, Ascot SL5 9NE

**ASHTON GROUP THEATRE The**
The Old Fire Station, Abbey Road, Barrow-in-Furness
Cumbria LA14 1XH Tel/Fax: 01229 430636
Website: www.ashtongroup.co.uk
e-mail: info@ashtongroup.co.uk

**ATC**
The Tab Centre
3 Godfrey Place, London E2 7NT
Website: www.atctheatre.com
e-mail: atc@atctheatre.com
Fax: 020-7033 7360 Tel: 020-7739 8298

**ATTIC THEATRE COMPANY (LONDON) Ltd**
Mitcham Library
157 London Road
Mitcham CR4 2YR Tel: 020-8640 6800
Website: www.attictheatrecompany.com
e-mail: info@attictheatrecompany.com

**BACKGROUND Ltd**
44 Carnaby Street, London W1F 9PP
e-mail: insight@background.co.uk
Fax: 020-7479 4710 Tel: 020-7479 4700

**BARKING PRODUCTIONS/INSTANT WIT**
(Comedy Improvisation Show/Corporate Entertainment &
Drama Based Training)
Regus, 1 Friary, Temple Quay
Bristol BS1 6EA Tel/Fax: 0117-908 5384
Website: www.barkingproductions.co.uk
e-mail: info@barkingproductions.co.uk

**BARNES Andy PRODUCTIONS**
Ambassadors Theatre
West Street, London WC2H 9ND Tel: 020-7395 5460
Website: www.andybarnesproductions.com
e-mail: andy@andybarnesproductions.com

**BEE & BUSTLE ENTERPRISES**
32 Exeter Road, London NW2 4SB
Website: www.beeandbustle.co.uk
e-mail: info@beeandbustle.co.uk
Fax: 020-8450 1057 Tel: 020-8450 0371

**BIRMINGHAM STAGE COMPANY The**
Suite 228, The Linen Hall
162 Regent Street, London W1B 5TB
Website: www.birminghamstage.net
e-mail: info@birminghamstage.net
Fax: 020-7437 3395 Tel: 020-7437 3391

**BLUE BOX ENTERTAINMENT Ltd**
Top Floor, 80-81 St Martin's Lane, London WC2N 4AA
Website: www.newbluebox.com
e-mail: info@newbluebox.com
Fax: 020-3292 1699 Tel: 020-7395 7520

**BLUE STAR PRODUCTIONS / BARRIE STACEY**
7-8 Shaldon Mansions
132 Charing Cross Road
London WC2H 0LA
Website: www.barriestacey.com
e-mail: hopkinstacey@aol.com
Fax: 020-7836 2949 Tel: 020-7836 6220

**BORDER CROSSINGS**
13 Bankside, Enfield EN2 8BN
Website: www.bordercrossings.org.uk
e-mail: info@bordercrossings.org.uk
Fax: 020-8366 5239 Tel: 020-8829 8928

**BORDERLINE THEATRE COMPANY**
North Harbour Street
Ayr KA8 8AA Tel: 01292 281010
e-mail: enquiries@borderlinetheatre.co.uk

**BOTELLO Catalina**
48 New Cavendish Street
London W1G 8TG
Website: www.catalinabotello.com
e-mail: contact@catalinabotello.com
Mobile: 07939 060434 Tel: 020-7935 1360

# infopage

## What is a theatre producer?

A theatre producer is someone who oversees and organises a theatre show. He or she will find, or arrange for other professionals to find, a suitable script, design, director and cast for each production, while also managing all finances and marketing.

## How should I use these listings?

Theatre producers tend to use casting directors to put forward suitable actors for the parts in forthcoming productions, but you could also try approaching them yourself. Rather than sending your CV and headshot to every producer listed, it would be best to do some research first in order to target your search. You need to decide what type of work you want to do first, as there is no need to waste your time and the producer's time sending your CV to unsuitable companies. Then find out what each company has produced in the past, what they are currently working on, and if possible what they are considering producing in the future, and only send your CV to those most relevant to the roles you want to play. Don't forget to include a covering letter which states why you are contacting this producer in particular: this could be because you feel you are perfect for a particular role in their next production, for example. Personalising and targeting your correspondence in this way gives you the best chance of your CV being considered in a favourable light.

## How should I approach theatre producers?

You should contact theatre producers by post or e-mail only. We would advise against calling them, especially when approaching them for the first time. Address your correspondence to an individual within the company, as this demonstrates that you have done your research. If you are unsure as to the best method of applying to theatre producers, as with other casting professionals it is safest to post your CV and headshot in the traditional way rather than e-mailing it. Remember to put your name and telephone number on the back of the photo in case it gets separated from your CV. It would be a good idea to include a SAE big enough to contain your 10 x 8 photo and with sufficient postage to increase your chances of getting a reply. Do not enclose your showreel but you can mention that you have one available in your covering letter, and if the producer is interested in viewing it they will contact you.

## When should I approach theatre producers?

Listen to industry news and have a look at theatre producers' websites for forthcoming production details. The casting process usually takes place around three months prior to rehearsals, so bear this in mind when you are writing your covering letter.

**Ian formed The Hiss & Boo Company over thirty years ago and combines the roles of Artistic Director and Executive Producer. Once a much feared pantomime villain and prolific actor with many TV roles (including long running soaps *Crossroads* and *Coronation Street*) and films such as *Star Wars: The Empire Strikes Back* to his credit, Ian now concentrates his activities on producing quality pantomimes for half a dozen top venues together with Variety and Revue-type shows. Many of these, including The Hiss & Boo Show and *The Shakespeare Revue* are regular audience pleasers on the touring circuit and frequently play overseas.**

Whilst preparing this article I came across a box full of old theatre reference books which included an early edition of Contacts. Looking through the well-thumbed and annotated pages of that very slim publication reminded me of how essential it was to me when starting out in the business as a young actor.

You've already bought this new edition so you don't need convincing of its usefulness; nevertheless there are many pitfalls for the unwary in an age when information is now such a hard currency.

Today's edition offers more information and resources for every creative branch of the entertainment industry than could ever have been dreamed of even 10 years ago. As a theatre producer, mainly of touring plays, revues and pantomimes, I tend to be on the receiving end of hundreds of submissions a year from every conceivable branch of the entertainment profession.

The vast bulk of the letters and applications we receive will be from actors, the majority of whom make easily avoidable mistakes that spoil what little chance they may have of getting work. Sadly, despite the increasing number of drama schools and training courses, actors are offered little help and information on the practicalities of surviving in the profession once they've completed an arduous and often expensive period of training.

Whether you are an actor, writer, designer, director, wardrobe mistress, flyman or stunt man, you are empowered with Contacts at your fingertips to research all the production companies and potential employers in the industry. Don't waste the head start you've spent good money to buy!

Find out what the producers produce and what the production companies actually do: it's the easiest of tasks to click on to their websites to do your research and even the occasional phone call to get more detail might not go amiss.

Select the ones that may be most interested in what you have to offer. For example, you will find from a visit to our website that we usually cast our pantomimes in the February-May period, that we don't hold general auditions, that casting breakdowns are sent out via Spotlight Interactive and that we don't use a casting director - all casting and crewing is done by me, in conjunction with the director of each show, and the co-producer from our partner theatre. We don't encourage unsolicited scripts and will only return something if it is accompanied by a stamped addressed envelope - the time and cost of replying to everything we receive would be prohibitive.

Websites for other producers will tell you different information about their requirements, which are always highly individual from one producer to the next. Although we are a theatrical production company we get our fair share of applications from film stunt men, location caterers, walk-on artistes and the like who simply haven't bothered to find out what we do. What a waste of their money!

Being a relatively small company it's likely that most incoming post will land on my desk. I'm the one you need to persuade that you have something to offer and you're not going to do that with a "To whom it may concern" or a "Dear Sir or Madam" introduction. You will have even less chance if you haven't spent a bit of time and effort to offer a smart, concise CV with a decent photo; preferably printed on paper that's at least 100gsm as it may get a lot of passing around to various interested parties! If you are sending a photograph, make sure your name is on the back. More than three-quarters of the photos we receive have neither name nor contact information on the reverse.

Be just as careful with e-mail submissions. Keep the size of your message small: a few hundred KB should be enough. Files of 1 MB or more are totally unnecessary and rarely make it through our spam filters.

Just because you don't receive a reply doesn't mean that your letter has been ignored. We get dozens of applications every month and, much as we'd like to, we have neither the time nor the money to reply to them all.

Finally please, if sending mail, check the postage. You're not likely to endear yourself to anyone, let alone a producer you're trying to impress, if they have to pay to receive your casting letter or script submission. Odds are that they won't!

**BRIT-POL THEATRE Ltd**
10 Bristol Gardens
London W9 2JG     Tel: 020-7266 0323
Website: www.britpoltheatre.com
e-mail: admin@britpoltheatre.com

**BRITISH SHAKESPEARE COMPANY**
Website: www.britishshakespearecompany.com
info@britishshakespearecompany.com   Mobile: 07502 245540

**BRITISH THEATRE SEASON IN MONACO**
1 Hogarth Hill
London NW11 6AY     Tel: 020-8455 3278
Website: www.montecarlotheatre.co.uk
e-mail: mail@montecarlotheatre.co.uk

**BROADHOUSE PRODUCTIONS Ltd**
Lodge Rocks House
Bilbrook
Minehead, Somerset TA24 6RD
e-mail: admin@broadhouse.co.uk
Fax: 01984 641027     Tel: 01984 640773

**BROOKE Nick Ltd**
2nd Floor, 80-81 St Martin's Lane
London WC2N 4AA
Website: www.nickbrooke.com
e-mail: nick@nickbrooke.com
Fax: 020-7240 2947     Tel: 020-7240 3901

**BUSH THEATRE**
Shepherd's Bush Green
London W12 8QD     Tel: 020-8743 3584
Website: www.bushtheatre.co.uk
e-mail: info@bushtheatre.co.uk

**BYAM SHAW Matthew for ST ELMO PRODUCTIONS**
2nd Floor, 20-22 Stukeley Street
London WC2B 5LR
Fax: 020-7242 3548     Tel: 020-7438 9520

**CAHOOTS THEATRE COMPANY**
Contact: Denise Silvey
St Martin's Theatre
West Street, London WC2N 9NH     Tel: 020-7240 3659
e-mail: ds@denisesilvey.com

**CAP PRODUCTION SOLUTIONS Ltd**
116 Wigmore Road
Carshalton, Surrey SM5 1RQ
e-mail: leigh@leighporter.com
Fax: 07970 763480     Mobile: 07973 432576

**CAPRICORN STAGE (& SCREEN) DIRECTIONS**
9 Spencer House, Vale of Health
Hampstead, London NW3 1AS     Tel: 020-7794 5843

**CELEBRATION**
(Theatre Company for the Young)
48 Chiswick Staithe, London W4 3TP
Website: www.speakwell.co.uk
Mobile: 07976 805976     Tel: 020-8994 8886

**CENTRELINE PRODUCTIONS**
293 Lea Bridge Road
London E10 7NE     Mobile: 07710 522438
Website: www.centrelinenet.com
e-mail: jenny@centrelinenet.com

**CHAIN REACTION THEATRE COMPANY**
Three Mills Studios
Sugar House Yard, Sugar House Lane
London E15 2QS     Tel/Fax: 020-8534 0007
Website: www.chainreactiontheatre.co.uk
e-mail: mail@chainreactiontheatre.co.uk

**CHANNEL THEATRE PRODUCTIONS**
Central Studios, 36 Park Place
Margate, Kent CT9 1LE
Website: www.channel-theatre.co.uk
e-mail: info@channel-theatre.co.uk
Fax: 01843 280088     Tel: 01843 280077

**CHAPMAN Duggie ASSOCIATES**
(Concerts, Musicals, Pantomime)
The Old Coach House
202 Common Edge Road
Blackpool FY4 5DG     Tel/Fax: 01253 691823
Website: www.duggiechapman.co.uk
e-mail: duggie@chapmanassociates.fsnet.co.uk

**CHEEK BY JOWL**
Contact: Declan Donnellan, Nick Ormerod
Stage Door, Barbican Centre
Silk Street, London EC2Y 8DS     Tel: 020-7382 7281
Website: www.cheekbyjowl.com
e-mail: info@cheekbyjowl.com

**CHICHESTER FESTIVAL THEATRE**
Oaklands Park, Chichester, West Sussex PO19 6AP
Website: www.cft.org.uk
e-mail: admin@cft.org.uk
Fax: 01243 787288     Tel: 01243 784437

**CHICKENSHED**
Chase Side, Southgate
London N14 4PE     Tel: 020-8351 6161
Website: www.chickenshed.org.uk
e-mail: info@chickenshed.org.uk

**CHOL THEATRE**
Contact: Andrew Loretto (Director, Theatre &
International), Susan Burns (Director,
Education & Community)
Lawrence Batley Theatre
8 Queen Street, Huddersfield, West Yorkshire HD1 2SP
Website: www.choltheatre.co.uk
e-mail: info@choltheatre.co.uk
Fax: 01484 425336     Tel: 01484 536008

**CHURCHILL THEATRE BROMLEY Ltd**
The Churchill, High Street
Bromley, Kent BR1 1HA
Website: www.churchilltheatre.co.uk
Fax: 020-8290 6968     Tel: 020-8464 7131

**CLEAN BREAK**
(Theatre Education, New Writing)
2 Patshull Road, London NW5 2LB
Website: www.cleanbreak.org.uk
e-mail: general@cleanbreak.org.uk
Fax: 020-7482 8611     Tel: 020-7482 8600

**CLUBWEST PRODUCTIONS**
Arundel Town Hall, Arundel
West Sussex BN18 9AP     Tel/Fax: 01903 889821
Website: www.clubwest.co.uk
e-mail: admin@clubwest.co.uk

**CODRON Michael PLAYS Ltd**
Aldwych Theatre Offices
London WC2B 4DF
Fax: 020-7240 8467     Tel: 020-7240 8291

**COLE KITCHENN PERSONAL MANAGEMENT Ltd**
212 Strand, London WC2R 1AP
Website: www.colekitchenn.com
e-mail: info@colekitchenn.com
Fax: 020-7353 9639     Tel: 020-7427 5682

**COMPLICITE**
14 Anglers Lane, London NW5 3DG
Website: www.complicite.org
e-mail: email@complicite.org
Fax: 020-7485 7701      Tel: 020-7485 7700

**CONCORDANCE**
Contact: Neil McPherson
Finborough Theatre
118 Finborough Road, London SW10 9ED
Website: www.concordance.org.uk
e-mail: admin@concordance.org.uk
Fax: 020-7835 1853      Tel: 020-7244 7439

**CONRADD Michael PROMOTIONS**
455 Waterloo Road
Blackpool FY4 4BW      Tel/Fax: 01253 692289
e-mail: miconproms@aol.com

**CONTEMPORARY STAGE COMPANY**
3 Etchingham Park Road, Finchley, London N3 2DU
Website: www.contemporarystage.co.uk
e-mail: contemp.stage@hotmail.co.uk
Fax: 020-8349 2458      Tel: 020-8349 4402

**CONWAY Clive CELEBRITY PRODUCTIONS Ltd**
32 Grove Street, Oxford OX2 7JT
e-mail: info@celebrityproductions.org
Fax: 01865 514409      Tel: 01865 514830

**CREATIVE MANAGEMENT & PRODUCTIONS (CMP) Ltd**
1st Floor, 26-28 Neal Street, London WC2H 9QQ
Website: www.cmplimited.com
e-mail: mail@cmplimited.com
Fax: 020-7240 3037      Tel: 020-7240 3033

**DEAD EARNEST THEATRE**
Sheffield Design Studio
40 Ball Street, Sheffield S3 8DB      Tel: 0114-321 0450
Website: www.deadearnest.co.uk
e-mail: info@deadearnest.co.uk

**DEAN Lee**
PO Box 10703, London WC2H 9ED
e-mail: admin@leedean.co.uk
Fax: 020-7836 6968      Tel: 020-7497 5111

**DEBUT PRODUCTIONS**
(Actor Showcases in London's West End & Manchester)
65 Norton Way North
Letchworth, Herts SG6 1BH      Mobile: 07505 677994
Website: www.debutproductions.co.uk
e-mail: enquiries@debutproductions.co.uk

**DISNEY THEATRICAL PRODUCTIONS (UK)**
Lyceum Theatre
21 Wellington Street, London WC2E 7RQ
Fax: 020-7845 0999      Tel: 020-7845 0900

**DONEGAN David Ltd**
PO Box LB689
London W1A 9LB      Mobile: 07957 358909
e-mail: daviddonegan@hotmail.co.uk

**DRAMATIS PERSONAE Ltd**
Contact: Nathan Silver, Nicolas Kent
19 Regency Street
London SW1P 4BY      Tel: 020-7834 9300
e-mail: ns@nathansilver.com

**DU FER Paul TOUR BOOKING SERVICES**
27 Kingfisher Court, Bridge Road
Hampton Court, East Molesey
Surrey KT8 9HL      Tel: 020-8941 8122
Website: www.pauldufer.com
e-mail: info@pauldufer.com

---

**Richard Jordan Productions Ltd**

- **Producing**
- **General Management**
  UK and International Productions,
  and International Festivals
- **Consultancy**
- **Richard Jordan Productions Ltd**
  Mews Studios, 16 Vernon Yard
  London W11 2DX

  Tel:      020 7243 9001
  Fax:      020 7313 9667
  e-mail:   richard.jordan@virgin.net

---

**EASTERN ANGLES THEATRE COMPANY**
(Touring)
Sir John Mills Theatre
Gatacre Road, Ipswich, Suffolk IP1 2LQ
Website: www.easternangles.co.uk
e-mail: admin@easternangles.co.uk
Fax: 01473 384999      Tel: 01473 218202

**EASY TIGER PRODUCTIONS Ltd**
7 Caroline House
London W6 9RG      Tel/Fax: 020-7371 8656
Website: www.easytigerproductions.com
e-mail: anything@easytigerproductions.com

**ELLIOTT Paul Ltd**
1st Floor, 18 Exeter Street, London WC2E 7DU
e-mail: pre@paulelliott.ltd.uk
Fax: 020-7379 4860      Tel: 020-7379 4870

**ENGLISH CHAMBER THEATRE The**
(No Drama School Applicants)
6 St Simon's Avenue
London SW15 6DU      Mobile: 07951 912425
Website: www.janemcculloch.com
e-mail: jane@janemcculloch.com

**ENGLISH NATIONAL OPERA**
London Coliseum, St Martin's Lane
London WC2N 4ES
Website: www.eno.org
Fax: 020-7845 9277      Tel: 020-7836 0111

**ENGLISH STAGE COMPANY Ltd**
Royal Court Theatre, Sloane Square, London SW1W 8AS
Website: www.royalcourttheatre.com
e-mail: info@royalcourttheatre.com
Fax: 020-7565 5001      Tel: 020-7565 5050

**ENGLISH TOURING THEATRE (ETT)**
25 Short Street, London SE1 8LJ
Website: www.ett.org.uk
e-mail: admin@ett.org.uk
Fax: 020-7633 0188      Tel: 020-7450 1990

**ENTERTAINMENT BUSINESS Ltd The**
Cameo House, 11 Bear Street, London WC2H 7AS
Website: www.entbiz.co.uk
e-mail: info@entbiz.co.uk
Fax: 020-7766 5275      Tel: 020-7766 5274

**EUROPEAN THEATRE COMPANY The**
39 Oxford Avenue, London SW20 8LS
Website: www.europeantheatre.co.uk
e-mail: admin@europeantheatre.co.uk
Fax: 020-8544 1999      Tel: 020-8544 1994

**FACADE**
(Musicals)
43A Garthorne Road, London SE23 1EP
e-mail: facade@cobomedia.com
Fax: 020-8291 4969                    Tel: 020-8291 7079

**FAIRBANK PRODUCTIONS**
Contact: Gerald Armin
27 Harcourt Road
London E15 3DX                Tel/Fax: 020-8555 3085
Website: www.fairbankproductions.co.uk
e-mail: info@fairbankproductions.co.uk

**FEATHER PRODUCTIONS Ltd**
The Studio, 137 Sheen Road
Richmond, Surrey TW9 1YJ
Website: www.featherproductions.com
e-mail: info@featherproductions.com
Fax: 020-8940 2335                    Tel: 020-8439 9848

**FELL Andrew Ltd**
4 Ching Court, 49-51 Monmouth Street
London WC2H 9EY
e-mail: hq@andrewfell.co.uk
Fax: 020-7240 2499                    Tel: 020-7240 2420

**FIELD Anthony ASSOCIATES Ltd**
Top Floor, 80-81 St Martin's Lane
London WC2N 4AA
Website: www.anthonyfieldassociates.com
e-mail: info@anthonyfieldassociates.com
Fax: 020-7240 2947                    Tel: 020-7240 5453

**FIELDER Simon PRODUCTIONS**
The Leatherhead Theatre
7 Church Street, Leatherhead
Surrey KT22 8DN
e-mail: enquiries@simonfielder.com
Fax: 01372 365135                    Tel: 01372 365134

**FIERY ANGEL Ltd**
22-24 Torrington Place
London WC1E 7HJ
Website: www.fiery-angel.com
e-mail: mail@fiery-angel.com
Fax: 020-7436 6287                    Tel: 020-7907 7012

**FORBIDDEN THEATRE COMPANY**
20 Rupert Street
London W1D 6DF                    Tel: 0845 0093084
Website: www.forbidden.org.uk
e-mail: info@forbidden.org.uk

**FORD Vanessa PRODUCTIONS Ltd**
Upper House Farm, Upper House Lane
Shamley Green, Surrey GU5 0SX        Tel: 01483 278203
Website: www.vfpltd.com
e-mail: vanessa.ford8@googlemail.com

**FOX Robert Ltd**
6 Beauchamp Place, London SW3 1NG
Website: www.robertfoxltd.com
e-mail: info@robertfoxltd.com
Fax: 020-7225 1638                    Tel: 020-7584 6855

**FREEDMAN Bill Ltd**
Colebrooke House
10-12 Gaskin Street
London N1 2RY                    Tel: 020-7226 5554

**FRESH GLORY PRODUCTIONS**
59 St Martin's Lane
London WC2N 4JS                    Tel: 020-7240 1941
Website: www.freshglory.com
e-mail: info@freshglory.com

**FRICKER Ian (THEATRE) Ltd**
3rd Floor, 146 Strand, London WC2R 1JD
Website: www.ianfricker.com
e-mail: mail@ianfricker.com
Fax: 020-7836 3078                    Tel: 020-7836 3090

**FRIEDMAN Sonia PRODUCTIONS**
Duke of York's Theatre
104 St Martin's Lane, London WC2N 4BG
Website: www.soniafriedman.com
e-mail: office@soniafriedman.com
Fax: 020-7845 8759                    Tel: 020-7845 8750

**GALLEON THEATRE COMPANY Ltd**
Contact: Alice De Sousa
Greenwich Playhouse
Greenwich BR Station Forecourt
189 Greenwich High Road, London SE10 8JA
Website: www.galleontheatre.co.uk
e-mail: boxoffice@galleontheatre.co.uk
Fax: 020-8310 7276                    Tel: 020-8858 9256

**GBM PRODUCTIONS Ltd**
Bidlake Toft, Roadford Lake
Germansweek, Devon EX21 5BD
Website: www.musicaltheatrecreations.com
e-mail: gbm@bidlaketoft.com
Fax: 01837 871123                    Tel: 01837 871522

**GIANT STEPS Ltd**
41 Parfrey Street, London W6 9EW
Website: www.rolandjaquarello.com
e-mail: giantstepstheatre@googlemail.com
Mobile: 07808 742307            Tel/Fax: 020-8741 2446

**GODOT COMPANY**
51 The Cut
London SE1 8LF                    Tel: 020-7633 0599
e-mail: godot@calderpublications.com

**GOODNIGHTS ENTERTAINMENT Ltd**
74 Pannier Place
Milton Keynes MK14 7QP                Tel: 01908 672077
Website: www.goodnights.org
e-mail: goodnights@talk21.com

**GOUCHER Mark Ltd**
3rd Floor, 20-22 Stukeley Street
London WC2B 5LR
e-mail: jess@markgoucher.com
Fax: 020-7438 9577                    Tel: 020-7438 9570

**GRAEAE THEATRE COMPANY**
Bradbury Studios
138 Kingsland Road, London E2 8DY    Tel: 020-7613 6900
Website: www.graeae.org
e-mail: info@graeae.org

**GRAHAM David ENTERTAINMENT Ltd**
72 New Bond Street, London W1S 1RR
Website: www.davidgrahamentertainment.com
e-mail: info@davidgraham.co.uk
Fax: 0870 3211700                    Tel: 0870 3211600

**HAMPSTEAD THEATRE PRODUCTIONS Ltd**
Eton Avenue, Swiss Cottage, London NW3 3EU
Website: www.hampsteadtheatre.com
e-mail: info@hampsteadtheatre.com
Fax: 020-7449 4201                    Tel: 020-7449 4200

**HANDSTAND PRODUCTIONS**
13 Hope Street, Liverpool L1 9BH
Website: www.handstand-uk.com
e-mail: info@handstand-uk.com
Fax: 0151-709 3515                    Tel: 0151-708 7441

**HARLEY PRODUCTIONS**
68 New Cavendish Street, London W1G 8TE
e-mail: harleyprods@aol.com
Fax: 020-8202 8863      Tel: 020-7580 3247

**HAYDEN SCOTT PRODUCTIONS**
Contact: Daniel Sparrow, Mike Walsh
44B Floral Street
London WC2E 9DA      Mobile: 07879 897900
Website: www.danielsparrowproductions.com
e-mail: info@danielsparrowproductions.com

**HAYMARKET The**
c/o The Anvil Trust, Wote Street
Basingstoke, Hampshire RG21 7NW
Website: www.anvilarts.org.uk
e-mail: christine.bradwell@anvilarts.org.uk
Fax: 01256 331733      Tel: 01256 819797

**HEADLONG THEATRE Ltd**
3rd Floor, 34-35 Berwick Street
London W1F 8RP
Website: www.headlongtheatre.co.uk
e-mail: info@headlongtheatre.co.uk
Fax: 020-7438 1749      Tel: 020-7438 0270

**HENDERSON Glynis PRODUCTIONS Ltd**
69 Charlotte Street, London W1T 4PJ
Website: www.ghmp.co.uk
e-mail: info@ghmp.co.uk
Fax: 020-7436 1489      Tel: 020-7580 9644

**HENDRY Jamie PRODUCTIONS Ltd**
Amadeus House, Floral Street, London WC2E 9DP
Website: www.jamiehendryproductions.com
e-mail: office@jamiehendryproductions.com
Fax: 020-7812 6495      Tel: 020-7812 7296

**HENNEGAN Nicholas Ltd**
33A Prebend Mansions
Chiswick High Road, London W4 2LU    Tel: 020-8582 7506
Website: www.nicholashennegan.com
e-mail: info@nicholashennegan.com

**HESTER John PRODUCTIONS (Intimate Mysteries Theatre Company)**
105 Stoneleigh Park Road
Epsom, Surrey KT19 0RF      Tel/Fax: 020-8393 5705
e-mail: hjohnhester@aol.com

**HISS & BOO COMPANY Ltd The**
Contact: Ian Liston. By Post (SAE) (No unsolicited scripts)
Nyes Hill, Wineham Lane
Bolney, West Sussex RH17 5SD
Website: www.hissboo.co.uk
e-mail: email@hissboo.co.uk
Fax: 01444 882057      Tel: 01444 881707

**HISTORIA THEATRE COMPANY**
8 Cloudesley Square, London N1 0HT
Website: www.historiatheatre.com
e-mail: kateprice@lineone.net
Fax: 020-7278 4733      Tel: 020-7837 8008

**HOIPOLLOI**
Office F, Dale's Brewery
Gwydir Street, Cambridge CB1 2LJ      Tel: 01223 322748
Website: www.hoipolloi.org.uk
e-mail: info@hoipolloi.org.uk

**HOLLOW CROWN PRODUCTIONS**
2 Norfolk Road
London E17 5QS      Mobile: 07930 530948
Website: www.hollowcrown.co.uk
e-mail: enquiries@hollowcrown.co.uk

**HOLMAN Paul ASSOCIATES Ltd**
Morritt House, 58 Station Approach
South Ruislip, Middlesex HA4 6SA
Website: www.paulholmanassociates.co.uk
e-mail: enquiries@paulholmanassociates.co.uk
Fax: 020-8839 3124      Tel: 020-8845 9408

**HOLT Thelma Ltd**
Noel Coward Theatre
85 St Martin's Lane, London WC2N 4AU
Website: www.thelmaholt.co.uk
e-mail: thelma@dircon.co.uk
Fax: 020-7812 7550      Tel: 020-7812 7455

**HOUSE OF GULLIVER**
Contact: By Post
60 Beaconsfield Road
Tring, Herts HP23 4DW

**HUGHES Steve**
Oakwood, 4 Armitage Road
Armitage Bridge HD4 7PG      Mobile: 07816 844024
Website: www.hughes-productions.co.uk
e-mail: steve@hughes-productions.co.uk

**HULL TRUCK THEATRE**
50 Ferensway, Hull HU2 8LB
Website: www.hulltruck.co.uk
e-mail: admin@hulltruck.co.uk
Fax: 01482 581182      Tel: 01482 224800

**IAN David PRODUCTIONS**
Third Floor
33 Henrietta Street, London WC2E 8NA
Website: www.davidianproductions.com
Fax: 020-7257 6381      Tel: 020-7257 6380

**IBSEN STAGE COMPANY**
434B Hornsey Road
London N19 4EB      Tel: 020-7281 4322
Website: www.ibsenstage.com
e-mail: ask@ibsenstage.com

**ICARUS THEATRE COLLECTIVE**
33 Portland Place
London W1B 1QU      Tel: 020-3239 7033
Website: www.icarustheatre.co.uk
e-mail: info@icarustheatre.co.uk

**IMAGE MUSICAL THEATRE**
23 Sedgeford Road
Shepherd's Bush, London W12 0NA
Website: www.imagemusicaltheatre.co.uk
e-mail: brian@imagemusicaltheatre.co.uk
Fax: 020-8749 9294      Tel: 020-8743 9380

**INCISOR**
Flat 1, 5 York Avenue
Hove BN3 1PH
Website: www.theatre-company-incisor.com
e-mail: sarahmann7@hotmail.co.uk
Fax: 020-8830 4992      Mobile: 07979 498450

**INDIGO ENTERTAINMENTS**
Tynymynydd, Bryneglwys
Corwen, Denbighshire LL21 9NP      Tel: 01978 790211
Website: www.indigoentertainments.com
e-mail: info@indigoentertainments.com

**INGRAM Colin Ltd**
Suite 526, Linen Hall
162-168 Regent Street, London W1B 5TE
Website: www.coliningramltd.com
e-mail: info@coliningramltd.com
Fax: 020-7038 3907      Tel: 020-7038 3906

**INSIDE INTELLIGENCE**
(Theatre, Contemporary Opera, Music & Theatre)
13 Athlone Close, London E5 8HD
Website: www.inside-intelligence.org.uk
e-mail: admin@inside-intelligence.org.uk
Fax: 020-8985 7211                Tel: 020-8986 8013

**INTERNATIONAL THEATRE & MUSIC Ltd**
Contact: Piers Chater Robinson
Garden Studios
11-15 Betterton Street
Covent Garden, London WC2H 9BP
Website: www.it-m.co.uk
e-mail: info@it-m.co.uk
Fax: 020-7379 0801                Tel: 020-7470 8786

**ISLEWORTH ACTORS COMPANY**
38 Eve Road, Isleworth
Middlesex TW7 7HS              Tel/Fax: 020-8891 1073

**JAM THEATRE COMPANY**
21 Beechtree Avenue
Marlow, Bucks SL7 3NH            Tel: 01628 487773
Website: www.jamtheatre.co.uk
e-mail: office@jamtheatre.co.uk

**JAMES Bruce PRODUCTIONS Ltd**
68 St Georges Park Avenue
Westcliff-on-Sea, Essex SS0 9UD
Website: www.brucejamesproductions.co.uk
e-mail: info@brucejamesproductions.co.uk
Mobile: 07850 369018          Tel/Fax: 01702 335970

**JENKINS Andrew Ltd**
63 Kidbrooke Park Road
London SE3 0EE
Website: www.andrewjenkinsltd.com
e-mail: info@andrewjenkinsltd.com
Fax: 020-8856 7106                Tel: 020-8319 3657

**JOHNSON David**
85B Torriano Avenue
London NW5 2RX                  Tel: 020-7284 3733
e-mail: david@johnsontemple.co.uk

**JOHNSON Gareth Ltd**
Plas Hafren, Eglwyswrw
Crymych, Pembrokeshire SA41 3UL
e-mail: gjltd@mac.com
Mobile: 07770 225227            Tel: 01239 891368

**JORDAN Andy PRODUCTIONS Ltd**
Studio D, 413-419 Harrow Road
Maida Vale, London W9 3QJ        Mobile: 07775 615205
e-mail: andy@andyjordanproductions.co.uk

**JORDAN PRODUCTIONS Ltd**
Phoenix Auction Rooms
142 Langney Road, Eastbourne
East Sussex BN22 8AQ
e-mail: info@jordanproductionsltd.co.uk
Fax: 01323 417766                Tel: 01323 417745

**JORDAN Richard PRODUCTIONS Ltd**
Mews Studios
16 Vernon Yard, London W11 2DX
e-mail: richard.jordan@virgin.net
Fax: 020-7313 9667                Tel: 020-7243 9001

**KELLY Robert C Ltd**
The Alhambra Suite
82 Mitchell Street, Glasgow G1 3NA
Website: www.robertckelly.co.uk
e-mail: robert@robertckelly.co.uk
Fax: 0141-229 1441                Tel: 0141-229 1444

**KENWRIGHT Bill Ltd**
BKL House, 1 Venice Walk, London W2 1RR
Website: www.kenwright.com
e-mail: info@kenwright.com
Fax: 020-7446 6222                Tel: 020-7446 6200

**KING'S HEAD THEATRE PRODUCTIONS Ltd**
115 Upper Street
London N1 1QN                    Tel: 020-7226 8561
Website: www.kingsheadtheatre.org

**LATCHMERE THEATRE**
Contact: Chris Fisher
Unit 5A, Spaces Business Centre
Ingate Place, London SW8 3NS
e-mail: latchmere@fishers.org.uk
Fax: 020-7978 2631                Tel: 020-7978 2620

**LHP Ltd**
PO Box 60231
London EC1P 1FL                Mobile: 07973 938634
e-mail: lhpltd@msn.com

**LIMELIGHT PRODUCTIONS**
Unit 13, The io Centre, The Royal Arsenal
Seymour Street, London SE18 6SS
e-mail: enquiries@mcmlimelight.co.uk
Fax: 020-8305 2684                Tel: 020-8858 6141

**LINNIT PRODUCTIONS Ltd**
123A King's Road, London SW3 4PL
Fax: 020-7352 3450                Tel: 020-7352 7722

**LIVE THEATRE**
Broad Chare, Quayside
Newcastle upon Tyne NE1 3DQ      Tel: 0191-261 2694
Website: www.live.org.uk
e-mail: info@live.org.uk

**LONDON BUBBLE THEATRE COMPANY Ltd**
5 Elephant Lane, London SE16 4JD
Website: www.londonbubble.org.uk
e-mail: admin@londonbubble.org.uk
Fax: 020-7231 2366                Tel: 020-7237 4434

**LONDON CLASSIC THEATRE**
The Production Office
63 Shirley Avenue
Sutton, Surrey SM1 3QT           Tel: 020-8395 2095
Website: www.londonclassictheatre.co.uk
e-mail: admin@londonclassictheatre.co.uk

**LONDON PRODUCTIONS Ltd**
PO Box 10703, London WC2H 9ED
e-mail: admin@leedean.co.uk
Fax: 020-7836 6968                Tel: 020-7497 5111

**LONDON REPERTORY COMPANY**
27 Old Gloucester Street
London WC1N 3XX              Tel/Fax: 020-7258 1944
Website: www.londonrepertorycompany.com
e-mail: info@londonrepertorycompany.com

**MACKINTOSH Cameron Ltd**
1 Bedford Square, London WC1B 3RB
Fax: 020-7436 2683                Tel: 020-7637 8866

**MACNAGHTEN PRODUCTIONS**
19 Grange Court, Grange Road
Cambridge CB3 9BD                Tel: 01223 577974

**MALCOLM Christopher PRODUCTIONS Ltd**
11 Claremont Walk, Bath BA1 6HB
Website: www.christophermalcolm.co.uk
e-mail: cm@christophermalcolm.co.uk
Fax: 01225 480077                Tel: 01225 445459

**MANS Johnny PRODUCTIONS Ltd**
PO Box 196, Hoddesdon, Herts EN10 7WG
Website: www.johnnymansproductions.co.uk
e-mail: johnnymansagent@aol.com
Fax: 01992 470516                    Tel: 01992 470907

**MASTERSON Guy PRODUCTIONS**
Millfield House & Theatre
Silver Street, Edmonton N18 1PJ     Tel/Fax: 020-8807 5770
Website: www.theatretoursinternational.com
e-mail: admin@theatretoursinternational.com

**MEADOW Jeremy Ltd**
73 Great Titchfield Street, London W1W 6RD
e-mail: info@jeremymeadow.com
Fax: 0870 7627882                    Tel: 020-7436 2244

**MENZIES Lee Ltd**
118-120 Wardour Street, London W1F 0TU
Website: www.leemenzies.co.uk
e-mail: leemenzies@leemenzies.co.uk
Fax: 020-7734 4224                    Tel: 020-7734 9559

**MIDDLE GROUND THEATRE CO Ltd**
3 Gordon Terrace, Malvern Wells
Malvern, Worcestershire WR14 4ER
Website: www.middlegroundtheatre.co.uk
e-mail: middleground@middlegroundtheatre.co.uk
Fax: 01684 574472                    Tel: 01684 577231

**MILLIONTH MUSE PRODUCTIONS**
1st & 2nd Floors
20 Stansfield Road
Stockwell, London SW9 9RZ      Tel/Fax: 020-7737 5300
Website: www.millionthmuse.com
e-mail: paul@millionthmuse.com

**MITCHELL Matthew Ltd**
New Barn Farm, London Road
Hassocks, West Sussex BN6 9ND      Tel/Fax: 01273 842572
e-mail: info@matthewmitchell.org

**MJE PRODUCTIONS Ltd**
Contact: Carole Winter, Michael Edwards
Amadeus House, Floral Street
Covent Garden, London WC2E 9DP
Website: www.mjeproductions.com
e-mail: info@mjeproductions.com
Fax: 020-7812 6495                    Tel: 020-7812 7290

**MMP**
2nd Floor
23 Tavistock Street, London WC2E 7NX
Website: www.michaelmccabeproductions.com
e-mail: mailbox@michaelmccabe.net
Fax: 020-7420 7748                    Tel: 020-7420 7744

**MOKITAGRIT**
6 Addington Road
London N4 4RP                    Mobile: 07980 564849
Website: www.mokitagrit.com
e-mail: mail@mokitagrit.com

**MONSTAR PRODUCTIONS**
65A Huddleston Road
London N7 0AE                    Mobile: 07900 864694
Website: www.monstarproductions.co.uk
e-mail: monstar@fsmail.net

**MONSTER THEATRE PRODUCTIONS**
c/o 17 Prince Road, Wallsend
Tyne & Wear NE28 8DN
Website: www.monsterproductions.co.uk
e-mail: info@monsterproductions.co.uk
Fax: 0191-240 4016                    Tel: 0191-240 4011

**MOVING THEATRE**
16 Laughton Lodge, Nr Lewes, East Sussex BN8 6BY
Website: www.movingtheatre.com
e-mail: info@movingtheatre.com
Fax: 01323 815736                    Tel: 01323 815726

**MUSIC THEATRE LONDON**
Chertsey Chambers, 12 Mercer Street
London WC2H 9QD                    Mobile: 07831 243942
Website: www.capriolfilms.com
e-mail: musictheatre.london@virgin.net

**NATIONAL ANGELS**
123A Kings Road, London SW3 4PL
e-mail: admin@nationalangels.com
Fax: 020-7352 3450                    Tel: 020-7376 4878

**NATIONAL THEATRE**
South Bank, London SE1 9PX
Website: www.nationaltheatre.org.uk
Fax: 020-7452 3344                    Tel: 020-7452 3333

**NEAL STREET PRODUCTIONS Ltd**
1st Floor, 26-28 Neal Street, London WC2H 9QQ
e-mail: post@nealstreetproductions.com
Fax: 020-7240 7099                    Tel: 020-7240 8890

**NEW SHAKESPEARE COMPANY Ltd The**
Regent's Park Open Air Theatre
The Iron Works, Inner Circle
Regent's Park, London NW1 4NR
Website: www.openairtheatre.com
Fax: 020-7487 4562                    Tel: 0844 3753460

**NEWPALM PRODUCTIONS**
26 Cavendish Avenue, London N3 3QN
e-mail: newpalm@btopenworld.com
Fax: 020-8346 8257                    Tel: 020-8349 0802

**NICHOLAS Paul & IAN David ASSOCIATES Ltd**
c/o Third Floor
33 Henrietta Street, London WC2E 8NA
Fax: 020-7257 6381                    Tel: 020-7257 6380

**NITRO**
(Formerly Black Theatre Co-operative)
6 Brewery Road, London N7 9NH
Website: www.nitro.co.uk
e-mail: info@nitro.co.uk
Fax: 020-7609 1221                    Tel: 020-7609 1331

**NORDIC NOMAD PRODUCTIONS**
Contact: Tanja Raaste, Creative Producer (Specialising in
New Work and Business Skills Training)
64 Tulse Hill, London SW2 2PT      Mobile: 07980 619165
Website: www.nordicnomad.com
e-mail: info@nordicnomad.com

**NORTHERN BROADSIDES THEATRE COMPANY**
Dean Clough, Halifax HX3 5AX
Website: www.northern-broadsides.co.uk
e-mail: sue@northern-broadsides.co.uk
Fax: 01422 383175                    Tel: 01422 369704

**NORTHERN STAGE (THEATRICAL PRODUCTIONS) Ltd**
Barras Bridge, Newcastle upon Tyne NE1 7RH
Website: www.northernstage.co.uk
e-mail: info@northernstage.co.uk
Fax: 0191-261 8093                    Tel: 0191-232 3366

**NORTHUMBERLAND THEATRE COMPANY (NTC)**
The Playhouse, Bondgate Without, Alnwick
Northumberland NE66 1PQ
Website: www.northumberlandtheatre.co.uk
e-mail: admin@northumberlandtheatre.co.uk
Fax: 01665 605837                    Tel: 01665 602586

**NOT THE NATIONAL THEATRE**
Contact: By Post (Small/Mid-Scale Touring - UK & Abroad)
116 Dalberg Road
London SW2 1AW

**NOTIONAL THEATRE Ltd**
PO Box 130, Hexham NE46 4WA
e-mail: notional.theatre@virgin.net

**O'BRIEN Barry (1968) Ltd**
26 Cavendish Avenue, London N3 3QN
Fax: 020-8346 8257          Tel: 020-8349 0802

**OFF THE CUFF THEATRE COMPANY**
2nd Floor, 91A Rivington Street, London EC2A 3AY
Website: www.otctheatre.co.uk
e-mail: otctheatre@aol.com
Fax: 020-7739 3852          Tel: 020-7739 2857

**OLD VIC PRODUCTIONS Plc**
The Old Vic Theatre
The Cut, Waterloo, London SE1 8NB
e-mail: becky.barber@oldvictheatre.com
Fax: 020-7981 0991          Tel: 020-7928 2651

**ONE NIGHT BOOKING COMPANY The**
1 Hogarth Hill, London NW11 6AY     Tel: 020-8455 3278
Website: www.onenightbooking.com
e-mail: mail@onenightbooking.com

**OPEN AIR THEATRE**
(See NEW SHAKESPEARE COMPANY Ltd The)

**OPERATING THEATRE COMPANY**
22 Burghley Road
London NW5 1UE          Tel: 020-7419 2476
Website: www.operating-theatre.co.uk
e-mail: info@operating-theatre.co.uk

**OUT OF JOINT**
7 Thane Works, Thane Villas, London N7 7NU
Website: www.outofjoint.co.uk
e-mail: ojo@outofjoint.co.uk
Fax: 020-7609 0203          Tel: 020-7609 0207

**OVATION**
Upstairs at The Gatehouse
The Gatehouse
Highgate Village, London N6 4BD
Website: www.ovationtheatres.com
e-mail: events@ovationproductions.com
Fax: 020-8340 3466          Tel: 020-8340 4256

**P&S PRODUCTIONS**
Top Flat, 51 Norroy Road
London SW15 1PQ          Tel: 020-8788 8521
e-mail: timsawers@msn.com

**PAINES PLOUGH**
Fourth Floor
43 Aldwych, London WC2B 4DN
Website: www.painesplough.com
e-mail: office@painesplough.com
Fax: 020-7240 4534          Tel: 020-7240 4533

**PASSWORD PRODUCTIONS Ltd**
Contact: John Mackay
85B Torriano Avenue
London NW5 2RX          Tel: 020-7284 3733
e-mail: johnmackay2001@aol.com

**PENDLE PRODUCTIONS**
Bridge Farm, 249 Hawes Side Lane, Blackpool FY4 4AA
Website: www.pendleproductions.co.uk
e-mail: admin@pendleproductions.co.uk
Fax: 01253 792930          Tel: 01253 839375

**PENTABUS THEATRE**
(National Touring Company for New Writing)
Bromfield, Ludlow
Shropshire SY8 2JU          Tel: 01584 856564
Website: www.pentabus.co.uk
e-mail: john@pentabus.co.uk

**PEOPLE SHOW**
People Show Studios
Pollard Row, London E2 6NB
Website: www.peopleshow.co.uk
e-mail: people@peopleshow.co.uk
Fax: 020-7739 0203          Tel: 020-7729 1841

**PERFECT PITCH MUSICALS Ltd**
Ambassadors Theatre
West Street
London WC2H 9ND          Tel: 020-7395 5460
Website: www.perfectpitchmusicals.com
e-mail: wendy@perfectpitchmusicals.com

**PERFORMANCE BUSINESS The**
78 Oatlands Drive
Weybridge, Surrey KT13 9HT          Tel: 01932 888885
Website: www.theperformance.biz
e-mail: info@theperformance.biz

**PILOT THEATRE**
(New Writing & Multimedia YPT)
York Theatre Royal
St Leonard's Place, York YO1 7HD
Website: www.pilot-theatre.com
e-mail: info@pilot-theatre.com
Fax: 01904 656378          Tel: 01904 635755

**PLANTAGENET PRODUCTIONS**
Westridge (Open Centre), (Drawing Room Recitals)
Star Lane, Highclere
Nr Newbury RG20 9PJ          Tel: 01635 253322

**PLAYHOUSE ENTERTAINMENT GROUP The**
Playhouse Studios
First Floor, 104 Cavendish Place
Eastbourne
East Sussex BN21 3TZ          Tel/Fax: 01323 638980
Website: www.playhousecostumes.co.uk
e-mail: enquiries@playhousecostumes.co.uk

**PLUTO PRODUCTIONS Ltd**
New End Theatre
27 New End
Hampstead, London NW3 1JD
Website: www.newendtheatre.co.uk
e-mail: briandaniels@newendtheatre.co.uk
Fax: 020-7794 4044          Tel: 020-7472 5800

**POLKA THEATRE**
240 The Broadway
Wimbledon SW19 1SB
Website: www.polkatheatre.com
e-mail: admin@polkatheatre.com
Fax: 020-8545 8365          Tel: 020-8545 8320

**POPULAR PRODUCTIONS Ltd**
18B High Street, London N8 7PB
Website: www.popularproductions.com
e-mail: info@popularproductions.com
Mobile: 07812 859767          Tel: 020-8347 0221

**PORTER Richard Ltd**
214 Grange Road
London SE1 3AA          Mobile: 07884 183404
Website: www.richardporterltd.com
e-mail: office@richardporterltd.com

**POSTER Kim**
4th Floor, 80-81 St Martin's Lane
London WC2N 4AA
e-mail: admin@stanhopeprod.com
Fax: 020-7504 8656 Tel: 020-7240 3098

**PREMIER SHOWS Ltd**
PO Box 638, Chichester
West Sussex PO19 9HB Mobile: 07071 888990
Website: www.premiershows.co.uk
e-mail: mail@premiershows.co.uk

**PROMENADE PRODUCTIONS**
6 Russell Grove
London SW9 6HS Tel: 020-7582 9354
Website: www.promenadeproductions.com
e-mail: info@promenadeproductions.com

**PUGH David & ROGERS Dafydd**
Wyndhams Theatre
Charing Cross Road, London WC2H 0DA
e-mail: dpl@davidpughltd.com
Fax: 020-7292 0399 Tel: 020-7292 0390

**PURSUED BY A BEAR PRODUCTIONS**
Farnham Maltings, Bridge Square
Farnham GU9 7QR Tel: 01252 745445
Website: www.pursuedbyabear.co.uk
e-mail: pursuedbyabear@yahoo.co.uk

**PW PRODUCTIONS Ltd**
2nd Floor, 80-81 St Martin's Lane
London WC2N 4AA
Website: www.pwprods.co.uk
Fax: 020-7240 2947 Tel: 020-7395 7580

**QDOS ENTERTAINMENT**
Qdos House, Queen Margaret's Road
Scarborough, North Yorkshire YO11 2YH
Website: www.qdosentertainment.com
e-mail: info@qdosentertainment.co.uk
Fax: 01723 361958 Tel: 01723 500038

**QUANTUM THEATRE**
The Old Button Factory
1-11 Bannockburn Road, Plumstead
London SE18 1ET Tel: 020-8317 9000
Website: www.quantumtheatre.co.uk
e-mail: office@quantumtheatre.co.uk

**RAGS & FEATHERS THEATRE COMPANY**
80 Summer Road, Thames Ditton, Surrey KT7 0QP
e-mail: jill@ragsandfeathers.freeserve.co.uk
Mobile: 07958 724374 Tel: 020-8224 2203

**RAIN OR SHINE THEATRE COMPANY**
25 Paddock Gardens, Longlevens
Gloucester GL2 0ED Tel/Fax: 01452 521575
Website: www.rainorshine.co.uk
e-mail: theatre@rainorshine.co.uk

**RATTLING TONGUE THEATRE COMPANY**
44 Fairfield South, Kingston Upon Thames
Surrey KT1 2UW Tel: 020-7419 7851
Website: www.rattlingtongue.com
e-mail: info@rattlingtongue.com

**REAL CIRCUMSTANCE THEATRE COMPANY**
100 Lexden Road, West Bergholt
Colchester CO6 3BW
Website: www.realcircumstance.com
e-mail: info@realcircumstance.com

**REALLY USEFUL THEATRE COMPANY The**
22 Tower Street, London WC2H 9TW
Fax: 020-7240 1293 Tel: 020-7240 0880

**RED ROOM The**
11-15 Betterton Street
Covent Garden, London WC2H 9PB Tel: 020-7470 8790
Website: www.theredroom.org.uk
e-mail: info@theredroom.org.uk

**RED ROSE CHAIN**
1 Fore Hamlet, Ipswich IP3 8AA Tel: 01473 288886
Website: www.redrosechain.co.uk
e-mail: info@redrosechain.co.uk

**RED SHIFT THEATRE COMPANY**
PO Box 60151
London SW19 2TB Tel/Fax: 020-8540 1271
Website: www.redshifttheatreco.co.uk
e-mail: jane@redshifttheatreco.co.uk

**REVEAL THEATRE COMPANY Ltd**
The Creative Village
Staffordshire Univeristy Business Village
72 Leek Road
Stoke on Trent ST4 2AR Tel: 01782 294871
Website: www.revealtheatre.co.uk
e-mail: enquiries@revealtheatre.co.uk

**RGC PRODUCTIONS**
260 Kings Road, Kingston
Surrey KT2 5HX Mobile: 07740 286727
Website: www.rgcproductions.com
e-mail: info@rgcproductions.com

**RHO DELTA Ltd**
Contact: Greg Ripley-Duggan
26 Goodge Street
London W1T 2QG Tel: 020-7436 1392
e-mail: info@ripleyduggan.com

**ROCKET THEATRE**
32 Baxter Road
Sale, Manchester M33 3AL
Website: www.rockettheatre.co.uk
e-mail: martin@rockettheatre.co.uk
Mobile: 07788 723570 Tel: 0161-969 1444

**ROSE Michael Ltd**
The Old Dairy, Throop Road
Holdenhurst
Bournemouth, Dorset BH8 0DL
e-mail: firstname@michaelroseltd.com
Fax: 01202 522311 Tel: 01202 522711

**ROSENTHAL Suzanna Ltd**
PO Box 40001
London N6 4YA Tel/Fax: 020-8340 4421
e-mail: admin@suzannarosenthal.com

**ROYAL COURT THEATRE PRODUCTIONS Ltd**
Sloane Square, London SW1W 8AS
Website: www.royalcourttheatre.com
e-mail: info@royalcourttheatre.com
Fax: 020-7565 5001 Tel: 020-7565 5050

**ROYAL EXCHANGE THEATRE**
St Ann's Square
Manchester M2 7DH Tel: 0161-833 9333
Website: www.royalexchange.co.uk

**ROYAL SHAKESPEARE COMPANY**
The Courtyard Theatre
Southern Lane
Stratford-upon-Avon CV37 6BB
Website: www.rsc.org.uk
Fax: 01789 272509 Tel: 01789 296655

1 Earlham Street, London WC2H 9LL
Fax: 020-7845 0505 Tel: 020-7845 0500

**RUBINSTEIN Mark Ltd**
25 Short Street, London SE1 8LJ
e-mail: info@mrluk.com
Fax: 0870 7059731
Tel: 020-7021 0787

**SALBERG & STEPHENSON Ltd**
18 Soho Square, London W1D 3QL
e-mail: soholondon@aol.com
Fax: 020-7025 8100
Tel: 020-7025 8701

**SCAMP**
(Sutherland Callow Arts Management & Production)
44 Church Lane, Arlesey, Beds SG15 6UX
Website: www.scamptheatre.com
e-mail: admin@scamptheatre.com
Mobile: 07710 491111
Tel: 01462 734843

**SCARLET THEATRE**
Studio 4, The Bull
68 High Street, Barnet
Herts EN5 5SJ
Tel: 020-8441 9779
Website: www.scarlettheatre.co.uk
e-mail: admin@scarlettheatre.co.uk

**SEABRIGHT James**
3rd Floor, 118-120 Wardour Street
London W1F OTU
Website: www.seabright.info
e-mail: contacts@seabright.info
Fax: 08701 255706
Tel: 020-7439 1173

**SHAKESPEARE'S MEN**
10 Dee Close, Upminster
Essex RM14 1QD
Tel: 01708 222938
Website: www.terencemustoo.com
e-mail: terence@terencemustoo.com

**SHARED EXPERIENCE**
(National/International Touring)
13 Riverside House
27-29 Vauxhall Grove, London SW8 1SY
Website: www.sharedexperience.org.uk
e-mail: admin@sharedexperience.org.uk
Fax: 020-7735 0374
Tel: 020-7587 1596

**SHOW OF STRENGTH**
74 Chessel Street, Bedminster
Bristol BS3 3DN
Tel: 0117-902 0235
Website: www.showofstrength.org.uk
e-mail: info@showofstrength.org.uk

**SHOWCASE ENTERTAINMENTS PRODUCTIONS Ltd**
Contact: Geoffrey J.L. Hindmarch (Executive Producer)
Paul W. Morgan (Stage Director)
2 Lumley Close, Newton Aycliffe
Co Durham DL5 5PA
Tel: 01325 316224
Website: www.showcaseproductions.co.uk
e-mail: gjl@showcaseproductions.co.uk

**SIMPLY THEATRE**
Chemin des Couleuvres 8B
1295 Tannay, Switzerland 1295
Tel: 00 41 22 8600518
Website: www.simplytheatre.com
e-mail: info@simplytheatre.com

**SINDEN Marc PRODUCTIONS**
1 Hogarth Hill, London NW11 6AY
Tel: 020-8455 3278
Website: www.sindenproductions.com
e-mail: mail@sindenproductions.com

**SIXTEENFEET PRODUCTIONS**
25 Rattray Road, London SW2 1AZ
Website: www.sixteenfeet.co.uk
e-mail: info@sixteenfeet.co.uk
Mobile: 07958 448690
Tel: 020-7326 4417

**SOHO THEATRE COMPANY**
21 Dean Street, London W1D 3NE
Website: www.sohotheatre.com
Fax: 020-7287 5061
Tel: 020-7287 5060

**SPARROW Daniel PRODUCTIONS**
47A Trinity Street
London SE1 4JA
Mobile: 07879 897900
Website: www.danielsparrowproductions.com
e-mail: info@danielsparrowproductions.com

**SPHINX THEATRE COMPANY**
13 Riverside House
27-29 Vauxhall Grove
London SW8 1SY
Tel: 020-7587 1596
Website: www.sphinxtheatre.co.uk
e-mail: info@sphinxtheatre.co.uk

**SPINNING WHEEL THEATRE**
Contact: By Post/e-mail
5 Haughmond, Woodside Grange Road
Finchley, London N12 8ST
Website: www.spinningwheeltheatre.com
e-mail: georgia@spinningwheeltheatre.com

**SPLATS ENTERTAINMENT**
5 Denmark Street
London WC2H 8LP
Tel: 020-7240 8400
Website: www.splatsentertainment.co.uk
e-mail: admin@splatsentertainment.co.uk

**SPLITMOON THEATRE**
Flat 1, 17 Westgrove Lane
London SE10 8QP
Tel: 020-8694 3703
Website: www.splitmoontheatre.org
e-mail: info@splitmoontheatre.org

**SQUAREDEAL PRODUCTIONS Ltd**
Contact: Jenny Topper
24 De Beauvoir Square
London N1 4LE
e-mail: jenny@jennytopper.com
Fax: 020-7275 7553
Tel: 020-7249 5966

**SQUIRES & JOHNS PRODUCTIONS Ltd**
Sullon Lodge, Sullon Side Lane
Garstang PR3 1GH
Website: www.trendsgroup.co.uk
e-mail: info@trendsgroup.co.uk
Fax: 01253 407715
Tel: 0871 2003343

**STAGE ENTERTAINMENT UK Ltd**
6th Floor, Swan House
52 Poland Street, London W1F 7NQ
Website: www.stage-entertainment.co.uk
Fax: 020-7025 6971
Tel: 020-7025 6970

**STAGE FURTHER PRODUCTIONS Ltd**
Westgate House, Stansted Road
Eastbourne
East Sussex BN22 8LG
e-mail: davidsfp@hotmail.com
Fax: 01323 736127
Tel: 01323 739478

**STAND UP DRAMA Ltd**
Unit 8, 8 Balmes Road
London N1 5TQ
Tel: 020-7923 2295
Website: www.standupdrama.com
e-mail: info@standupdrama.com

**STANHOPE PRODUCTIONS Ltd**
4th Floor, 80-81 St Martin's Lane
London WC2N 4AA
e-mail: admin@stanhopeprod.com
Fax: 020-7504 8656
Tel: 020-7240 3098

**STRAIGHT LINE PRODUCTIONS**
58 Castle Avenue
Epsom, Surrey KT17 2PH
e-mail: hilary@straightlinemanagement.co.uk
Fax: 020-8393 8079          Tel: 020-8393 4220

**SUPPORT ACT PRODUCTIONS**
Contact: Ian McCracken
243A Lynmouth Avenue
Morden, Surrey SM4 4RX          Tel: 0845 0940796
Website: www.supportact.co.uk
e-mail: info@supportact.co.uk

**TALAWA THEATRE COMPANY**
Ground Floor, 53-55 East Road, London N1 6AH
Website: www.talawa.com
e-mail: hq@talawa.com
Fax: 020-7251 5969          Tel: 020-7251 6644

**TAMASHA THEATRE COMPANY**
Unit 220, Great Guildford Business Square
30 Great Guildford Street, London SE1 0HS
Website: www.tamasha.org.uk
e-mail: info@tamasha.org.uk
Fax: 020-7021 0421          Tel: 020-7633 2270

**TBA MUSIC**
1 St Gabriels Road, London NW2 4DS
e-mail: peter@tbagroup.co.uk
Fax: 0700 607 0808          Tel: 0845 1203722

**TEG PRODUCTIONS Ltd**
73 Great Titchfield Street, London W1W 6RD
e-mail: info@tegproductions.com
Fax: 0870 7627882          Tel: 020-7436 2244

**THAT'S ENTERTAINMENT PRODUCTIONS**
PO Box 4766
Worthing BN11 9NY          Tel: 01903 263454
Website: www.thatsentertainmentproductions.co.uk
e-mail: info@thatsentertainmentproductions.co.uk

**THEATRE ABSOLUTE**
Insititute for Creative Enterprise
Technology Park, Puma Way
Coventry CV1 2TT          Tel: 024-7615 8340
Website: www.theatreabsolute.co.uk
e-mail: info@theatreabsolute.co.uk

**THEATRE ALIVE!**
13 St Barnabas Road, London E17 8JZ
Website: www.theatrealive.org.uk
e-mail: theatrealive@tiscali.co.uk

**THEATRE BABEL**
PO Box 5103, Glasgow G78 9AR          Tel: 0141-416 0051
Website: www.theatrebabel.co.uk
e-mail: admin@theatrebabel.co.uk

**THEATRE NORTH**
Woodlands, The Mains, Giggleswick
Settle, North Yorkshire BD24 0AX          Tel/Fax: 01729 822058
Website: www.theatrenorth.co.uk
e-mail: info@theatrenorth.co.uk

**THEATRE OF COMEDY COMPANY Ltd**
Shaftesbury Theatre
210 Shaftesbury Avenue
London WC2H 8DP
Fax: 020-7836 8181          Tel: 020-7379 3345

**THEATRE PARTNERS Ltd**
PO Box 293, Letchworth Garden City SG6 9EU
Website: www.theatrepartners.com
e-mail: info@theatrepartners.com
Fax: 0870 2359519          Tel: 020-7240 9941

**THEATRE ROYAL HAYMARKET PRODUCTIONS**
Theatre Royal Haymarket
18 Suffolk Street, London SW1Y 4HT          Tel: 020-7389 9669
e-mail: jaqui@trh.co.uk

**THEATRE ROYAL STRATFORD EAST**
Gerry Raffles Square, Stratford, London E15 1BN
Website: www.stratfordeast.com
e-mail: theatreroyal@stratfordeast.com
Fax: 020-8534 8381          Tel: 020-8534 7374

**THEATRE SANS FRONTIERES**
The Queen's Hall Arts Centre
Beaumont Street, Hexham NE46 3LS
Website: www.tsf.org.uk
e-mail: admin@tsf.org.uk
Fax: 01434 607206          Tel: 01434 652484

**THEATRE SET-UP**
12 Fairlawn Close, Southgate
London N14 4JX          Tel: 020-8886 9572
Website: www.ts-u.co.uk

**THEATRE TOURS INTERNATIONAL**
Contact: Guy Masterson, Rebecca Vaughan
Millfield House & Theatre
Silver Street, Edmonton N18 1PJ          Tel: 020-8807 5770
Website: www.theatretoursinternational.com
e-mail: mail@theatretoursinternational.com

**THEATRE WORKOUT Ltd**
13A Stratheden Road
Blackheath, London SE3 7TH          Tel: 020-8144 2290
Website: www.theatreworkout.co.uk
e-mail: enquiries@theatreworkout.co.uk

**THEATREWORKS**
2 Hanley Road, Malvern Wells
Worcs WR14 4PQ          Tel: 01684 578342
Website: www.theatreworks.info
e-mail: info@theatreworks.info

**THIRD PARTY PRODUCTIONS Ltd**
87 St Thomas' Road, Hastings, East Sussex TN34 3LD
Website: www.thirdparty.org.uk
e-mail: gleave@thirdparty.org.uk
Mobile: 07768 694211          Mobile: 07768 694212

**TIATA FAHODZI**
AH 112 Aberdeen Centre
22-24 Highbury Grove
London N5 2EA          Tel/Fax: 020-7226 3800
Website: www.tiatafahodzi.com
e-mail: info@tiatafahodzi.com

**TOLD BY AN IDIOT**
Unit LF 1.7 Lafone House
The Leathermarket
11-13 Weston Street, London SE1 3ER
Website: www.toldbyanidiot.org
e-mail: info@toldbyanidiot.org
Fax: 020-7407 9002          Tel: 020-7407 4123

**TOPPER Jenny**
(Squaredeal Productions Ltd)
24 De Beauvoir Square, London N1 4LE
e-mail: jenny@jennytopper.com
Fax: 020-7275 7553          Tel: 020-7249 5966

**TOWER THEATRE COMPANY**
(Full-time non-professional)
St Bride Foundation
Bride Lane, London EC4Y 8EQ          Tel/Fax: 020-7353 5700
Website: www.towertheatre.org.uk
e-mail: info@towertheatre.freeserve.co.uk

**TREAGUS Andrew ASSOCIATES Ltd**
5th Floor, 35 Soho Square, London W1D 3QX
e-mail: admin@at-assoc.co.uk
Fax: 020-7851 0151          Tel: 020-7851 0150

**TREAGUS STONEMAN ASSOCIATES Ltd**
5th Floor, 35 Soho Square, London W1D 3QX
Website: www.treagusstoneman.com
e-mail: info@treagusstoneman.com
Fax: 020-7851 0151          Tel: 020-7851 0150

**TRESTLE THEATRE COMPANY**
(Visual/Physical Theatre, Music, Choreography, New
Writing)
Trestle Arts Base, Russet Drive, Herts, St Albans AL4 0JQ
Website: www.trestle.org.uk
e-mail: admin@trestle.org.uk
Fax: 01727 855558          Tel: 01727 850950

**TRICYCLE LONDON PRODUCTIONS**
269 Kilburn High Road, London NW6 7JR
Website: www.tricycle.co.uk
e-mail: admin@tricycle.co.uk
Fax: 020-7328 0795          Tel: 020-7372 6611

**TRIUMPH PROSCENIUM PRODUCTIONS Ltd**
1 Lumley Court, Off 402 The Strand
London WC2R 0NB          Tel: 020-7836 0186

**TURTLE KEY ARTS**
Ladbroke Hall, 79 Barlby Road, London W10 6AZ
Website: www.turtlekeyarts.org.uk
e-mail: admin@turtlekeyarts.org.uk
Fax: 020-8964 4080          Tel: 020-8964 5060

**TWO'S COMPANY**
244 Upland Road, London SE22 0DN
e-mail: graham@2scompanytheatre.co.uk
Fax: 020-8299 3714          Tel: 020-8299 4593

**UK ARTS INTERNATIONAL**
First Floor, 6 Shaw Street, Worcester WR1 3QQ
Website: www.ukarts.com
e-mail: janryan@ukarts.com
Fax: 01905 22868          Tel: 01905 26424

**UK PRODUCTIONS Ltd**
Churchmill House, Ockford Road
Godalming, Surrey GU7 1QY
Website: www.ukproductions.co.uk
e-mail: mail@ukproductions.co.uk
Fax: 01483 418486          Tel: 01483 423600

**UNRESTRICTED VIEW**
Above Hen & Chickens Theatre Bar
109 St Paul's Road, London N1 2NA          Tel: 020-7704 2001
Website: www.henandchickens.com
e-mail: james@henandchickens.com

**VANDER ELST Anthony PRODUCTIONS**
The Studio, 14 College Road, Bromley, Kent BR1 3NS
Fax: 020-8313 0443          Tel: 020-8466 5580

**VAYU NAIDU COMPANY**
Unit LFB2, Lafone House, The Leathermarket
11-13 Leathermarket Street
London SE1 3HN          Tel/Fax: 020-7720 0707
Website: www.vayunaiducompany.org.uk
e-mail: info@vayunaiducompany.org.uk

**VOLCANO THEATRE COMPANY Ltd**
Swansea Metropolitan University
Townhill Road, Swansea SA2 0UT
Website: www.volcanotheatre.co.uk
e-mail: volcano.tc@virgin.net
Fax: 01792 281282          Tel: 01792 281280

**WALKING FORWARD Ltd**
Studio 6, Aberdeen Centre
22-24 Highbury Grove
London N5 2EA          Tel/Fax: 020-7359 5249
Website: www.walkingforward.co.uk
e-mail: info@walkingforward.co.uk

**WALLACE Kevin Ltd**
10 (H) St Martin's Place, London WC2N 4JL
e-mail: info@kevinwallace.co.uk
Fax: 020-7836 9587          Tel: 020-7836 9586

**WAREHOUSE THEATRE COMPANY**
Dingwall Road, Croydon CR0 2NF
Website: www.warehousetheatre.co.uk
e-mail: info@warehousetheatre.co.uk
Fax: 020-8688 6699          Tel: 020-8681 1257

**WAX Kenny Ltd**
3rd Floor, 25 Lexington Street
London W1F 9AG
Website: www.kennywax.com
Fax: 020-3214 6063          Tel: 020-7437 1736

**WELDON Duncan C PRODUCTIONS Ltd**
1 Lumley Court, Off 402 The Strand
London WC2R 0NB          Tel: 020-7836 0186

**WEST END PROPERTY PRODUCTIONS**
29 Creek Road, Hayling Island
Hampshire PO11 9QZ
Website: www.soultraders-themusical.com
e-mail: directaccounts@btconnect.com
Fax: 023-9263 7264          Tel: 023-9263 7067

**WEYLAND Valerie**
29 Darby Crescent
Lower Sunbury TW16 5LB          Tel: 01932 886413
e-mail: valweyland@hotmail.com

**WHITALL Keith**
25 Solway, Hailsham
East Sussex BN27 3HB          Tel: 01323 844882

**WHITEHALL Michael**
10 Lower Common South
London SW15 1BP
e-mail: mwhitehall@msn.com
Fax: 020-8788 2340          Tel: 020-8785 3737

**WILDCARD THEATRE COMPANY**
Suite A, Swan House
White Hart Street
High Wycombe, Bucks HP11 2HL
Website: www.wildcardtheatre.org.uk
e-mail: admin@wildcardtheatre.org.uk
Fax: 07092 024967          Tel: 0870 7606158

**WILLS Newton MANAGEMENT**
The Studio, 29 Springvale Avenue
Brentford, Middlesex TW8 9QH
Website: www.newtonwills.com
e-mail: newtoncttg@aol.com
Fax: 00 33 468 218685          Mobile: 07989 398381

**YELLOW EARTH THEATRE**
3rd Floor, 20 Rupert Street
London W1D 6DF          Tel: 020-7734 5988
Website: www.yellowearth.org
e-mail: admin@yellowearth.org

**YOUNG VIC THEATRE**
66 The Cut, London SE1 8LZ
Website: www.youngvic.org
e-mail: info@youngvic.org
Fax: 020-7922 2802          Tel: 020-7922 2800

**1623 THEATRE COMPANY**
61 Haven Baulk Lane
Littleover, Derby DE23 4AD          Mobile: 07867 996959
Website: www.1623theatre.co.uk
e-mail: messages@1623theatre.co.uk

**ABERYSTWYTH ARTS CENTRE**
Penglais Campus, Aberystwyth, Ceredigion SY23 3DE
Website: www.aber.ac.uk/artscentre
e-mail: ggo@aber.ac.uk
Fax: 01970 622883          Tel: 01970 621512

**ADMIRATION THEATRE**
PO Box 50255, London EC3A 5WA          Tel: 0870 7651584
Website: www.admirationtheatre.com
e-mail: admiration@admirationtheatre.com

**AGE EXCHANGE THEATRE TRUST**
Contact: Suzanne Lockett (Administrator)
The Reminiscence Centre
11 Blackheath Village, London SE3 9LA
Website: www.age-exchange.org.uk
e-mail: administrator@age-exchange.org.uk
Fax: 020-8318 0060          Tel: 020-8318 9105

**ALTERNATIVE ARTS**
Top Studio, Montefiore Centre
Hanbury Street, London E1 5HZ
Website: www.alternativearts.co.uk
e-mail: info@alternativearts.co.uk
Fax: 020-7375 0484          Tel: 020-7375 0441

**ANGLES THEATRE The**
Alexandra Road, Wisbech, Cambridgeshire PE13 1HQ
e-mail: astromanis@anglestheatre.co.uk
Fax: 01945 581967          Tel: 01945 585587

**ASHTON GROUP THEATRE The**
The Old Fire Station, Abbey Road, Barrow-in-Furness
Cumbria LA14 1XH          Tel/Fax: 01229 430636
Website: www.ashtongroup.co.uk
e-mail: theashtongroup@btconnect.com

**ATTIC THEATRE COMPANY**
Mitcham Library, 157 London Road
Mitcham CR4 2YR          Tel: 020-8640 6800
Website: www.attictheatrecompany.com
e-mail: info@attictheatrecompany.com

**BANNER THEATRE**
Oaklands New Church Centre
Winleigh Road, Handsworth Wood
Birmingham B20 2HN          Tel: 0845 4581909
e-mail: info@bannertheatre.co.uk

**BECK THEATRE**
Grange Road, Hayes
Middlesex UB3 2UE          Tel: 020-8561 7506
Website: www.becktheatre.org.uk
e-mail: enquiries@becktheatre.org.uk

**BENT BACK TULIPS THEATRE COMPANY**
16 Brunel Close, Crystal Palace
London SE19 3AE          Mobile: 07971 159940
Website: www.bentbacktulips.com
e-mail: info@bentbacktulips.com

**BISHOPS GREAVES THEATRE**
Bishop Grosseteste University College
Newport, Lincoln, Lincolnshire, LN1 3DY          Tel: 01522 583761
Website: www.bishopg.ac.uk/theatre
e-mail: theatre@bishopg.ac.uk

**BLUEYED THEATRE PRODUCTIONS**
76 Barcombe Avenue
London SW2 3AZ          Mobile: 07957 215965
Website: www.blueyedtheatreproductions.co.uk
e-mail: info@blueyedtheatreproductions.co.uk

**BLUNDERBUS THEATRE COMPANY Ltd**
The Studio, Ollerton Primary School, Whinney Lane
New Ollerton, Newark, Notts NG22 9TH
Website: www.blunderbus.co.uk
e-mail: admin@blunderbus.co.uk
Fax: 01623 869559          Tel: 01623 835888

**BORDERLINE THEATRE COMPANY**
Contact: Eddie Jackson
North Harbour Street, Ayr KA8 8AA
Website: www.borderlinetheatre.co.uk
e-mail: enquiries@borderlinetheatre.co.uk
Fax: 01292 618685          Tel: 01292 281010

**BRUVVERS THEATRE COMPANY**
36 Lime Street, Ouseburn
Newcastle upon Tyne NE1 2PQ          Tel: 0191-261 9230
Website: www.bruvvers.co.uk
e-mail: mikeofbruvvers@hotmail.com

**CAPITAL ARTS YOUTH THEATRE**
Wyllyotts Centre, Darkes Lane, Potters Bar, Herts EN6 2HN
e-mail: capitalarts@btconnect.com
Mobile: 07885 232414          Tel/Fax: 020-8449 2342

**CARIB THEATRE COMPANY**
73 Lancelot Road, Wembley
Middlesex HA0 2AN          Tel/Fax: 020-8903 4592
e-mail: antoncarib@yahoo.co.uk

**CENTRE FOR PERFORMANCE RESEARCH**
The Foundry, Parry Williams, Penglais Campus SY23 3AJ
Website: www.thecpr.org.uk
e-mail: cprwww@aber.ac.uk
Fax: 01970 622132          Tel: 01970 622133

**CHAIN REACTION THEATRE COMPANY**
Three Mills Studios, Sugar House Yard
Sugar House Lane
London E15 2QS          Tel/Fax: 020-8534 0007
Website: www.chainreactiontheatre.co.uk
e-mail: mail@chainreactiontheatre.co.uk

**CHALKFOOT THEATRE ARTS**
Central Studios, 36 Park Place, Margate, Kent CT9 1LE
Website: www.chalkfoot.org.uk
e-mail: info@chalkfoot.org.uk
Fax: 01843 280088          Tel: 01843 280077

**CHATS PALACE ARTS CENTRE**
42-44 Brooksby's Walk
Hackney, London E9 6DF          Tel: 020-8533 0227
Website: www.chatspalace.com
e-mail: info@chatspalace.com

**CHERUB COMPANY LONDON The**
Office: 9 Park Hill, London W5 2JS
Website: www.cherub.org.uk
e-mail: casting@cherub.org.uk
Fax: 020-8248 0318          Tel/Fax: 020-8723 4358

**CHICKENSHED**
Chase Side, Southgate, London N14 4PE
Website: www.chickenshed.org.uk
e-mail: info@chickenshed.org.uk
Fax: 020-8292 0202          Tel: 020-8351 6161

**CHOL THEATRE**
Contact: Andrew Loretto (Director, Theatre &
International), Susan Burns (Director, Education &
Community)
Lawrence Batley Theatre, 8 Queen Street
Huddersfield, West Yorkshire HD1 2SP
Website: www.choltheatre.co.uk
e-mail: info@choltheatre.co.uk
Fax: 01484 425336          Tel: 01484 536008

**CLOSE FOR COMFORT THEATRE COMPANY**
34 Boleyn Walk, Leatherhead, Surrey KT22 7HU
Website: www.closeforcomforttheatre.co.uk
e-mail: close4comf@aol.com
Mobile: 07710 258290                    Tel: 01372 378613

**COLLUSION THEATRE COMPANY**
131 Renfrew Street, Glasgow G3 6QZ
Website: www.collusiontheatre.co.uk
e-mail: admin@collusiontheatre.co.uk
Fax: 0141-644 4163                    Tel: 0141-332 7001

**COMPLETE WORKS CREATIVE COMPANY Ltd The**
The Old Truman Brewery, 91 Brick Lane, London E1 6QL
Website: www.tcw.org.uk
e-mail: theatre@tcw.org.uk
Fax: 020-7247 7405                    Tel: 020-7377 0280

**CORNELIUS & JONES ORIGINAL PRODUCTIONS**
49 Carters Close, Sherington, Newport Pagnell
Buckinghamshire MK16 9NW          Tel/Fax: 01908 612593
Website: www.corneliusjones.com
e-mail: admin@corneliusjones.com

**CRAGRATS THEATRE**
The Mill, Dunford Road, Holmfirth, Huddersfield HD9 2AR
Website: www.cragrats.com
e-mail: info@cragrats.com
Fax: 01484 686212                    Tel: 01484 686451

**CUT-CLOTH THEATRE**
41 Beresford Road, Highbury
London N5 2HR                         Tel: 020-7503 4393

**DRAMA ZONE**
Arundel Town Hall, Arundel
West Sussex BN18 9AP                 Tel/Fax: 01903 889821
Website: www.dramazone.net
e-mail: admin@dramazone.net

**ELAN WALES**
(European Live Arts Network)
17 Douglas Buildings, Royal Stuart Lane
Cardiff CF10 5EL                     Tel/Fax: 029-2019 0077
Website: www.elanwales.org
e-mail: elanwales@ntlbusiness.com

**ELECTRIC CABARET**
107 High Street, Brackley, Northants NN13 7BN
Website: www.electricccabaret.co.uk
e-mail: richard@electriccabaret.co.uk
Mobile: 07714 089763                 Tel: 01280 700956

**EUROPEAN THEATRE COMPANY The**
39 Oxford Avenue, London SW20 8LS
Website: www.europeantheatre.co.uk
e-mail: admin@europeantheatre.co.uk
Fax: 020-8544 1999                   Tel: 020-8544 1994

**FOREST FORGE THEATRE COMPANY**
The Theatre Centre, Endeavour Park, Crow Arch Lane
Ringwood, Hampshire BH24 1SF
Website: www.forestforge.co.uk
e-mail: info@forestforge.co.uk
Fax: 01425 471158                    Tel: 01425 470188

**FOUND THEATRE**
The Byways, Church Street
Monyash, Derbyshire DE45 1JH         Tel: 01629 813083
Website: www.foundtheatre.org.uk
e-mail: found_theatre@yahoo.co.uk

**FOURSIGHT THEATRE Ltd**
Newhampton Arts Centre
Dunkley Street, Wolverhampton WV1 4AN
Website: www.foursighttheatre.co.uk
e-mail: admin@foursighttheatre.co.uk
Fax: 01902 428413                    Tel: 01902 714257

**FRANTIC THEATRE COMPANY**
32 Woodlane
Falmouth TR11 4RF                    Tel/Fax: 0870 1657350
Website: www.frantictheatre.com
e-mail: info@frantictheatre.com

**GALLEON THEATRE COMPANY Ltd**
Greenwich Playhouse, Greenwich BR Station Forecourt
189 Greenwich High Road, London SE10 8JA
Website: www.galleontheatre.co.uk
e-mail: alice@galleontheatre.co.uk
Fax: 020-8310 7276                   Tel: 020-8858 9256

**GOOD NIGHT OUT PRESENTS**
Contact: Adam Spreadbury-Maher (Artistic Director)
The Cock Tavern Theatre, 125 Kilburn High Road
London NW6 6JH                       Mobile: 07704 321469
Website: www.goodnightout.org.uk
e-mail: info@goodnightout.org.uk

**GRANGE ARTS CENTRE**
Rochdale Road, Oldham, Greater Manchester OL9 6EA
Website: www.grangeartsoldham.co.uk
e-mail: grangearts@oldham.ac.uk
Fax: 0161-785 4263                   Tel: 0161-785 4239

**GREASEPAINT ANONYMOUS**
(Youth Theatre Company)
4 Gallus Close, Winchmore Hill, London N21 1JR
e-mail: info@greasepaintanonymous.co.uk
Fax: 020-8882 9189                   Tel: 020-8886 2263

**HALL FOR CORNWALL**
Contact: Anna Coombs (Head of Projects)
Back Quay, Truro, Cornwall TR1 2LL
Website: www.hallforcornwall.co.uk
e-mail: annac@hallforcornwall.org.uk
Fax: 01872 260246                    Tel: 01872 321970

**HIJINX THEATRE**
(Touring Theatre Company, Community, Adults with
Learning Disabilities)
Wales Millennium Centre, Bute Place, Cardiff CF10 5AL
Website: www.hijinx.org.uk
e-mail: info@hijinx.org.uk
Fax: 029-2063 5621                   Tel: 029-2030 0331

**HISTORIA THEATRE COMPANY**
8 Cloudesley Square, London N1 0HT
Website: www.historiatheatre.com
e-mail: kateprice@lineone.net
Fax: 020-7278 4733                   Tel: 020-7837 8008

**ICON THEATRE**
The Brook Theatre, Old Town Hall
Chatham, Kent ME4 4SE                Tel: 01634 813179
Website: www.icontheatre.org.uk
e-mail: nancy@icontheatre.org.uk

**IMAGE MUSICAL THEATRE**
23 Sedgeford Road, Shepherd's Bush, London W12 0NA
Website: www.imagemusicaltheatre.co.uk
e-mail: brian@imagemusicaltheatre.co.uk
Fax: 020-8749 9294                   Tel: 020-8743 9380

**IMMEDIATE THEATRE**
1.2 Hoxton Works, 128 Hoxton Street, London N1 6SH
Website: www.immediate-theatre.com
e-mail: info@immediate-theatre.com
Fax: 020-7012 1682                   Tel: 020-7012 1677

**INOCENTE ART & FILM Ltd**
(Film, Multimedia, Music Videos & two Rock 'n' Roll
Musicals)
5 Denmans Lane, Haywards Heath
West Sussex RH16 2LA                 Mobile: 07973 518132
e-mail: tarascas@btopenworld.com

There are hundreds of theatres in the UK, varying dramatically in size and type. The theatre sections are organised under headings which best indicate a theatre's principal area of work. A summary of each of these is below.

## Alternative and Community

Many of these companies tour to Arts Centres, small and middle-scale theatres, and non-theatrical venues which do not have a resident company, or they may be commissioned to develop site specific projects. The term 'alternative' is sometimes used to describe work that is more experimental in style and execution.

## Children's, Young People's and TIE

The primary focus of these theatre companies is to reach younger audiences. They often tour to smaller theatres, schools and non-theatrical venues. Interactive teaching - through audience participation and workshops - is often a feature of their work.

## English Speaking Theatre Companies in Europe

These work principally outside of the UK. Some are based in one venue whilst others are touring companies. Their work varies enormously and includes Young People's Theatre, large scale musicals, revivals of classics and dinner theatre. Actors are employed either for an individual production or a 'season' of several plays.

## London Theatres

Larger theatres situated in the West End and Central London. A few are producing houses, but most are leased to Theatre Producers who take responsibility for putting together a company for a run of a single show. In such cases it is they and not the venue who cast productions (often with the help of Casting Directors). Alternatively, a production will open outside London and tour to Provincial Theatres, then subsequently, if successful, transfer to a London venue.

## Outer London, Fringe and Venues

Small and middle-scale theatres in Outer London and around the country. Some are producing houses, others are only available for hire. Many of the London venues have provided useful directions on how they may be reached by public transport.

## Provincial / Touring

Theatre Producers and other companies sell their ready-made productions to the Provincial/Touring Theatres, a list of larger venues outside London. A run in each theatre varies between a night and several weeks, but a week per venue for tours of plays is usual. Even if a venue is not usually a producing house, most Provincial Theatres and Arts Centres put on a family show at Christmas.

## Puppet Theatre Companies

Some Puppet Theatres are one-performer companies who literally create their own work from scratch. The content and style of productions varies enormously. For example, not all are aimed at children, and some are more interactive than others. Although we list a few theatres with Puppet Companies in permanent residence, this kind of work often involves touring. As with all small and middle scale touring, performers who are willing, and have the skills, to involve themselves with all aspects of company life are always more valuable.

## Repertory (Regional) Theatres

Theatres situated outside London which employ a resident company of actors (i.e. the 'repertory company') on a play-by-play basis or for a season of several plays. In addition to the main auditorium (usually the largest acting space) these theatres may have a smaller studio theatre attached, which will be home to an additional company whose focus is education or the production of new plays (see Children's, Young People's and TIE). In recent years the length of repertory seasons has become shorter; this means that a number of productions are no longer in-house. It is common for gaps in the performance calendar to be filled by tours mounted by Theatre Producers, other Repertory (Regional) Theatres and non-venue based production companies.

**ISOSCELES**
7 Amity Grove, Raynes Park
London SW20 0LQ                    Tel: 020-8946 3905
Website: www.isosceles.biz
e-mail: patanddave@isosceles.biz

**KOMEDIA**
44-47 Gardner Street, Brighton BN1 1UN
Website: www.komedia.co.uk
e-mail: info@komedia.co.uk
Fax: 01273 647102
                                   Tel: 01273 647101

**KORU THEATRE**
11 Clovelly Road, London W5 5HF       Tel: 020-8579 1029
Website: www.korutheatre.com
e-mail: info@korutheatre.com

**LADDER TO THE MOON ENTERTAINMENT**
Unit 105, Battersea Business Centre
99-109 Lavender Hill, London SW11 5QL    Tel: 020-7228 9700
e-mail: enquiries@laddertothemoon.co.uk

**LIVE THEATRE**
(New Writing)
Broad Chare, Quayside, Newcastle upon Tyne NE1 3DQ
Website: www.live.org.uk
e-mail: info@live.org.uk
Fax: 0191-232 2224
                                   Tel: 0191-261 2694

**LONDON ACTORS THEATRE COMPANY**
Unit 5A, Imex Bus Centre, Ingate Place, London SW8 3NS
e-mail: latchmere@fishers.org.uk
Fax: 020-7978 2631                 Tel: 020-7978 2620

**LONDON BUBBLE THEATRE COMPANY Ltd**
5 Elephant Lane, London SE16 4JD
Website: www.londonbubble.org.uk
e-mail: admin@londonbubble.org.uk
Fax: 020-7231 2366                 Tel: 020-7237 4434

**LONG OVERDUE THEATRE COMPANY The**
37 Barnfield Rise, Andover SP10 2UQ    Mobile: 07971 277479
Website: www.longoverdue.co.uk
e-mail: admin@longoverdue.co.uk

**LSW JUNIOR INTER-ACT**
PO Box 31855, London SE17 3XP     Tel/Fax: 020-7793 9755
Website: www.londonshakespeare.org.uk
e-mail: londonswo@hotmail.com

**LSW PRISON PROJECT**
PO Box 31855, London SE17 3XP     Tel/Fax: 020-7793 9755
Website: www.lswproductions.co.uk
e-mail: londonswo@hotmail.com

**LSW SENIOR RE-ACTION**
PO Box 31855, London SE17 3XP     Tel/Fax: 020-7793 9755
Website: www.lswproductions.co.uk
e-mail: londonswo@hotmail.com

**LUNG HA'S THEATRE COMPANY**
Eric Liddell Centre, 15 Morningside Rd, Edinburgh EH10 4DP
Website: www.lunghas.co.uk
e-mail: info@lunghas.co.uk
Fax: 0131-447 3290
                                   Tel: 0131-447 8496

**M6 THEATRE COMPANY**
Studio Theatre, Hamer CP School
Albert Royds Street, Rochdale OL16 2SU
Website: www.m6theatre.co.uk
e-mail: info@m6theatre.co.uk
Fax: 01706 712601                  Tel: 01706 355898

**MADDERMARKET THEATRE**
(Resident Community Theatre Company & Small-Scale
Producing & Receiving House)
St John's Alley, Norwich NR2 1DR
Website: www.maddermarket.co.uk
e-mail: mmtheatre@btconnect.com
Fax: 01603 661357                  Tel: 01603 626560

**MAGIC HAT PRODUCTIONS**
Brookslee, Brookshill Drive
Harrow HA3 6SB                     Mobile: 07769 560991
Website: www.magichat-productions.com
e-mail: general@magichat-productions.com

**MANCHESTER ACTORS COMPANY**
PO Box 54, Manchester M60 7AB        Tel: 0161-227 8702
Website: www.manactco.org.uk
e-mail: manactco@aol.com

**MAVERICK THEATRE COMPANY Ltd**
12 Lydney Grove, Northfield, Birmingham
West Midlands B31 1RB
Website: www.mavericktheatre.co.uk
e-mail: info@mavericktheatre.co.uk
Mobile: 07531 138248
                                   Tel: 0121-444 0933

**MAYA PRODUCTIONS Ltd**
156 Richmond Road
London E8 3HN                   Tel/Fax: 020-7923 0675
Website: www.mayaproductions.co.uk
e-mail: mayachris@aol.com

**MIKRON THEATRE COMPANY Ltd**
Marsden Mechanics, Peel Street
Marsden, Huddersfield HD7 6BW        Tel: 01484 843701
Website: www.mikron.org.uk
e-mail: admin@mikron.org.uk

**MONTAGE THEATRE ARTS**
Contact: Judy Gordon (Artistic Director)
The Albany, Douglas Way
London SE8 4AG                       Tel: 020-8692 7007
Website: www.montagetheatre.com
e-mail: office@montagetheatre.com

**NATURAL THEATRE COMPANY**
(Street Theatre, Touring, Corporate)
Widcombe Institute, Widcombe Hill, Bath BA2 6AA
Website: www.naturaltheatre.co.uk
e-mail: info@naturaltheatre.co.uk
Fax: 01225 442555                  Tel: 01225 469131

**NET CURTAINS THEATRE COMPANY**
Contact: Claire Farrington (Artistic Director)
Scurms, Rye Road, Sandhurst
Kent TN18 5PQ                      Mobile: 07968 564687
Website: www.netcurtains.org
e-mail: claire@netcurtains.org

**NETTLEFOLD The**
West Norwood Library Centre
1 Norwood High Street
London SE27 9JX                     Tel: 020-7926 8070
e-mail: thenettlefold@lambeth.gov.uk

**NEW PERSPECTIVES THEATRE COMPANY**
(Regional/National New Writing Touring Theatre)
Park Lane Business Centre, Park Lane
Basford, Nottinghamshire NG6 0DW     Tel: 0115-927 2334
Website: www.newperspectives.co.uk
e-mail: info@newperspectives.co.uk

**NEWFOUND THEATRE COMPANY**
18 India House, 73 Whitworth Street, Manchester M1 6LG
Website: www.newfoundtheatre.com
e-mail: newfoundtheatre@gmail.com

**NORTH COUNTRY THEATRE**
3 Rosemary Lane, Richmond
North Yorkshire DL10 4DP             Tel: 01748 825288
Website: www.northcountrytheatre.com
e-mail: office@northcountrytheatre.com

**NORTHERN STAGE (THEATRICAL PRODUCTIONS) Ltd**
Barras Bridge, Newcastle upon Tyne NE1 7RH
Website: www.northernstage.co.uk
e-mail: info@northernstage.co.uk
Fax: 0191-261 8093                   Tel: 0191-232 3366

**NORTHUMBERLAND THEATRE COMPANY (NTC)**
(Touring Regionally & Nationally)
The Playhouse, Bondgate Without
Alnwick, Northumberland NE66 1PQ
Website: www.northumberlandtheatre.co.uk
e-mail: admin@northumberlandtheatre.co.uk
Fax: 01665 605837      Tel: 01665 602586

**NUFFIELD THEATRE**
(Touring & Projects)
University Road, Southampton SO17 1TR
Website: www.nuffieldtheatre.co.uk
e-mail: annie.reilly@nuffieldtheatre.co.uk
Fax: 023-8031 5511      Tel: 023-8031 5500

**OLD TYME PLAYERS THEATRE COMPANY**
(Music Hall, Revues - Locally Based)
35 Barton Court Avenue
Barton on Sea, Hants BH25 7EP      Tel: 01425 612830
Website: www.oldetymeplayers.co.uk
e-mail: oldetymeplayers@tiscali.co.uk

**ONATTI PRODUCTIONS**
9 Field Close, Warwick
Warwickshire CV34 4QD
Website: www.onatti.co.uk
e-mail: info@onatti.co.uk
Fax: 0870 1643629      Tel: 01926 495220

**OPEN STAGE PRODUCTIONS**
49 Springfield Road, Moseley
Birmingham B13 9NN      Tel/Fax: 0121-777 9086
e-mail: info@openstage.co.uk

**ORMSGARD! DARK AGES THEATRE**
12 Carleton Close
Great Yeldham, Essex CO9 4QJ      Tel: 01787 238257
Website: www.ormsgard.org
e-mail: pete@gippeswic.demon.co.uk

**OXFORDSHIRE TOURING THEATRE COMPANY**
The Annexe, SS Mary & John School
Meadow Lane, Oxford OX4 1TJ
Website: www.oxfordshiretheatrecompany.co.uk
e-mail: info@oxfordshiretheatrecompany.co.uk
Fax: 01865 247266      Tel: 01865 249444

**PASCAL THEATRE COMPANY**
35 Flaxman Court, Flaxman Terrace
Bloomsbury, London WC1H 9AR      Tel: 020-7383 0920
Website: www.pascal-theatre.com
e-mail: pascaltheatreco@aol.com

**PAUL'S THEATRE COMPANY**
Ardleigh House, 42 Ardleigh Green Road
Hornchurch, Essex RM11 2LG      Tel: 01708 447123
Website: www.paulstheatreschool.com
e-mail: info@paulstheatreschool.com

**PEOPLE'S THEATRE COMPANY The**
12E High Street, Egham
Surrey TW20 9EA      Tel: 01784 470439
Website: www.ptc.org.uk
e-mail: admin@ptc.org.uk

**PHANTOM CAPTAIN The**
618B Finchley Road
London NW11 7RR      Tel: 020-8455 4564
Website: www.phantomcaptain.netfirms.com
e-mail: lambhorn@gmail.com

**PLAYTIME THEATRE COMPANY**
18 Bennells Avenue
Whitstable, Kent CT5 2HP
Website: www.playtimetheatre.co.uk
e-mail: playtime@dircon.co.uk
Fax: 01227 266648      Tel: 01227 266272

**POWERHOUSE THEATRE COMPANY**
Castle Arch, Quarry Street, Guildford, Surrey GU1 3SX
Website: www.powerhousetheatre.co.uk
e-mail: geoff@powerhousetheatre.co.uk
Mobile: 07949 821567      Tel: 01483 444787

**PRIME PRODUCTIONS**
54 Hermiston Village
Currie EH14 4AQ      Tel/Fax: 0131-449 4055
Website: www.primeproductions.co.uk
e-mail: primeproductions@talktalk.net

**PROTEUS THEATRE COMPANY**
(Multimedia and Cross-art Form Work)
Queen Mary's College, Cliddesden Road, Basingstoke
Hampshire RG21 3HF      Tel: 01256 354541
Website: www.proteustheatre.com
e-mail: info@proteustheatre.com

**PURSUED BY A BEAR PODUCTIONS**
Farnham Maltings, Bridge Square
Farnham GU9 7QR      Tel: 01252 745445
Website: www.pursuedbyabear.co.uk
e-mail: pursuedbyabear@yahoo.co.uk

**Q20 THEATRE COMPANY**
19 Wellington Crescent, Shipley
West Yorkshire BD18 3PH      Tel: 0845 1260632
e-mail: info@q20theatre.co.uk

**QUICKSILVER THEATRE**
The Glasshouse, 4 Enfield Road, London N1 5AZ
Website: www.quicksilvertheatre.org
e-mail: talktous@quicksilvertheatre.org
Fax: 020-7254 3119      Tel: 020-7241 2942

**RIDING LIGHTS THEATRE COMPANY**
Friargate Theatre, Lower Friargate, York YO1 9SL
Website: www.ridinglights.org
e-mail: info@rltc.org
Fax: 01904 651532      Tel: 01904 655317

**SALTMINE THEATRE COMPANY**
61 The Broadway, Dudley DY1 3EB      Tel: 01384 454807
Website: www.saltminetrust.org.uk
e-mail: creative@saltmine.org

**SCRATCH PRODUCTIONS**
64 York Road, Bridgwater
Somerset TA6 6CE      Tel: 01278 422681
Website: www.scratchproductions.org.uk
e-mail: markscott.ison@yahoo.co.uk

**SPANNER IN THE WORKS**
PO Box 239, Sidcup DA15 0DP
Website: www.spannerintheworks.org.uk
e-mail: info@spannerintheworks.org.uk
Mobile: 07850 313986      Tel: 020-7193 7995

**SPARE TYRE THEATRE COMPANY**
Contact: Bonnie Mitchell (General Manager)
(Community Drama & Music Projects)
Hampstead Town Hall, 213 Haverstock Hill
London NW3 4QP      Tel/Fax: 020-7419 7007
Website: www.sparetyre.org
e-mail: info@sparetyre.org

**SPECTACLE THEATRE**
Coleg Morgannwg Rhondda
Llwynypia, Tonypandy CF40 2TQ
Website: www.spectacletheatre.co.uk
e-mail: info@spectacletheatre.co.uk
Fax: 01443 439640      Tel: 01443 430700

**SPONTANEITY SHOP The**
85-87 Bayham St., London NW1 0AG      Tel: 020-7788 4080
Website: www.the-spontaneity-shop.com
e-mail: info@the-spontaneity-shop.com

**STABLES GALLERY & ARTS CENTRE**
Gladstone Park, Dollis Hill Lane
London NW2 6HT                      Tel: 020-8452 8655
Website: www.brentarts.org.uk
e-mail: stablesgallery@msn.com

**TAG CITIZENS**
Citizens' Theatre, 119 Gorbals Street
Glasgow G5 9DS
Website: www.tag-theatre.co.uk
e-mail: info@tag-theatre.co.uk
Fax: 0141-429 7374                  Tel: 0141-429 5561

**TAKING FLIGHT THEATRE COMPANY**
79 Kings Road, Canton
Cardiff CF11 9DB                    Tel: 029-2064 5505
Website: www.takingflighttheatre.com
e-mail: takingflighttheatre@yahoo.co.uk

**TARA ARTS GROUP**
356 Garratt Lane, London SW18 4ES
Website: www.tara-arts.com
e-mail: tara@tara-arts.com
Fax: 020-8870 9540                  Tel: 020-8333 4457

**THEATR POWYS**
The Drama Centre
Tremont Road
Llandrindod Wells, Powys LD1 5EB
Website: www.theatrpowys.co.uk
e-mail: theatr.powys@powys.gov.uk
Fax: 01597 824381                   Tel: 01597 824444

**THEATRE & Ltd**
Church Hall
St James Road, Marsh
Huddersfield HD1 4QA
Website: www.theatreand.com
e-mail: cmitchell@theatreand.com
Fax: 01484 532962                   Tel: 01484 532967

**THEATRE IN EDUCATION TOURS (TIE TOURS)**
PO Box 433, Weston Super Mare
Somerset BS24 0WY                   Tel: 01934 815163
Website: www.actionwork.com
e-mail: admin@actionwork.com

**THEATRE IS, ...**
The Innovation Centre, College Lane
Hatfield AL10 9AB                   Tel: 01707 281100
Website: www.theatreis.org
e-mail: info@theatreis.org

**THEATRE OF LITERATURE The**
(Dramatised Readings)
51 The Cut, London SE1 8LF          Tel: 020-7633 0599
e-mail: info@calderpublications.com

**THEATRE PECKHAM**
Havil Street, London SE5 7SD        Tel: 020-7708 5401
Website: www.theatrepeckham.co.uk
e-mail: admin@theatrepeckham.co.uk

**THEATRE WORKSHOP**
34 Hamilton Place
Edinburgh EH3 5AX
Website: www.theatre-workshop.com
Fax: 0131-220 0112                  Tel: 0131-225 7942

**TIME OF OUR LIVES MUSIC THEATRE Ltd**
5 Monkhams Drive
Woodford Green
Essex IG8 0LG                       Tel/Fax: 020-8505 3197
Website: www.toolmusictheatre.co.uk
e-mail: dympna@toolmusictheatre.co.uk

**TOBACCO FACTORY THEATRE**
Raleigh Road, Southville
Bristol BS3 1TF                     Tel: 0117-902 0345
Website: www.tobaccofactorytheatre.com
e-mail: theatre@tobaccofactory.com

**TRICYCLE THEATRE**
269 Kilburn High Road
London NW6 7JR
Website: www.tricycle.co.uk
e-mail: admin@tricycle.co.uk
Fax: 020-7328 0795                  Tel: 020-7372 6611

**WAREHOUSE THEATRE COMPANY**
Dingwall Road
Croydon CR0 2NF
Website: www.warehousetheatre.co.uk
e-mail: info@warehousetheatre.co.uk
Fax: 020-8688 6699                  Tel: 020-8681 1257

**WIGAN PIER THEATRE COMPANY**
Wigan Leisure & Culture Trust
The Stables
Haigh Hall, Wigan
Lancashire WN2 1PE                  Tel: 01942 486919
Website: www.wclt.org/wptc
e-mail: mpj.green@@wlct.org

**WINCHESTER HAT FAIR, FESTIVAL OF STREET THEATRE**
5A Jewry Street, Winchester
Hampshire SO23 8RZ                  Tel: 01962 849841
Website: www.hatfair.co.uk
e-mail: info@hatfair.co.uk

**WOMEN & THEATRE BIRMINGHAM Ltd**
220 Moseley Road
Highgate, Birmingham B12 0DG
e-mail: info@womenandtheatre.co.uk
Fax: 0121-446 4280                  Tel: 0121-440 4203

**Y TOURING THEATRE COMPANY**
One KX, 120 Cromer Street
London WC1H 8BS
Website: www.ytouring.org.uk
e-mail: d.jackson@ytouring.org.uk
Fax: 020-7520 3099                  Tel: 020-7520 3092

**YELLOW EARTH THEATRE**
3rd Floor, 20 Rupert Street
London W1D 6DF                      Tel: 020-7734 5988
Website: www.yellowearth.org
e-mail: admin@yellowearth.org

**YORICK INTERNATIONALIST THEATRE ENSEMBLE**
(Yorick Theatre & Film)
4 Duval Court
36 Bedfordbury
Covent Garden
London WC2N 4DQ                     Tel/Fax: 020-7836 7637
e-mail: yorickx@hotmail.com

**YOUNG VIC THEATRE**
66 The Cut, London SE1 8LZ
Website: www.youngvic.org
e-mail: info@youngvic.org
Fax: 020-7922 2801                  Tel: 020-7922 2800

**ZIP THEATRE**
Newhampton Arts Centre
Dunkley Street
Wolverhampton WV1 4AN
Website: www.ziptheatre.co.uk
e-mail: admin@ziptheatre.co.uk
Fax: 01902 572251                   Tel: 01902 572250

**ACTION TRANSPORT THEATRE**
(New Writing, Professional Production for, by and with Young People)
Whitby Hall, Stanney Lane
Ellesmere Port, Cheshire CH65 9AE          Tel: 0151-357 2120
Website: www.actiontransporttheatre.org
e-mail: info@actiontransporttheatre.org

**ACTIONWORK**
(Theatre & Film Productions with Young People)
PO Box 433, Weston-super-Mare
Somerset BS24 0WY          Tel: 01934 815163
Website: www.actionwork.com
e-mail: admin@actionwork.com

**ARTY-FACT THEATRE COMPANY Ltd**
18 Weston Lane, Crewe, Cheshire CW2 5AN
Website: www.arty-fact.co.uk
Fax: 07020 982098          Tel: 07020 962096

**ASHCROFT YOUTH THEATRE**
Ashcroft Academy of Dramatic Art, Malcolm Primary
School, Malcolm Road, Penge, London SE20 8RH
Website: www.ashcroftacademy.com
e-mail: geraldi.gillma@btconnect.com
Mobile: 07799 791586          Tel: 0844 8005328

**BARKING DOG THEATRE COMPANY**
14 Leaside Mansions
Fortis Green, London N10 3EB          Tel: 020-8883 0034
Website: www.barkingdog.co.uk
e-mail: mike@barkingdog.co.uk

**BECK THEATRE**
Grange Road, Hayes, Middlesex UB3 2UE
Website: www.becktheatre.org.uk
e-mail: enquiries@becktheatre.org.uk
BO: 020-8561 8371          Tel: 020-8561 7506

**BIG WOODEN HORSE THEATRE COMPANY Ltd**
30 Northfield Road
West Ealing, London W13 9SY          Tel: 020-8567 8431
Website: www.bigwoodenhorse.com
e-mail: info@bigwoodenhorse.com

**BIRMINGHAM STAGE COMPANY The**
Contact: Neal Foster (Actor/Manager), Philip Compton
(Executive Producer)
Suite 228, The Linen Hall
162 Regent Street, London W1B 5TB
Website: www.birminghamstage.net
e-mail: info@birminghamstage.net
Fax: 020-7437 3395          Tel: 020-7437 3391

**BITESIZE THEATRE COMPANY**
8 Green Meadows, New Broughton, Wrexham LL11 6SG
Website: www.bitesizetheatre.co.uk
e-mail: admin@bitesizetheatre.co.uk
Fax: 01978 756308          Tel: 01978 358320

**BLAH BLAH BLAH THEATRE COMPANY The**
The West Park Centre, Spen Lane
Leeds LS16 5BE          Tel: 0113-274 0030
Website: www.blahs.co.uk
e-mail: admin@blahs.co.uk

**BLUE MOON THEATRE COMPANY**
20 Sandpiper Road, Blakespool Park
Bridgwater, Somerset TA6 5QU          Tel/Fax: 01278 458253
Website: www.bluemoontheatre.co.uk
e-mail: info@bluemoontheatre.co.uk

**BLUNDERBUS THEATRE COMPANY Ltd**
The Studio, Ollerton Primary School
Whinney Lane, New Ollerton
Newark, Notts NG22 9TH
Website: www.blunderbus.co.uk
e-mail: admin@blunderbus.co.uk
Fax: 01623 869559          Tel: 01623 835888

**BOOSTER CUSHION THEATRE Ltd**
75 How Wood, Park Street, St Albans, Herts AL2 2RW
Website: www.booster-cushion.co.uk
e-mail: boostercushion@hotmail.com
Fax: 01727 872597          Tel: 01727 873874

**BORDERLINE THEATRE COMPANY**
Contact: Eddie Jackson (Producer)
North Harbour Street, Ayr KA8 8AA
Website: www.borderlinetheatre.co.uk
e-mail: enquiries@borderlinetheatre.co.uk
Fax: 01292 618685          Tel: 01292 281010

**BRIDGE HOUSE THEATRE**
(Visiting Companies, Professional & School Productions)
Warwick School Site, Myton Road, Warwick CV34 6PP
Website: www.bridgehousetheatre.co.uk
Fax: 01926 776476          Tel: 01926 776437

**BRIEF CANDLE THEATRE**
Chesterfield Studios, 44 Newbold Rd, Derbyshire S41 7PL
Website: www.briefcandle.co.uk
e-mail: office@briefcandle.co.uk          Tel: 01246 556161

**CAMBRIDGE TOURING THEATRE**
29 Worts Causeway
Cambridge CB1 8RJ          Tel/Fax: 01223 246533
Website: www.cambridgetouringtheatre.co.uk
e-mail: info@cambridgetouringtheatre.co.uk

**CAUGHT IN THE ACT**
Conygree House, Church St, Kingham, Oxfordshire OX7 6YA
Website: www.caughtintheact.co.uk
e-mail: cita@caughtintheact.co.uk    Tel/Fax: 01608 659555

**CHAIN REACTION THEATRE COMPANY**
Three Mills Studios, Sugar Hse Yard, Sugar House Lane
London E15 2QS          Tel/Fax: 020-8534 0007
Website: www.chainreactiontheatre.co.uk
e-mail: mail@chainreactiontheatre.co.uk

**CHALKFOOT THEATRE ARTS**
Contact: Philip Dart (Artistic Director)
Central Studios, 36 Park Place, Margate, Kent CT9 1LE
Website: www.chalkfoot.org.uk
e-mail: info@chalkfoot.org.uk          Tel: 01843 280077

**CHICKENSHED**
Contact: Mary Ward MBE (Artistic Director)
Chase Side, Southgate, London N14 4PE
Website: www.chickenshed.org.uk
e-mail: info@chickenshed.org.uk
BO: 020-8292 9222          Tel: 020-8351 6161

**CIRCUS MANIACS YOUTH CIRCUS**
(International Award-Winning Youth Circus Company)
Office 8A, The Kingswood Foundation
Britannia Road, Kingswood, Bristol BS15 8DB
e-mail: info@circusmaniacs.com
Mobile: 07977 247287          Tel/Fax: 0117-947 7042

**CLWYD THEATR CYMRU THEATRE FOR YOUNG PEOPLE**
Contact: Education Administator
Mold, Flintshire CH7 1YA
Website: www.ctctyp.co.uk
e-mail: education@clwyd-theatr-cymru.co.uk
Fax: 01352 701558          Tel: 01352 701575

**COMPLETE WORKS CREATIVE COMPANY Ltd The**
Contact: Phil Evans (Artistic Director)
The Old Truman Brewery, 91 Brick Lane, London E1 6QL
Website: www.tcw.org.uk
e-mail: info@tcw.org.uk
Fax: 020-7247 7405          Tel: 020-7377 0280

**CRAGRATS Ltd**
The Mill, Dunford Road, Holmfirth, Huddersfield HD9 2AR
Website: www.cragrats.com
e-mail: info@cragrats.com
Fax: 01484 686212          Tel: 01484 686451

**DAYLIGHT THEATRE**
66 Middle Street, Stroud
Gloucestershire GL5 1EA · Tel: 01453 763808

**DONNA MARIA COMPANY**
16 Bell Meadow, Dulwich, London SE19 1HP
Website: www.donna-marias-world.co.uk
e-mail: info@donnamariasworld.co.uk · Tel: 020-8670 7814

**DRAGON DRAMA**
(Theatre Company, Tuition, Workshops, Parties)
347 Hanworth Road, Surrey TW12 3EJ
Website: www.dragondrama.co.uk
e-mail: info@dragondrama.co.uk · Tel/Fax: 020-8255 8356

**EUROPA CLOWN THEATRE SHOW**
36 St Lukes Road
Tunbridge Wells, Kent TN4 9JH · Tel: 01892 537964
Website: www.clownseuropa.co.uk
e-mail: mike@heypresto.orangehome.co.uk

**EUROPEAN THEATRE COMPANY The**
39 Oxford Avenue, London SW20 8LS
Website: www.europeantheatre.co.uk
e-mail: admin@europeantheatre.co.uk
Fax: 020-8544 1999 · Tel: 020-8544 1994

**FUSE: NEW THEATRE FOR YOUNG PEOPLE**
Contact: Michael Quirke (General Manager), Andrew Raffle
(Artistic Producer)
13 Hope Street, Liverpool L1 9BH
Website: www.fusetheatre.com
e-mail: info@fusetheatre.com
Fax: 0151-707 9950 · Tel/Fax: 0151-708 0877

**FUTURES THEATRE COMPANY**
St John's Crypt, 73 Waterloo Road, London SE1 8UD
Website: www.futurestheatrecompany.co.uk
e-mail: info@futurestheatrecompany.co.uk
Fax: 020-7928 6724 · Tel: 020-7928 2832

**GAZEBO TIE COMPANY Ltd**
Bilston Town Hall, Church Street
Bilston, West Midlands WV14 0AP
Website: www.gazebotie.org
e-mail: info@gazebotie.org
Fax: 01902 497244 · Tel: 01902 497222

**GRANT Derek ORGANISATION Ltd**
13 Beechwood Road, West Moors, Dorset BH22 0BN
Website: www.derekgrant.co.uk
e-mail: admin@derekgrant.co.uk · Tel: 01202 855777

**GREENWICH & LEWISHAM YOUNG PEOPLES' THEATRE (GLYPT)**
The Tramshed, Woolwich New Road, London SE18 6ES
Website: www.glypt.co.uk
e-mail: postbox@glypt.co.uk
Fax: 020-8317 8595 · Tel: 020-8854 1316

**GROUP 64 YOUTH THEATRE**
Putney Arts Theatre, Ravenna Road, London SW15 6AW
Website: www.putneyartstheatre.org.uk
Fax: 020-8788 6940 · Tel: 020-8788 6935

**GWENT TIE COMPANY**
The Drama Centre Pen-y-pound
Abergavenny, Monmouthshire NP7 5UD
Website: www.gwenttheatre.com
e-mail: gwenttie@uwclub.net
Fax: 01873 853910 · Tel: 01873 853167

**HALF MOON YOUNG PEOPLE'S THEATRE**
43 White Horse Road, London E1 0ND
Website: www.halfmoon.org.uk
e-mail: admin@halfmoon.org.uk
Fax: 020-7709 8914 · Tel: 020-7265 8138

**HOXTON HALL YOUTH ARTS CENTRE**
130 Hoxton Street, London N1 6SH
Website: www.hoxtonhall.co.uk
e-mail: info@hoxtonhall.co.uk
Fax: 020-7729 3815 · Tel: 020-7684 0060

**IMAGE MUSICAL THEATRE**
23 Sedgeford Road, Shepherd's Bush, London W12 0NA
Website: www.imagemusicaltheatre.co.uk
e-mail: brian@imagemusicaltheatre.co.uk
Fax: 020-8749 9294 · Tel: 020-8743 9380

**IMPACT UNIVERSAL Ltd**
Hopebank House, Woodhead Road
Honley, Huddersfield HD9 6PF
Website: www.impactuniversal.com
e-mail: jill.beckwith@impactuniversal.com
Fax: 01484 660088 · Tel: 01484 660077

**INDIGO MOON THEATRE**
35 Waltham Court, Beverley
East Yorkshire HU17 9JF · Mobile: 07855 328552
Website: www.indigomoontheatre.com
e-mail: info@indigomoontheatre.com

**INTERPLAY THEATRE**
Armley Ridge Road, Leeds LS12 3LE
Website: www.interplayleeds.co.uk
e-mail: info@interplayleeds.co.uk · Tel: 0113-263 8556

**KINETIC THEATRE COMPANY Ltd**
Suite H, The Jubilee Centre
Lombard Road, Wimbledon, London SW19 3TZ
Website: www.kinetictheatre.co.uk
e-mail: paul@kinetictheatre.co.uk
Fax: 020-8286 2645 · Tel: 020-8286 2613

**KOMEDIA**
44-47 Gardner Street, Brighton BN1 1UN
Website: www.komedia.co.uk/brighton
e-mail: info@komedia.co.uk
BO: 01273 647100 · Tel: 01273 647101

**LEIGHTON BUZZARD YOUTH THEATRE**
6 Hillside Road
Leighton Buzzard LU7 3BU · Tel: 01525 377222
e-mail: sarah.cavender@tesco.net

**LITTLE ACTORS THEATRE COMPANY**
16 Hawthorn Road, Parkgate
Cheshire CH64 6SX · Tel: 0151-336 4302
e-mail: mail@littleactorstheatre.com

**M6 THEATRE COMPANY**
Studio Theatre, Hamer C. P. School
Albert Royds Street, Rochdale OL16 2SU
Website: www.m6theatre.co.uk
e-mail: info@m6theatre.co.uk
Fax: 01706 712601 · Tel: 01706 355898

**MAGIC CARPET THEATRE**
18 Church Street, Sutton-on-Hull HU7 4TS
Website: www.magiccarpettheatre.com
e-mail: admin@magiccarpettheatre.com
Fax: 01482 787362 · Tel: 01482 709939

**NATIONAL ASSOCIATION OF YOUTH THEATRES (NAYT)**
Arts Centre, Vane Terrace
Darlington, County Durham DL3 7AX
Website: www.nayt.org.uk
e-mail: nayt@btconnect.com
Fax: 01325 363313 · Tel: 01325 363330

**NATIONAL STUDENT DRAMA FESTIVAL**
Aberdeen Centre, 22-24 Highbury Grove, London N5 2DQ
Website: www.nsdf.org.uk
e-mail: admin@nsdf.org.uk · Tel: 020-7354 8070

**NATIONAL YOUTH MUSIC THEATRE The**
2-4 Great Eastern Street, London EC2A 3NW
Website: www.nymt.org.uk
e-mail: enquiries@nymt.org.uk
Fax: 0870 9033785 · Tel: 020-7422 8290

**NATIONAL YOUTH THEATRE OF GREAT BRITAIN**
443-445 Holloway Road, London N7 6LW
Website: www.nyt.org.uk
e-mail: info@nyt.org.uk
Fax: 020-7281 8246 · Tel: 020-7281 3863

**NETTLEFOLD The**
West Norwood Library Centre, 1 Norwood High Street
London SE27 9JX     Tel: 020-7926 8070
e-mail: thenettlefold@lambeth.gov.uk

**OILY CART**
(Create work for the under 5's and young people 3-19 with
complex disabilities or ASD)
Smallwood School Annexe
Smallwood Road, London SW17 0TW
Website: www.oilycart.org.uk
e-mail: oilies@oilycart.org.uk
Fax: 020-8672 0792     Tel: 020-8672 6329

**ONATTI PRODUCTIONS**
Contact: Andrew Bardwell (Artistic Director)
9 Field Close, Warwick, Warwickshire CV34 4QD
Website: www.onatti.co.uk
e-mail: info@onatti.co.uk
Fax: 0870 1643629     Tel: 01926 495220

**PANDEMONIUM TOURING PARTNERSHIP**
228 Railway Street
Cardiff CF24 2NJ     Tel: 029-2047 2060
e-mail: paul@pandemoniumtheatre.com

**PANDORA'S BOX THEATRE COMPANY**
(National Touring Young Children's Theatre)
43 Fallsbrook Road
London SW16 6DU     Tel/Fax: 020-8769 8710
Website: www.pandorasboxtheatre.co.uk
e-mail: info@pandorasboxtheatre.co.uk

**PAUL'S THEATRE COMPANY**
Ardleigh House, 42 Ardleigh Green Road
Hornchurch, Essex RM11 2LG     Tel: 01708 447123
Website: www.paulstheatreschool.com
e-mail: info@paulstheatreschool.com

**PIED PIPER COMPANY**
1 Lilian Place, Coxcombe Lane
Chiddingfold, Surrey GU8 4QA     Tel/Fax: 01428 684022
Website: www.piedpipertheatre.co.uk
e-mail: twpiedpiper@aol.com

**PILOT THEATRE**
York Theatre Royal, St Leonard's Place, York YO1 7HD
Website: www.pilot-theatre.com
e-mail: info@pilot-theatre.com
Fax: 01904 656378     Tel: 01904 635755

**PLAY HOUSE The**
(Language Alive!/Catalyst Theatre/Project)
Longmore Street, Birmingham B12 9ED
Website: www.theplayhouse.org.uk
e-mail: info@theplayhouse.org.uk
Fax: 0121-464 5713     Tel: 0121-464 5712

**PLAYTIME THEATRE COMPANY**
18 Bennells Avenue, Whitstable, Kent CT5 2HP
Website: www.playtimetheatre.co.uk
e-mail: playtime@dircon.co.uk
Fax: 01227 266648     Tel: 01227 266272

**POLKA THEATRE**
240 The Broadway, Wimbledon SW19 1SB
Website: www.polkatheatre.com
e-mail: admin@polkatheatre.com
Fax: 020-8545 8365     Tel: 020-8545 8320

**Q20 THEATRE COMPANY**
19 Wellington Crescent, Shipley, West Yorkshire BD18 3PH
e-mail: info@q20theatre.co.uk     Tel: 0845 1260632

**QUAKER YOUTH THEATRE**
Ground Floor, 1 The Lodge
1046 Bristol Road, Birmingham B29 6LJ
Website: www.leaveners.org
e-mail: qyt@leaveners.org
Fax: 0121-414 0090     Tel: 0121-414 0099

**QUANTUM THEATRE**
Contact: Michael Whitmore, Jessica Selous (Artistic
Directors)
The Old Button Factory
1-11 Bannockburn Road
Plumstead, London SE18 1ET     Tel: 020-8317 9000
Website: www.quantumtheatre.co.uk
e-mail: office@quantumtheatre.co.uk

**QUICKSILVER THEATRE COMPANY**
(National Touring - New Writing for the under 12's,
Participatory Outreach Projects)
4 Enfield Road, London N1 5AZ
Website: www.quicksilvertheatre.org
e-mail: talktous@quicksilvertheatre.org
Fax: 020-7254 3119     Tel: 020-7241 2942

**RAINBOW BIGBOTTOM & Co Ltd/**
**THE MR PANDA ADVENTURES**
The Studio, 1A Park View
Stanley Avenue, Chesham, Bucks HP5 2JF
Website: www.rainbowbigbottom.com
e-mail: laneatrainbows@aol.com
Mobile: 07778 106552     Tel: 01494 771029

**REDROOFS THEATRE COMPANY**
Contact: By Post
The Novello Theatre, Sunninghill
Nr Ascot, Berkshire SL5 9NE
Website: www.novellotheatre.co.uk

**ROUNDABOUT THEATRE IN EDUCATION**
Nottingham Playhouse
Wellington Circus, Nottingham NG1 5AF
e-mail: roundabout@nottinghamplayhouse.co.uk
Fax: 0115-947 5759     Tel: 0115-947 4361

**ROYAL & DERNGATE**
19-21 Guildhall Road, Northampton NN1 1DP
Website: www.royalandderngate.co.uk
e-mail: education@ntt.org     Tel: 01604 627566

**ROYAL COURT YOUNG WRITERS PROGRAMME**
(Playwriting Projects for Young People aged 13-25)
Royal Court Theatre, Sloane Square, London SW1W 8AS
Website: www.royalcourttheatre.com
e-mail: ywp@royalcourttheatre.com
Fax: 020-7565 5001     Tel: 020-7565 5050

**SCOTTISH YOUTH THEATRE**
The Old Sheriff Court
105 Brunswick Street, Glasgow G1 1TF
Website: www.scottishyouththeatre.org
e-mail: info@scottishyouththeatre.org
Fax: 0141-552 7615     Tel: 0141-552 3988

**SEAHORSE THEATRE & PARTY COMPANY**
Ealing House, 33 Hanger Lane, London W5 3HJ
e-mail: revampevents@aol.com     Tel: 020-8997 3355

**SHAKESPEARE 4 KIDZ THEATRE COMPANY The**
Drewshearne Barn
Crowhurst Lane End
Oxted, Surrey RH8 9NT
Website: www.shakespeare4kidz.com
e-mail: theatre@shakespeare4kidz.com
Fax: 01342 893754     Tel: 01342 894548

**SHAKESPEAREWORKS**
22 Chilswell Road, Oxford OX1 4PJ     Tel/Fax: 01865 241281
Website: www.shakespeareworks.co.uk
e-mail: info@shakespeareworks.co.uk

**SHARED EXPERIENCE YOUTH THEATRE**
13 Riverside House
27-29 Vauxhall Grove, London SW8 1SY
Website: www.sharedexperience.org.uk
e-mail: admin@sharedexperience.org.uk
Fax: 020-7735 0374     Tel: 020-7587 1596

**SHEFFIELD THEATRES**
Contact: Sue Burley (Education Administrator), Dan Bales (Chief Executive)
55 Norfolk Street, Sheffield S1 1DA
www.sheffieldtheatres.co.uk/creativedevelopmentprogramme
e-mail: info@sheffieldtheatres.co.uk
Fax: 0114-249 6003          Tel: 0114-249 5999

**SOLOMON THEATRE COMPANY**
Penny Black, High Street, Damerham, Fordingbridge
Hants SP6 3EU          Tel/Fax: 01725 518760
Website: www.solomon-theatre.co.uk
e-mail: office@solomon-theatre.co.uk

**SPECTACLE THEATRE**
Coleg Morgannwg, Rhondda
Llwynypia, Tonypandy CF40 2TQ
Website: www.spectacletheatre.co.uk
e-mail: info@spectacletheatre.co.uk
Fax: 01443 423080          Tel: 01443 430700

**STOPWATCH THEATRE COMPANY**
Unit 318 Solent Business Centre
Millbrook Road West, Southampton SO15 0HW
Website: www.stopwatchtheatre.com
e-mail: info@stopwatchtheatre.com          Tel: 023-8078 3800

**STORYTELLERS THEATRE COMPANY The**
Bridge Farm, 249 Hawes Side Lane, Blackpool FY4 4AA
Website: www.pendleproductions.co.uk
e-mail: admin@pendleproductions.co.uk
Fax: 01253 792930          Tel: 01253 839375

**SUPPORT ACT PRODUCTIONS**
Contact: Ian McCracken
243A Lynmouth Avenue, Morden
Surrey SM4 4RX          Tel: 0845 0940796
Website: www.supportact.co.uk
e-mail: info@supportact.co.uk

**TEAM PLAYERS THEATRE COMPANY**
Lingfield Countryside Centre
Mount Pleasant Way
Coulby Newham, Middlesbrough TS8 0XF
Website: www.teamplayerstheatre.com
e-mail: info@teamplayerstheatre.com
Fax: 01642 577121          Tel: 01642 592648

**THEATR IOLO Ltd**
The Old School Building, Cefn Road
Mynachdy, Cardiff CF14 3HS
Website: www.theatriolo.com
e-mail: info@theatriolo.com
Fax: 029-2052 2225          Tel: 029-2061 3782

**THEATRE & Ltd**
Church Hall, St James Road, Marsh, Huddersfield HD1 4QA
Website: www.theatreand.com
e-mail: cmitchell@theatreand.com
Fax: 01484 532962          Tel: 01484 532967

**THEATRE ALIBI**
(Adult & Young People)
Northcott Studio Theatre
Emmmanuel Road, Exeter EX4 1EJ          Tel/Fax: 01392 217315
Website: www.theatrealibi.co.uk
e-mail: info@theatrealibi.co.uk

**THEATRE CENTRE**
(National Touring & New Writing for Young Audiences)
Shoreditch Town Hall, 380 Old Street, London EC1V 9LT
Website: www.theatre-centre.co.uk
e-mail: admin@theatre-centre.co.uk
Fax: 020-7739 9741          Tel: 020-7729 3066

**THEATRE HULLABALOO**
(Formerly CTC Theatre)
Arts Centre, Vane Terrace
Darlington, County Durham DL3 7AX
Website: www.theatrehullabaloo.org.uk
e-mail: info@theatrehullabaloo.org.uk
Fax: 01325 369404          Tel: 01325 352004

**THEATRE IS.......**
The Innovation Centre
College Lane, Hatfield AL10 9AB
Website: www.theatreis.org
e-mail: info@theatreis.org          Tel: 01707 281100

**THEATRE NA N'OG**
Unit 3
Millands Road Industrial Estate
Neath SA11 1NJ
Website: www.theatr-nanog.co.uk
e-mail: drama@theatr-nanog.co.uk
Fax: 01639 647941          Tel: 01639 641771

**THEATRE WORKOUT Ltd**
13A Stratheden Road
Blackheath, London SE3 7TH          Tel: 020-8144 2290
Website: www.theatreworkout.co.uk
e-mail: enquiries@theatreworkout.co.uk

**TICKLISH ALLSORTS SHOW**
57 Victoria Road
Wilton, Salisbury, Wiltshire SP2 0DZ
Website: www.ticklishallsorts.co.uk
e-mail: garynunn@ntlworld.com          Tel/Fax: 01722 744949

**TIE ACTION WORK**
PO Box 433
Weston-Super-Mare
Somerset BS24 0WY
Website: www.actionwork.com
e-mail: admin@actionwork.com          Tel: 01934 815163

**TOURING TALES THEATRE COMPANY Ltd**
Suite 228 The Linen Hall
162 Regent Street, London W1B 5TB
Website: www.birminghamstage.net
e-mail: info@birminghamstage.net
Fax: 020-7437 3395          Tel: 020-7437 3391

**TRICYCLE THEATRE**
Contact: Gillian Christie (Education Director)
269 Kilburn High Road
London NW6 7JR          Tel/Fax: 020-7372 6611
Website: www.tricycle.co.uk
e-mail: education@tricycle.co.uk

**UNICORN THEATRE**
147 Tooley Street, London SE1 2HZ
Website: www.unicorntheatre.com
e-mail: admin@unicorntheatre.com
Fax: 020-7645 0550          Tel: 020-7645 0500

**WEST YORKSHIRE PLAYHOUSE**
(Touring Company)
Playhouse Square
Quarry Hill, Leeds LS2 7UP
e-mail: gail.mcintyre@wyp.org.uk          Tel: 0113-213 7225

**WIZARD THEATRE**
Contact: Leon Hamilton (Director), Emmy Bradbury (Company Manager)
175 Royal Crescent
Ruislip, Middlesex HA4 0PN
Website: www.wizardtheatre.co.uk
e-mail: admin@wizardtheatre.co.uk          Tel: 0800 5832373

**WYTHENSHAWE YOUTH THEATRE**
17 Kennett Road, Newall Green
Wythenshawe
Manchester, Lancashire M23 2XS          Tel: 0161-493 9160
Website: www.wythenshaweyouththeatre.piczo.com
e-mail: wythyyouththeatre@btinternet.com

**YOUNG SHAKESPEARE COMPANY**
Contact: Christopher Geelan & Sarah Gordon (Artistic Directors)
31 Bellevue Road
Friern Barnet, London N11 3ET
e-mail: youngshakespeare@mac.com
Fax: 020-8368 6713          Tel: 020-8368 4828

## AUSTRIA
VIENNA
**Vienna's English Theatre**
(See website for casting requirements), UK Representative:
VM Theatre Productions Ltd, 16 The Street, Ash Canterbury,
Kent CT3 2HJ     Tel/Fax: 01304 813330
Website: www.englishtheatre.at
Casting: Vanessa Mallatratt

## DENMARK
COPENHAGEN
**The English Theatre of Copenhagen**
London Toast Theatre, Kochsvej 18
DK-1812 Frb. C, Denmark     Tel: + 45 33 22 8686
Website: www.londontoast.dk
e-mail: mail@londontoast.dk
Artistic Director: Vivienne McKee
Administrator: Soren Hall

## FRANCE
PARIS
**ACT Company**
25 Avenue Mal Leclerc
92240 Malakoff, France     Tel: + 33 1 46 56 20 50
Website: www.actheatre.com
e-mail: andrew@actheatre.com
Artistic Director: Andrew Wilson
Administrator: Anne Wilson

## FRANCE
LYON
**Theatre From Oxford (Touring Europe & Beyond)**
B.P. 10, F-42750 St-Denis-de-Cabanne
e-mail: theatre.oxford@virgin.net
Contact: Robert Southam. By Post

## GERMANY
FRANKFURT AM MAIN
**The English Theatre Frankfurt**
Gallusanlage 7, 60329, Frankfurt am Main, Germany
Website: www.english-theatre.org
e-mail: mail@english-theatre.org
Fax: + 49 69 242 316 45     Tel: + 49 69 242 316 20
Artistic Director: Daniel John Nicolai
Casting: Amy Rycroft (See RYCROFT CASTING)

## GERMANY
HAMBURG
**The English Theatre of Hamburg**
Lerchenfeld 14, 22081 Hamburg, Germany
Website: www.englishtheatre.de
Fax: + 49 40 227 7927     Tel: + 49 40 227 7089
Contact: Robert Rumpf, Clifford Dean

## GERMANY
TOURING GERMANY
**White Horse Theatre**
Boerdenstrasse 17, 59494 Soest-Muellingsen, Germany
Website: www.whitehorse.de
e-mail: theatre@whitehorse.de
Fax: + 49 29 21 33 93 36     Tel: + 49 29 21 33 93 39
Contact: Peter Griffith, Michael Dray

## HUNGARY
BUDAPEST
**Merlin International Theatre**
Gerloczy Utca 4
1052 Budapest, Hungary
Website: www.merlinszinhaz.hu
e-mail: angol@merlinszinhaz.hu
Fax: + 36 1 2660904     Tel: + 36 1 3179338
Contact: Laszlo Magacs

## ICELAND
REYKJAVIK
**Light Nights - The Summer Theatre**
The Travelling Theatre
Baldursgata 37
IS-101 Reykjavik, Iceland     Tel: + 354 551 9181
Website: www.lightnights.com
Artistic Director: Kristine G Magnus

## ITALY
SANREMO
**Theatrino & Melting Pot Theatre - ACLE**
Via Roma 54, 18038 Sanremo (IM), Italy
Website: www.acle.org
e-mail: info@acle.org
Fax: + 39 0184 509996     Tel: + 39 0184 506070

## SWITZERLAND
TANNAY
**Simply Theatre**
Chemin des Couleuvres 8B
1295 Tannay, Switzerland
Website: www.simplytheatre.com
e-mail: info@simplytheatre.com
Fax: + 41 22 8600519     Tel: + 41 22 8600518

## UNITED KINGDOM
WARWICK
**Onatti Productions**
9 Field Close, Warwick, Warwickshire CV34 4QD
Website: www.onatti.co.uk
e-mail: info@onatti.co.uk
Fax: 0870 1643629     Tel: 01926 495220
Contact: Andrew Bardwell

**ADELPHI**
Strand, London WC2E 7NN
Manager:      -------------------
Stage Door:   020-7836 1166
Box Office:   0870 8955598

**ALDWYCH**
Aldwych, London WC2B 4DF
Manager:      020-7836 5537
Stage Door:   020-7836 5537
Box Office:   020-7379 3367
Website:      www.aldwychtheatre.co.uk

**ALMEIDA**
Almeida Street, London N1 1TA
Manager:      020-7288 4900
Stage Door:   -------------------
Box Office:   020-7359 4404

**AMBASSADORS**
West Street, London WC2H 9ND
Manager:      020-7395 5410
Stage Door:   020-7395 5400
Box Office:   020-7395 5405
Website:      www.theambassadorstheatre.co.uk
e-mail:       boxofficemanager@theambassadorstheatre.co.uk

**APOLLO**
Shaftesbury Avenue, London W1D 7EZ
Manager:      020-7494 5834
Stage Door:   020-7851 2711
Box Office:   0844 4124658
Website:      www.nimaxtheatres.com
e-mail::      enquiries@nimaxtheatres.com

**APOLLO VICTORIA**
17 Wilton Road, London SW1V 1LG
Manager:      020-7834 6318
Stage Door:   020-7834 6318
Box Office:   0870 4000650
Website:      www.apollovictorialondon.org.uk

**ARTS**
6-7 Great Newport Street, London WC2H 7JB
Manager:      020-7836 2132
Stage Door:   020-7836 2132
Box Office:   0845 0175584
Website:      www.artstheatrelondon.com
e-mail:       info@artstheatrewestend.com

**BARBICAN**
Barbican, London EC2Y 8DS
Manager:      020-7628 3351
Stage Door:   020-7628 3351
Box Office:   0845 1207511
Website:      www.barbican.org.uk

**BLOOMSBURY**
15 Gordon Street, London WC1H 0AH
Manager:      020-7679 2777
Stage Door:   020-7679 2922
Box Office:   020-7388 8822
Website:      www.thebloomsbury.com
e-mail:       blooms.theatre@ucl.ac.uk

**BUSH**
Shepherds Bush Green, London W12 8QD
Manager:      020-8743 3584
Stage Door:   -------------------
Box Office:   020-8743 5050
Website:      www.bushtheatre.co.uk
e-mail:       info@bushtheatre.co.uk

**CAMBRIDGE**
Earlham Street, Seven Dials
Covent Garden, London WC2H 9HU
Manager:      020-7850 8711
Stage Door:   020-7850 8710
Box Office:   020-7850 8715
Website:      www.cambridgetheatre.co.uk

**COLISEUM (English National Opera)**
St Martin's Lane, London WC2N 4ES
Manager:      020-7836 0111
Stage Door:   020-7845 9397
Box Office:   0870 1450200
Website:      www.eno.org

**COMEDY**
Panton Street, London SW1Y 4DN
Manager:      020-7321 5310
Stage Door:   020-7321 5300
Box Office:   0870 0606637
e-mail:       comedymanager@theambassadors.com

**CRITERION**
2 Jermyn Street, Piccadilly, London SW1Y 4XA
Manager:      020-7839 8811
Stage Door:   020-7839 8811
Box Office:   0844 8471778
Website:      www.criterion-theatre.co.uk
e-mail:       admin@criterion-theatre.co.uk

**DOMINION**
268-269 Tottenham Court Road, London W1T 7AQ
Manager:      -------------------
Stage Door:   020-7927 0900
Box Office:   0870 7490587
Website:      www.dominiontheatrelondon.org.uk

**DONMAR WAREHOUSE**
41 Earlham Street, London WC2H 9LX
Manager:      020-7240 4882
Stage Door:   020-7438 9200
Box Office:   0870 060 6624
Website:      www.donmarwarehouse.com
e-mail:       office@donmarwarehouse.com

**DRURY LANE**
Theatre Royal
Catherine Street, London WC2B 5JF
Manager:      -------------------
Stage Door:   020-7850 8790
Box Office:   020-7494 5060
Website:      www.rutheatres.com

**DUCHESS**
Catherine Street, London WC2B 5LA
Manager:      020-7632 9601
Stage Door:   020-7632 9600
Box Office:   0844 4124659
e-mail:       enquiries@nimaxtheatres.com

**DUKE OF YORK'S**
St Martin's Lane, London WC2N 4BG
Manager:      020-7836 4615
Stage Door:   020-7836 4615
Box Office:   0870 0606623

**FORTUNE**
Russell Street
Covent Garden, London WC2B 5HH
Manager:      020-7010 7901
Stage Door:   020-7010 7901
Box Office:   0870 0606626

**GARRICK**
2 Charing Cross Road, London WC2H 0HH
Manager:       020-7520 5692
Stage Door: 020-7520 5690
Box Office:   020-7520 5693
e-mail:         enquiries@nimaxtheatres.com

**GIELGUD**
Shaftesbury Avenue, London W1D 6AR
Manager:       020-7292 1321
Stage Door: 020-7292 1320
Box Office:   020-7812 7480

**HACKNEY EMPIRE**
291 Mare Street, London E8 1EJ
Manager:       020-8510 4500
Stage Door: 020-8510 4500
Box Office:   020-8985 2424
Website:      www.hackneyempire.co.uk
e-mail:         info@hackneyempire.co.uk

**HAMMERSMITH APOLLO**
Queen Caroline Street, London W6 9QH
Manager:       -------------------
Stage Door: -------------------
Box Office:   0844 8444748
Website:      www.hammersmithapollo.net

**HAMPSTEAD**
Eton Avenue
Swiss Cottage, London NW3 3EU
Manager:       020-7449 4200
Stage Door: -------------------
Box Office:   020-7722 9301
Website:      www.hampsteadtheatre.com
e-mail:         info@hampsteadtheatre.com

**HER MAJESTY'S**
Haymarket, London SW1Y 4QL
Manager:       020-7850 8750
Stage Door: 020-7850 8750
Box Office:   0844 4122707

**LONDON PALLADIUM**
Argyll Street, London W1F 7TF
Manager:       020-7850 8777
Stage Door: 020-7850 8770
Box Office:   0870 8901108

**LYCEUM**
21 Wellington Street
London WC2E 7RQ
Manager:       020-7420 8100
Stage Door: 020-7420 8100
Box Office:   0844 8440005

**LYRIC**
29 Shaftesbury Avenue
London W1D 7ES
Manager:       020-7494 5840
Stage Door: 020-7494 5841
Box Office:   0844 4124661
e-mail:         enquiries@nimaxtheatres.com

**LYRIC HAMMERSMITH**
King Street, London W6 0QL
Manager:       -------------------
Stage Door: -------------------
Box Office:   0871 2211722
Website:      www.lyric.co.uk
e-mail:         enquiries@lyric.co.uk

**NATIONAL**
South Bank, Upper Ground, London SE1 9PX
Manager:       020-7452 3280
Stage Door: 020-7452 3333
Box Office:   020-7452 3000
Website:      www.nationaltheatre.org.uk

**NEW LONDON**
Drury Lane, London WC2B 5PW
Manager:       020-7242 9802
Stage Door: 020-7242 9802
Box Office:   0870 8900141
e-mail:         cuqui.rivera@reallyuseful.co.uk

**NEW PLAYERS**
The Arches, Off Villiers Street, London WC2N 6NG
Manager:       020-7930 5868
Stage Door: -------------------
Box Office:   -------------------
Website:      www.newplayerstheatre.com
e-mail:         info@newplayerstheatre.com

**NOEL COWARD (Previously ALBERY)**
85 St Martin's Lane, London WC2N 4AU
Manager:       020-7759 8011
Stage Door: 020-7759 8010
Box Office:   0844 482 5140

**NOVELLO (Previously STRAND)**
Aldwych, London WC2B 4LD
Manager:       020-7759 9611
Stage Door: 020-7759 9611
Box Office:   0844 4825171

**OLD VIC**
The Cut, London SE1 8NB
Manager:       020-7928 2651
Stage Door: 020-7928 2651
Box Office:   0870 0606628
Website:      www.oldvictheatre.com
e-mail:         ovtcadmin@oldvictheatre.com

**PALACE**
Shaftesbury Avenue, London W1D 5AY
Manager:       020-7434 0088
Stage Door: 020-7434 0088
Box Office:   0844 7550016
Website:      www.rutheatres.com
e-mail:         info@reallyuseful.co.uk

**PEACOCK**
(For Administration See SADLER'S WELLS)
Portugal Street, Kingsway London WC2A 2HT
Manager:       -------------------
Stage Door: 020-7863 8268
Box Office:   0844 4124322
Website:      www.sadlerswells.com
e-mail:         info@sadlerswells.com

**PHOENIX**
110 Charing Cross Road, London WC2H 0JP
Manager:       020-7438 9610
Stage Door: 020-7438 9600
Box Office:   020-7438 9605
e-mail:         phoenixmanager@theambassadors.com

**PICCADILLY**
Denman Street, London W1D 7DY
Manager:       020-7478 8800
Stage Door: 020-7478 8800
Box Office:   020-7478 8805
e-mail:         piccadillymanager@theambassadors.com

**PLAYHOUSE**
Northumberland Avenue, London WC2N 5DE
Manager:     020-7839 4292
Stage Door: 020-7839 4292
Box Office:   020-7839 4401

**PRINCE EDWARD**
28 Old Compton Street, London W1D 4HS
Manager:     020-7440 3021
Stage Door: 020-7440 3020
Box Office:   020-7447 5459
Website:      www.delfont-mackintosh.com

**PRINCE OF WALES**
Coventry Street, London W1D 6AS
Manager:     020-7766 2101
Stage Door: 020-7766 2100
Box Office:   0844 4825115
Website:      www.delfontmackintosh.co.uk

**QUEEN'S**
51 Shaftesbury Avenue, London W1D 6BA
Manager:     020-7292 1350
Stage Door: 020-7292 1350
Box Office:   0844 4825160

**REGENT'S PARK OPEN AIR**
Inner Circle, Regent's Park, London NW1 4NR
Manager:     0844 3753460
Stage Door: 0844 3753460
Box Office:   0844 8264242
Website:      www.openairtheatre.com

**RIVERSIDE STUDIOS**
Crisp Road, Hammersmith, London W6 9RL
Manager:     020-8237 1000
Stage Door: 020-8237 1000
Box Office:   020-8237 1111
Website:      www.riversidestudios.co.uk
e-mail:       online@riversidestudios.co.uk

**ROYAL COURT**
Sloane Square, London SW1W 8AS
Manager:     020-7565 5050
Stage Door: 020-7565 5050
Box Office:   020-7565 5000
Website:      www.royalcourttheatre.com
e-mail:       info@royalcourttheatre.com

**ROYAL OPERA HOUSE**
Covent Garden, London WC2E 9DD
Manager:     020-7240 1200
Stage Door: 020-7240 1200
Box Office:   020-7304 4000

**SADLER'S WELLS**
Rosebery Avenue, London EC1R 4TN
Manager:     020-7863 8034
Stage Door: 020-7863 8198
Box Office:   0844 4124300
Website:      www.sadlerswells.com
e-mail:       info@sadlerswells.com

**SAVOY**
Strand, London WC2R 0ET
Manager:     --------------------
Stage Door: 020-7845 6050
Box Office:   0870 1648787

**SHAFTESBURY**
210 Shaftesbury Avenue, London WC2H 8DP
Manager:     020-7379 3345
Stage Door: 020-7379 3345
Box Office:   020-7379 5399
e-mail:       info@toc.dltentertainment.co.uk

**SHAKESPEARE'S GLOBE**
21 New Globe Walk
Bankside, London SE1 9DT
Manager:     020-7902 1400
Stage Door: 020-7902 1400
Box Office:   020-7401 9919
Website:      www.shakespeares-globe.org
e-mail:       info@shakespearesglobe.com

**SHAW**
100-110 Euston Road, London NW1 2AJ
Manager:     020-7666 9037
Stage Door: --------------------
Box Office:   --------------------
Website:      www.shaw-theatre.com
e-mail:       info@shaw-theatre.com

**SOHO**
21 Dean Street
London W1D 3NE
Manager:     020-7287 5060
Stage Door: --------------------
Box Office:   020-7478 0100
Website:      www.sohotheatre.com

**ST MARTIN'S**
West Street, London WC2H 9NZ
Manager:     020-7497 0578
Stage Door: 020-7836 1086
Box Office:   0844 4991515
e-mail:       enquiries@the-mousetrap.co.uk

**THEATRE ROYAL**
Haymarket, London SW1Y 4HT
Manager:     020-7930 8890
Stage Door: 020-7930 8890
Box Office:   0845 4811870

**TRICYCLE**
269 Kilburn High Road
London NW6 7JR
Manager:     020-7372 6611
Stage Door: 020-7372 6611
Box Office:   020-7328 1000
Website:      www.tricycle.co.uk
e-mail:       info@tricycle.co.uk

**VAUDEVILLE**
404 Strand, London WC2R 0NH
Manager:     020-7836 1820
Stage Door: 020-7836 3191
Box Office:   0870 8900511

**VICTORIA PALACE**
Victoria Street
London SW1E 5EA
Manager:     020-7828 0600
Stage Door: 020-7834 2781
Box Office:   0844 2485000
e-mail:       enquiries@victoriapalace.co.uk

**WYNDHAM'S**
Charing Cross Road
London WC2H 0DA
Manager:     020-7759 8077
Stage Door: 020-7759 8010
Box Office:   0870 9500925

**YOUNG VIC**
66 The Cut, London SE1 8LZ
Manager:     020-7922 2800
Stage Door: 020-7922 2800
Box Office:   020-7922 2922
Website:      www.youngvic.org
e-mail:       info@youngvic.org

**ALBANY The**
Douglas Way, Deptford, London SE8 4AG
Website: www.thealbany.org.uk
e-mail: boxoffice@thealbany.org.uk
Fax: 020-8469 2253
BO: 020-8692 4446 · · · · · Admin: 020-8692 0231

**ARCOLA THEATRE**
Contact: Mehmet Ergen (Artistic Director), Leyla Nazli
(Executive Producer)
27 Arcola Street, Dalston
(Off Kingsland High Street), London E8 2DJ
Website: www.arcolatheatre.com
e-mail: info@arcolatheatre.com
BO: 020-7503 1646 · · · · · Admin: 020-7503 1645
Route: Victoria Line to Highbury & Islington, then North
London Line to Dalston Kingsland (Main Line) - 5 min walk.
Buses: 38 or 242 from West End, 149 from London Bridge or
30, 67, 76, 243

**ARTSDEPOT**
5 Nether Street, Tally Ho Corner
North Finchley, London N12 0GA · · · · · BO: 020-8369 5454
Website: www.artsdepot.co.uk
e-mail: info@artsdepot.co.uk

**BAC**
(Battersea Arts Centre)
Lavender Hill, London SW11 5TN
Website: www.bac.org.uk
e-mail: mailbox@bac.org.uk
Fax: 020-7978 5207
BO: 020-7223 2223 · · · · · Admin: 020-7223 6557
Route: Victoria or Waterloo (Main Line) to Clapham
Junction then 5 min walk or Northern Line to Clapham
Common then 20 min walk

**BARONS COURT THEATRE**
'The Curtain's Up'
28A Comeragh Road
West Kensington, London W14 9HR
Website: www.offwestend.com
e-mail: londontheatre@gmail.com
Admin/BO: 020-8932 4747
Route: West Kensington or Barons Court tube, Piccadilly &
District Lines

**BATES Tristan THEATRE**
Contact: Laura Kriefman (Creative Producer)
(adjoining The Actors Centre)
1A Tower Street, London WC2H 9NP
Website: www.tristanbatestheatre.co.uk
e-mail: tbt@actorscentre.co.uk
Fax: 020-7240 3896
BO: 020-7240 6283 · · · · · Admin: 020-7632 8010

**BECK THEATRE**
Grange Road, Hayes, Middlesex UB3 2UE
Website: www.becktheatre.org.uk
e-mail: enquiries@becktheatre.org.uk
BO: 020-8561 8371 · · · · · Admin: 020-8561 7506
Route: Metropolitan Line to Uxbridge then buses 427 or
607 to Theatre or Paddington (Main Line) to Hayes
Harlington then buses 90, H98 or 195 (10 min)

**BEDLAM THEATRE**
11B Bristo Place, Edinburgh EH1 1EZ
Website: www.bedlamtheatre.co.uk
e-mail: info@bedlamtheatre.co.uk
BO: 0131-225 9893 · · · · · Admin/Fax: 0131-225 9873

**BELLAIRS PLAYHOUSE**
Millmead Terrace
Guildford GU2 4YT
Website: www.gsauk.org
e-mail: enquiries@gsauk.org
BO: 01483 444789 · · · · · Admin: 01483 560701 (Mon-Fri)

**BLACKHEATH HALLS**
23 Lee Road, Blackheath, London SE3 9RQ
Website: www.blackheathhalls.com
e-mail: programming@blackheathhalls.com
Fax: 020-8852 5154
Tel: 020-8318 9758

**BLOOMSBURY THEATRE**
15 Gordon Street
Bloomsbury, London WC1H 0AH
Website: www.thebloomsbury.com
e-mail: blooms.theatre@ucl.ac.uk
BO: 020-7388 8822 · · · · · Admin: 020-7679 2777
Route: Tube to Euston, Euston Square or Warren Street

**BORLASE THEATRE The**
Sir William Borlase's Grammar School
West Street, Marlow SL7 2BR · · · · · Tel: 01628 816500
Website: www.swbgs.com
e-mail: mhartley@swbgs.com

**BRENTWOOD THEATRE**
Contact: Mark P. Reed (Theatre Administrator)
15 Shenfield Road, Brentwood, Essex CM15 8AG
Website: www.brentwood-theatre.org
e-mail: admin@brentwood-theatre.org
SD: 01277 226658
BO: 01277 200305 · · · · · Admin/Fax: 01277 230833
Route: Liverpool Street (Main Line) to Shenfield, then 15
min walk

**BRIDEWELL THEATRE The**
St Bride Foundation, Bride Lane
Fleet Street, London EC4Y 8EQ
Website: www.bridewelltheatre.org
e-mail: info@stbridefoundation.org
Fax: 020-7353 1547 · · · · · Admin: 020-7353 3331
Route: Circle Line to St Paul's. City Thameslink Capital
Connect. Fifteen different bus routes

**BROADWAY STUDIO THEATRE The**
Contact: Martin Costello (Director)
Catford, London SE6 4RU
Website: www.broadwaytheatre.org.uk
e-mail: martin@broadwaytheatre.org.uk
BO: 020-8690 0002 · · · · · Admin: 020-8690 1000
Route: Charing Cross to Catford Bridge

**BROADWAY The**
Broadway, Barking IG11 7LS
Website: www.thebroadwaybarking.com
e-mail: admin@thebroadwaybarking.com
Fax: 020-8507 5611
BO: 020-8507 5607 · · · · · Admin: 020-8507 5610

**CAMDEN PEOPLE'S THEATRE**
Contact: Matt Ball (Artistic Director)
58-60 Hampstead Road, London NW1 2PY
Website: www.cptheatre.co.uk
e-mail: admin@cptheatre.co.uk
Fax: 020-7813 3889 · · · · · Tel: 020-7419 4841
Route: Victoria or Northern Line to Euston or Warren
Street, Metropolitan or Circle Line to Euston Square (2 min
walk either way)

**CANAL CAFE THEATRE The**
Contact: Emma Taylor (Artistic Director)
The Bridge House
Delamere Terrace
Little Venice
London W2 6ND
Website: www.canalcafetheatre.com
e-mail: mail@canalcafetheatre.com
BO: 020-7289 6054                    Admin: 020-7289 6056

**CHATS PALACE ARTS CENTRE**
Contact: Sarah Wickens
42-44 Brooksby's Walk
Hackney, London E9 6DF              Tel: 020-8533 0227
Website: www.chatspalace.com
e-mail: info@chatspalace.com

**CHELSEA THEATRE**
World's End Place
King's Road, London SW10 0DR
e-mail: admin@chelseatheatre.org.uk
Fax: 020-7352 2024                   Tel: 020-7349 7811
Route: District or Circle Line to Sloane Square then short
bus ride 11 or 22 down King's Road

**CHICKENSHED**
Contact: Mary Ward MBE (Artistic Director)
Chase Side
Southgate, London N14 4PE
Website: www.chickenshed.org.uk
e-mail: info@chickenshed.org.uk
Fax: 020-8292 0202
BO: 020-8292 9222                    Admin: 020-8351 6161
Route: Piccadilly Line to Oakwood, turn left outside tube &
walk 8 min down Bramley Road or take 307 bus. Buses 298,
299, 699 or N19. Car parking available & easy access
parking by reservation

**CHRIST'S HOSPITAL THEATRE**
Contact: Jeff Mayhew (Director)
Horsham, West Sussex RH13 7LW
e-mail: jm@christs-hospital.org.uk
BO: 01403 247434                     Admin: 01403 247435

**CHURCHILL The**
Contact: John Bartliff (Administrator)
High Street
Bromley, Kent BR1 1HA
Website: www.churchilltheatre.co.uk
Fax: 020-8290 6968
BO: 0870 0606620                     Tel: 020-8464 7131

**CLUB FOR ACTS & ACTORS The**
Contact: Malcolm Knight (Concert Artistes Association)
20 Bedford Street
London WC2E 9HP                      Admin: 020-7836 3172
Website: www.thecaa.org
e-mail: office@thecaa.org
Route: Piccadilly or Northern Line to Leicester Square then
few mins walk

**COCHRANE THEATRE**
Contact: Deirdre Malynn
Southampton Row
London WC1B 4AP
e-mail: info@cochranetheatre.co.uk
BO: 020-7269 1606                    Admin: 020-7269 1600
Route: Central or Piccadilly Line to Holborn then 3 min
walk

**COCK TAVERN THEATRE The**
Contact: Adam Spreadbury-Maher (Artistic Director)
125 Kilburn High Road
London NW6 6JH
Website: www.cocktaverntheatre.com
e-mail: info@cocktaverntheatre.com
BO: 0844 4771000                     Mobile: 07704 321469

**COCKPIT THEATRE**
Gateforth Street
London NW8 8EH
Website: www.cockpittheatre.org.uk
e-mail: admin@cockpittheatre.org.uk
Fax: 020-7258 2921
BO: 020-7258 2925                    Admin: 020-7258 2920
Route: Tube to Marylebone/Edgware Road then short walk
or bus 139 to Lisson Grove & 6, 8 or 16 to Edgware Road

**COLOUR HOUSE THEATRE The**
Merton Abbey Mills
Watermill Way, London SW19 2RD       Tel: 020-8542 5511
Website: www.colourhousetheatre.co.uk
e-mail: info@colourhousetheatre.co.uk

**CORBETT THEATRE**
(East 15 Acting School)
Hatfields, Rectory Lane
Loughton IG10 3RY
Website: www.east15.ac.uk
e-mail: east15@essex.ac.uk
Fax: 020-8508 7521                   Admin/BO: 020-8508 5983
Route: Central Line (Epping Branch) to Debden then 6 min
walk

**COURTYARD THEATRE The**
Contact: June Abbott, Tim Gill (Joint Artistic Directors)
Bowling Green Walk
40 Pitfield Street, London N1 6EU
Website: www.thecourtyard.org.uk
e-mail: info@thecourtyard.org.uk
BO: 0870 1630717                     Admin/Fax: 020-7251 6018

**CROYDON CLOCKTOWER**
Katharine Street
Croydon CR9 1ET                      Admin/BO: 020-8253 1030
Website: www.croydonclocktower.org.uk
e-mail: arts@croydon.gov.uk

**CUSTARD FACTORY**
Gibb Street, Digbeth
Birmingham B9 4AA
Website: www.custardfactory.co.uk
e-mail: info@custardfactory.co.uk
Fax: 0121-604 8888                   Tel: 0121-224 7777

**DARTFORD ORCHARD THEATRE**
Contact: Andy Hill
Home Gardens
Dartford, Kent DA1 1ED
Website: www.orchardtheatre.co.uk
Fax: 01322 227122
BO: 01322 220000                     Admin: 01322 220099
Route: Charing Cross (Main Line) to Dartford

**DRILL HALL The**
16 Chenies Street, London WC1E 7EX
Website: www.drillhall.co.uk
e-mail: box.office@drillhall.co.uk
Fax: 020-7307 5062                   BO: 020-7307 5060
Route: Northern Line to Goodge Street then 1 min walk

**EDINBURGH FESTIVAL FRINGE**
180 High Street
Edinburgh EH1 1QS
Website: www.edfringe.com
e-mail: admin@edfringe.com
Fax: 0131-226 0016          Tel: 0131-226 0026

**EDINBURGH UNIVERSITY THEATRE COMPANY**
(See BEDLAM THEATRE)

**EMBASSY THEATRE & STUDIOS**
(The Central School of Speech & Drama)
64 Eton Avenue
Swiss Cottage
London NW3 3HY          Tel: 020-7722 8183
Website: www.cssd.ac.uk
e-mail: enquiries@cssd.ac.uk
Route: Jubilee Line to Swiss Cottage then 1 min walk

**ETCETERA THEATRE CLUB**
Contact: Zena Barrie, Michelle Flower (Directors)
Oxford Arms
265 Camden High Street
London NW1 7BU
Website: www.etceteratheatre.com
e-mail: etc@etceteratheatre.com
Fax: 020-7482 0378          Admin/BO: 020-7482 4857

**FAIRFIELD HALLS**
Ashcroft Theatre & Concert Hall
Park Lane
Croydon CR9 1DG
Website: www.fairfield.co.uk
e-mail: info@fairfield.co.uk
BO: 020-8688 9291          Admin/SD: 020-8681 0821
Route: Victoria & London Bridge (Main Line) to East
Croydon then 5 min walk

**FINBOROUGH THEATRE**
Contact: Neil McPherson (Artistic Director)
The Finborough
118 Finborough Road
London SW10 9ED
Website: www.finboroughtheatre.co.uk
e-mail: admin@finboroughtheatre.co.uk
Fax: 020-7835 1853
BO: 020-7373 3842          Admin: 020-7244 7439
Route: District or Piccadilly Line to Earls Court then 5 min
walk. Buses 74, 328, C1, C3, 74 then 3 min walk

**GATE THEATRE**
Contact: Natalie Abrahami, Carrie Cracknell
(Artistic Directors)
11 Pembridge Road
Above Prince Albert Pub
Notting Hill, London W11 3HQ
Website: www.gatetheatre.co.uk
e-mail: gate@gatetheatre.co.uk
Fax: 020-7221 6055
BO: 020-7229 0706          Admin: 020-7229 5387
Route: Central, Circle or District Line to Notting Hill Gate
then 1 min walk

**GBS THEATRE (George Bernard Shaw)**
Malet Street
London WC1E 7JN
Website: www.radaenterprises.org
e-mail: bookings@rada.ac.uk
BO: 020-7908 4800          Tel: 020-7908 4754

**GIELGUD John THEATRE**
Malet Street, London WC1E 7JN
Website: www.radaenterprises.org
e-mail: bookings@rada.ac.uk
BO: 020-7908 4800          Tel: 020-7908 4754

**GREENWICH PLAYHOUSE**
Contact: Alice de Sousa
Greenwich BR Station Forecourt
189 Greenwich High Road, London SE10 8JA
Website: www.galleontheatre.co.uk
e-mail: alice@galleontheatre.co.uk
Fax: 020-8310 7276          Tel: 020-8858 9256
Route: Main Line from Charing Cross, Waterloo East or
London Bridge, DLR to Greenwich

**GREENWICH THEATRE**
Contact: James Haddrell (Executive Director)
Crooms Hill, Greenwich, London SE10 8ES
Website: www.greenwichtheatre.org.uk
e-mail: info@greenwichtheatre.org.uk
Fax: 020-8858 8042
BO: 020-8858 7755          Admin: 020-8858 4447
Route: Jubilee Line (change Canary Wharf) then DLR to
Greenwich Cutty Sark, 3 min walk or Charing Cross (Main
Line) to Greenwich, 5 min walk

**GUILDHALL SCHOOL OF MUSIC & DRAMA**
Silk Street, Barbican, London EC2Y 8DT
Website: www.gsmd.ac.uk
e-mail: info@gsmd.ac.uk
Fax: 020-7256 9438          Tel: 020-7628 2571
Route: Hammersmith & City, Circle or Metropolitan line to
Barbican or Moorgate (also served by Northern line) then 5
min walk

**HACKNEY EMPIRE THEATRE**
291 Mare Street, Hackney, London E8 1EJ
e-mail: info@hackneyempire.co.uk
BO: 020-8985 2424          Press/Admin: 020-8510 4500
Route: North London Line to Hackney Central

**HEN & CHICKENS THEATRE**
Unrestricted View
Above Hen & Chickens Theatre Bar
109 St Paul's Road, Islington
London N1 2NA          Tel: 020-7704 2001
Website: www.henandchickens.com
e-mail: james@henandchickens.com
Route: Victoria Line or Main Line to Highbury & Islington
directly opposite station

**ICA THEATRE**
(No CVs, Venue only)
The Mall, London SW1Y 5AH
Website: www.ica.org.uk
Fax: 020-7873 0051
BO: 020-7930 3647          Admin: 020-7930 0493
Route: Nearest stations Piccadilly & Charing Cross

**JACKSONS LANE**
269A Archway Road
London N6 5AA          Tel: 020-8340 5226
Website: www.jacksonslane.org.uk
e-mail: reception@jacksonslane.org.uk

**JERMYN STREET THEATRE**
Contact: Gene David Kirk (Artistic Director), Penny Horner
(General Manager)
16B Jermyn Street, London SW1Y 6ST
Website: www.jermynstreettheatre.co.uk
e-mail: info@jermynstreettheatre.co.uk
Fax: 020-7287 3232
BO: 020-7287 2875          Admin: 020-7434 1443

**JERWOOD VANBRUGH THEATRE**
Malet Street, London WC1E 7JN
Website: www.radaenterprises.org
e-mail: bookings@rada.ac.uk
BO: 020-7908 4800          Tel: 020-7908 4754

**KING'S HEAD THEATRE**
115 Upper Street
Islington, London N1 1QN
Website: www.kingsheadtheatre.org
BO: 0844 2090326          Admin: 020-7226 8561
Route: Northern Line to Angel then 5 min walk. Approx
halfway between Angel and Highbury & Islington tube
stations

**KING'S LYNN CORN EXCHANGE**
Tuesday Market Place
King's Lynn, Norfolk PE30 1JW
Website: www.kingslynncornexchange.co.uk
e-mail: entertainment_admin@west-norfolk.gov.uk
Fax: 01553 762141
BO: 01553 764864          Admin: 01553 765565

**KOMEDIA**
Contact: Marina Kobler (Programmer)
44-47 Gardner Street
Brighton BN1 1UN
Website: www.komedia.co.uk/brighton
e-mail: info@komedia.co.uk
Fax: 01273 647102
BO: 0845 2938480          Tel: 01273 647101

**LANDMARK ARTS CENTRE**
Ferry Road
Teddington Lock
Middlesex TW11 9NN
Website: www.landmarkartscentre.org
e-mail: info@landmarkartscentre.org
Fax: 020-8977 4830          Tel: 020-8977 7558

**LANDOR THEATRE The**
Contact: Robert McWhir (Artistic Director)
70 Landor Road
London SW9 9PH          Admin/BO: 020-7737 7276
Website: www.landortheatre.co.uk
e-mail: info@landortheatre.co.uk
Route: Northern Line Clapham North then 2 min walk

**LEICESTER SQUARE THEATRE**
5 Leicester Place
London WC2H 7BP
Website: www.leicestersquaretheatre.com
BO: 0844 8472475          Tel: 0870 8993335

**LEIGHTON BUZZARD THEATRE**
Lake Street, Leighton Buzzard
Bedfordshire LU7 1RX
Website: www.leightonbuzzardtheatre.co.uk
BO: 01582 818801          Tel: 01582 818800

**LILIAN BAYLIS THEATRE**
(Information: Sadler's Wells Theatre)
Rosebery Avenue, London EC1R 4TN
Website: www.sadlerswells.com
e-mail: info@sadlerswells.com
BO: 0844 4124300          SD: 020-7863 8198

**LIVE THEATRE**
Broad Chare
Quayside, Newcastle upon Tyne NE1 3DQ
Website: www.live.org.uk
e-mail: info@live.org.uk
Fax: 0191-232 2224
BO: 0191-232 1232          Admin: 0191-261 2694

**MACOWAN THEATRE**
(LAMDA)
1-2 Logan Place, London W8 6QN
Website: www.lamda.org.uk
Fax: 020-7370 1980          Tel: 020-7244 8744
Route: District or Piccadilly Line to Earl's Court then 6 min
walk

**MADDERMARKET THEATRE**
Contact: Michael Lyas (General Manager)
St John's Alley, Norwich NR2 1DR
Website: www.maddermarket.co.uk
e-mail: mmtheatre@btconnect.com
Fax: 01603 661357
BO: 01603 620917          Admin: 01603 626560

**MENIER CHOCOLATE FACTORY**
53 Southwark Street
London SE1 1RU
Website: www.menierchocolatefactory.com
e-mail: office@menierchocolatefactory.com
Fax: 020-7378 1713
BO: 020-7907 7060          Tel: 020-7378 1712

**MILLFIELD ARTS CENTRE**
Silver Street, London N18 1PJ
Website: www.millfieldtheatre.co.uk
e-mail: info@millfieldtheatre.co.uk
Fax: 020-8807 3892
BO: 020-8807 6680          Admin: 020-8803 5283
Route: Liverpool Street (Main Line) to Silver Street or tube
to Turnpike Lane then bus 144 (15 min to Cambridge
Roundabout)

**MYERS STUDIO THEATRE The**
Contact: Trevor Mitchell (General Manager & Artistic
Director)
The Epsom Playhouse, Ashley Avenue
Epsom, Surrey KT18 5AL
Website: www.epsomplayhouse.co.uk
e-mail: tmitchell@epsom-ewell.gov.uk
Fax: 01372 726228
BO: 01372 742555          Tel: 01372 742226

## NADINE'S WINDOW
(Showcase Theatre Company)
Website: www.myspace.com/nadineswindow
e-mail: nadineswindow@yahoo.co.uk

## NETTLEFOLD The
West Norwood Library Centre
1 Norwood High Street, London SE27 9JX
e-mail: thenettlefold@lambeth.gov.uk
Fax: 020-7926 8071          Admin/BO: 020-7926 8070
Route: Victoria, West Croydon or London Bridge (Main Line)
to West Norwood then 2 min walk, or tube to Brixton then
buses 2, 196, 322, 432, or buses 68, 468

## NEW DIORAMA THEATRE The
(Hire Venue)
Regents Place, London NW1          Admin: 020-7916 5467
Website: www.diorama-arts.org.uk
e-mail: admin@diorama-arts.org.uk
Route: Circle & District Line to Great Portland Street then 5
min walk, or Victoria/Northern line to Warren Street then 1
min walk

## NEW END THEATRE
27 New End, Hampstead, London NW3 1JD
Website: www.newendtheatre.co.uk
e-mail: info@newendtheatre.co.uk
Fax: 020-7794 4044
BO: 0870 0332733          Admin: 020-7472 5800
Route: Northern Line to Hampstead then 2 min walk off
Heath Street

## NEW PLAYERS THEATRE The
(Formerly The Players Theatre)
The Arches, Villiers Street
London WC2N 6NG          Tel: 020-7930 5868
Website: www.newplayerstheatre.com
e-mail: info@newplayerstheatre.com

## NEW WIMBLEDON THEATRE & STUDIO
The Broadway, Wimbledon, London SW19 1QG
Website: www.newwimbledontheatre.co.uk
Fax: 020-8543 6637
BO: 0870 0606646          Admin: 020-8545 7900
Route: Main Line or District Line to Wimbledon, then 3 min
walk. Buses 57, 93, 155

## NORTHBROOK THEATRE The
Contact: Dave Manley (Theatre Co-ordinator)
Littlehampton Road
Goring-by-Sea, Worthing
West Sussex BN12 6NU
Website: www.northbrooktheatre.co.uk
e-mail: box.office@nbcol.ac.uk
Fax: 01903 606141          Admin/BO: 01903 606162

## NORWICH PUPPET THEATRE
St James, Whitefriars
Norwich NR3 1TN
Website: www.puppettheatre.co.uk
e-mail: info@puppettheatre.co.uk
Fax: 01603 617578
BO: 01603 629921          Admin: 01603 615564

## NOVELLO THEATRE The
(Redroofs Theatre Company)
2 High Street, Sunninghill
Nr Ascot, Berkshire          Tel: 01344 620881
Route: Waterloo (Main Line) to Ascot then 1 mile from
station

## OLD RED LION THEATRE PUB
Contact: Helen Devine (Theatre Manager)
418 St John Street
Islington, London EC1V 4NJ
BO: 020-7837 7816          Admin: 020-7833 3053
Route: Northern Line to Angel then 1 min walk

## ORANGE TREE
Contact: Sam Walters (Artistic Director)
1 Clarence Street
Richmond TW9 2SA
e-mail: admin@orangetreetheatre.co.uk
Fax: 020-8332 0369
BO: 020-8940 3633          Admin: 020-8940 0141
Route: District Line, Waterloo (Main Line) or North London
Line then virtually opposite station

## OVAL HOUSE THEATRE
52-54 Kennington Oval, London SE11 5SW
Website: www.ovalhouse.com
e-mail: info@ovalhouse.com
Fax: 020-7820 0990
BO: 020-7582 7680          Admin: 020-7582 0080
Route: Northern Line to Oval then 1 min walk, Victoria Line
& Main Line to Vauxhall then 10 min walk

## PAVILION THEATRE
Marine Road, Dun Laoghaire, County Dublin, Ireland
Website: www.paviliontheatre.ie
e-mail: info@paviliontheatre.ie
Fax: 00 353 1 663 6328          Tel: 00 353 1 231 2929

## PENTAMETERS
(Theatre Entrance in Oriel Place), 28 Heath Street
London NW3 6TE          Admin/BO: 020-7435 3648
Website: www.pentameters.co.uk
Route: Northern Line to Hampstead then 1 min walk. Buses
268, 46

## PLACE The
(Main London Venue for Contemporary Dance)
17 Duke's Road, London WC1H 9PY
Website: www.theplace.org.uk
e-mail: theatre@theplace.org.uk
BO: 020-7121 1100          Admin: 020-7121 1101
Route: Northern or Victoria Line to Euston or King's Cross
then 5 min walk (Opposite rear of St Pancras Church)

## PLEASANCE ISLINGTON
Contact: Anthony Alderson
Carpenters Mews, North Road, (Off Caledonian Road)
London N7 9EF
Website: www.pleasance.co.uk
e-mail: info@pleasance.co.uk
Fax: 020-7700 7366
BO: 020-7609 1800          Admin: 020-7619 6868
Route: Piccadilly Line to Caledonian Road, turn left, walk
50 yds, turn left into North Road, 2 min walk. Buses 17, 91,
259, N91, 393

## POLKA THEATRE
240 The Broadway, Wimbledon SW19 1SB
Website: www.polkatheatre.com
e-mail: admin@polkatheatre.com
Fax: 020-8545 8365
BO: 020-8543 4888          Admin: 020-8545 8320
Route: Waterloo (Main Line) or District Line to Wimbledon
then 10 min walk. Northern Line to South Wimbledon then
10 min walk. Tram to Wimbledon, Buses 57, 93, 219, 493

## PRINCESS THEATRE HUNSTANTON
The Green
Hunstanton, Norfolk PE36 5AH
Website: www.princesstheatrehunstanton.co.uk
Fax: 01485 534463
BO: 01485 532252    Admin: 01485 535937

## PUTNEY ARTS THEATRE
Ravenna Road, Putney SW15 6AW
Website: www.putneyartstheatre.org.uk
e-mail: info@putneyartstheatre.org.uk
Fax: 020-8788 6940    Tel: 020-8788 6943

## QUEEN'S THEATRE
Contact: Bob Carlton (Artistic Director)
Billet Lane
Hornchurch, Essex RM11 1QT
Website: www.queens-theatre.co.uk
e-mail: info@queens-theatre.co.uk
Fax: 01708 462363
BO: 01708 443333    Admin/SD: 01708 462362
Route: District Line to Hornchurch, Main Line to
Romford/Gidea Park. 15 miles from West End take A13,
A1306 then A125 or A12 then A127

## QUESTORS THEATRE EALING The
12 Mattock Lane, London W5 5BQ
Website: www.questors.org.uk
e-mail: enquiries@questors.org.uk
Fax: 020-8567 2275
BO: 020-8567 5184    Admin/SD: 020-8567 0011
Route: Central or District Line to Ealing Broadway then 5
min walk. Buses 207, 83, 65, 427, 607, E2, E7, E8, E11

## RED LADDER THEATRE COMPANY Ltd
3 St Peter's Buildings
York Street, Leeds LS9 8AJ
Website: www.redladder.co.uk
e-mail: rod@redladder.co.uk
Fax: 0113-245 5351    Tel: 0113-245 5311

## RICHMOND THEATRE
Contact: Karin Gartzke
The Green, Richmond, Surrey TW9 1QJ
Website: www.ambassadortickets.com/richmond
e-mail: richmondstagedoor@theambassadors.com
Fax: 020-8332 4509
BO: 0844 8717651    Admin/SD: 020-8332 4500
Route: 20 minutes from Waterloo (South West Trains) or
District Line to Richmond then 2 min walk

## RIDWARE THEATRE
Contact: Alan & Margaret Williams (Venue only. No resident
performing company)
Wheelwright's House
Pipe Ridware
Rugeley, Staffs WS15 3QL
Website: www.ridwares.co.uk
e-mail: al@christmas-time.com
Tel: 01889 504380

## RIVERSIDE STUDIOS
Crisp Road, London W6 9RL
Website: www.riversidestudios.co.uk
e-mail: info@riversidestudios.co.uk
BO: 020-8237 1111    Admin: 020-8237 1000
Route: District, Piccadilly or Hammersmith & City Line to
Hammersmith then 5 min walk. Buses 9, 10, 27, 33, 72, 190,
209, 211, 266, 267, 283, 295, 391, 419

## ROSE THEATRE
24-26 High Street, Kingston upon Thames, Surrey KT1 1HL
Website: www.rosetheatrekingston.org
e-mail: admin@rosetheatrekingston.org
Fax: 020-8546 8783    Tel: 020-8546 6983

## ROSEMARY BRANCH THEATRE
2 Shepperton Road
London N1 3DT    Tel: 020-7704 6665
Website: www.rosemarybranch.co.uk
e-mail: cecilia@rosemarybranch.co.uk
Route: Tube to Bank, Moorgate or Old Street (exit 5), then
No 21, 76 or 141 bus to Baring Street, or 271 bus from
Highbury and Islington

## SCOTTISH STORYTELLING CENTRE
(Netherbow Theatre)
43-45 High Street, Edinburgh EH1 1SR    Tel: 0131-556 9579
Website: www.scottishstorytellingcentre.co.uk
e-mail: reception@scottishstorytellingcentre.com

## SHAW THEATRE
Contact: John-Jackson Almond (Artistic Director)
100-110 Euston Road, London NW1 2AJ
Fax: 020-7666 9025
BO: 0871 5943123    Admin: 020-7666 9037

## SOUTH HILL PARK ARTS CENTRE
Bracknell
Berkshire RG12 7PA
Website: www.southhillpark.org.uk
e-mail: admin@southhillpark.org.uk
BO: 01344 484123    Admin/SD: 01344 484858
Route: Waterloo (Main Line) to Bracknell then 10 min bus
ride or taxi rank at station

## SOUTH LONDON THEATRE
(Bell Theatre & Prompt Corner)
2A Norwood High Street
London SE27 9NS    Tel: 020-8670 3474
Website: www.southlondontheatre.co.uk
e-mail: southlondontheatre@yahoo.co.uk
Route: Victoria or London Bridge (Main Line) to West
Norwood then 2 min walk, or Victoria Line to Brixton then
buses 2, 68, 196, 322

## SOUTHWARK PLAYHOUSE
Contact: Chris Smyrnios (Chief Executive)
Ellie Jones (Artistic Director)
Shipwright Yard
Corner of Tooley Street & Bermondsey Street
London SE1 2TF    Admin/BO: 020-7407 0234
Website: www.southwarkplayhouse.co.uk
e-mail: admin@southwarkplayhouse.co.uk
Route: Trains to London Bridge, Jubilee/Northern Line to
London Bridge. Buses 47, 381, RV1, N47, N381. River service
to London Bridge City

## SPACE ARTS CENTRE The
269 Westferry Road, London E14 3RS    Tel: 020-7515 7799
Website: www.space.org.uk
e-mail: info@space.org.uk

## TABARD THEATRE
Contact: Collin Hilton, Fred Perry (Artistic Directors)
Simon Reilly (Theatre Manager)
2 Bath Road, London W4 1LW
Website: www.tabardtheatre.co.uk
e-mail: info@tabardtheatre.co.uk
Fax: 020-8994 6985    Tel: 020-8995 6035

## THEATRE 503
The Latchmere Pub
503 Battersea Park Road
London SW11 3BW     BO: 020-7978 7040
Website: www.theatre503.com
e-mail: info@theatre503.com
Route: Victoria or Waterloo (Main Line) to Clapham
Junction then 10 min walk or buses 44, 319, 344, 345 or
tube to South Kensington then buses 49 or 345 or tube to
Sloane Square then bus 319

## THEATRE ROYAL STRATFORD EAST
Contact: Kerry Michael (Artistic Director)
Gerry Raffles Square
London E15 1BN
Website: www.stratfordeast.com
e-mail: theatreroyal@stratfordeast.com
Fax: 020-8534 8381
BO: 020-8534 0310     Admin: 020-8534 7374
Route: Central or Jubilee Lines, DLR, Overground or
National Express trains to Stratford then 2 min walk

## THEATRO TECHNIS
Contact: George Eugeniou (Artistic Director)
26 Crowndale Road
London NW1 1TT     Admin/BO: 020-7387 6617
Website: www.theatrotechnis.com
e-mail: info@theatrotechnis.com
Route: Northern Line to Mornington Crescent then 3 min
walk

## TRICYCLE THEATRE
Contact: Nicolas Kent (Artistic Director), Mary Lauder
(General Manager)
269 Kilburn High Road
London NW6 7JR
Website: www.tricycle.co.uk
e-mail: admin@tricycle.co.uk
Fax: 020-7328 0795
BO: 020-7328 1000     Admin: 020-7372 6611
Route: Jubilee Line to Kilburn then 5 min walk or buses 16,
189, 32 pass the door, 98, 31, 206, 316, 332 pass nearby

## TRON THEATRE
63 Trongate, Glasgow G1 5HB
Website: www.tron.co.uk
e-mail: casting@tron.co.uk
Fax: 0141-552 6657
BO: 0141-552 4267     Admin: 0141-552 3748

## UNION THEATRE The
Contact: Sasha Regan (Artistic Director), Ben De Wynter
(Associate Director), Steve Miller (Technical Director)
Paul Flynn (All Casting Enquiries)
204 Union Street, Southwark
London SE1 0LX     Tel/Fax: 020-7261 9876
Website: www.uniontheatre.biz
e-mail: sasha@uniontheatre.freeserve.co.uk
Route: Jubilee Line to Southwark then 2 min walk

## UPSTAIRS AT THE GATEHOUSE
(Ovation Theatres Ltd)
The Gatehouse Pub
Corner of Hampstead Lane/
North Road, London N6 4BD
Website: www.upstairsatthegatehouse.com
e-mail: events@ovationproductions.com
BO: 020-8340 3488     Admin: 020-8340 4256
Route: Northern Line to Highgate then 10 min walk. Buses
143, 210, 214, 271

## WAREHOUSE THEATRE
Contact: Ted Craig (Artistic Director)
Dingwall Road, Croydon CRO 2NF
Website: www.warehousetheatre.co.uk
e-mail: info@warehousetheatre.co.uk
Fax: 020-8688 6699
BO: 020-8680 4060     Admin: 020-8681 1257
Route: Adjacent to East Croydon (Main Line). Direct from
Victoria (15 min), Clapham Junction (10 min) or by First
Capital Connect from West Hampstead, Kentish Town,
Kings Cross (25 Mins) & London Bridge (10 mins)

## WATERMANS
40 High Street, Brentford TW8 0DS
Website: www.watermans.org.uk
e-mail: info@watermans.org.uk
Fax: 020-8232 1030
BO: 020-8232 1010     Admin: 020-8232 1020
Route: Buses: 237, 267, 65, N9. Tube: Gunnersbury or South
Ealing. Main Line: Kew Bridge then 5 min walk, Gunnersbury
then 10 min walk, or Brentford

## WESTRIDGE (OPEN CENTRE)
(Drawing Room Recitals)
Star Lane, Highclere, Nr Newbury
Berkshire RG20 9PJ     Tel: 01635 253322

## WHITE BEAR THEATRE
(Favours New Writing)
138 Kennington Park Road
London SE11 4DJ     Admin/BO: 020-7793 9193
Website: www.whitebeartheatre.co.uk
e-mail: info@whitebeartheatre.co.uk
Route: Northern Line to Kennington (2 min walk)

## WILTONS MUSIC HALL
Graces Alley, Off Ensign Street, London E1 8JB
Website: www.wiltons.org.uk
Fax: 0871 2532424     Tel: 020-7702 9555
Route: Tube: Under 10 minutes walk from Aldgate East (exit
for Leman Street)/Tower Hill. DLR: Shadwell or Tower
Gateway. Car: Follow the yellow AA signs to Wiltons Music
Hall from the Highway, Aldgate or Tower Hill

## WIMBLEDON STUDIO THEATRE
(See NEW WIMBLEDON THEATRE & STUDIO)

## WYCOMBE SWAN
St Mary Street, High Wycombe
Buckinghamshire HP11 2XE
Website: www.wycombeswan.co.uk
e-mail: enquiries@wycombeswan.co.uk
BO: 01494 512000     Admin: 01494 514444

## ABERDEEN

**His Majesty's Theatre**
Rosemount Viaduct, Aberdeen AB25 1GL
**Box Office:** 01224 641122
**Stage Door:** 01224 337673
**Admin:** 0845 2708200
**Website:** www.boxofficeaberdeen.com
**e-mail:** hmtinfo@aberdeenperformingarts.com

## ABERYSTWYTH

**Aberystwyth Arts Centre**
University of Wales
Aberystwyth SY23 3DE
**Box Office:** 01970 623232
**Stage Door:** 01970 624239
**Admin:** 01970 622882
**Website:** www.aber.ac.uk/artscentre
**e-mail:** ggo@aber.ac.uk

## BACUP

**Royal Court Theatre**
Rochdale Road, Bacup OL13 9NR
**Box Office:** 01706 874080
**Stage Door:** ------------------
**Admin:** ------------------

## BASINGSTOKE

**The Haymarket Theatre**
Wote Street
Basingstoke RG21 7NW
**Box Office:** 01256 844244
**Stage Door:** 01256 819797
**Admin:** 01256 819797
**Website:** www.haymarket.org.uk
**e-mail:** info@haymarket.org.uk

## BATH

**Theatre Royal**
Sawclose, Bath BA1 1ET
**Box Office:** 01225 448844
**Stage Door:** 01225 448815
**Admin:** 01225 448815
**Website:** www.theatreroyal.org.uk
**e-mail:** forename.surname@theatreroyal.org.uk

## BELFAST

**Grand Opera House**
Great Victoria Street
Belfast BT2 7HR
**Box Office:** 028-9024 1919
**Stage Door:** 028-9024 0411
**Admin:** 028-9024 0411
**Website:** www.goh.co.uk
**e-mail:** info@goh.co.uk

## BILLINGHAM

**Forum Theatre**
Town Centre, Billingham TS23 2LJ
**Box Office:** 01642 552663
**Stage Door:** ------------------
**Admin:** 01642 551389
**Website:** www.forumtheatrebillingham.co.uk
**e-mail:** forumtheatre@btconnect.com

## BIRMINGHAM

**Alexandra Theatre**
Station Street, Birmingham B5 4DS
**Box Office:** 0844 8472301
**Stage Door:** 0121-230 9102
**Admin:** 0121-643 5536
**Website:** www.alexandratheatre.org.uk

## BIRMINGHAM

**Hippodrome**
Hurst Street
Birmingham B5 4TB
**Box Office:** 0844 3385000
**Stage Door:** 0121-689 3020
**Admin:** 0870 7305555
**Website:** www.birminghamhippodrome.com

## BLACKPOOL

**Grand Theatre**
33 Church Street
Blackpool FY1 1HT
**Box Office:** 01253 290190
**Stage Door:** 01253 743218
**Admin:** 01253 290111
**Website:** www.blackpoolgrand.co.uk
**e-mail:** box@blackpoolgrand.co.uk

## BLACKPOOL

**Opera House**
Church Street, Blackpool FY1 1HW
**Box Office:** 0844 8561111
**Stage Door:** 01253 629732
**Admin:** 01253 625252
**Website:** www.blackpoollive.com

## BOURNEMOUTH

**Pavilion Theatre**
Westover Road
Bournemouth BH1 2BU
**Box Office:** 0844 5763000
**Stage Door:** 01202 451863
**Admin:** 01202 456400
**Website:** www.bic.co.uk

## BRADFORD

**Alhambra Theatre**
Morley Street, Bradford BD7 1AJ
**Box Office:** 01274 432000
**Stage Door:** 01274 432375
**Admin:** 01274 432375
**Website:** www.bradford-theatres.co.uk
**e-mail:** administration@ces.bradford.gov.uk

## BRADFORD

**Theatre in the Mill**
University of Bradford
Shearbridge Road, Bradford BD7 1DP
**Box Office:** 01274 233200
**Stage Door:** 01274 233187
**Admin:** 01274 233185
**Website:** www.bradford.ac.uk/theatre
**e-mail:** theatre@bradford.ac.uk

## BRIGHTON
**Theatre Royal**
New Road, Brighton BN1 1SD
**Box Office:** 0870 0606650
**Stage Door:** 01273 764400
**Admin:** 01273 764400
**Website:** www.theambassadors.com/brighton
**e-mail:** brightontheatremanager@theambassadors.com

## BRIGHTON
**The Dome, Corn Exchange & Pavilion Theatres**
12A Pavilion Buildings, Castle Square, Brighton BN1 1EE
**Box Office:** 01273 709709
**Stage Door:** 01273 261550
**Admin:** 01273 700747
**Website:** www.brightondome.org
**e-mail:** info@brightondome.org

## BRISTOL
**Hippodrome**
St Augustines Parade, Bristol BS1 4UZ
**Box Office:** 0844 8472325
**Stage Door:** 0117-302 3251
**Admin:** 0117-302 3310
**Website:** www.bristolhippodrome.org.uk

## BROXBOURNE (Herts)
**Broxbourne Civic Hall**
High Street
Hoddesdon, Herts EN11 8BE
**Box Office:** 01992 441946
**Stage Door:** ------------------
**Admin:** 01992 441931
**Website:** www.broxbourne.gov.uk/whatson
**e-mail:** civic.leisure@broxbourne.gov.uk

## BURY ST EDMUNDS
**Theatre Royal**
Westgate Street, Bury St Edmunds IP33 1QR
**Box Office:** 01284 769505
**Stage Door:** ------------------
**Admin:** 01284 755127
**Website:** www.theatreroyal.org
**e-mail:** admin@theatreroyal.org

## BUXTON
**Buxton Opera House**
Water Street, Buxton SK17 6XN
**Box Office:** 0845 1272190
**Stage Door:** 01298 72524
**Admin:** 01298 72050
**Website:** www.buxtonoperahouse.org.uk
**e-mail:** admin@boh.org.uk

## CAMBERLEY
**The Camberley Theatre**
Knoll Road
Camberley, Surrey GU15 3SY
**Box Office:** 01276 707600
**Stage Door:** ------------------
**Admin:** 01276 707512
**Website:** www.camberleytheatre.biz
**e-mail:** camberleytheatre@surreyheath.gov.uk

## CAMBRIDGE
**Cambridge Arts Theatre Trust Ltd**
6 St Edward's Passage, Cambridge CB2 3PJ
**Box Office:** 01223 503333
**Stage Door:** 01223 578933
**Admin:** 01223 578904
**Website:** www.cambridgeartstheatre.com
**e-mail:** info@cambridgeartstheatre.com

## CAMBRIDGE
**Mumford Theatre**
Anglia Ruskin University, East Road, Cambridge CB1 1PT
**Box Office:** 0845 1962320
**Stage Door:** 0845 1962848
**Admin:** 0845 1962848
**e-mail:** mumford@anglia.ac.uk

## CANTERBURY
**Gulbenkian Theatre**
University of Kent, Canterbury CT2 7NB
**Box Office:** 01227 769075
**Stage Door:** ------------------
**Admin:** 01227 827861
**Website:** www.gulbenkiantheatre.co.uk
**e-mail:** gulbenkian@kent.ac.uk

## CANTERBURY
**The Marlowe Theatre**
(Closed until 2011 for redevelopment)

## CARDIFF
**New Theatre**
Park Place, Cardiff CF10 3LN
**Box Office:** 029-2087 8889
**Stage Door:** 029-2087 8900
**Admin:** 029-2087 8787
**Website:** www.newtheatrecardiff.co.uk

## CARDIFF
**Wales Millennium Centre**
Bute Place, Cardiff CF10 5AL
**Box Office:** 0870 0402000
**Stage Door:** 029-2063 4630
**Admin:** 029-2063 6400
**Website:** www.wmc.org.uk

## CHELTENHAM
**Everyman Theatre**
Regent Street, Cheltenham GL50 1HQ
**Box Office:** 01242 572573
**Stage Door:** 01242 512515
**Admin:** 01242 512515
**Website:** www.everymantheatre.org.uk
**e-mail:** admin@everymantheatre.org.uk

## CHICHESTER
**Festival Theatre**
Oaklands Park, Chichester PO19 6AP
**Box Office:** 01243 781312
**Stage Door:** 01243 784437
**Admin:** 01243 784437
**Website:** www.cft.org.uk
**e-mail:** admin@cft.org.uk

## CRAWLEY

**The Hawth**
Hawth Avenue
Crawley, West Sussex RH10 6YZ
**Box Office:** 01293 553636
**Stage Door:** ------------------
**Admin:** 01293 552941
**Website:** www.hawth.co.uk
**e-mail:** info@hawth.co.uk

## CREWE

**Lyceum Theatre**
Heath Street
Crewe CW1 2DA
**Box Office:** 01270 537333
**Stage Door:** 01270 537336
**Admin:** 01270 537243

## DARLINGTON

**Civic Theatre**
Parkgate
Darlington DL1 1RR
**Box Office:** 01325 486555
**Stage Door:** ------------------
**Admin:** 01325 387775
**Website:** www.darlingtonarts.co.uk

## DUBLIN

**Gaiety Theatre**
South King Street, Dublin 2
**Box Office:** 00 353 1 6771717
**Stage Door:** 00 353 1 6795622
**Admin:** 00 353 1 6795622
**Website:** www.gaietytheatre.com

## DUBLIN

**Gate Theatre**
1 Cavendish Row, Dublin 1
**Box Office:** 00 353 1 8744045
**Stage Door:** ------------------
**Admin:** 00 353 1 8744368
**Website:** www.gate-theatre.ie
**e-mail:** info@gate-theatre.ie

## DUBLIN

**Olympia Theatre**
72 Dame Street
Dublin 2
**Box Office:** 00 353 1 6793323
**Stage Door:** 00 353 1 6771400
**Admin:** 00 353 1 6725883
**Website:** www.olympia.ie
**e-mail:** info@olympia.ie

## EASTBOURNE

**Congress Theatre**
Admin: Winter Garden
Compton Street, Eastbourne BN21 4BP
**Box Office:** 01323 412000
**Stage Door:** 01323 410048
**Admin:** 01323 415500
**Website:** www.eastbournetheatres.co.uk
**e-mail:** theatres@eastbourne.gov.uk

## EASTBOURNE

**Devonshire Park Theatre**
Admin: Winter Garden
Compton Street, Eastbourne BN21 4BP
**Box Office:** 01323 412000
**Stage Door:** 01323 410074
**Admin:** 01323 415500
**Website:** www.eastbournetheatres.co.uk
**e-mail:** theatres@eastbourne.gov.uk

## EDINBURGH

**King's Theatre**
2 Leven Street, Edinburgh EH3 9LQ
**Box Office:** 0131-529 6000
**Stage Door:** 0131-229 3416
**Admin:** 0131-662 1112
**Website:** www.eft.co.uk
**e-mail:** empire@eft.co.uk

## EDINBURGH

**Playhouse Theatre**
18-22 Greenside Place, Edinburgh EH1 3AA
**Box Office:** 0844 8471660
**Stage Door:** 0131-524 3324
**Admin:** 0131-524 3333
**Website:** www.livenation.co.uk/edinburgh

## GLASGOW

**King's Theatre**
297 Bath Street, Glasgow G2 4JN
**Box Office:** 0844 8717648
**Stage Door:** 0141-240 1300
**Admin:** 0141-240 1300
**Website:** www.kings-glasgow.co.uk
**e-mail:** glasgowstagedoor@theambassadors.com

## GLASGOW

**Theatre Royal**
282 Hope Street
Glasgow G2 3QA
**Box Office:** 0870 0606647
**Stage Door:** 0141-332 3321
**Admin:** 0141-332 3321
**Website:** www.ambassadortickets.com/glasgow

## GRAYS THURROCK

**Thameside Theatre**
Orsett Road, Grays Thurrock RM17 5DX
**Box Office:** 0845 3005264
**Stage Door:** ------------------
**Admin:** 01375 413981
**Website:** www.thurrock.gov.uk/theatre
**e-mail:** thameside.theatre@thurrock.gov.uk

## HARLOW

**The Playhouse**
Playhouse Square
Harlow CM20 1LS
**Box Office:** 01279 431945
**Stage Door:** ------------------
**Admin:** 01279 446760
**Website:** www.playhouseharlow.com
**e-mail:** playhouse@harlow.gov.uk

## HARROGATE
**Harrogate International Centre**
Kings Road, Harrogate HG1 5LA
**Box Office:** 0845 1308840
**Stage Door:** ------------------
**Admin:** 01423 500500
**Website:** www.harrogateinternationalcentre.co.uk
**e-mail:** sales@harrogateinternationalcentre.co.uk

## HASTINGS
**White Rock Theatre**
White Rock, Hastings TN34 1JX
**Box Office:** 01424 462288
**Stage Door:** ------------------
**Admin:** 01424 462283
**Website:** www.whiterocktheatre.org.uk
**e-mail:** info@whiterocktheatre.org.uk

## HAYES (Middlesex)
**Beck Theatre**
Grange Road, Hayes
Middlesex UB3 2UE
**Box Office:** 020-8561 8371
**Stage Door:** ------------------
**Admin:** 020-8561 7506
**Website:** www.becktheatre.org.uk
**e-mail:** enquiries@becktheatre.org.uk

## HIGH WYCOMBE
**Wycombe Swan**
St Mary Street, High Wycombe HP11 2XE
**Box Office:** 01494 512000
**Stage Door:** 01494 514444
**Admin:** 01494 514444
**Website:** www.wycombeswan.co.uk
**e-mail:** enquiries@wycombeswan.co.uk

## HUDDERSFIELD
**Cragrats Ltd**
The Mill, Dunford Road
Holmfirth, Huddersfield HD9 2AR
**Stage Door:** ------------------
**Box Office:** ------------------
**Admin:** 01484 686451
**Website:** www.cragrats.com
**e-mail:** info@cragrats.com

## HUDDERSFIELD
**Lawrence Batley Theatre**
Queen Street, Huddersfield HD1 2SP
**Box Office:** 01484 430528
**Stage Door:** --------------------
**Admin:** 01484 425282
**Website:** www.lawrencebatleytheatre.co.uk
**e-mail:** theatre@lbt-uk.org

## HULL
**Hull New Theatre**
Kingston Square, Hull HU1 3HF
**Box Office:** 01482 226655
**Stage Door:** 01482 318300
**Admin:** 01482 613818
**Website:** www.hullcc.gov.uk
**e-mail:** theatre.management@hullcc.gov.uk

## HULL
**Hull Truck Theatre**
50 Ferensway
Hull HU2 8LB
**Box Office:** 01482 323638
**Stage Door:** ------------------
**Admin:** 01482 224800
**Website:** www.hulltruck.co.uk
**e-mail:** admin@hulltruck.co.uk

## ILFORD
**Kenneth More Theatre**
Oakfield Road
Ilford IG1 1BT
**Box Office:** 020-8553 4466
**Stage Door:** 020-8553 4465
**Admin:** 020-8553 4464
**Website:** www.kenneth-more-theatre.co.uk
**e-mail:** kmtheatre@aol.com

## IPSWICH
**Sir John Mills Theatre (Hire Only)**
Gatacre Road, Ipswich IP1 2LQ
**Box Office:** 01473 211498
**Stage Door:** ------------------
**Admin:** 01473 218202
**Website:** www.easternangles.co.uk
**e-mail:** admin@easternangles.co.uk

## JERSEY
**Opera House**
Gloucester Street
St Helier, Jersey JE2 3QR
**Box Office:** 01534 511115
**Stage Door:** ------------------
**Admin:** 01534 511100
**Website:** www.jerseyoperahouse.co.uk
**e-mail:** admin@jerseyoperahouse.co.uk

## KIRKCALDY
**Adam Smith Theatre**
Bennochy Road, Kirkcaldy KY1 1ET
**Box Office:** 01592 583302
**Stage Door:** ------------------
**Admin:** 01592 583301

## LEATHERHEAD
**The Leatherhead Theatre**
7 Church Street
Leatherhead, Surrey KT22 8DN
**Box Office:** 01372 365141
**Stage Door:** ------------------
**Admin:** 01372 365130
**Website:** www.the-theatre.org
**e-mail:** info@the-theatre.org

## LEEDS
**City Varieties Music Hall**
Swan Street, Leeds LS1 6LW
**Box Office:** 0845 6441881
**Stage Door:** ------------------
**Admin:** 0845 1260696
**Website:** www.cityvarieties.co.uk
**e-mail:** info@cityvarieties.co.uk

## LEEDS

**Grand Theatre & Opera House**
46 New Briggate, Leeds LS1 6NZ
**Box Office:** 0844 8482700
**Stage Door:** 0113-245 6014
**Admin:** 0113-245 6014
**Website:** www.leedsgrandtheatre.com
**e-mail:** boxoffice@leedsgrandtheatre.com

## LICHFIELD

**The Lichfield Garrick**
Castle Dyke, Lichfield WS13 6HR
**Box Office:** 01543 412121
**Stage Door:** ------------------
**Admin:** 01543 412110
**Website:** www.lichfieldgarrick.com

## LINCOLN

**Theatre Royal**
Clasketgate, Lincoln LN2 1JJ
**Box Office:** 01522 525555
**Stage Door:** ------------------
**Admin:** 01522 523303
**Website:** www.theatreroyallincoln.com
**e-mail:** trl@dial.pipex.com

## LIVERPOOL

**Empire Theatre**
Lime Street, Liverpool L1 1JE
**Box Office:** 0844 8472525
**Stage Door:** 0151-708 3200
**Admin:** 0151-708 3200
**Website:** www.liverpoolempire.org.uk

## LLANDUDNO

**Venue Cymru**
Promenade, Llandudno, Conwy, North Wales, LL30 1BB
**Tel:** 01492 879771
**Box Office:** 01492 872000
**Stage Door:** ------------------
**Website:** www.venuecymru.co.uk
**e-mail:** info@venuecymru.co.uk

## MALVERN

**Malvern Theatres (Festival & Forum Theatres)**
Grange Road, Malvern WR14 3HB
**Box Office:** 01684 892277
**Stage Door:** ------------------
**Admin:** 01684 569256
**Website:** www.malvern-theatres.co.uk
**e-mail:** post@malvern-theatres.co.uk

## MANCHESTER

**Manchester Apollo**
Stockport Road, Ardwick Green, Manchester M12 6AP
**Box Office:** 0844 4777677
**Stage Door:** 0161-273 2416
**Admin:** 0161-273 6921
**Website:** www.livenation.co.uk
**e-mail:** manchester.apollo@livenation.co.uk

## MANCHESTER

**Opera House**
Quay Street, Manchester M3 3HP
**Box Office:** 0844 8472328
**Stage Door:** 0161-828 1700
**Admin:** 0161-828 1700
**Website:** www.palaceandoperahouse.org.uk

## MANCHESTER

**Palace Theatre**
Oxford Street, Manchester M1 6FT
**Box Office:** 0844 8472275
**Stage Door:** 0161-245 6600
**Admin:** 0161-245 6600
**Website:** www.manchesterpalace.org.uk

## MARGATE

**Theatre Royal**
Addington Street, Margate, Kent CT9 1PW
**Box Office:** 0845 1301786
**Stage Door:** 01843 293397
**Admin:** 01843 293397
**Website:** www.theatreroyalmargate.com

## MILTON KEYNES

**Milton Keynes Theatre**
500 Marlborough Gate, Central Milton Keynes MK9 3NZ
**Box Office:** 0870 0606652
**Stage Door:** 01908 547500
**Admin:** 01908 547500
**Website:** www.ambassadortickets.com/miltonkeynes

## NEWARK

**Palace Theatre**
Appletongate, Newark NG24 1JY
**Box Office:** 01636 655755
**Stage Door:** ------------------
**Admin:** 01636 655750
**Website:** www.palacenewark.com
**e-mail:** kevan.jackson@nsdc.info

## NEWCASTLE UPON TYNE

**Northern Stage**
Barras Bridge, Haymarket, Newcastle upon Tyne NE1 7RH
**Box Office:** 0191-230 5151
**Stage Door:** ------------------
**Admin:** 0191-232 3366
**Website:** www.northernstage.co.uk
**e-mail:** info@northernstage.co.uk

## NEWCASTLE UPON TYNE

**Theatre Royal**
Grey Street, Newcastle upon Tyne NE1 6BR
**Box Office:** 0844 8112121
**Stage Door:** 0191-244 2500
**Admin:** 0191-244 2500
**Website:** www.theatreroyal.co.uk

## NORTHAMPTON

**Royal & Derngate Theatres**
19-21 Guildhall Road, Northampton NN1 1DP
**Box Office:** 01604 624811
**Stage Door:** 01604 626222
**Admin:** 01604 626222
**Website:** www.royalandderngate.co.uk
**e-mail:** postbox@royalandderngate.co.uk

## NORWICH

**Theatre Royal**
Theatre Street, Norwich NR2 1RL
**Box Office:** 01603 630000
**Stage Door:** 01603 598500
**Admin:** 01603 598500
**Website:** www.theatreroyalnorwich.co.uk

## NOTTINGHAM
**Theatre Royal & Royal Concert Hall**
Theatre Square
Nottingham NG1 5ND
**Box Office:** 0115-989 5555
**Stage Door:** 0115-989 5500
**Admin:** 0115-989 5500
**Website:** www.royalcentre-nottingham.co.uk
**e-mail:** enquiry@royalcentre-nottingham.co.uk

## OXFORD
**New Theatre**
George Street
Oxford OX1 2AG
**Box Office:** 0844 8471588
**Stage Door:** 01865 320760
**Admin:** 01865 320760

## OXFORD
**Oxford Playhouse**
11-12 Beaumont Street
Oxford OX1 2LW
**Box Office:** 01865 305305
**Stage Door:** 01865 305301
**Admin:** 01865 305300
**Website:** www.oxfordplayhouse.com
**e-mail:** admin@oxfordplayhouse.com

## POOLE
**Lighthouse, Poole's Centre for The Arts**
Kingland Road
Poole BH15 1UG
**Box Office:** 0844 4068666
**Stage Door:** ------------------
**Admin:** ------------------
**Website:** www.lighthousepoole.co.uk

## READING
**The Hexagon**
Queen's Walk, Reading RG1 7UA
**Box Office:** 0118-960 6060
**Stage Door:** 0118-939 0018
**Admin:** 0118-939 0123
**Website:** www.readingarts.com
**e-mail:** boxoffice@readingarts.com

## RICHMOND (N Yorks)
**Georgian Theatre Royal**
Victoria Road
Richmond, North Yorkshire DL10 4DW
**Box Office:** 01748 825252
**Stage Door:** ------------------
**Admin:** 01748 823710
**Website:** www.georgiantheatreroyal.co.uk
**e-mail:** admin@georgiantheatreroyal.co.uk

## RICHMOND (Surrey)
**Richmond Theatre**
The Green
Richmond, Surrey TW9 1QJ
**Box Office:** 0844 8717651
**Stage Door:** 020-8332 4500
**Admin:** 020-8332 4500
**Website:** www.ambassadortickets.com/richmond
**e-mail:** richmondstagedoor@theambassadors.com

## SHEFFIELD
**Sheffield Theatres - Crucible, Lyceum & Crucible Studio**
55 Norfolk Street, Sheffield S1 1DA
**Box Office:** 0114-249 6000
**Stage Door:** 0114-249 5999
**Admin:** 0114-249 5999
**Website:** www.sheffieldtheatres.co.uk
**e-mail:** info@sheffieldtheatres.co.uk

## SHERINGHAM
**The Little Theatre**
2 Station Road, Sheringham, Norfolk NR26 8RE
**Box Office:** 01263 822347
**Stage Door:** ------------------
**Admin:** 01263 822117
**Website:** www.sheringhamlittletheatre.com
**e-mail:** enquiries@sheringhamlittletheatre.com

## SOUTHAMPTON
**The Mayflower**
Commercial Road, Southampton SO15 1GE
**Box Office:** 023-8071 1811
**Stage Door:** ------------------
**Admin:** 023-8071 1800
**Website:** www.mayflower.org.uk
**e-mail:** info@mayflower.org.uk

## SOUTHEND
**Southend Theatres**
**(Cliffs Pavilion, Palace Theatre & Dixon Studio)**
Cliffs Pavilion, Station Road
Westcliff-on-Sea, Essex SS0 7RA
**Box Office:** 01702 351135
**Stage Door:** 01702 347394
**Admin:** 01702 390657
**Website:** www.southendtheatres.org.uk
**e-mail:** info@southendtheatres.org.uk

## ST ALBANS
**Abbey Theatre**
Holywell Hill, St Albans AL1 2DL
**Box Office:** 01727 857861
**Stage Door:** ------------------
**Admin:** 01727 847472
**Website:** www.abbeytheatre.org.uk
**e-mail:** manager@abbeytheatre.org.uk

## ST ALBANS
**Alban Arena**
Civic Centre, St Albans AL1 3LD
**Box Office:** 01727 844488
**Stage Door:** ------------------
**Admin:** 01727 861078
**Website:** www.alban-arena.co.uk
**e-mail:** alban.arena@leisureconnection.co.uk

## ST HELENS
**Theatre Royal**
Corporation Street
St Helens WA10 1LQ
**Box Office:** 01744 756000
**Stage Door:** ------------------
**Admin:** 01744 756333
**Website:** www.sthelenstheatreroyal.co.uk

## STAFFORD

**Stafford Gatehouse Theatre**
Eastgate Street, Stafford ST16 2LT
**Box Office:** 01785 254653
**Stage Door:** -------------------
**Admin:** 01785 253595
**Website:** www.staffordgatehousetheatre.co.uk
**e-mail:** gatehouse@staffordbc.gov.uk

## STEVENAGE

**Gordon Craig Theatre**
Arts & Leisure Centre, Lytton Way, Stevenage SG1 1LZ
**Box Office:** 0870 0131030
**Stage Door:** 01438 242629
**Admin:** 01438 242679
**Website:** www.gordon-craig.co.uk
**e-mail:** gordoncraig@stevenage-leisure.co.uk

## SUNDERLAND

**Sunderland Empire**
High Street West, Sunderland SR1 3EX
**Box Office:** 0844 8472499
**Stage Door:** 0191-566 1057
**Admin:** 0191-566 1040

## SWANAGE

**Mowlem Theatre**
Shore Road, Swanage BH19 1DD
**Box Office:** 01929 422239
**Stage Door:** -------------------
**Admin:** -------------------
**e-mail:** briantraversmowlem@yahoo.co.uk

## TAMWORTH

**Assembly Rooms**
Corporation Street, Tamworth B79 7DN
**Box Office:** 01827 709618
**Stage Door:** -------------------
**Admin:** 01827 709619
**Website:** www.tamworthassemblyrooms.gov.uk
**e-mail:** assemblyrooms@tamworth.gov.uk

## TEWKESBURY

**The Roses**
Sun Street, Tewkesbury GL20 5NX
**Box Office:** 01684 295074
**Stage Door:** -------------------
**Admin:** 01684 290734
**Website:** www.rosestheatre.org
**e-mail:** admin@rosestheatre.org

## TORQUAY

**Babbacombe Theatre**
Babbacombe Downs, Torquay TQ1 3LU
**Box Office:** 01803 328385
**Stage Door:** 01803 328385
**Admin:** 01803 322233
**Website:** www.babbacombe-theatre.com
**e-mail:** mail@matpro-show.biz

## TORQUAY

**Princess Theatre**
Torbay Road, Torquay TQ2 5EZ
**Box Office:** 0844 8472315
**Stage Door:** 01803 290068
**Admin:** 01803 290288
**Website:** www.princesstheatre.org.uk
**e-mail:** wendy.bennett@livenation.co.uk

## TRURO

**Hall For Cornwall**
Back Quay
Truro, Cornwall TR1 2LL
**Box Office:** 01872 262466
**Stage Door:** 01872 262465
**Admin:** 01872 262465
**Website:** www.hallforcornwall.co.uk
**e-mail:** admin@hallforcornwall.org.uk

## WINCHESTER

**Theatre Royal**
21-23 Jewry Street, Winchester SO23 8SB
**Box Office:** 01962 840440
**Stage Door:** -------------------
**Admin:** 01962 844600
**Website:** www.theatreroyalwinchester.co.uk
**e-mail:** comms@theatreroyalwinchester.co.uk

## WOLVERHAMPTON

**Grand Theatre**
Lichfield Street
Wolverhampton WV1 1DE
**Box Office:** 01902 429212
**Stage Door:** 01902 573320
**Admin:** 01902 573320
**Website:** www.grandtheatre.co.uk
**e-mail:** marketing@grandtheatre.co.uk

## WORCESTER

**Swan Theatre**
The Moors
Worcester WR1 3ED
**Box Office:** 01905 611427
**Stage Door:** -------------------
**Admin:** 01905 726969
**Website:** www.worcesterlive.co.uk
**e-mail:** chris@worcesterlive.co.uk

## WORTHING

**Connaught Theatre**
Union Place
Worthing BN11 1LG
**Box Office:** 01903 206206
**Stage Door:** -------------------
**Admin:** 01903 231799
**Website:** www.worthingtheatres.co.uk
**e-mail:** theatres@worthing.gov.uk

## YEOVIL

**Octagon Theatre**
Hendford
Yeovil BA20 1UX
**Box Office:** 01935 422884
**Stage Door:** -------------------
**Admin:** 01935 845900
**Website:** www.octagon-theatre.co.uk
**e-mail:** octagontheatre@southsomerset.gov.uk

## YORK

**Grand Opera House**
Cumberland Street
York YO1 9SW
**Box Office:** 0844 8472322
**Stage Door:** -------------------
**Admin:** 01904 678700
**Website:** www.grandoperahouseyork.org.uk
**e-mail:** lizzie.richards@livenation.co.uk

## AUTHENTIC PUNCH & JUDY
Contact: John Styles (Puppets, Booths & Presentations)
42 Christchurch Road
Sidcup
Kent DA15 7HQ
Tel/Fax: 020-8300 3579
Website: www.johnstylesentertainer.co.uk

## BUCKLEY Simon
(Freelance Puppeteer/Presenter)
12 College Green
55-57 Barrington Road
London SW9 7JG
Mobile: 07976 290351
Website: www.simonbuckley.co.uk
e-mail: puppet.buckley@virgin.net

## COMPLETE WORKS CREATIVE COMPANY Ltd The
Contact: Phil Evans (Artistic Director)
The Old Truman Brewery
91 Brick Lane
London E1 6QL
Website: www.tcw.org.uk
e-mail: info@tcw.org.uk
Fax: 0870 1431979
Tel: 0870 1431969

## CORNELIUS & JONES
49 Carters Close
Sherington
Newport Pagnell
Buckinghamshire MK16 9NW
Tel/Fax: 01908 612593
Website: www.corneliusjones.com
e-mail: admin@corneliusjones.com

## DYNAMIC NEW ANIMATION
Unit 13
The Watermark
Ribbleton Lane, Preston PR1 5EZ
Website: www.dynamicnewanimation.co.uk
e-mail: info@dynamicnewanimation.co.uk
Mobile: 07976 946003
Tel: 01772 253100

## INDIGO MOON THEATRE
35 Waltham Court
Beverley
East Yorkshire HU17 9JF
Mobile: 07855 328552
Website: www.indigomoontheatre.com
e-mail: info@indigomoontheatre.com

## JACOLLY PUPPET THEATRE
Kirkella Road
Yelverton
West Devon PL20 6BB
Tel: 01822 852346
Website: www.jacolly-puppets.co.uk
e-mail: theatre@jacolly-puppets.co.uk

## LITTLE ANGEL THEATRE
14 Dagmar Passage
Cross Street
London N1 2DN
Tel: 020-7226 1787
Website: www.littleangeltheatre.com
e-mail: info@littleangeltheatre.com

## MAJOR MUSTARD'S TRAVELLING SHOW
1 Carless Avenue
Harborne
Birmingham B17 9EG
Tel: 0121-426 4329
e-mail: mm@majormustard.com

## NORWICH PUPPET THEATRE
St James
Whitefriars
Norwich NR3 1TN
Website: www.puppettheatre.co.uk
e-mail: info@puppettheatre.co.uk
Fax: 01603 617578
Tel: 01603 615564

## PEKKO'S PUPPETS
Contact: Stephen Novy (Director)
92 Stanley Avenue
Greenford
Middlesex UB6 8NP
Tel: 020-8575 2311
e-mail: enquiries@pekkospuppets.co.uk

## POM POM PUPPETS
9 Fulham Park Gardens
London SW6 4JX
Mobile: 07974 175247

## PROFESSOR PATTEN'S PUNCH & JUDY
(Puppetry & Magic)
14 The Crest
Goffs Oak, Herts EN7 5NP
Tel: 01707 873262
Website: www.dennispatten.co.uk

## PUPPET THEATRE WALES
22 Starling Road
St Athan
Vale of Glamorgan CF62 4NJ
Tel: 01446 790634
Website: www.puppettheatrewales.co.uk
e-mail: info@puppettheatrewales.co.uk

## TALK TO THE HAND PRODUCTIONS
(Custom Characters Created & Performed)
Studio 277
Wimbledon Art Studios
Riverside Yard, Riverside Road
Earlsfield, London SW17 0BB
Website: www.talktothehandpuppets.com
e-mail: info@talktothehandpuppets.com
Mobile: 07813 682293
Mobile: 07855 421454

## TICKLISH ALLSORTS SHOW
57 Victoria Road, Wilton, Salisbury
Wiltshire SP2 0DZ
Tel/Fax: 01722 744949
Website: www.ticklishallsorts.co.uk
e-mail: garynunn@ntlworld.com

## TOPPER Chris PUPPETS
(Puppets & Costume Characters, Created & Performed)
75 Barrows Green Lane
Widnes
Cheshire WA8 3JH
Tel: 0151-424 8692
Website: www.christopperpuppets.co.uk
e-mail: christopper@ntlworld.com

**ALDEBURGH**
Summer Theatre (July & August) The Jubilee Hall
Crabbe Street
Aldeburgh IP15 5BW
BO: 01728 453007/454022 (Evening)
Admin: (Oct-May) 020-7724 5432    Admin: (June-Sept) 01502 723077
Website: www.southwoldtheatre.org

**BELFAST**
Lyric Theatre
88A Starnmillis Road
Belfast BT9 5AD
Fax: 028-9038 1395      Admin: 028-9038 5685
Website: www.lyrictheatre.co.uk
e-mail: info@lyrictheatre.co.uk
Artistic Director: Richard Croxford
Production Manager: Marianne Crosslé
Administration Manager: Clare Gault
Executive Director: Ciaran McAuley
Finance Manager: Deírdre Ferguson

**BIRMINGHAM**
Birmingham Stage Company
The Old Rep Theatre, Station Street
Birmingham B5 4DY
BO: 0121-303 2323      Admin: 0121-643 9050
Website: www.birminghamstage.net
e-mail: info@birminghamstage.net
Actor/Manager: Neal Foster

**BIRMINGHAM**
Birmingham Stage Company
London Office:
Suite 228 The Linen Hall
162 Regent Street, London W1B 5TB
Fax: 020-7437 3395      Admin: 020-7437 3391
Website: www.birminghamstage.net
e-mail: info@birminghamstage.net
Actor/Manager: Neal Foster
Executive Producer: Philip Compton

**BIRMINGHAM**
Repertory Theatre
Centenary Square, Broad Street
Birmingham B1 2EP
Press Office: 0121-245 2072
BO: 0121-236 4455      Tel: 0121-245 2000
e-mail: info@birmingham-rep.co.uk
Artistic Director: Rachel Kavanaugh
Executive Director: Stuart Rogers

**BOLTON**
Octagon Theatre
Howell Croft South, Bolton BL1 1SB
Fax: 01204 556502
BO: 01204 520661      Admin: 01204 529407
Website: www.octagonbolton.co.uk
e-mail: info@octagonbolton.co.uk
Artistic Director: David Thacker
Executive Director: John Blackmore
Head of Administration: Lesley Etherington
Head of Production: Lesley Chenery

**BRISTOL**
Theatre Royal & Studio
Bristol Old Vic
King Street, Bristol BS1 4ED
Fax: 0117-949 3996
BO: 0117-987 7877      Tel: 0117-949 3993
Website: www.bristololdvic.org.uk
e-mail: admin@bristol-old-vic.co.uk
Artistic Director: Tom Morris
Executive Director: Emma Stenning

**CARDIFF**
Sherman Cymru
Senghennydd Road, Cardiff CF24 4YE
Fax: 029-2064 6902
BO: 029-2064 6900      Tel: 029-2064 6901
Director: Chris Ricketts
General Manager: Margaret Jones

**CHICHESTER**
Chichester Festival Theatre
Oaklands Park, Chichester, West Sussex PO19 6AP
Fax: 01243 787288
BO: 01243 781312      Admin/SD: 01243 784437
Website: www.cft.org.uk
e-mail: admin@cft.org.uk
Artistic Director: Jonathan Church
Executive Director: Alan Finch
Theatre Manager: Janet Bakose

**CHICHESTER**
Minerva Theatre at Chichester Festival Theatre
Oaklands Park, Chichester, West Sussex PO19 6AP
Fax: 01243 787288
BO: 01243 781312      Admin/SD: 01243 784437
Website: www.cft.org.uk
e-mail: admin@cft.org.uk
Artistic Director: Jonathan Church
Executive Director: Alan Finch
Theatre Manager: Janet Bakose

**COLCHESTER**
Mercury Theatre, Balkerne Gate, Colchester, Essex CO1 1PT
Fax: 01206 769607
BO: 01206 573948      Admin: 01206 577006
Website: www.mercurytheatre.co.uk
e-mail: info@mercurytheatre.co.uk
Chief Executive: Dee Evans
General Manager: Adrian Grady

**COVENTRY**
Belgrade Main Stage & B2 Auditorium
Belgrade Square, Coventry, West Midlands CV1 1GS
BO: 024-7655 3055      Admin: 024-7625 6431
Website: www.belgrade.co.uk
e-mail: admin@belgrade.co.uk
Artistic Director & CEO: Hamish Glen
Executive Director: Joanna Reid
Director of Marketing: Antony Flint

**DUBLIN**
Abbey Theatre Amharclann na Mainistreach
26 Lower Abbey Street, Dublin 1, Ireland
Fax: 00 353 1 872 9177
BO: 00 353 1 878 7222      Admin: 00 353 1 887 2200
Website: www.abbeytheatre.ie
e-mail: info@abbeytheatre.ie
Director: Fiach MacConghail

**DUNDEE**
Dundee Repertory Theatre, Tay Square, Dundee DD1 1PB
Fax: 01382 228609
BO: 01382 223530      Admin: 01382 227684
Website: www.dundeereptheatre.co.uk
Artistic Director & Chief Executive: James Brining
Associate Director: Jemima Levick
General Manager: Ian Alexander

**EDINBURGH**
Royal Lyceum Theatre Company
30B Grindlay Street, Edinburgh EH3 9AX
Fax: 0131-228 3955
BO: 0131-248 4848      Admin/SD: 0131-248 4800
Website: www.lyceum.org.uk
e-mail: info@lyceum.org.uk
Artistic Director: Mark Thomson

**EDINBURGH**
Traverse Theatre
(New Writing, Own Productions, Touring & Visiting
Companies)
10 Cambridge Street, Edinburgh EH1 2ED
Fax: 0131-229 8443
BO: 0131-228 1404     Admin: 0131-228 3223
Website: www.traverse.co.uk
e-mail: admin@traverse.co.uk
Artistic Director: Dominic Hill
Administrative Director: Mike Griffiths

**EXETER**
Exeter Northcott Theatre
Stocker Road, Exeter, Devon EX4 4QB
Fax: 01392 223996
BO: 01392 493493     Admin: 01392 223999
Website: www.exeternorthcott.co.uk
e-mail: info@exeternorthcott.co.uk
Chief Executive: Kate Tyrrell

**FRINTON**
Frinton Summer Theatre
(July-Sept)
The McGrigor Hall, Fourth Avenue, Frinton-on-Sea
Essex CO13 9EB     BO: 07905 589792 (July-Sept only)
e-mail: ed.max@frintonsummertheatre.co.uk
Producer/Artistic Director: Edward Max

**GLASGOW**
Citizens Theatre, Gorbals, Glasgow G5 9DS
Fax: 0141-429 7374
BO: 0141-429 0022     Admin: 0141-429 5561
Website: www.citz.co.uk
e-mail: info@citz.co.uk
Artistic Directors: Jeremy Raison, Guy Hollands
Administrative Director: Anna Staples

**GUILDFORD**
Yvonne Arnaud Theatre
Millbrook, Guildford, Surrey GU1 3UX
Fax: 01483 564071
BO: 01483 440000     Admin: 01483 440077
Website: www.yvonne-arnaud.co.uk
e-mail: yat@yvonne-arnaud.co.uk
Director: James Barber

**HARROGATE**
Harrogate Theatre
(Mainly Co-productions, Touring & Visiting Companies)
Oxford Street, Harrogate HG1 1QF
Fax: 01423 563205
BO: 01423 502116     Admin: 01423 502710
Website: www.harrogatetheatre.co.uk
e-mail: info@harrogatetheatre.co.uk
Chief Executive: David Bown

**HULL**
Hull Truck Theatre, 50 Ferensway, Hull HU2 8LB
Fax: 01482 581182     Tel: 01482 224800
Website: www.hulltruck.co.uk
e-mail: admin@hulltruck.co.uk
Artistic Directors: John Godber & Gareth Tudor Price
Executive Director: Paul Marshall
Associate Director: Nick Lane

**IPSWICH**
The New Wolsey Theatre
Civic Drive, Ipswich, Suffolk IP1 2AS
BO: 01473 295900
Admin Fax: 01473 295910     Admin: 01473 295911
Website: www.wolseytheatre.co.uk
e-mail: info@wolseytheatre.co.uk
Artistic Director: Peter Rowe
Chief Executive: Sarah Holmes

**KESWICK**
Theatre by the Lake
Lakeside, Keswick
Cumbria CA12 5DJ
Fax: 01768 774698
BO: 01768 774411     Admin: 01768 772282
Website: www.theatrebythelake.com
e-mail: enquiries@theatrebythelake.com
Artistic Director: Ian Forrest

**LANCASTER**
The Dukes
Moor Lane
Lancaster
Lancashire LA1 1QE
Fax: 01524 598519
BO: 01524 598500     Admin: 01524 598505
Website: www.dukes-lancaster.org
e-mail: info@dukes-lancaster.org
Director: Joe Sumsion

**LEEDS**
West Yorkshire Playhouse
Playhouse Square
Quarry Hill, Leeds LS2 7UP
Fax: 0113-213 7250
BO: 0113-213 7700     Admin: 0113-213 7800
Website: www.wyp.org.uk
Artistic Director (Chief Executive): Ian Brown
Joint Chief Executive: Sheena Wrigley
Producer: Henrietta Duckworth

**LEICESTER**
Leicester Theatre Trust
Curve Theatre
Rutland Street, Leicester LE1 1SB
Fax: 0870 7065241     Admin: 0116-242 3595
Website: www.curveonline.co.uk
e-mail: enquiries@leicestertheatretrust.co.uk
Artistic Director: Paul Kerryson
Chief Executive: Ruth Eastwood

**LIVERPOOL**
Everyman & Playhouse Theatres
Everyman: 13 Hope Street
Liverpool L1 9BH
Playhouse: Williamson Square
Liverpool L1 1EL
Fax: 0151-709 0398
BO: 0151-709 4776     Admin: 0151-708 0338
Website: www.everymanplayhouse.com
e-mail: reception@everymanplayhouse.com
Artistic Director: Gemma Bodinetz
Executive Director: Deborah Aydon

**MANCHESTER**
Contact Theatre Company
Oxford Road, Manchester M15 6JA
Fax: 0161-274 0640
BO: 0161-274 0600     Admin: 0161-274 0623
Website: www.contact-theatre.org
e-mail: info@contact-theatre.org
Chief Executive/Artistic Director: Baba Israel

**MANCHESTER**
Library Theatre Company
St Peter's Square
Manchester M2 5PD
Fax: 0161-274 7055
BO: 0161-236 7110     Admin: 0161-234 1913
Website: www.librarytheatre.com
e-mail: ltcadmin@manchester.gov.uk
Artistic Director: Chris Honer
General Manager: Adrian J. P. Morgan

## MANCHESTER
Royal Exchange Theatre
St Ann's Square, Manchester M2 7DH
Fax: 0161-832 0881
BO: 0161-833 9833                Admin: 0161-833 9333
Website: www.royalexchange.co.uk
Artistic Directors: Braham Murray, Gregory Hersov
& Sarah Frankcom
Executive Director: Paul Clay
Producer (Studio): Richard Morgan
Casting Director: Jerry Knight-Smith

## MILFORD HAVEN
Torch Theatre
St Peter's Road
Milford Haven, Pembrokeshire SA73 2BU
Fax: 01646 698919
BO: 01646 695267                Admin: 01646 694192
Website: www.torchtheatre.co.uk
e-mail: info@torchtheatre.co.uk
Artistic Director: Peter Doran

## MOLD
Clwyd Theatr Cymru
(Repertoire, 4 Weekly, also touring)
Mold, Flintshire, North Wales CH7 1YA
Fax: 01352 701558
BO: 0845 3303565                Admin: 01352 756331
Website: www.clwyd-theatr-cymru.co.uk
e-mail: admin@clwyd-theatr-cymru.co.uk

## MUSSELBURGH
The Brunton Theatre
(Annual programme of Theatre, Dance, Music, Comedy &
Children's Work)
Ladywell Way, Musselburgh EH21 6AA
Fax: 0131-653 5265
BO: 0131-665 2240                Admin: 0131-665 9900
Website: www.bruntontheatre.co.uk
General Manager: Lesley Smith

## NEWBURY
Watermill Theatre
(4-8 Weekly) (Feb-Jan)
Bagnor, Nr Newbury, Berkshire RG20 8AE
Fax: 01635 523726
BO: 01635 46044                Admin: 01635 45834
Website: www.watermill.org.uk
e-mail: admin@watermill.org.uk
Artistic & Executive Director: Hedda Beeby
General Manager: Clare Lindsay

## NEWCASTLE UNDER LYME
New Vic Theatre
(3-4 Weekly)
Etruria Road, Newcastle-under-Lyme, Staffordshire ST5 0JG
Fax: 01782 712885
BO: 01782 717962                Tel: 01782 717954
Website: www.newvictheatre.org.uk
e-mail: casting@newvictheatre.org.uk
Artistic Director: Theresa Heskins
Managing Director: Nick Jones

## NEWCASTLE UPON TYNE
Northern Stage (Theatrical Productions) Ltd
Barras Bridge, Newcastle upon Tyne NE1 7RH
Fax: 0191-261 8093
BO: 0191-230 5151                Admin: 0191-232 3366
Website: www.northernstage.co.uk
e-mail: info@northernstage.co.uk
Chief Executive: Erica Whyman

## NORTHAMPTON
Royal & Derngate
Guildhall Road, Northampton, Northamptonshire NN1 1DP
TIE: 01604 655740
BO: 01604 624811                Admin: 01604 626222
e-mail: postbox@royalandderngate.co.uk
Chief Executive: Martin Sutherland
Artistic Director: Laurie Sansom
Associate Director: Dani Parr

## NOTTINGHAM
Nottingham Playhouse
(3/4 Weekly)
(Nottingham Playhouse Trust Ltd)
Wellington Circus, Nottingham NG1 5AL
Fax: 0115-947 5759
BO: 0115-941 9419                Admin: 0115-947 4361
Website: www.nottinghamplayhouse.co.uk
e-mail: enquiry@nottinghamplayhouse.co.uk
Chief Executive: Stephanie Sirr
Artistic Director: Giles Croft
Director, Roundabout and Education: Andrew Breakwell

## OLDHAM
Coliseum Theatre
(3-4 Weekly)
Fairbottom Street, Oldham, Lancashire OL1 3SW
Fax: 0161-624 5318
BO: 0161-624 2829                Admin: 0161-624 1731
Website: www.coliseum.org.uk
e-mail: mail@coliseum.org.uk
Chief Executive: Kevin Shaw

## PERTH
Perth Theatre
(2-3 Weekly)
Horsecross Arts, 185 High Street, Perth PH1 5UW
Fax: 01738 624576
BO: 01738 621031                Admin: 01738 472700
Website: www.horsecross.co.uk
e-mail: info@horsecross.co.uk
Artistic Director: Ian Grieve
Head of Planning & Resources: Paul Hackett
Chief Executive: Jane Spiers

## PETERBOROUGH
Key Theatre
(Touring & Occasional Seasonal)
Embankment Road, Peterborough, Cambridgeshire PE1 1EF
Fax: 01733 567025
BO: 01733 207239                Admin: 01733 207237
e-mail: key.theatre@peterborough.gov.uk

## PITLOCHRY
Pitlochry Festival Theatre
Pitlochry, Perthshire PH16 5DR
Fax: 01796 484616
BO: 01796 484626                Admin: 01796 484600
Website: www.pitlochry.org.uk
e-mail: admin@pitlochry.org.uk
Chief Executive/Artistic Director: John Durnin

## PLYMOUTH
Theatre Royal & Drum Theatre
Royal Parade, Plymouth, Devon PL1 2TR
Fax: 01752 230506
BO: 01752 267222                Admin: 01752 668282
Website: www.theatreroyal.com
e-mail: info@theatreroyal.com
Artistic Director: Simon Stokes
Chief Executive: Adrian Vinken

## READING
The Mill at Sonning Theatre
(5-6 Weekly)
Sonning Eye
Reading RG4 6TY
BO: 0118-969 8000     Admin: 0118-969 6039
Website: www.millatsonning.com
Artistic Director: Sally Hughes
Assistant Administrator: Ann Seymour

## SALISBURY
Playhouse & Salberg Studio
(3-4 Weekly)
Malthouse Lane
Salisbury, Wiltshire SP2 7RA
Fax: 01722 421991
BO: 01722 320333     Admin: 01722 320117
Website: www.salisburyplayhouse.com
e-mail: info@salisburyplayhouse.com
Artistic Director: Philip Wilson
Executive Director: Michelle Carwardine-Palmer

## SCARBOROUGH
Stephen Joseph Theatre
(Repertoire/Repertory)
Westborough, Scarborough
North Yorkshire YO11 1JW
Fax: 01723 360506
BO: 01723 370541     Admin: 01723 370540
e-mail: enquiries@sjt.uk.com
Artistic Director: Chris Monks
Executive Director: Stephen Wood

## SHEFFIELD
Crucible, Studio & Lyceum Theatres
55 Norfolk Street
Sheffield S1 1DA
Fax: 0114-249 6003
BO: 0114-249 6000     Admin: 0114-249 5999
Website: www.sheffieldtheatres.co.uk
e-mail: info@sheffieldtheatres.co.uk
Chief Executive: Dan Bates

## SHERINGHAM
Summer Repertory
The Little Theatre
2 Station Road
Sheringham, Norfolk NR26 8RE
BO: 01263 822347
Website: www.sheringhamlittletheatre.com
e-mail: enquiries@sheringhamlittletheatre.com
Producer: Sheringham Little Theatre
Artistic Director: Debbie Thompson

## SIDMOUTH
Manor Pavilion Theatre
(Weekly) (July-Sept)
Manor Road
Sidmouth, Devon EX10 8RP
BO: 01395 579977 (June-Sept)

## SOUTHAMPTON
Nuffield Theatre
(Sept-July, Sunday Night Concerts, Tours)
University Road
Southampton SO17 1TR
Fax: 023-8031 5511
BO: 023-8067 1771     Admin: 023-8031 5500
Website: www.nuffieldtheatre.co.uk
Artistic Director: Patrick Sandford
Executive Director: Kate Anderson

## SOUTHWOLD
Summer Theatre
(July-Sept)
St Edmund's Hall, Cumberland Road
Southwold IP18 6JP
Admin: (Oct-May) 020-7724 5432
Admin: (June-Sept) 01502 723077
Website: www.southwoldtheatre.org
e-mail: enquiries@southwoldtheatre.org
Producer: Jill Freud & Company

## ST ANDREWS
Byre Theatre
(Not producing, Co-productions only)
Abbey Street
St Andrews KY16 9LA
Fax: 01334 475370
BO: 01334 475000     Admin: 01334 475000
Website: www.byretheatre.com
e-mail: enquiries@byretheatre.com
Chief Executive: Jacqueline McKay

## STRATFORD-UPON-AVON
Royal Shakespeare Company & Courtyard Theatre
Southern Lane
Stratford-upon-Avon CV37 6BB
Fax: 01789 272560
BO: 0844 8001110     Admin: 01789 296655
Website: www.rsc.org.uk
e-mail: info@rsc.org.uk

## WATFORD
Watford Palace Theatre
(3-4 Weekly) Weds 2.30pm, Sat 3pm
20 Clarendon Road
Watford, Herts WD17 1JZ
Fax: 01923 819664
BO: 01923 225671     Admin: 01923 810300
Website: www.watfordpalacetheatre.co.uk
e-mail: enquiries@watfordpalacetheatre.co.uk
Artistic Director & Chief Executive: Brigid Larmour
Executive Director: Mathew Russell

## WINDSOR
Theatre Royal
Thames Street
Windsor, Berkshire SL4 1PS
Fax: 01753 831673
BO: 01753 853888     Admin: 01753 863444
Website: www.theatreroyalwindsor.co.uk
e-mail: info@theatreroyalwindsor.co.uk
Director: Simon Pearce

## WOKING
New Victoria Theatre
The Ambassadors
Peacocks Centre, Woking GU21 6GQ
SD: 01483 545855
BO: 0870 0606645     Admin: 01483 545800
Website: www.theambassadors.com/woking
e-mail: boxoffice@theambassadors.com

## YORK
Theatre Royal
St Leonard's Place, York YO1 7HD
Fax: 01904 550164
BO: 01904 623568     Admin: 01904 658162
Website: www.yorktheatreroyal.co.uk
e-mail: admin@yorktheatreroyal.co.uk
Artistic Director: Damian Cruden
Chief Executive: Daniel Bates

**Unions, Professional Guilds and Associations**

**BROADCASTING ENTERTAINMENT CINEMATOGRAPH & THEATRE UNION (BECTU) (Formerly BETA & ACTT)**
373-377 Clapham Road
London SW9 9BT
e-mail: smacdonald@bectu.org.uk
Fax: 020-7346 0901          Tel: 020-7346 0900

**CASTING DIRECTORS' GUILD**
PO Box 64973
London SW20 2AW
Website: www.thecdg.co.uk
e-mail: info@thecdg.co.uk

**DIRECTORS GUILD OF GREAT BRITAIN**
Top Floor, Julian House
4 Windmill Street, London W1T 2HZ
Website: www.dggb.org
e-mail: info@dggb.org
Fax: 020-7580 9132          Tel: 020-7580 9131

**EQUITY inc Variety Artistes' Federation**
Guild House
Upper St Martin's Lane
London WC2H 9EG
Website: www.equity.org.uk
e-mail: info@equity.org.uk
Fax: 020-7379 7001          Tel: 020-7379 6000

**(Midlands)**
Office 1
Steeple House, Percy Street
Coventry CV1 3BY          Tel/Fax: 024-7655 3612
e-mail: tjohnson@midlands-equity.org.uk

**(North West & Isle of Man)**
Express Networks
1 George Leigh Street
Manchester M4 5DL
e-mail: info@manchester-equity.org.uk
Fax: 0161-244 5971          Tel: 0161-244 5995

**(Scotland & Northern Ireland)**
114 Union Street
Glasgow G1 3QQ
e-mail: igilchrist@glasgow.equity.org.uk
Fax: 0141-248 2473          Tel: 0141-248 2472

**(Wales & South West)**
Transport House
1 Cathedral Road
Cardiff CF11 9SD
e-mail: info@cardiff-equity.org.uk
Fax: 029-2023 0754          Tel: 029-2039 7971

**FILM ARTISTS ASSOCIATION**
(Amalgamated with BECTU)
373-377 Clapham Road
London SW9
Website: www.bectu.org.uk
Fax: 020-7346 0925          Tel: 020-7346 0900

**INTERNATIONAL FEDERATION OF ACTORS (FIA)**
Guild House
Upper St Martin's Lane, London WC2H 9EG
Website: www.fia-actors.com
e-mail: office@fia-actors.com
Fax: 020-7379 8260          Tel: 020-7379 0900

**[CONTACTS 2010]**

**MUSICIANS' UNION**
60-62 Clapham Road
London SW9 0JJ
Website: www.musiciansunion.org.uk
Fax: 020-7582 9805　　　Tel: 020-7582 5566

**NASAA - NATIONAL ASSOCIATION OF SUPPORTING
ARTISTES AGENTS**
Website: www.nasaa.org.uk
e-mail: info@nasaa.org.uk

**NORTH AMERICAN ACTORS ASSOCIATION**
Contact: By Telephone/e-mail only
Website: www.naaa.org.uk
e-mail: admin@naaa.org.uk　　　Mobile: 07873 371891

**PERSONAL MANAGERS' ASSOCIATION Ltd**
PO Box 63819
London N1P 1HL　　　Tel: 0845 6027191
Website: www.thepma.com
e-mail: info@thepma.com

**WRITERS' GUILD OF GREAT BRITAIN The**
40 Rosebery Avenue
London EC1R 4RX
Website: www.writersguild.org.uk
e-mail: admin@writersguild.org.uk
Fax: 020-7833 4777　　　Tel: 020-7833 0777

**BELGIUM**

**ACV/TRANSCOM - CULTUUR**
Galerij Agora
Grasmarkt 105 bus 40
1000 Brussels
Website: www.acvcultuur.be
e-mail: info@acvcultuur.be
Fax: 00 32 2 512 8591　　　Tel: 00 32 2 289 0830

**CENTRALE GÉNÉRALE DES SERVICES PUBLICS**
Place Fontainas 9-11
1000 Brussels
Website: www.cgsp-culture.be
e-mail: mylene.paon@cgsp.be
Fax: 00 32 2 508 5902　　　Tel: 00 32 2 508 5811

**DENMARK**

**DAF - DANSK ARTIST FORBUND**
Dronningensgade 68
1420 Copenhagen K
Website: www.artisten.dk
e-mail: artisten@artisten.dk
Fax: 00 45 33 33 73 30　　　Tel: 00 45 33 32 66 77

**DANSK SKUESPILLERFORBUND**
Sankt Knuds Vej 26
1903 Frederiksberg C
Website: www.skuespillerforbundet.dk
e-mail: dsf@skuespillerforbundet.dk
Fax: 00 45 33 24 81 59　　　Tel: 00 45 33 24 22 00

**FINLAND**

**SUOMEN NÄYTTELIJÄLIITTO**
Meritullinkatu 33, 00170 Helsinki, Finland
Website: www.nayttelijaliitto.fi
e-mail: toimisto@nayttelijaliitto.fi
Fax: 00 358 9 2511 2139　　　Tel: 00 353 9 2511 2135

**FRANCE**

**SYNDICAT FRANÇAIS DES ARTISTES-INTERPRÈTES**
1 rue Janssen, 75019 Paris
Website: www.sfa-cgt.fr
e-mail: info@sfa-cgt.fr
Fax: 00 33 1 53 25 09 01　　　Tel: 00 33 1 53 25 09 09

**GERMANY**

**GENOSSENSCHAFT DEUTSCHER
BUEHNENANGEHOERIGER**
Feldbrunnenstrasse 74, 20148 Hamburg
Website: www.buehnengenossenschaft.de
e-mail: gdba@buehnengenossenschaft.de
Fax: 00 49 40 45 93 52　　　Tel: 00 49 40 44 51 85

**GREECE**

**HAU - HELLENIC ACTORS' UNION**
33 Kaniggos Street, 106 82 Athens
Website: www.sei.gr
e-mail: sei@sei.gr
Fax: 00 30 210 380 8651　　　Tel: 00 30 210 383 3742

**IRELAND**

**IEG - IRISH EQUITY GROUP**
SIPTU
Liberty Hall, Dublin 1
Website: www.irishequity.ie
e-mail: equity@siptu.ie
Fax: 00 353 1 874 3691　　　Tel: 00 353 1 858 6403

**ITALY**

**SINDACATO ATTORI ITALIANO**
Via Ofanto 18, 00198 Rome
Website: www.cgil.it/sai-slc
e-mail: sai-slc@cgil.it
Fax: 00 39 06 854 6780　　　Tel: 00 39 06 841 7303

**LUXEMBOURG**

**ONOFHANGEGE GEWERKSCHAFTSBOND LETZEBUERG**
60 bd. Kennedy
B.P. 149, L-4002 Esch/Alzette
Website: www.ogb-l.lu
e-mail: ogbl@ogbl.lu
Fax: 00 352 541 620　　　Tel: 00 352 540 545-1

**NETHERLANDS**

**FNV - KUNSTEN INFORMATIE EN MEDIA**
Jan Tooropstraat 1
Postbus 9354, 1006 AJ Amsterdam
Website: www.fnv.nl/kiem
e-mail: algemeen@fnv-kiem.nl
Fax: 00 31 20 355 3737　　　Tel: 00 31 20 355 3636

**NORWAY**

**NSF - NORSK SKUESPILLERFORBUND**
Welhavensgate 3, 0166 Oslo
Website: www.skuespillerforbund.no
e-mail: nsf@skuespillerforbund.no
Fax: 00 47 21 02 71 91　　　Tel: 00 47 21 02 71 90

# infopage

## What are performers' unions?

The unions listed over the next few pages exist to protect and improve the rights, interests and working conditions of performers. They offer very important services to their members, such as advice on pay and conditions, help with contracts and negotiations, legal support and welfare advice. To join a performers' union there is usually a one-off joining fee and then an annual subscription fee calculated in relation to an individual's total yearly earnings. Equity is the main actors' union in the UK. See www.equity.org.uk and page 406 for more details.

## Do similar organisations exist for other sectors of the entertainment industry?

In addition to representation by trade unions, some skills also have professional bodies, guilds and associations which complement the work of trade unions. These include directors, producers, stage managers, designers and casting directors. These are also listed over the following pages.

## What is the FIA?

The FIA (International Federation of Actors) www.fia-actors.com is an organisation which represents performers' trade unions, guilds and associations from all around the world. It tackles the same issues as individual actors' unions, but on an international rather than local level. Please see their article on page 407 for further information.

## I'm a professionally trained actor from overseas and I want to work in the UK. How do I get started?

As with all forms of employment, to work as an actor in the UK you will need to have a relevant work permit / working visa. You might want to visit www.bia.homeoffice.gov.uk/workingintheuk for full information. You may also wish to join the UK's actors' union, Equity. For more information please visit their website www.equity.org.uk. If you can prove that you have relevant professional acting training and/or experience, you can also apply to join Spotlight to promote yourself to casting opportunities.

## I am a UK resident and I want to work as an actor elsewhere in Europe. Where do I start?

A good starting point would be to contact the actors' union in the country in which you are hoping to work for information on their employment legislation. Contact details for performers' unions in Europe can be found over the next few pages or obtained from the FIA www.fia-actors.com, who in most cases will be able to advise on what criteria you need to fulfil to be eligible for work.

As a UK national, you have the right to work in any country which is a member of the European Union (EU) without a work permit. You will be given the same employment rights as nationals of the country you are working in, but these rights will change according to the country you choose to work in and may not be the same as the UK.

For more general advice, the Foreign and Commonwealth Office (FCO) offers advice on living overseas and provides information on contacting the UK embassy in and relevant entry requirements for the country of your choice. Please see www.fco.gov.uk/en/travelling-and-living-overseas for more details. You could also visit Directgov's website www.direct.gov.uk/en/BritonsLivingAbroad/index.htm for further useful guidance for British citizens living abroad.

You should also go further and start researching agents, casting directors, production companies and so on which are based in the country you wish to live and work in. Begin your search online and you may decide to approach a person or company for further information once you have found out more about them. Learning the culture and becoming as fluent as possible in the language of your chosen country would be advisable, as this opens up a far wider range of job opportunities.

## What are English Speaking Theatres?

English Speaking Theatres can provide British actors with an opportunity to work abroad in theatre. These companies vary greatly in terms of the plays they put on and the audiences they attract: they may aim to teach English to schoolchildren; help audiences develop an appreciation of English plays; or may exist simply because there is a demand for English speaking entertainment. Some are based in one venue while others tour round the country. Actors may be employed for an individual production or, especially if touring, for a series of plays. Performers interested in the possibility of working for this type of theatre company should refer to the 'Theatre - English Speaking in Europe' section for listings.

## I am a UK resident and I want to work as an actor in the USA. Where do I start?

To work in America you will need a Green Card, a visa which entitles the holder to live and work there permanently as an immigrant, but you will not qualify for one unless you are sponsored by a prospective employer in the US or a relative who is a US citizen. It would be worth visiting the US Embassy's website www.usembassy.org.uk/cons_new/visa/index.html or the US Department of State's Bureau of Consular Affairs' website http://travel.state.gov/visa/visa_1750.html for information about the criteria you must meet and the fees you will have to pay. Relocation companies and legal services tailored to helping performers move to America can be found in the 'Accountants, Insurance & Law' section of Contacts.

Don't expect to be granted immediate entry to the USA. There is a limit to the number of people who can apply for immigrant status every year, so you could be on the waiting list for several years depending on the category of your application. You could enter the Green Card Lottery at www.greencard.co.uk for a chance to fast-track the processing of your application, although your visa will still have to be approved.

Finding employment from outside the USA will be difficult. You might want to try signing with an American talent agent to submit you for work, although there is huge competition for agents. Try the Association of Talent Agents (ATA) www.agentassociation.com for US agent details. The most effective way to gain an American agent's interest would be to get a personal referral from an industry contact, such as a casting director or acting coach. You should also promote yourself as you would with Spotlight by signing up with casting directories such as www.breakdownservices.com.

Acting employment in America is divided into union work and non-union work. The major actors' unions are SAG www.sag.org, AEA www.actorsequity.org, and AFTRA www.aftra.com. As with any other union they protect and enhance the rights of their members and offer various services and benefits. You will only become eligible for membership once you have provided proof of a contract for a job which comes under a particular union's jurisdiction. Non-members can work on union jobs if a producer is willing to employ them. You can join more than one union, but once you have joined at least one you will be unable to accept any non-union work.

You may have to begin your career in America with non-union work, as experience or union membership in the UK does not make you eligible to join a union in the US. Work ungoverned by the unions could include student and independent films, small stage productions, commercials, voice-overs, extra work, and so on. You are unlikely to be paid well as non-union contracts are not governed by the minimum wages set by the unions, but you will be able to build on your CV and begin making yourself known in the US acting industry.

# infopage

**Martin McGrath is the Campaigns & Publications Officer at Equity, the trade union for the UK entertainment industry. He works to provide a voice of authority for performers and the industry in general.**

There are lots of good reasons to join a performers' union. The issues that impact most upon you as a performer will depend on your personal circumstances and your career, amongst other things, but the one thing that performers can be sure of is that Equity is the union that best represents your interests.

So, why should you join Equity? Here are ten good reasons to get you thinking...

1. **PAY:** Equity contracts set the minimum rates for employment throughout the entertainment industry and the provisions in our contracts protect members from exploitation and deliver minimum standards. The stronger we become, the more we push for improved deals. When members come together we can make real progress. In the last twelve months we've achieved a minimum wage of £500 in West End theatres.

2. **DECENT TREATMENT AT WORK:** On everything from holiday entitlement to meal breaks and from health and safety protection to maximum working time, Equity has negotiated agreements across the industry to protect you from exploitation by unscrupulous employers and to increase awareness of best practice.

3. **EQUAL TREATMENT:** Regardless of your gender, your race or your sexuality, Equity works for equal opportunities across the entertainment industry and to end discrimination. Recent campaigns for greater opportunities for older women and for a media that is more representative of all sectors of the community have been high profile and continue to attract considerable support.

4. **PROTECTION:** If your employers, managers or agents are treating you unfairly, Equity will be by your side to ensure that your rights are protected. Equity has a team of specialist organisers working full-time to represent your needs and we have strong legal support for when you need it.

5. **PUBLIC LIABILITY:** For many performers, Equity's public liability insurance (which provides coverage of up to £10million) is an essential protection for their working lives and provides unbeatable value. If someone gets hurt during your act or if something gets damaged, then the knowledge that full insurance comes with your membership can help take the drama out of a crisis.

6. **COMPENSATION:** If you are injured or get ill because of your working conditions our legal services can ensure you get proper compensation. We have specialist legal support and a 24 hour helpline if you need to make a personal injury claim.

7. **BELONGING:** By becoming an Equity member you make a statement about your commitment to your vocation and your place within our industry. For almost 80 years Equity membership has been a symbol of unity in an industry where work is often transitory and geographically diverse. Your Equity card is a symbol of your professionalism.

8. **CONTRIBUTE:** If you are serious about making a contribution to improving conditions for yourself and those you work with, the best way to help is to get involved in your union. In Equity our democratic structures mean your voice can be heard and that you can genuinely make a difference to your own working life and that of your fellow performers.

9. **INFLUENCE:** Equity is a major voice in the entertainment industry, contributing to public debate at local, regional, national and international levels. Our influence comes from the strength of our membership. Although we are not affiliated to any political party, we work with other entertainment unions to influence politicians and to protect your interests and the interests of the arts and media in general.

10. **PRIDE:** By being part of Equity you can be proud of your contribution to making your industry a safer and more rewarding place for everyone who works. Your membership makes our union stronger; your involvement gives your union greater influence. Working together we can make Equity a union we can all be proud of.

For more information about Equity contact:
Post: Equity, Guild House, Upper St Martin's Lane, London WC2H 9EG
Telephone: 020-7379 6000  Website: www.equity.org.uk  e-mail: info@equity.org.uk

**The International Federation of Actors (FIA) is the umbrella organisation representing performers' unions, guilds and professional associations beyond national borders. Set up in 1952 by Equity and the French Actors' Union (SFA), it has spread to gather more than 100 affiliates in about 80 countries around the world. Together with its sister federation FIM (International Federation of Musicians) it is the only international trade body voicing the professional interests of performers at global level. It enjoys consultative status with the World Intellectual Property Organisation, the International Labour Organisation, UNESCO and the Council of Europe.**

Increasingly, decisions are taken at supranational level that may have serious repercussions for the daily lives of hundreds of thousands of professional performers. Our remit at FIA is to anticipate change and ensure that performers' legitimate concerns are duly taken into account. Whether the focus is on intellectual property, core labour rights, cultural diversity, mobility, new media or any other issue that is relevant to them, we bring performers and their livelihoods right to the heart of the decision-making process. As other industrial players also actively foster their own interests at international level, our presence is essential to preserve an equitable level playing field for all. We work closely with other interested parties and their trade bodies across the industry to seek solutions to common problems, wherever possible, through dialogue and negotiation.

Our ability to speak with an authoritative voice relies on the collective strength of our members. To this aim, we relentlessly work to help performers around the world build knowledgeable and effective trade unions. Unions are a vital tool for performers as they secure them decent working conditions and a minimum safety net for them to make a living. They are resourceful contributors to the entertainment industry, as they structure dialogue, help prevent and solve conflicts, raise professional standards, promote excellence and campaign for the industry to continue to be successful and fairly reward its creative talent. Our committed work carries us to countries where our knowledge can truly make a difference and bring local performers hope for a better future. To this end, FIA is particularly active in Africa, Latin America and Asia where we organise regular workshops and grow partnerships to reduce the divide between creative industries in developed and developing countries. We organise several regional meetings each year where unions in North America and in Europe can share experience, coordinate policies and respond to industrial developments.

We are committed to raising professional standards in the industry and regularly publish researches, guidelines and basic advice for performers. With the cooperation of the International Labour Organisation, we recently completed a Health & Safety brief for performers working in live shows as well as in television and film production. We also released a collection of minimum terms of reference for dancers working in countries where there are no collective agreements in place as well as a pan-European study on gender portrayal in the entertainment industry.

We always strongly encourage performers to join and support their unions and offer our services to strengthen their network. We channel solidarity and expertise to our members and create mechanisms to extend assistance to performers when their work brings them far from their union's jurisdiction. Active membership in one of our affiliated unions gives performers privileged access to advice and counselling in many other countries where FIA affiliates are established.

FIA is the voice of performers in the world. By joining local unions, they can help us protect their interests more effectively beyond national borders. They can also help us make a real difference to many other fellow performers who still face very difficult conditions as they struggle to live by their creative work in less fortunate countries.

For more information about FIA contact:
Post: FIA, Guild House, Upper St. Martin's Lane, London WC2H 9EG
Telephone: 020-7379 0900   Website: www.fia-actors.com   e-mail: office@fia-actors.com

SOME THINGS ARE ONLY POSSIBLE WITH THE PROPER SUPPORT

www.equity.org.uk ● info@equity.org.uk ● 020 7379 6000    Equity

## PORTUGAL

**STE - SINDICATO DOS TRABALHADORES DE ESPECTÁCULOS**
Rua da Fe 232do piso
1150-149 Lisbon
e-mail: startistas@mail.telepac.pt
Fax: 00 351 21 885 3787          Tel: 00 351 21 885 2728

## SPAIN

**CC.OO. COMISIONES OBRERAS - SERVICIOS A LA CIUDADANÍA SECTOR DE MEDIOS, ARTES, CULTURA Y DEPORTE**
Plaza Cristino Martos 4
6A Planta
28015 Madrid
Website: www.fct.ccoo.es/webfctmedios
e-mail: medios@fsc.ccoo.es
Fax: 00 34 91 548 1613          Tel: 00 34 91 540 9295

**FAEE - FEDERACIÓN DE ARTISTAS DEL ESTADO ESPAÑOL**
C/ Montera 34
1ro Piso
28013 Madrid
Website: www.faee.net
e-mail: faee@wanadoo.es
Fax: 00 34 91 522 6055          Tel: 00 34 91 522 2804

## SWEDEN

**TF TEATERFÖRBUNDET**
Kaplansbacken 2A
Box 12 710, 112 94 Stockholm
Website: www.teaterforbundet.se
e-mail: info@teaterforbundet.se
Fax: 00 46 8 653 9507          Tel: 00 46 8 441 1300

## UNITED STATES OF AMERICA

**AFTRA**
**(American Federation of Television & Radio Artists)**
260 Madison Avenue, New York NY 10016
Website: www.aftra.com
Fax: (212) 545-1238          Tel: (212) 532-0800

5757 Wilshire Boulevard
9th Floor, Los Angeles CA 90036
Website: www.aftra.com
Fax: (323) 634-8246          Tel: (323) 634-8100

**S A G**
**(Screen Actors Guild)**
7th Floor, 5757 Wilshire Boulevard
Los Angeles, CA 90036-3600
Website: www.sag.org          Tel: (323) 954-1600

360 Madison Avenue, 12th Floor, New York NY 10017
Website: www.sag.org
e-mail: nymember@sag.org
Fax: (212) 944-6774          Tel: (212) 944-1030

# Index To Advertisers

[ CONTACTS 2010 ]

## PHOTOGRAPHERS

## TRAINING
## (Schools, Companies & Workshops)

## VEHICLES & TRANSPORT

## WIG SUPPLIERS

## U

## V

## W

## XYZ